Third Edition

BSCS
Biology
A Human Approach

5415 Mark Dabling Boulevard
Colorado Springs, CO 80918-3842

BSCS

KENDALL/HUNT PUBLISHING COMPANY
4050 Westmark Drive   Dubuque, Iowa 52002

Teacher Guide

BSCS ADMINISTRATIVE STAFF, THIRD EDITION

Carlo Parravano, *Chair, Board of Directors*
Rodger W. Bybee, *Executive Director*
Janet Carlson Powell, *Director and Chief Science Education Officer*
Pamela Van Scotter, *Director,*
       The BSCS Center for Curriculum Development
Marcia Mitchell, *Director of Finance*

BSCS THIRD EDITION PROJECT STAFF

Anne L. Westbrook, *Project Director*
Dottie Watkins, *Revision Coordinator*
Barbara Perrin, *Production Manager*
Stacey Luce, Lisa Rasmussen, *Production Staff*
Steve Getty, *Unit 1, Review*

BSCS SECOND EDITION PROJECT STAFF

Hedi F. Baxter, *Project Director*
April Gardner, *Curriculum Developer*
Sherry Herron, *Curriculum Developer*
Rose M. Johnson, *Project Assistant*
Janet Carlson Powell, *Science Education Advisor*
Pamela Van Scotter, *Director of Curriculum Development*

BSCS SECOND EDITION PRODUCTION STAFF

Richard Bascobert, *Editor*
Joan Bolen, *Production Assistant*
Diane Gionfriddo, *Photo Researcher*
Stacey Luce, *Production Specialist*
Barbara Perrin, *Production Manager*
Lisa Rasmussen, *Graphic Designer*

SECOND EDITION CONTRIBUTORS

Edward Drexler, Pius XI High School, Milwaukee, WI
The Jane Goodall Institute, Silver Spring, MD
Tim Myles, University of Toronto, Toronto, Ontario
Douglas Niles, Delavan, WI

SECOND EDITION ARTISTS AND EDITORS

Fran Sevin
Susan Bartel
Marjorie C. Leggitt
Robert F. Schwengel
Paige Louis Thomas
MiRobin Webster

FIRST EDITION BSCS DEVELOPMENT TEAM

Rodger W. Bybee, *Principal Investigator*
Michael J. Dougherty, *Project Director, 1995–1996*
Janet Carlson Powell, *Project Director, 1993–1995*
Gordon E. Uno, *Project Director, 1992*

Staff Associates

Randall K. Backe, Wilbur Bergquist, William J. Cairney, Michael J. Dougherty, B. Ellen Friedman, Philip Goulding, David A. Hanych, Laura J. Laughran, Lynda B. Micikas, Jean P. Milani, Josina Romero-O'Connell, Jenny Sigsted, Pamela Van Scotter.

FIRST EDITION ARTISTS AND EDITORS

Jan Chatlain Girard
Mark Handy
Becky Hill
Brent Sauerhagen

Copyright © 1997, 2003, 2006 by BSCS
ISBN 0-7575-1251-8

This material is based on work supported by the National Science Foundation under Grant No. ESI 9252974. Any opinions, findings, conclusions, or recommendations expressed in this publication are those of the authors and do not necessarily reflect the views of the granting agency.

Printed in the United States of America
1 2 3 4 5 6 7 8 9 10   09 08 07 06 05

Acknowledgments
Second Edition Contributors

Pedagogical Advisors

Scott Charleton, Lebanon High School, Lebanon, OH

Frank Girolami, Mason High School, Mason, OH

Barbara Grosz, Pine Crest Preparatory School, Fort Lauderdale, FL

Melanie Hardel, Hartford Union High School, Hartford, WI

Terry Houchens, Joliet Central High School, Joliet, IL

Mary McClellan, Seattle School District, Seattle, WA

Kimberly Noethen, Cornell University, Ithaca, NY

Eugene O'Brien, Hartford Union High School, Hartford, WI

Members of the BSCS-Human listserv

Content Reviewers

Dr. John G. Bailey, College of Veterinary Medicine, Mississippi State, MS (Chapter 7)

Dr. Marvin Druger, Syracuse University, Syracuse, NY (Chapter 1)

Dr. Diane Ebert-May, Michigan State University, East Lansing, MI (Chapter 9)

Dr. James J. Gallagher, Michigan State University, East Lansing, MI (Chapter 3)

Dr. Burnette W. Hamil, Mississippi State University, Mississippi State, MS (Chapter 16)

Dr. Craig Hanke, University of Wisconsin Green Bay, Green Bay, WI (Chapter 5)

Dr. Ross Jilk, Rochester University, Kansas City, MO (Chapter 12)

Carolyn W. Keys, The University of Georgia, Athens, GA (Engage, Explain, Evaluate)

Dr. Norman G. Lederman, Illinois Institute of Technology, Chicago, IL (Chapter 2)

Dr. Sarah H. Martin, University of Southern Mississippi, Hattiesburg, MS (Chapters 13 and 14)

Dr. Rhonda A. Patterson, University of Southern Mississippi, Hattiesburg, MS (Chapter 6)

Dr. Montgomery Slatkin, University of California, Berkeley, CA (Chapter 11)

Dr. Marshall Sundberg, Emporia State University, Emporia, KS (Chapter 15)

Dr. James H. Wandersee, Louisiana State University, Baton Rouge, LA (Chapter 8)

Dr. Richard E. Wilson, Rockhurst University, Kansas City, MO (Chapter 4)

Consultants

Dr. Robert D. Carlson, Marshfield Clinic, Marshfield, WI

Diana Gordon, Vernier Software & Technology, Beaverton, OR

Dr. Eileen M. Lento, PASCO Scientific, Roseville, CA

Dr. Gerald Saunders, University of Northern Colorado, Greeley, CO

Geof Smith, Ward's Natural Science Establishment, Inc., Rochester, NY

Dr. Edward B. Whitney, Colorado Department of Labor, Denver, CO

First Edition Contributors

Contributors

Robert A. Bouchard, College of Wooster, Wooster, OH; Edward Drexler, Pius XI High School, Milwaukee, WI; Kim Finer, Kent State University, Canton, OH; Ann Haley-Oliphant, Miami University, Oxford, OH; Laura J. Laughran, New Directions, Tucson, AZ

Consultants

Susan Speece, External Evaluator, Fresno City College, Fresno, CA; Constance Bouchard, College of Wooster, Wooster, OH; Ted Dunning, New Mexico State University, Las Cruces, NM; Irene Pepperberg, University of Arizona, Tucson, AZ; Bert Kempers, Will Allgood, and Mark Viner, Media Design Associates, Inc., Boulder, CO; Larry N. Norton, Quantum Technology, Inc.,

Evergreen, CO; Chester Penk, Quantum Technology, Inc., Evergreen, CO; Ward's Natural Science Establishment, Inc., Rochester, NY.

Advisory Board

Judy Capra, Jefferson County Public Schools, Golden, CO; Mack Clark, Academy School District 20, Colorado Springs, CO; Diane Ebert-May, Northern Arizona University, Flagstaff, AZ; Philip R. Elliott, The Colorado College, Colorado Springs, CO; April Gardner (*Executive Committee*), University of Northern Colorado, Greeley, CO; Michele Girard, Peyton High School, Peyton, CO; Eville Gorham, University of Minnesota, Minneapolis, MN; Joseph Graves, Arizona State University—West, Phoenix, AZ; Ann Haley-Oliphant (*Executive Committee*), Miami

University, Oxford, OH; Paul DeHart Hurd, Prof. Emeritus, Stanford University, Stanford, CA; Mary Kiely, Stanford University, Stanford, CA; Douglas Kissler, Douglas County High School, Castle Rock, CO; Carole Kubota, University of Washington, Seattle, WA; Douglas Lundberg, Air Academy High School, United States Air Force Academy, CO; Michael E. Martinez (*Executive Committee*), University of California, Irvine, CA; Donald E. Mason, Mitchell High School, Colorado Springs, CO; Laurence McCullough, Baylor College of Medicine, Houston, TX; Martin K. Nickels, Illinois State University, Normal, IL; Floyd Nordland, Prof. Emeritus, Purdue University, West Lafayette, IN; S. Scott Obenshain, University of New Mexico, Albuquerque, NM; William O'Rourke,

Harrison School District, Colorado Springs, CO; Ann Pollet, Pueblo County High School, Pueblo, CO; Jerry Resnick, Clara Barton High School, Brooklyn, NY; Parker A. Small, Jr., University of Florida, Gainesville, FL; Gordon E. Uno, University of Oklahoma, Norman, OK; Betty M. Vetter, Commission on Professionals in Science and Technology, Washington, DC; Bruce Wallace (*Executive Committee*), Virginia Polytechnic Institute and State University, Blacksburg, VA; Harry Zimbrick, School District 11, Colorado Springs, CO.

Reviewers

Douglas Allchin, University of Texas, El Paso, TX; Tom Anderson, University of Illinois, Champaign, IL; James Botsford, New Mexico State University, Las Cruces, NM; Robert A. Bouchard, College of Wooster, Wooster, OH; Jack Carter, Prof. Emeritus, The Colorado College, Colorado Springs, CO; Frank Cassel, Prof. Emeritus, North Dakota St. University, Fargo, ND; Angelo Collins, Vanderbilt University, Nashville, TN; Robert Cook-Degan, Institute of Medicine, Washington, DC; David Corbin, Monsanto Company, Chesterfield, MO; Jorge Crisci, Museo de La Plata, Argentina; Mary Ann Cutter, University of Colorado, Colorado Springs, CO; Hans Dethlefs, The Neighborhood Health Center—South, Omaha, NE; Edward Drexler, Pius XI High School, Milwaukee, WI; James Ebersole, The Colorado College, Colorado Springs, CO; Diane Ebert-May, Northern Arizona University, Flagstaff, AZ; Philip R. Elliott, The Colorado College, Colorado Springs, CO; Michael Fatone, United States Air Force Academy, CO; Kim Finer, Kent State University, Canton, OH; Steven Fleck, United States Olympic Center, Colorado Springs, CO; Geoff Gamble, Washington State University, Pullman, WA; Barbara Grosz, Pine Crest School, Fort Lauderdale, FL; Topper Hagerman, Steadman-Hawkins Sports Medicine Foundation, Vail, CO; Jerry Harder, NOAA Aeronomy Laboratory, Boulder, CO; Jeff Hays, United States Air Force Academy, CO; Werner Heim, Prof. Emeritus, The Colorado College, Colorado Springs, CO; Barry Hewlett, Washington State University, Pullman, WA; Michael Hoffman, The Colorado College, Colorado Springs, CO; Michael Keelan, Medical College of Wisconsin, Milwaukee, WI; Rich Kulmacz, University of Texas Health Science Center, Houston, TX; Linda Lundgren, Bear Creek High School, Lakewood, CO; Thomas Manney, Kansas State University, Manhattan, KS; Cheryl Mason, San Diego State University, San Diego, CA; Jeffry Mitton, University of Colorado, Boulder, CO; Adrian Morrison, University of Pennsylvania, Philadelphia, PA; Jamie Nekoba, Waiákea High School, Hilo, HI; Gene O'Brien, Hartford Union High School, Hartford, WI; John Opitz, Montana State University, Helena, MT; Carl Pierce, Harrington Cancer Center, Amarillo, TX; Tracy Posnanski, University of Wisconsin, Milwaukee, WI; Ken Rainis, Ward's Natural Science Establishment, Inc., Rochester, NY; Barbara Saigo, Saiwood Biology Resources, Montgomery, AL; Orwyn Sampson, Brigadier General Retired, United States Air Force Academy, CO; James Short, Packer Collegiate Institute, Brooklyn, NY; James Siedow, Duke University, Durham, NC; Fran Slowiczek, San Diego City Schools, San Diego, CA; Susan Speece, Fresno City College, Fresno, CA; Sam Stoler, National Institutes of Health, Washington, DC; Richard Storey, The Colorado College, Colorado Springs, CO; Gordon E. Uno, University of Oklahoma, Norman, OK; Jeff Velten, New Mexico State University, Las Cruces, NM; Mariana Wolfner, Cornell University, Ithaca, NY.

Field-Test Centers and Coordinators

First Edition

Arizona

Northern Arizona University, Flagstaff, AZ: Diane Ebert-May, Julie McCormick, Brownie Sternberg

Colorado

BSCS, Colorado Springs, CO: Laura J. Laughran, Randall K. Backe

University of Northern Colorado, Greeley, CO: April Gardner, Alan Lennon, Brenda Zink

Florida

University of South Florida, Tampa, FL: Barbara Spector, Leslie Brackin, Craig Holm

Kansas

Kansas State University, Manhattan, KS: Gail Shroyer, Carol Arjona

Ohio

Miami University, Oxford, OH: Jane Butler Kahle, Rick Fairman

Washington

University of Washington, Seattle, WA: Carole Kubota, Claire McDaniel Orner

Field-Test Schools and Teachers

First Edition

Colombia, South America
Haydée Bejardno de Cadena, Marcela Melendez, Monica Sarmiento, Colegio Los Nogales, Bogotá

Arizona
Marcia Fisher, Arcadia High School, Scottsdale; Doug Davis, Dub Manis, Dee Schwartz, Chinle High School, Chinle; Geri Fisher, Jo Quintenz, Desert View High School, Tucson; Kathy Thayer, Ray High School, Ray; Clyde Christensen, Scott Greenhalgh, Ray Pool, Mary Southall, Elizabeth Stone, Tempe High School, Tempe; Willie Long Reed, Tuba City High School, Tuba City; Jack Johnson, Williams High School, Williams; Carlos Estrada, Karen Steele, Window Rock High School, Fort Defiance

Colorado
Don Born, Peggy Wickliff, Air Academy High School, United States Air Force Academy; Linda Lynch, Douglas County High School, Castle Rock; Doug Hewins, Liberty High School, Colorado Springs; Barbara Andrews, Mitchell High School, Colorado Springs; Rata Clarke, Ray Coddington, Jean Orton, Jim Snare, Palmer High School, Colorado Springs; Rod Baker, Michele Girard, Peyton High School, Peyton; Kathy Dorman, Malcom Hovde, Ponderosa High School, Parker; Ann Pollet, Deborah Walters, Pueblo County High School, Pueblo; Glen Smith, Sabin Junior High School, Colorado Springs; Jeff Cogburn, B.J. Stone, Valley High School, Gilcrest; Bill Bragg, Wasson High School, Colorado Springs; Larry Jakel, Doug Steward, Weld Central High School, Keenesburg; Jay Matheson, West Center for Intergenerational Learning, Colorado Springs; Christy Beauprez, Glenn Peterson, Windsor High School, Windsor

Florida
James Happel, Constance Hopkins, Manatee High School, Bradenton; Scott MacGregor, Joe Martin, Palmetto High School, Palmetto; Barbara Grosz, Pine Crest School, Fort Lauderdale

Hawaii
Jamie Nekoba, Waiákea High School, Hilo; Jennifer Busto, Maryknoll Schools, Honolulu

Illinois
Shelly Peretz, Thornridge High School, Dolton

Kansas
J.D. Hand, Chuck Mowry, Gina Whaley, Junction City Senior High School, Junction City

Minnesota
Clyde Cummins, St. Paul Academy Summit School, St. Paul

Missouri
David Jungmeyer, California R-1 High School, California

New Jersey
Judith Jones, Saint John Vianney High School, Holmdel; Margaret Sheldon, West Morris Central High School, Chester; Karen Martin, West Morris Mendham High School, Mendham

Ohio
Barbara Blackwell, Susan Keiffer-Barone, Aiken High School, Cincinnati; Scott Popoff, Sycamore High School, Cincinnati

Texas
Peter Mariner, Francis Mikan, Dean Mohlman, Tom Stege, St. Stephen's Episcopal School, Austin

Washington
Kathleen Heidenrich, Vicky Lamoreaux, River Ridge High School, Lacey; Larry Bencivengo, Mary Margaret Welch, Mercer Island High School, Mercer Island; Mary Ketchum, Jeannie Wenndorf, Lindberg High School, Renton; Gro Buer, Carol Nussbaum, B.E.S.T. Alternative School, Kirkland; Connie Kelly, Diane Lashinsky, Patrick Taylor, Shorecrest High School, Seattle

Wisconsin
Gene O'Brien, Hartford Union High School, Hartford

Contents

PEDAGOGICAL OVERVIEW

The Biological Sciences Curriculum Study has developed *BSCS Biology: A Human Approach*, an innovative, activity-driven biology program that is appropriate for *all* high school students. It is a sequential, full-year, general biology curriculum that makes frequent use of human examples to engage 9th- and 10th-grade students in the fundamental concepts of biology.

Foremost among the program's innovative features is a comprehensive emphasis on the unifying concepts of biology and less emphasis on vocabulary and the memorization of disconnected facts. Instead of the typical encyclopedic approach to biology, broad concepts and the factual content that elaborates those concepts are presented in ways that demonstrate biological interconnections, permit an in-depth exploration of life, and establish a relevance to students' lives. Such an approach necessarily means that certain topics often covered in survey courses must be omitted. In deciding what content to retain, we relied on the recommendations of the impressive group of scientists and educators who developed the *National Science Education Standards* (NRC, 1996) and *Developing Biological Literacy* (BSCS, 1993). Complementing the conceptual approach to biology is the program's explicit instruction model, which is based on the constructivist philosophy of learning.

BSCS Biology: A Human Approach also strongly emphasizes the development of students' problem-solving, critical-thinking, and inquiry skills. This curriculum allows learners to conduct investigations that are meaningful to them and that highlight experimental design, analysis, and the application of concepts, rather than the perfunctory verification of processes about which students already have learned. And to accommodate the demand that students be able to apply their understanding of biology to the personal, social, and ethical demands of scientific literacy, this program uses real-world connections and thematic approaches that bridge the gap between familiar student experiences and more abstract biology theories.

One of our goals in designing *BSCS Biology: A Human Approach* was to develop a curriculum that meets the needs of a changing discipline and a changing education environment. The rapid increase in the knowledge base of biology demands that students develop lifelong-learning skills that encourage continued science literacy. In this course, we believe that we have provided the tools to meet this need by presenting biology in a way that unifies life and establishes a relevance to students' lives. In addition, our careful treatment of the nature and methods of science helps to develop students' own scientific habits of mind.

To meet the needs of teachers who must facilitate learning in classrooms characterized by student populations with multiple abilities and learning styles, we have developed a flexible curriculum that can be individualized to suit particular teaching styles and unique classroom settings. An explicit instructional model, collaborative and cooperative learning opportunities, ongoing assessment, alternative and optional activities, and a variety of educational technologies all can be used to adapt the curriculum to virtually any learning situation. Chapter implementation flowcharts at the beginning of each chapter in the teacher's guide alert teachers to tools, skills, and concepts that are pertinent to the chapter. Together, the elements of this program support the following goals for teachers:

- ◆ Decreased dependence on a central text and increased use of a variety of instructional materials and strategies
- ◆ Decreased use of lecture, and increased use of activities including laboratory and educational courseware

- Decreased perceptions that science is a body of knowledge and that technology is the application of knowledge, and increased understanding that science is a way of knowing and technology is a way of adapting
- Decreased use of structured materials, and increased empowerment through the decision-making process for curriculum and instruction
- Decreased use of traditional tests, and increased use of authentic science assessment, such as portfolios, hands-on performance tests, and checklists for skills

The same innovations that support a teacher's role as a facilitator of learning also help students assume greater responsibility for their own learning. This program supports the following goals for students:

- Understand major biological concepts
- Understand the role, place, and interactions of humans in the biosphere
- Appreciate the diversity of living systems
- Demonstrate mastery of the processes of scientific inquiry
- Use such cognitive skills as critical thinking, problem solving, and ethical analysis
- Understand that science is a way of knowing and that technology is a way of adapting
- Understand the personal, social, and ethical implications of biology and biotechnology
- Use educational technologies as tools for learning

The rest of this front matter has four sections—the Program Overview, which includes information about the content, the components, and the distinguishing characteristics of *BSCS Biology: A Human Approach*; Guidelines for Laboratory Safety; teacher's notes for Appendix B, *Technique 4 The Compound Microscope*; and a Master Materials List.

PROGRAM OVERVIEW

A. Content

We organized this program into three sections and six core units. The three sections are the Engage, Explain, and Evaluate Sections. They come at the beginning, middle, and end of the program and are described in the following pages as part of the description of the instructional model. The six core units are (1) Evolution: Patterns and Products of Change in Living Systems, (2) Homeostasis: Maintaining Dynamic Equilibrium in Living Systems, (3) Energy, Matter, and Organization: Relationships in Living Systems, (4) Continuity: Reproduction and Inheritance in Living Systems, (5) Development: Growth and Differentiation in Living Systems, and (6) Ecology: Interaction and Interdependence in Living Systems.

Six key features distinguish this program, and they are described in the following pages. (The *Implementation Guide*, Section 1 on the *Teacher Resource CD*, contains a more detailed discussion of each of these features.)

Unifying Themes

Before beginning the development of *BSCS Biology: A Human Approach*, BSCS conducted a design study to determine what biological concepts and principles are critical to the study of biology at the high school level. The subsequent report, *Developing Biological Literacy*, published by BSCS in 1993, listed six unifying principles or themes that we have used for the conceptual organization of the program. The *National Science Education Standards*, published by the National Research Council in 1996, also identify six broad conceptual themes in the life sciences, five of which correlate directly with the themes used to organize the units in *BSCS Biology: A Human Approach*, thus reinforcing the wisdom of this program's organization. (The sixth theme in the standards, Behavior, does not serve as the focal point for any single unit, but instead is discussed in the context of several other unifying themes, including Development.)

Evolution: Patterns and Products of Change in Living Systems. What does it mean to be human? That is the central question of Unit 1. Learners will assess the unique qualities of humans and the diversity of life while trying to place humans in the scheme of living systems. Then they will consider characteristics that are common to all living systems as well as those that are unique to humans, and they will grapple with the question of whether life is definable. Unity, diversity, genetic variation, and evolution, including cultural evolution, are the major conceptual themes in Unit 1.

Homeostasis: Maintaining Dynamic Equilibrium in Living Systems. Unit 2 explores the requirement of a controlled internal environment for optimal functioning of an organism. Learners will use familiar examples to develop an understanding of the concepts of response, regulation, and feedback. Then they will examine the division between internal and external conditions and the processes by which internal conditions are maintained in spite of changes in external conditions. In the final chapter of the unit, they expand these concepts by analyzing the way health and disease affect both the individual human and society as a group.

Energy, Matter, and Organization: Relationships in Living Systems. Unit 3 begins by letting students explain the requirements of physical performance and by considering the effects of fitness, drugs, and alcohol on performance. They will develop an understanding of the relationship between structure and function by using mobility as an example of activity. Then they will explore the interplay between energy and matter through the organization of metabolic processes, such as photosynthesis and cellular respiration, as well as through interactions in a community. Finally, they will consider the role of producers, consumers, and decomposers in the flow of energy and cycling of matter in a community.

Continuity: Reproduction and Inheritance in Living Systems. Unit 4 focuses on reproduction, patterns of inheritance, and the role of genes and DNA in inheritance. The discussion of human sexual reproduction includes reproductive systems and cycles, reproductive behavior, and ethical issues, such as contraception, abortion, and sexually transmitted diseases. Students will consider continuity and variation in the context of inheritance, and genes as a source of information that is organized as a genetic code stored in DNA. In conclusion, learners will study the dynamics of gene expression and replication at a molecular level, which provides a basis for understanding genetic engineering.

Development: Growth and Differentiation in Living Systems. As Unit 5 begins, students will consider development as a process that involves differentiation and growth and that requires regulation. They will explore patterns of development, which appear in stages such as reproductive maturity, aging, and death. Development is affected by evolutionary history and provides opportunities for evolutionary change, and it depends on communication. Finally, learners consider human life stages, looking at biologically programmed events as well as the cultural environment in which they occur.

Ecology: Interaction and Interdependence in Living Systems. Unit 6 centers on issues in the major conceptual area of ecology, including dilemmas about the interactions among populations, resources, and environments. Students will examine the concepts involved in population dynamics, which set the stage for studying the interactions between humans and their environment. Next, learners will focus on how human actions can modify the environment, especially through the use of technology. The final emphasis is on the ethical issues raised by human actions and technology.

B. Components

Student Book

The student book contains activities and essays. The activities are the core of the program, and they drive the conceptual learning. Activities involve hands-on/minds-on manipulation, laboratory activities, paper-and-pencil inquiries, computer simulations, video learning, and other activities. The essays introduce, formalize, or elaborate concepts; provide historical insights; provide cultural, social, technological, and ethical perspectives; and reveal the nature of science. The essays, which follow each unit, are organized in a magazine format that appeals to most students. Each essay is self-contained, that is, essays do not generally have transitions connecting one to the next as do standard texts.

Teacher Guide

The teacher guide includes overviews of the activities, materials lists, preparations, strategies for guiding learners, assessment strategies (noted by icons), flowcharts for chapter implementation, appropriate uses for educational technologies (video activities noted by DVD icons), and student responses to procedural and Analysis questions.

Teacher Resource CD

The *Teacher Resource CD (TRCD)* contains the following:

◆ An implementation guide, which offers detailed strategies for using the innovations in this program as well as a model for a week-long training institute
◆ A guide to cooperative learning
◆ A correlation of this program to the *National Science Education Standards*
◆ Copymasters for all activities that require them
◆ Optional activities
◆ A guide to educational technology and the DVD video library

Unlike some other programs, the *TRCD* is not an ancillary component of *BSCS Biology: A Human Approach.* In addition to the required instruction tools, such as assessments and DVD narratives, the *TRCD* is a valuable professional development resource that most teachers will want to use during the first several years of implementing the innovations in this program.

Guide to Assessment CD

The *Guide to Assessment CD (GACD)* contains:

◆ A guide to assessment, which includes a complete set of assessment instruments

Interactive DVD Video Library

The program includes a DVD that contains motion sequences and still pictures. Students will work with the DVD videos in large groups, small groups, or individually.

Educational Technology

Educational technology is part of each instructional unit. Several laboratory investigations are designed to allow students to use probe ware and microcomputers to collect data. SciLinks reference Internet sites that provide additional information about specific topics. *The Commons* CD-ROM provides experience with simulations and modeling.

Materials and Equipment

Ward's Natural Science Establishment, Inc., is the official supplier for this program and develops and provides special materials and kits as needed. Ward's also offers a master materials list for this program in disk format, which may expedite ordering.

C. Distinguishing Characteristics

Subthemes

Science as Inquiry. The Science as Inquiry subtheme refers both to the discovery process by which information is obtained and evaluated and to the changing body of knowledge that characterizes scientific understanding. We use this theme to expose learners systematically to the processes of science, including making observations, making inferences, assembling evidence, developing hypotheses, designing experiments, collecting data, analyzing and presenting results, and communicating and evaluating conclusions. Students' scientific habits of mind and inquiry abilities culminate in a full inquiry, which students begin following Unit 3.

Science and Humanity. The Science and Humanity subtheme makes the students' study of biology more relevant and approachable by incorporating the critical elements of human culture: the history of science; the place of ethics, ethical analysis, and decision making in today's controversial science world; and the importance of human technology as a way of adapting.

Science and Culture. Many aspects of culture influence the biological world. We want learners to become aware of the role that culture plays in environmental and health care issues, and to appreciate the diversity of cultural approaches to various situations in the natural world.

Science and Change. Biology is not a static body of knowledge. We want students to appreciate that biological knowledge changes across time as scientists collect more evidence, as they view the same evidence in a different way, and as they develop different ways of observing and collecting data.

Science for All. It is important for all future citizens to be able to think clearly and critically about a variety of personal and societal issues. In this program, we provide students with opportunities to develop skills related to ethical analysis and decision making in contexts that are relevant to them.

Science and Technology. We define technology as the use of knowledge to achieve a practical solution to a perceived problem and recognize that the ultimate effects of the technological process or product on society and the biosphere may extend beyond the intended effects.

Instructional Model

The instruction of major concepts is organized around an instructional model that is based on the constructivist philosophy of learning. This philosophy of learning maintains that learners build or construct new ideas on top of their old ideas.

We call the instructional model the "5Es" because each chapter is organized around *five* phases of learning that we best can describe using five words that begin with "E": *Engage*, *Explore*, *Explain*, *Elaborate*, and *Evaluate*. This instructional model allows students and teachers to experience common activities, to use and build on prior knowledge and experience, to construct meaning, and to assess their understanding of a concept continually.

Engage: This phase of the instructional model initiates the learning task. The activity should (1) activate prior knowledge and make connections between past and present learning experiences, and (2) anticipate activities and focus students' thinking on the learning outcomes of current activities. The learner should become mentally engaged in the concept, process, or skill to be explored.

Explore: This phase of the instructional model provides students with a common base of experiences within which they identify and develop current concepts, processes, and skills. During this phase, students actively explore their environment or manipulate materials.

Explain: This phase of the instructional model focuses learners on developing an explanation for the concepts they have been exploring. As a result, they have opportunities to verbalize their conceptual understanding or to demonstrate their skills or behaviors. This phase also provides opportunities for teachers to introduce formal labels, definitions, and explanations for concepts, processes, skills, or behaviors.

Elaborate: This phase of the instructional model challenges and extends students' conceptual understanding and allows further opportunity for students to practice desired skills and behaviors. Through new experiences, the learners develop deeper and broader understanding of major concepts, obtain more information about areas of interest, and refine their scientific skills.

Evaluate: This phase of the instructional model encourages learners to assess their understanding and abilities and provides opportunities for teachers to evaluate students' understanding of key concepts and development of essential skills.

In addition to this chapter-level organization, the program is organized around the 5Es. Students experience an overview of the program, including the prominent role that inquiry plays in biology, by completing the Engage Section. Units 1–3 allow learners to explore the first three unifying principles and to experience and practice all of the skills of scientific inquiry. The Explain Section then provides the students with a framework for conducting their own full, scientific inquiry. Units 4–6 are designed to allow learners to develop an understanding of the last three unifying principles and to elaborate on their understanding of the processes of science. The Evaluate Section provides several opportunities for students to evaluate their overall progress in learning biology.

Cooperative Learning

Cooperative and collaborative learning are used as strategies to decrease students' dependence on the teacher as the sole repository of information and to increase their responsibility for their own learning. Cooperative learning in this program also models the processes that scientists use when collaborating and helps teach the working-relationship skills necessary in today's team-based workforce.

In *BSCS Biology: A Human Approach*, you can use cooperative learning strategies in a significant number of the activities. These strategies will help the students achieve the program goals for the following reasons:

◆ Cooperative learning empowers the learners, making them responsible for seeking information and achieving a particular task

◆ Cooperative learning strategies model one feature of the nature of the scientific enterprise

◆ Research has shown that cooperative learning is an effective technique for involving learners from groups that are underrepresented in science, such as female and minority students

◆ Cooperative learning can be a powerful way to interest and motivate students who might not otherwise excel or even be interested in science

We have made every effort to make the cooperative learning experience at the high school level relevant without compromising the elements that are critical to successful cooperative learning. Those elements include the use of roles, the use of working-relationship skills, positive interdependence, individual accountability, distributed leadership, group autonomy, heterogeneous grouping, and team self-evaluation. *A Guide to Cooperative Learning,* Section 2 on the *TRCD,* explains these roles and provides more information about cooperative learning.

Assessment

Assessment opportunities, which allow you to evaluate your students' progress on an ongoing basis, are embedded throughout the program and are based on the philosophy that assessment itself should be a learning experience. The following strategies, which include both formal and informal assessment techniques, are included in the program:

◆ Performance-based assessments such as experiments

◆ Written tests with a variety of short-answer and essay questions

◆ Working-relationship assessments in cooperative learning activities

◆ Debates

◆ Presentations, both team and individual

◆ Written assignments, both team and individual

◆ Journal assignments that include short-term and long-term work

◆ Projects, both ongoing and one-time

◆ A folder activity for a newly discovered organism

◆ Portfolios

◆ Opportunities for self-assessment and peer-assessment

◆ Discussions, both team and whole-class

You will find more information on assessment in the *Guide to Assessment CD.*

Educational Technology

Educational technology is integral to the program and is used as a tool to enhance learning and understanding whenever it provides the best learning experience. With the exception of the video DVD activities, which are used at some point in nearly every chapter, nontechnological alternatives are available for most of the electronic technology-based activities. The program includes four major electronic technologies:

◆ Video DVDs, which include interactive, inquiry-based video activities

◆ Probe ware instructions for microcomputer-based laboratories

◆ A computer simulation, which allows students to explore complex biological interactions

◆ SciLinks, which provide links to supplemental Internet resources

Journals

Students use a journal throughout the course as a key piece of developing conceptual continuity. The use of the journal is integral to student participation and growth. At different times, students will use their journals in the following ways:

◆ Recording data

◆ Taking notes

◆ Responding to questions in the activities

◆ Responding to Further Challenges in the activities

◆ Keeping track of questions they may have

◆ Keeping track of their cooperative-learning responsibilities as part of assessments

◆ Keeping long-term records and projects.

You can build on the role of the journal by recommending that students record upcoming assignments there or by adding reflective exercises of your own. The Engage Section and Appendix B in the student book have information for learners about keeping a journal.

D. Icons

In *BSCS Biology: A Human Approach*, we use various icons to identify elements of the program that affect safety, learning, and instruction. Tell your students about the following icons, which they will see throughout the activity pages.

Student Page Icons

Essay icon. In *BSCS Biology: A Human Approach*, we provide essays that the learners can use as one resource to complete activity tasks, questions, labs, and projects. The essays, which are short, self-contained, magazine-style articles, are grouped at the end of each unit in the student book. Essay icons appear in the activity pages the first time an essay is referenced. Tell your students about this feature of the student pages.

Safety icons. In *BSCS Biology: A Human Approach*, we use safety icons to alert students to potential hazards and to strategies that they can use to protect themselves, such as wearing goggles and aprons. See Appendix A at the back of the student pages for detailed descriptions of each of the student safety icons.

Lab Gloves   Safety Goggles   Lab Apron

Flammable!   Poison!   Caution

Teacher Page Icons

In the teacher guide, the *TRCD* and the *GACD*, you will encounter the following icons, which identify assessment opportunities, uses of educational technology, and other instructional tools:

Assessment icon. In *BSCS Biology: A Human Approach*, we use assessment icons to alert you to opportunities to assess for students' prior knowledge, preconceptions, and current understanding. For a detailed discussion of the assessment philosophy and strategies in this program, see the *GACD*.

***Guide to Assessment CD* icon.** In *BSCS Biology: A Human Approach*, we use *Guide to Assessment CD* (*GACD*) icons to alert you to rubrics for clarifying the expectations of an assignment and providing an efficient means for evaluating student work. Consult the Rubrics section of the *GACD* to find these assessment tools.

***Teacher Resource CD* icon.** In *BSCS Biology: A Human Approach*, we use *Teacher Resource CD* (*TRCD*) icons to alert you to copymasters and optional activities that may be necessary or helpful in teaching a given activity. Consult the appropriate section of the *TRCD* to find these materials.

Computer icon. In *BSCS Biology: A Human Approach*, we use computer icons to alert you to the use of a computer or other probe ware system in an activity. Computers or other probe ware systems are used in microcomputer-based laboratories and in simulations of complex biological events. Consult the educational technology section of the *TRCD* for more information about probe ware, simulations, and system modeling.

Video DVD icon. In *BSCS Biology: A Human Approach*, we use DVD icons to alert you to the need for a DVD player for an activity. Descriptions of video segments and video strategies are described in an interactive DVD guide in the educational technology section of the *TRCD*.

Safety icon. In *BSCS Biology: A Human Approach*, we use a safety icon in the Preparations section to alert you to potentially hazardous materials or situations, such as preparing chemicals for a lab. We also use this icon in the strategies if students are doing something that is potentially dangerous.

***The Commons* icon.** In *BSCS Biology: A Human Approach*, we use *The Commons* icons to alert you to the use of *The Commons CD-ROM* in an activity. *The Commons CD* contains interactive environmental activities that are integrated into *Unit 6, Ecology: Interactions and Interdependence in Living Systems*. Consult the educational technology section of the *TRCD* for more information about installing, running, and setting the preferences for *The Commons CD-ROM*.

GUIDELINES FOR LABORATORY SAFETY

A. Overview

Safety must be a major consideration in a biology laboratory. The safety information in this teacher's guide is not intended to be a complete guide but rather to help you organize your own laboratory safety program. Consult your school authorities and local and state regulations for further information. Keep informed of new safety data made available by government agencies, educational organizations, and other sources, and update your safety programs as necessary.

Before each laboratory experience, anticipate possible accidents and take steps to prevent them. Preventing an accident is, after all, the goal of a safety program. Base your conduct and expectations on the students' age, background, and intelligence. Do not expect them to behave as responsible adults.

Post laboratory rules in a conspicuous place in the laboratory. Insist on a safety contract between the student and the school. Devise your own, or use the sample presented in this overview.

Instruct students in techniques of laboratory safety, and give them the opportunity to demonstrate their knowledge of proper safety practices. When students learn what is expected of them, and when you show that you are safety conscious, they will be more likely to follow appropriate safety procedures. A list of basic safety considerations follows.

1. Have a thorough understanding of each activity and the potential hazards of the materials, equipment, and procedures required.

2. Prior to conducting an activity, be sure that all safety and personal protective equipment is present and in good working order. Before students begin an activity, review specific safety rules and demonstrate proper procedures.

3. Never permit students to work in or be present in the laboratory without supervision. No unauthorized activity should be conducted, and no unauthorized materials should be brought into the laboratory.

4. Lock the laboratory and storeroom when you are not present. Do not allow students to enter the storeroom at any time.

5. Mark locations of, and call students' attention to, eyewash stations, safety showers, and fire blankets in the laboratory and storeroom. Also, mark locations of chemical spill kits, fire extinguishers (ABC tri-class), and first aid kits.

6. Post an evacuation diagram and procedure by each exit.

7. Provide for separate, labeled disposal containers for glass and sharp objects, and separate, labeled disposal containers for individual waste chemical reagents.

8. For safety and economy, use small hot plates with an on/off switch and indicator light whenever possible. Do not use alcohol lamps.

9. Allow no food or beverages in the laboratory and no application of cosmetics. Guard against toxic exposure by providing adequate ventilation. Remind students not to ingest chemicals, and identify plants or animals that may cause irritation or poisoning by contact or by bite. Caution students to keep their hands and fingers away from their faces and to wash their hands with soap and water before leaving the laboratory.

10. Know the location of the master shut-off for laboratory electrical circuits, gas, and water.

11. Notify those in authority of the existence or development of any hazard.

12. Remind students that they must report directly to you any accident, no matter how trivial. Keep written records of events related to accidents.

Laboratory Safety Agreement

I, _____ , agree to abide by these laboratory safety regulations whenever performing a biology activity. I will do the following:

1. Use the science laboratory for authorized work only
2. Remove contact lenses and wear safety goggles when instructed to do so
3. Know the four hazard classes and control measures
4. Study the laboratory activity before coming to the lab (If in doubt about any procedure, I will ask the teacher.)
5. Know how to use the safety equipment and know the location of the fire extinguisher, eyewash station, safety shower, and fire blanket
6. Alert the teacher in case of fire, and leave the laboratory
7. Check carefully for the presence of any ignition source (open flames, electric heating coils) before using flammable materials such as alcohol
8. Place broken glass and disposable materials in their designated containers
9. Report any incident, accident, injury, or unsafe procedure to the teacher at once
10. Never taste, touch, or smell any substance unless the teacher specifically directs me to do so
11. Handle chemicals carefully, check the label of every bottle or jar before removing the contents, and never return unused chemicals to reagent containers
12. Make sure that the mouth of the test tube points away from other people and away from myself when heating a substance in a test tube
13. Use proper equipment to handle hot glassware
14. Tie back long hair, remove dangling jewelry, roll up loose sleeves, and tuck in loose clothing
15. Clean the work area at the end of the lab, wash and store all materials and equipment, and turn off all water, gas, and electrical appliances
16. Wash my hands thoroughly with soap and water before leaving the laboratory

_____   _____
Student's signature   Parent's or guardian's signature

_____
Date

B. Personal Protective Equipment

Whenever chemicals or laboratory equipment are used, everyone in the laboratory should wear safety goggles and laboratory aprons. Loose clothing, full blouses, ties, bows, and so forth should be tucked in. Long hair should be tied back securely. If a chemical spill occurs on someone's clothing or soft cloth shoes, the individual should remove the article and wash the skin thoroughly with running water. Do not attempt to wash off a harmful chemical while the clothing is on the body. Use the safety shower in such cases. (See *safety shower* for details.) Contaminated shoes rarely can be reused; contaminated clothing must be laundered separately before reuse.

When corrosives are used, students should wear both safety goggles and a face shield, as well as a laboratory apron and impervious gloves (nitrile rubber). A safety shower and eyewash station should be within a 30-second walking distance. Specifications for protective equipment follow.

Lab apron. Gray or black rubber-coated cloth, Tyvek, or vinyl (nylon-coated), halter type are recommended when working with corrosives or solvents. Disposable polyethylene is recommended only to prevent physical contact with water-based reagents that are not, in themselves, corrosives or solvents.

Gloves. Nitrile or neoprene rubber is recommended when handling acids, caustics, or organic solvents. Polyethylene or natural latex gloves should be used only for protection against water-based reagents that are not corrosives or solvents.

Safety goggles. Clear, high-impact polystyrene; must meet ANSI Standard Z87.1.

Face shield. Must meet ANSI Standard Z87.1; should be used in combination with safety goggles when working with corrosives, reactives, or solvents.

Contact lenses. Liquids can be drawn under a contact lens by capillary action and into direct contact with the eyeball. Therefore, wearing contact lenses for cosmetic reasons should be prohibited in the laboratory. Students who must wear contact lenses prescribed by a physician should wear eye-cup ANSI Z87.1-approved safety goggles. These are similar to the goggles sometimes worn when swimming underwater. If an accident occurs (despite the protection of safety goggles), the student should immediately remove the goggles and the contact lenses and flush the eyes, including under the eyelids, while moving the eyeball from side to side and up and down, at the eyewash station for at least 15 minutes. Meanwhile, call a physician.

Eyewash station. Must meet ANSI Standard Z358.1 and be within a 30-second walking distance from any spot in the room. The device must be capable of delivering a gentle but full flow of water to both eyes for at least 15 minutes. Portable liquid supply devices are not satisfactory and should not be used. A plumbed-hose attached to a plumbed-in outlet and designed for use as an eyewash fountain is suitable if it meets ANSI Standard Z358.1. Demonstrate the use of the eyewash station to your students. Follow the procedure described in First Aid—Eyes on page xxi.

Safety shower. Must meet ANSI Standard Z358.1 and be within a 30-second walking distance from any spot in the room. Students should be instructed in the use of the safety shower in the event of a fire or chemical splash on clothing. Chemicals should be flushed off the bare skin for at least 15 minutes while under the safety shower. Make certain students understand that contaminated clothing, shoes, wristwatches, and so forth *must be removed while under the shower.* False modesty is a poor exchange for permanent injury. Call a doctor while the victim is still under the shower.

No safety shower is referred to in the cautionary statements that accompany each activity because the quantities of chemicals used in this laboratory program are kept sufficiently small. A safety shower should be present in the laboratory, however, as a precaution against fires or chemical spills related to other laboratory procedures.

C. Understanding Chemical Hazards

General Information

Some degree of hazard or risk is associated with every chemical that you or your students will handle. Using chemicals safely means understanding the hazards and taking the appropriate measures to prevent harm. A hazardous chemical is any substance likely to cause injury if precautionary measures are not taken. The hazards presented by any chemical can be grouped into the following categories: flammables, poisons (toxins), corrosives, and reactives. A particular chemical may present more than one hazard.

When dealing with chemical hazards, be aware of and follow general safety procedures regarding storage, disposal, spills, and first aid, as listed below. Detailed information about specific chemical categories follows this listing.

Signal Words

This program uses the signal words *CAUTION, WARNING,* and *DANGER* specifically to inform both the teacher and the student about the degree of risk or physical harm associated with a particular material or activity.

CAUTION: denotes a low level of risk associated with use.
WARNING: denotes a moderate level of risk associated with use.
DANGER: denotes a high level of risk associated with use.

For example, the signal word *DANGER* is used to denote a high potential of risk (corrosivity) when handling solid sodium hydroxide, but the signal word *CAUTION* is used when handling a 0.1M solution of this same material.

Chemical Hazard Labeling

Any container used by students must be labeled accurately with the following information:

◆ The *name of the material* and its concentration (if in solution)
◆ The *names of individual components* and their respective concentrations (if a mixture)
◆ The appropriate *signal word*
◆ An affirmative *statement of the potential hazard* or hazards
◆ *Precautionary measures* to be taken to avoid the hazards
◆ Immediate *first aid measures*

For example, a stock 70% isopropyl alcohol solution should be labeled as follows:

70% Isopropyl Alcohol
WARNING: Flammable liquid
Avoid open flame, heat, or sparks.
Do not ingest. Avoid skin/eye contact.
Flush spills and splashes with water
for 15 minutes; rinse mouth with water.
Call the teacher.

Small student-use containers such as dropping bottles must be labeled with the name of the chemical and the caution statement. Reagent bottles must have complete labels as shown in the example.

Refer to the materials lists for each activity for appropriate safety information when writing label warnings.

Storage

Specific information about chemical storage may be found in Management of Chemicals on page xxv. In general, chemicals should be stored in a cool, dry place away from direct sunlight and local heat and segregated according to storage colors.

Spills

These directions are generic and may not be appropriate in all cases. Refer to the Material Safety Data Sheet (MSDS) for the specific chemical for detailed instructions.

Solids. Sweep up material; avoid dusting; place in a suitable container; wash the area with water and discard water.

Liquids. Check the pH with litmus or other indicator; if necessary, adjust pH to neutrality with small amounts of $1M$ acid or base; wipe up with absorbent material and discard; wash spill area with water.

Disposal (for chemicals used in this program)

Recommended disposal procedures are included in the Preparations section of an activity for all prepared solutions that require special disposal steps. Keep in mind that these procedures may be preempted by state or local regulations. Consult the MSDS for specific procedures for stock reagents before disposal.

Aqueous liquids. Test the pH with litmus or other indicator; if necessary, adjust pH to neutrality by adding small amounts of an acid, base, or other reagent as required. (Exceptions are noted in Preparations.) In all cases, dilute aqueous liquid waste material at least 1:20 with water, and flush to a sanitary sewer (not a drain that leads to a septic tank).

Solids. Dissolve small amounts of the material completely in water; dilute this volume 1:20 with water again; flush to a sanitary sewer. (Exceptions are noted in Preparations.)

Biological materials. Actively growing culture materials should be autoclaved or steam-sterilized in a pressure cooker at 15 psi for 15 minutes. Use autoclavable bags. If an autoclave or pressure cooker is not available, aseptically add (in a fume hood) just enough full-strength chlorine laundry bleach or 70% isopropyl alcohol to cover the growing surface. Cover the container, close the hood door, and allow at least 8 hours contact time before disposal. **WARNING: Alcohol is flammable. Extinguish all flames and avoid other ignition sources.** Wear goggles, gloves, and lab apron. Dilute with water 1:20, and flush using copious amounts of water to a sanitary sewer. Autoclave or steam-sterilize contaminated objects, or place them, in the hood, in covered pans or trays containing liquid chlorine laundry bleach. Allow 24 hours contact before diluting with water 1:20 and discarding the bleach to a sanitary sewer. Wash decontaminated objects with soap and water.

First Aid

Before using any chemical, read the label and the MSDS and follow the recommended procedures. In case of spills or splashes, carry out the following immediate first aid measures:

Eyes. Immediately flush eyes, including under eyelids, with flowing water for at least 15 minutes at an eyewash station. Roll eye from side to side and up and down while flushing. Call a physician.

Skin. Wash with flowing water for at least 15 minutes. Contact a physician if redness, blisters, continued irritation, or painful symptoms develop.

Clothing. Remove any contaminated clothing within 5 minutes and wash skin as above. (For concentrated chemicals the teacher uses, go to the safety shower immediately and remove clothing while under the shower.) Launder or decontaminate any article before wearing. Contaminated clothing includes shoes, belts, watches and watchstraps, jewelry, and so forth. If laundering or decontamination is not possible, discard.

Inhalation. Remove to fresh air. Begin CPR if victim has stopped breathing. Get immediate medical attention.

Ingestion. For mouth contact, spit out, and wash mouth with running water for at least 15 minutes. Contact a physician immediately.

Poison (Toxins)

Protective equipment: Gloves, safety goggles, lab apron, container for sharp objects, chemical fume hood, secured storage ventilation sufficient to keep breathing-air concentrations well below the threshold limit value (TLV) and/or permissible exposure limit (PEL) limits

Typically, toxic chemicals can injure the body through one or more exposure routes: inhalation, ingestion, injection, and absorption through intact skin or through a break in the skin.

There are two types of toxic effects: acute and chronic. An acute effect usually occurs on exposure or within a few hours following exposure. A chronic effect is noted only following repeated exposures or after a prolonged single exposure.

Important information about toxicity in the MSDS for each substance is provided by the supplier. (See the section titled *Health Hazard Data,* or similar title, in the MSDS.)

Prevention/Control Measures

1. Treat all chemicals as potentially toxic. Use barriers, cleanliness, and avoidance when handling any chemical.

2. Wear eye protection.

3. Handle contaminated glass and metal carefully. Sharp objects are vehicles for injecting substances into the body.

4. Provide enough ventilation to keep vapor, mist, and dust concentrations well below the TLV or PEL as stated in the MSDS. Use a chemical fume hood if required.

5. Recognize symptoms of overexposure for each chemical used during an activity. These are usually described in the MSDS.

6. Become familiar with immediate first aid measures for each chemical used during an activity. See the MSDS and label.

7. Be scrupulous in housekeeping and personal hygiene.

8. Never consume food or beverages or apply cosmetics in the laboratory.

9. Wash your hands thoroughly with soap and water before leaving the laboratory.

10. Post the phone number of the nearest poison control center and consulting school physician on your telephone.

Flammables

Protective equipment: Safety goggles, approved flammables storage cabinets, fire blanket, safety shower, fire extinguishers (ABC tri-class)

Flammable substances are solids, liquids, or gases that will burn readily. The process of burning involves fuel, oxidizer, and ignition source. For burning to start, all three components must be present. To stop a fire or prevent it from starting, remove or make inaccessible at least one of those components.

Prevention/Control Measures

1. Store away from oxidizers.

2. Store only in approved containers in an approved flammable-liquid storage cabinet. Minimize the quantities available in the laboratory—usually 100 mL per bottle and 600 mL per room.

3. Remove ignition sources. Extinguish lighted burners. Check for and eliminate sources of ignition, such as sparks from static charge, friction, or electrical equipment, and hot objects such as hot plates or incandescent bulbs. Keep all ignition sources 30 feet away. If the ignition source is 6 feet above, a distance of 15 feet away is usually sufficient. (Flammable vapors are usually heavier than air and can travel long distances before being diluted below ignitable concentrations.)

4. Electrically bond and ground all metal containers before and during the dispensing of flammable liquids. Check with your local fire department for the correct procedure.

5. Ensure that ABC tri-class fire extinguishers are present in the laboratory and storeroom and that you have used these in at least one practice drill, supervised by a firefighting official, within the past year.

6. Drill students in exactly what should be done if clothes or hair catch fire. Practice "stop, drop, and roll" techniques. Be sure a safety shower is available and is in working order. A fire blanket should be available to cover a prone victim but should not be used to wrap smoldering or burning clothing, except in emergencies.

7. Conduct a fire inspection with members of the local fire department at least once a year. Practice fire drills at least annually.

8. Provide adequate ventilation to keep breathing-air concentrations well below TLV and/or PEL limits.

9. Prepare for spills by having absorbent, vapor-reducing materials close at hand. (These are available commercially.) Plan to have enough absorbent material to handle the volume of flammables on hand.

Reactives

Protective equipment: Safety goggles, lab apron, gloves, segregated storage location

Reactives are chemical substances that undergo violent reactions, generating heat, light, flammable and nonflammable gases, and toxicants under certain ambient or induced (by mixing, shock, or disturbance) conditions. Categories of reactives include, but are not limited to, the following:

◆ Acid-sensitives—react with acids or acid fumes
◆ Water-sensitives—react with moisture

- Oxidizers—promote rapid burning or explosion in materials that can burn
- Unstable—spontaneously explode when handled, moved, exposed to sunlight, rapid temperature changes, etc.

Prevention/Control Measures

1. In storage, isolate compounds of a given hazard class away from other hazard classes. Consult color storage codes. Note that certain chemicals classed "white" or "red" should be stored separately—away from other chemicals with the same storage code color. Chemicals requiring special storage assignments are identified in the Preparations section of the activities.

2. Protect from physical shock.

3. Provide a ready water source for dilution (except for water-sensitives).

4. Keep water away from water-sensitives.

5. Store in a cool, dry place away from sunlight and localized heat.

6. Familiarize yourself with any incompatibilities for *all* chemicals used or stored.

Corrosives

Protective equipment: Safety goggles, lab apron, face shield, nitrile rubber gloves, safety shower, eyewash station

Corrosives are solids, liquids, or gases that, by direct chemical action, destroy body tissues. Irritants are a group of chemicals that cause less serious injury. Sensitizers are allergenic. Hence, injury may range from sensitization/irritation to actual physical destruction of body tissues. Categories of corrosives include the following:

- Corrosive—causes destruction and irreversible alterations in living tissue
- Irritant—causes reversible inflammation in living tissue
- Sensitizer—causes allergic reaction in normal tissue of a substantial number of individuals after more than one exposure

Prevention/Control Measures

1. Store corrosives below eye level. Keep containers closed.

2. Always wear safety goggles and lab apron. Also, wear a face shield and gloves when handling any corrosive material above 1*M*.

3. Have at least one eyewash station and safety shower in close proximity. Be sure they are in working order.

4. Never wear cloth-covered, woven-leather, or open-toed shoes in the laboratory.

5. Prepare for spills by having neutralizing kits readily available in sufficient quantity for the corrosives on hand.

6. Always wash hands with soap and water after working with corrosives.

D. Management of Chemicals

Note: The following section about storage is for your general information. If you have any questions about the storage of chemicals, call the Safety Consultant at Ward's Natural Science Establishment, Inc., 800-962-2660.

Storage

Never store chemicals alphabetically unless they have been segregated into color-coded storage areas (see below). Alphabetical storage greatly increases the risk of promoting a violent reaction. A list of storage suggestions follows:

1. Store chemicals in a cool, dry place, away from sunlight and rapid temperature changes.

2. Never store chemicals on the floor or above eye level.

3. Firmly secure all shelf assemblies to the wall.

4. Use only shelves that have anti-roll lips.

5. Use permanently fixed, not adjustable, shelves.

6. Store flammables in a dedicated flammable-storage cabinet.

7. Store poisons in a locked, dedicated poison-storage cabinet.

8. Store chemicals by a color-code classification, in separate dedicated storage areas as described below.

Many chemical and biological supply companies use color codes to designate general hazards and to facilitate handling and storage of chemicals. These codes are present on reagent labels, but each chemical or biological supplier uses a different color-code scheme. Many, but not all, of the supplier color codes *appear* to be based on single hazardous characteristics, such as flammability or corrosivity. In fact, they are based on multiple reactivity characteristics. Be sure you are familiar with the color codes for the chemicals used in this program and make appropriate arrangements for safe storage.

Chemical Inventory

It is important to compile an inventory and location map of *all* chemicals and reagents in the school as well as to obtain a Material Safety Data Sheet for each. Together, these form a critical database for protecting your own health and safety and those of your students. Have this information available in a central location in the science area and also give it to your local fire marshal or fire chief. Your inventory form should include the following categories: substance, protective equipment, storage color code, hazards, amount on hand, location.

Material Safety Data Sheets

The purpose of a Material Safety Data Sheet (MSDS) is to protect users and others from harm by supplying readily accessible information about hazards and precautionary measures. Typically, an MSDS is organized into sections, which include the following: manufacturer and material identification, hazards, physical data, fire and explosion data, reactivity data, health hazard information, spill and leak procedures, special information, exposure, guidelines, and special handling precautions.

Under federal requirements, all manufacturers and suppliers of hazardous chemicals must provide MSDSs. Most biological supply houses include MSDSs with the chemical at the time of shipment. To request an MSDS, simply call or write the supplier, giving the product name and catalog number.

MSDSs should be kept on file and referred to *before* handling *any* chemical. The MSDSs also can be used to instruct students about chemical hazards and to evaluate spill and disposal procedures and incompatibilities with other chemicals or mixtures.

Emergency Procedures

What would you do if a student dropped a 1-L bottle of isopropyl alcohol or hydrochloric acid? Are you prepared? Could you have altered your handling and storage methods to prevent or lessen the severity of the incident? Plan now how to react effectively *before* you need to. Some planning tips include the following:

1. Post the phone numbers of your regional poison control center, fire, police, and hospital on your telephone.

2. Practice fire and evacuation drills as well as what students must do in case of fire or chemical contact or exposure.

3. Ensure that all personal and other safety equipment is available and tested, if appropriate.

4. Compile an MSDS database and inventory of all chemicals.

5. Prepare in advance for spill-control procedures.

6. Under no circumstances allow students to fight fires or handle spills.

7. Appoint a hazardous-material response team of knowledgeable individuals who are prepared to handle spills or leaks. Agree beforehand who in the school has the ultimate decision-making authority for evaluating a hazardous-material incident. Know who to call for help and when *not* to handle an incident yourself.

8. Be trained in first aid and basic life support (CPR) procedures. Have first aid kits readily available.

9. Fully document *any* incident that occurs. Documentation is a critical tool in helping to identify areas of laboratory safety that need improvement.

Additional Safety Notes

1. Use only nontoxic marking pens. Many types of permanent marking pens release hazardous vapors.

2. Use nonmercury or digital thermometers in the laboratory. Mercury vapors from broken thermometers are poisonous. In the event a mercury thermometer is broken, or if mercury is spilled, collect all droplets and pools at once with a suction pump and aspirator bottle with a long capillary tube (commercially available). Cover fine (invisible) droplets in inaccessible cracks with calcium polysulfide and excess sulfur. Combine all contaminated mercury in a tightly stoppered bottle. Contact a registered and approved disposal agency.

   Note: If the mercury in a small clinical thermometer were dispersed in a closed 30- × 30- × 4-meter room, the TLV (threshold limit value) would be exceeded. Thermometer mercury spills are insidious and potentially dangerous.

3. When treating a student who has a bleeding cut, follow the recent OSHA standard regarding blood-borne pathogens. At a minimum, wear safety goggles and impervious gloves.

4. Electrical sockets in the laboratory must be protected with a GFI (ground fault interrupter) type of circuit breaker. Each electrical outlet in the lab must be three-hole, and each set of three holes must be checked with a circuit tester in advance of any use to make certain that the wiring has been correctly connected to the three holes. (That is, there should be no "open ground," "open neutral," or "open hot" wiring, no "hot/ground reverse," and no "hot/neutral reverse" wiring. The circuit tester indicates these wrong conditions by various configurations of red and green lights. Circuit testers can be purchased at Radio Shack or an equivalent retailer for less than $5.)

5. All electrical equipment should have a three-wire code with an attached three-prong plug.

E. Safety Information Resources and References

A Guide to Information Sources Related to the Safety and Management of Laboratory Waste from Secondary Schools. (1985). New York: New York State Environmental Facilities Corp.

American Chemical Society Health and Safety Service. American Chemical Society, 1155 16th Street, NW, Washington, DC 20036, 202-872-4511. This service refers inquiries to appropriate resources to help find answers to questions about health and safety.

Council Committee on Chemical Safety. (1990). *Safety in Academic Chemistry Laboratories.* (4th ed.). Washington, DC: American Chemical Society.

Gerlovich, J. A., et al. (1984). *School Science Safety: Secondary School.* Batavia, IL: Flinn Scientific.

Hazardous Materials Information Exchange (HMIX). HMIX can be accessed at no charge (other than the telephone call) by personal computer having a modem (300, 1,200, or 2,500 baud) with communication parameters set to no parity, 8 data bits, and 1 bit stop. Dial 312-972-3275; the bulletin board is available 24 hours a day, 7 days a week. HMIX is sponsored by the Federal Emergency Management Agency and the U.S. Department of Transportation and serves as a reliable on-line database, accessed through an electronic bulletin board. It provides information about instructional material and literature listings, hazardous materials and emergencies, and applicable laws and regulations.

Lefevre, M. J. (1989). *The First Aid Manual for Chemical Accidents.* Revised by Shirley A. Conibeau. Stroudsburg, PA: Dowden.

Manual of Safety and Health Hazards in the School Science Laboratory. (1980). Cincinnati, OH: National Institute for Occupational Safety and Health. This publication is available through the Council of State Science Supervisors, Attention: Frank Kizer, Rt. 2, Box 637, Lancaster, VA 22503.

NIOSH Pocket Guide to Chemical Hazards. (1985). (5th ed.). United States Department of Health and Human Services. DHEW (NIOSH) Publication No. 78-210. Superintendent of Documents. Washington, DC: United States Government Printing Office.

Pipitone, D. (Ed.). (1984). *Safe Storage of Laboratory Chemicals.* New York: John Wiley.

Prudent Practices for Handling Hazardous Chemicals in Laboratories. (1981). Committee on Hazardous Substances in the Laboratory. National Research Council. Washington, DC: National Academy Press.

Safety Awareness of Teachers. (1987). Rochester, NY: Ward's Natural Science Establishment.

Stauss, H., and Kaufman M., (Eds.). (1981). *Handbook for Chemical Technicians.* New York: McGraw-Hill.

Ward's MSDS Users Guide. (1989). Rochester, NY: Ward's Natural Science Establishment.

Windholz, M. (Ed.). (1983). *The Merck Index.* (11th ed.). Rahway, NJ: Merck.

Young, J. A. (Ed.). (1987). *Improving Safety in the Chemical Laboratory: A Practical Guide.* New York: Wiley Interscience.

F. Special Guidelines for the Biology Laboratory

Because biology involves the study of organisms, both living and preserved, certain safety considerations are unique to the biology laboratory.

Safety Using Animals

A double safety standard must be maintained when live animals are used in the laboratory for observation and experimentation. The humane treatment of the animals is one objective and the safety of the student is the other. The following statement, *The Use of Animals in Biology Education,* from the National Association of Biology Teachers was adopted by its Board of Directors in May 2003. (This policy supersedes and replaces all previous NABT statements regarding animals in biology education.) It is considered a comprehensive policy concerning the use of live animals in the instruction of biology. The student text contains general rules on which you may elaborate.

The Use of Animals in Biology Education

The study of organisms, including nonhuman animals, is essential to the understanding of life on Earth. NABT recommends the prudent and responsible use of animals in the life science classroom. Biology teachers should foster a respect for life and should teach about the interrelationship and interdependency of all things.

Classroom experiences that involve nonhuman animals range from observation to dissection. As with any instructional activity, the use of nonhuman animals in the biology classroom must have sound educational objectives. Any use of animals must convey substantive knowledge of biology and be appropriate for the classroom and for the age of the students. Biology teachers are in the best position to make this determination for their students.

NABT supports these experiences so long as they are conducted within the established guidelines of proper care and use of animals, as developed by the scientific and educational community. NABT encourages the presence of live animals in the classroom with appropriate consideration to the age and maturity level of the students (elementary, middle school, high school or college).

No alternative can substitute for the actual experience of dissection or other use of animals. NABT urges teachers to be aware of the limitations of alternatives. When the teacher determines that the most effective means to meet the objectives of the class do not require dissection, NABT acknowledges the use of alternatives to dissection including, models and the various forms of multimedia. NABT encourages teachers to be sensitive to substantive student objections to dissection and to consider providing appropriate lessons for those students where necessary.

To implement this policy, NABT endorses and adopts the "Principles and Guidelines for the Use of Animals in Precollege Education" of the Institute of Laboratory Animals Resources (National Research Council). Copies of the "Principles and Guidelines" may be obtained from the ILAR at 500 Fifth Street NW, Washington, DC 20001, phone 202 334-2590, e-mail ILAR@nas.edu. The Principles and Guidelines may be downloaded at http://dels.nas.edu/ilar/prin_guide.asp.

In addition to the NABT guidelines, observe the following cautions for student safety.

1. All mammals used in the biology laboratory should have been inoculated for rabies unless they were purchased from a reliable biological supply house or pet dealer.
2. Wild animals never should be brought into the laboratory.
3. Any student who is scratched or bitten by an animal should receive immediate attention by the school nurse or a physician.

Safety Using Plants

1. Become familiar with poisonous plants common to your area.
2. Have students observe the following rules:
   a. Do not eat any parts of plants intended for use in laboratory work.
   b. Do not rub sap or plant juice on the eyes, mucous membranes, skin, or an open wound.
   c. Do not inhale, or expose skin or eyes to, the smoke of any burning plant.
   d. Do not pick wildflowers or cultivated plants with which you are unfamiliar.
   e. After handling any plants, wash your hands thoroughly with soap and water before leaving the laboratory.
3. Do not work with plants that may have been sprayed with insecticides.
4. If any student exhibits signs of plant poisoning, such as headaches, dizziness, nausea, constriction of pupils, sweating, muscle tremor, or indications of convulsion, call the school nurse or a physician. The poison control center may be able to offer suggestions for first aid.

The following is a partial list of potentially dangerous plants developed by the National Safety Council. Add to the list any dangerous plants specific to your area.

House and garden plants. autumn crocus, bleeding heart, castor bean (seeds), daffodil (bulbs), dieffenbachia, Dutchman's breeches (foliage, roots), elephant's ear (all parts), foxglove (leaves), hyacinth, iris (underground stems), larkspur (young plant, seeds), lily of the valley (leaves, flowers), mistletoe (berries), monkshood (fleshy roots), narcissus, oleander (leaves, branches), poinsettia (leaf), rhubarb (leaf blade), rosary pea, star-of-Bethlehem (bulbs)

Trees, shrubs, and vines. azalea (all parts), black locust (bark, sprouts, foliage), cherries, wild and cultivated (twigs, foliage), daphne (berries), elderberry (shoots, leaves, bark), golden chain (capsules), jessamine (berries), lantana (green berries), laurel, oaks (foliage, acorns), poison ivy (leaves and berries), poison oak (leaves), poison sumac (leaves), rhododendron, wisteria (seeds, pods), yew (berries, foliage)

Wildflowers. jack-in-the-pulpit (all parts, especially roots), mayapple (apple, foliage, roots), moonseed (berries), nightshade (all parts, especially the unripe berry), poison hemlock (all parts), thorn apple (all parts), water hemlock (all parts)

Pollen and Mold Spores

Handle pollen-producing plants and spore-producing fungi carefully so that pollen and spores are not spread throughout the classroom. Many people are allergic to either pollen, spores, or both.

Safety Using Microbes

1. Bacteria, fungi, protoctists, or helminths that are pathogenic are not appropriate activity tools in the high school laboratory, and should never be used.

2. Demonstrate correct aseptic technique to students prior to conducting an activity. Never transfer liquid media by mouth or mouth suction. Flame wire loops before and after transferring bacterial cultures.

3. Treat all microorganisms as pathogenic. Use tape to seal plates containing bacterial cultures. Do not use blood agar plates, and never attempt to cultivate flora from a human or animal source.

4. Never allow students to clean up bacteriological spills. Keep a spill kit on hand that contains 500 mL of chlorine laundry bleach, biohazard bags (autoclavable), forceps, and paper towels. In the event of a bacteriological spill, cover the area with a layer of paper towels. Wet the paper towels with the disinfectant solution; allow to stand for 15–20 minutes. Wearing gloves and using forceps, place the residue in the biohazard bag. If broken glass is present, place the bag in a suitably marked container.

5. Consult with the school nurse to screen students who may be receiving immunosuppressive drug therapy that could lower immune response. Such individuals are extraordinarily sensitive to potential infection from nonpathogenic microorganisms and should not participate in laboratory activities involving microorganisms unless permitted to do so by a physician. Do not allow students with cuts, abrasions, or open sores to work with microorganisms.

6. Never discard microbe cultures without first sterilizing. Wear safety goggles, lab apron, and gloves. Autoclave or steam-sterilize all used cultures and any materials that have come in contact with them at 15 psi for 15 minutes. If these devices are not available, flood or immerse these articles in either chlorine laundry bleach or 70% isopropyl alcohol for 30 minutes and then discard. While sterilizing the cultures, keep them covered and in a fume hood. **WARNING: Alcohol is flammable. Extinguish all flames and avoid other ignition sources.** Do not allow students to use a steam sterilizer or autoclave.

7. Wash the lab surface with a disinfectant solution before and after handling bacterial cultures. Wear safety goggles, lab apron, and gloves.

Safety Using Preserved Materials

Biological supply firms use dilute formalin-based fixatives of varying concentrations (0.9%–5%) for initially fixing zoological and botanical specimens. Usually, it is the practice to post-treat and ship specimens in holding fluids or preservatives that do not contain formalin. Ward's Natural Science Establishment, Inc., provides specimens that are freeze-dried and rehydrated in a 10% isopropyl alcohol solution. In these specimens, no other hazardous chemical is present. Many suppliers provide fixed botanical materials in 50% glycerin.

Because your lab supplies may contain specimens fixed with formaldehyde (in formalin), you should be aware of the following safety precautions. Be sure the formaldehyde concentration in the air is less than the permissible exposure level (PEL). (Currently the PEL is 0.75 ppm with an "action level" of 0.5 ppm.) To be sure that exposure levels do not exceed acceptable standards, you can measure the concentration of formaldehyde in the air. Your lab supplier can suggest appropriate measures and technical equipment.

The following personal protective safety equipment is mandated when handling preserved specimens or when in contact with preserving fluids: safety goggles; protective gloves (nitrile, polyethylene, latex, neoprene); and lab apron or smock.

To reduce free formaldehyde, prewash specimens in a container left ajar in running water for 1–4 hours to dilute the fixative. Formaldehyde also may be chemically bound to reduce offgassing by immersing washed specimens in a 0.5%–1.0% (mass/volume) potassium bisulfate solution overnight.

The following safety practices are recommended when handling or dissecting any preserved material specimen.

1. Never dissect road kills or nonpreserved slaughterhouse material. Doing so increases the risk of infection.

2. Have students wear prescribed personal protective equipment (see above). Additional safety equipment includes eyewash station(s) within a 30-second walk from any location in the lab.

3. Do not allow the preserving fluid to come into continuous contact with the skin. Follow supplier's recommendations for prolonged contact, ingestion, or eye contact.

4. Conduct dissections in an area sufficiently ventilated to keep hazardous substances well below their PEL in the air.

Disposal of Specimens/Preserving Fluids

Neither preserved specimens nor preserving fluids are considered by the Environmental Protection Agency (EPA) to be a "hazardous waste" under the Resource and Recovery Act (RCRA), but local regulations may take precedence. Contact your supplier for recommended disposal procedures for the specific fluids provided.

Release of Biological Organisms

Nonindigenous species and certain microorganisms should not be reintroduced into local habitats. The responsible handling of life-forms requires that you be informed of their specific habitat requirements or potential for negative impact on local fauna or flora. The acquisition of any exotic or nonindigenous life-form requires preplanning to assure that it can be properly maintained throughout the entire year. See the table at the end of this section for specific information about life-forms that may be used in *BSCS Biology: A Human Approach*.

Use the following guidelines in making a decision about the release of any organism into a local habitat:

1. Certain organisms, particularly insects, are specifically regulated, and you must have a permit to possess or release them. Check with your local office of the Animal and Plant Health Inspection Service (APHIS), U.S. Department of Agriculture, or contact your biological supplier. Examples of regulated organisms include cockroaches and termites.

2. Bacteria, fungi, yeasts, growth media, or materials that have been in contact with these organisms should never be discarded without prior sterilization. See Safety Using Microbes on page xxx. For certain microorganisms (*Agrobacterium, Erwinia*, and others), you will need a permit (in certain states) prior to shipment. Check with your biological supplier for restrictions before ordering.

3. Certain aquatic plants, particularly *Anacharis* (Elodea), should not be introduced into local habitats. This plant is regulated as a pest in Canada and certain northern U.S. locales.

4. Ornamental plants should not, as a rule, be introduced into native habitats but instead should be kept indoors. Some states (California and others) have strict rules regarding procurement or introduction of plants containing root-bearing soils from outside the state that may contain plant-damaging nematodes. Usually, plants shipped from outside these states must pass an inspection or have a shipping permit. Check with your biological supplier before purchasing plant materials outside your state. Locally cultivated plants, as a rule, may be reintroduced by replanting if desired.

5. Nonindigenous macroinvertebrates and vertebrates should not be introduced into native habitats. In many cases, these organisms will not survive local climates or may compete or otherwise interfere with local fauna and flora. Contact your local APHIS office or your biological supplier for specific information about whether a particular organism would be considered nonindigenous in *your* area. In extreme cases, when release or continued maintenance of an organism is impossible, the animal must be humanely destroyed. A recommended resource for the care and handling of invertebrate and vertebrate animals is F. B. Orlans, *Animal Care from Protozoa to Small Mammals* (Menlo Park, CA: Addison-Wesley, 1977). Biological supply companies usually provide information regarding proper euthanasia for animals supplied.

6. Most microinvertebrates and protists may be freely released in aquatic environments. Nematodes should never be introduced but should be destroyed by sterilization. Marine forms should be released only into marine habitats.

G. Care and Release of Life-Forms

Care and release of life-forms		
Life-form	**Care**	**Release**
Bacteria (eubacteria)	Slant or broth cultures may be stored for extended periods (up to 6 months) at refrigeration temperatures.	Discard only after autoclaving cultures or contaminated materials.
Butterflies/moths	House in a perforated box covered with muslin netting. Keep caterpillars dry. Provide a continuous supply of fresh leaves. Use egg cartons as surface for population. Keep humidity at 60 percent.	Require permit for release.
Chaetopterus	Requires either an established 25-gallon marine aquarium or an equal amount of conditioned seawater. Acclimate the animals to the seawater. Aerate. Feed by introducing hatched brine shrimp. If care is exercised, the animals may be returned to their tubes and left in the aquarium following the conclusion of the investigation. Do not attempt to maintain these animals except in an established marine aquarium.	Release only in Florida gulf area. Otherwise, euthanize using MS-222 (tricane methanesulfonate).

Care and release of life-forms (*continued*)		
Life-form	**Care**	**Release**
Termites/crickets/ grasshoppers/small insects	House in plastic containers that are "sealable." Screen in air holes. Use egg cartons as "apartments." Keep temperature between 21°C–31°C (70°F–88°F); humidity at around 60 percent. Feed dried food pellets. Provide a number of watering devices (pieces of wet sponge or cotton in plastic petri dish).	Do not release. Euthanize by freezing.
Earthworms/other worms	Place commercial earthworm bedding or rich soil in a plastic washtub. Introduce worms. Allow approximately 150 cm^3 per worm. Cover with sphagnum moss or leaves. Keep moist. Cover container with muslin. Long-term storage is best under refrigeration.	May be freely released.
Anacharis (Elodea)	Place in established freshwater aquarium. Provide a photoperiod of 16 hours light, 8 hours dark using plant grow lights (fluorescent or incandescent). Light source should be placed approximately 16–18 inches over plants.	Do not release.
Frogs	Southern species (*R. belandearei*): Place up to five animals in a 10-gallon aquarium or similar container that is slightly tilted. Provide about 1–2 inches of water in lower end. Feed crickets two to three times/week. Keep tank covered to prevent escape. Place tank in a suitable location away from direct sunlight and excessive temperature. Change water daily. Northern species (*R. pipiens*): These animals may be stored at refrigeration temperature for no longer than 5 days. They may be housed for longer periods as described above.	
Geraniums/coleus	Pot in potting soil. Maintain a 16 hours light, 8 hours dark photoperiod. Use of plant grow lights is recommended.	May be transplanted.
Hermit crabs	Place in plastic dishpan with 1–2 inches of dry aquarium gravel. Add two finger bowls, one containing dry pellet rat chow and the other filled with moderate-sized rocks submerged in water. Hermit crabs eat apples, will climb on a small branch, and need some cover under which to hide.	Release only in southern United States, subtropical climates

(*continued*)

Care and release of life-forms (*continued*)		
Life-form	**Care**	**Release**
Hydra	Store in jars at refrigeration temperature; change water (spring or pond) weekly. Feeding is not necessary unless animals are stored at room temperature; animals can be stored safely for up to 3 weeks at refrigeration temperatures. If stored at room temperature, feed weekly by introducing small *Daphnia* into jar.	May be freely released.
Gerbils	For up to three gerbils, provide a commercial enclosure or use a plastic washtub with screened cage top. Use a commercial water bottle introduced through the cage top. House at room temperature of 21°C–23°C (70°F–73°F). Use sawdust bedding changed at least weekly. May be fed commercial pellet food (rat/mice) or a mixture of seeds and cereals.	Not recommended. Usually, pet stores will accept these animals.
Goldfish	15–25 gallon aquarium; allow 1 gallon per inch of water for each fish. Use aeration. Maintain water at 20°C–24°C (68°F–75°F). Use of aquatic plants recommended. Goldfish are omnivorous; feed them commercially prepared food daily. Remove uneaten food.	Not recommended. Usually, pet stores will accept these animals.
Guppies	10–25 gallon aquarium; allow 10 cm^2 for each fish. Use aeration. Maintain water at 24°C–27°C (75°F–81°F). Use of aquatic plants recommended. Guppies are omnivorous; feed them commercially prepared food daily. Remove uneaten food.	Not recommended. Usually, pet stores will accept these animals.
Mice	For up to three mice, provide a commercial enclosure or use a plastic washtub with screen cage top. Use a commercial water bottle introduced through the cage top. House at room temperature of 21°C–23°C (70°F–74°F). Use sawdust bedding changed at least weekly. May be fed commercial pellet food (rat/mice) or a mixture of seeds and cereals.	Not recommended. Usually, pet stores will accept these animals.

Care and release of life-forms (*continued*)		
Life-form	**Care**	**Release**
Microinvertebrates	Short-term holding: Unscrew jar caps and place in a cool area of lab away from direct sunlight. For long-term culture, place in jar containing $1/2$-inch of pond mud that also contains sprigs of *Anacharis* (Elodea). Place in an area that will receive southern light exposure but not direct sunlight. Gentle aeration may be applied.	May be freely released.
Planaria	Store in jars at refrigeration temperature; change water (spring or pond) weekly. Feeding is not necessary unless animals are stored at room temperature; animals can be stored for up to 3 weeks at refrigeration temperatures. If stored at room temperature, feed weekly by introducing small strips of fresh liver into jar.	May be freely released.
Protoctists	Short-term holding: Unscrew jar caps and place in cool area of lab away from direct sunlight. Refer to culture instructions for long-term culture.	May be freely released.

THE COMPOUND MICROSCOPE

Teacher's Notes for Appendix B, Technique 4

Many of the investigations in this course involve microscopic examination of materials. It is to the student's advantage to learn to use a microscope efficiently at the beginning of the school year. Even students who have used a microscope before will find it useful to take part in this investigation along with inexperienced students.

Recommended Team Size: One student per microscope is preferable. A limited number of microscopes may make it necessary to work in teams of two or even three per microscope.

Estimated Time: One or two 50-minute periods. Learners who have had previous experience with the compound microscope may be able to complete the exercise within one period. Learners who have not used a microscope before may require two periods.

Materials (per class of 30, teams of 2)

45 coverslips
45 microscope slides
15 100-mL beakers or small jars
15 dropping pipets
15 compound microscopes

15 pairs of scissors
15 transparent metric rulers
15 pieces of lens paper
1 section newspaper want ads
water

Safety

Warn students *never* to point any optical device at the sun or its direct rays. They never should use the mirror to capture direct sunlight when illuminating objects viewed under a microscope. The mirror concentrates light rays, which can permanently damage the retina of the eye. Only indirect light should be used; southern exposure is best, if possible.

Preparations

Newspapers or the indexes of catalogs are a good source of lowercase letters in fine print. If the letters *o, c, e,* and *r* are in limited supply, you can substitute letters that demonstrate the same phenomena. The letter *o* shows the degree of magnification and detail, *c* shows the reversal feature, and *e* or *r* shows that images are inverted as well as reversed by the lenses of the microscope.

Potential Responses to Analysis

1. Summarize the differences between an image viewed through a microscope and the same image viewed with the naked eye.

    Images are larger. Type will be grainier and show a dot pattern. Objects are inverted and reversed. They appear to move in the opposite direction of actual motion of the slide.

2. When you view an object through the high-power objective, not all of the object may be in focus. Explain.

    The high-power objective can focus on only a portion of the depth of the object at any one time.

3. What is the relationship between magnification and the diameter of the field of view?

    As the magnification increases, the diameter of the field of view decreases.

4. What is the diameter in micrometers of the low-power field of view of your microscope?

    Answers depend on the microscope used.

5. Calculate the diameter in micrometers of the high-power field. Use the following equations:

    $$\frac{\text{magnification number of high-power objective}}{\text{magnification number of low-power objective}} = A$$

    $$\frac{\text{diameter of low-power field of view}}{A} = \text{diameter of high-power field of view}$$

    For example, if the magnification of your low-power objective is 12 × and that of your high-power is 48 ×, then A = 4. If the diameter of the low-power field of view is 1,600 µm, then the diameter of the high-power field of view is 1,600 ÷ 4, or 400 µm.

    Answers depend on the microscope used. 1 mm = 1,000 µm.

COMPLETE MASTER MATERIALS LIST

This materials list was prepared for use with *BSCS Biology: A Human Approach*. Items are listed alphabetically, followed by package size, number of packages or items needed for 1 year per class of 30, and the investigation in which the item is used. A list of materials organized by activity can be found on pages xlvi–lvi. To order, contact your local science supplier, your Kendall/Hunt representative, or Ward's Natural Science Establishment, Inc.

Item	Qty.	Chapter/Activity
Agar, (YEKAC) bottles, pkg/6	3	11/Yeast Protocol
Agar, complete YED plates, pkg/6	3	16/Optional Activity: The Sun and Life (or Death?); 11/Yeast Protocol
Alpha amylase, powder, btl/25 g	1	7/You Are What You Eat
Aluminum cans	3–4	9/A Matter of Trash
Aluminum foil roll, 12" wide, rl/25 ft	2	15/Optional Activity: A Jar Full of Interactions; 9/Exploring the Cycling of Matter in Communities; 8/Keep on Running!; 8/Using Light Energy to Build Matter, 16/Optional Activity: The Sun and Life (or Death?)
Ammonia, clear household, btl/28 oz	1	5/On a Scale of 0 to 14
Ammonium nitrate, crystals, LABgr., btl/500 g	1	8/Energy in Matter
Amphipods, living, pkg/40	2	16/Tri-Lakes: The Investigation
Apron, disposable polyethylene, box/100	3	4/A Cell Model; 4/Optional Activity: Cell Size and Diffusion; 8/Energy in Matter; 8/Keep on Running!; 5/On a Scale of 0 to 14; 12/The Stuff of Life; 7/What Is in the Food You Eat?; 7/You Are What You Eat; 4/Cells in Action
Art supplies, miscellaneous		15/Optional Activity: Changing Ecosystems; 14/Growing Up—What Does That Mean?; 4/Regulating the Internal Environment
Bags, resealable zipper, 4 × 6", pkg/10	10	2/Modeling Natural Selection; 5/On a Scale of 0 to 14; 16/Optional Activity: The Sun and Life (or Death?); 11/Yeast Protocol
Balance, triple beam, ea	10	9/Generating Some Heat; 8/Keep on Running!; 4/Cells in Action
Ball, Styrofoam™ 2", pkg/10	2	1/Primates Exploring Primates
Ball, Styrofoam™ 3", pkg/10	2	1/Primates Exploring Primates
Ball, Styrofoam™ 6", ea	15	1/Primates Exploring Primates
Beaker, low-form 50 mL griffin, ea	30	5/On a Scale of 0 to 14; 6/What's the Risk?; 16/Tri-Lakes: The Investigation
Beaker, low-form 100 mL griffin, ea	30	7/What Is in the Food You Eat?; 8/Using Light Energy to Build Matter
Beaker, low-form 250 mL griffin, ea	32	4/Optional Activity: Cell Size and Diffusion; 4/A Cell Model
Beaker, low-form 600 mL griffin, ea	24	4/Cells in Action; 12/The Stuff of Life; 7/What Is in the Food You Eat?; 16/Tri-Lakes: The Investigation
Beaker, low-form 1,000 mL griffin, ea	8	12/The Stuff of Life; 4/Cells in Action
Beaker, 2,000 mL Pyrex std. grade, ea	8	8/Using Light Energy to Build Matter
Benedict's solution, qualitative, btl/500 mL	1	7/What Is in the Food You Eat?
Biohazard bag, 12 × 24", pkg/100	1	16/Optional Activity: The Sun and Life (or Death?); 11/Yeast Protocol
Biuret reagent, urea protein test, btl/100 mL	1	7/What Is in the Food You Eat?
Bleach, Clorox, btl/1pt	1	5/On a Scale of 0 to 14

Item	Qty.	Chapter/Activity
Blender, laboratory mixer, ea	1	12/The Stuff of Life; 5/On a Scale of 0 to 14
Brass brads, $\frac{1}{2}$", box/100	1	7/Structures and Functions
Bromothymol blue 0.1%, aqueous solution, btl/500 mL	1	6/What's the Risk?; 8/Using Light Energy to Build Matter; 9/Exploring the Cycling of Matter in Communities
Brush, drosophila/camel hair, pkg/12	3	15/Optional Activity: On the Double
Bulb, floodlight 100W, ea	8	8/Using Light Energy to Build Matter
Buttons	15	1/Primates Exploring Primates
Calculator, Slimline TI-1100 +, ea	30	11/Can You Sort It Out?; 15/Optional Activity: On the Double; 15/ Optional Activity: Reindeer on St. Paul Island; 16/Optional Activity: The Ozone Layer: A Disappearing Act?; 11/Game of Chance
Can, metal "soup" w/o lid, 20 oz, ea	10	8/Keep on Running!
Cardboard boxes		1/Portraying Humankind
Cardboard squares	8	16/Optional Activity: The Sun and Life (or Death?)
Cardboard, thin	15	7/Structures and Functions
Cassette player/recorder, mini, ea	1	14/A View of Life; 1/What Does It Mean to Be Human?; 1/Portraying Humankind
Cellophane sheet, blue 20 × 60", ea	1	8/Using Light Energy to Build Matter
Cellophane sheet, green 20 × 60", ea	1	8/Using Light Energy to Build Matter
Cellophane sheet, red 20 × 60", ea	1	8/Using Light Energy to Build Matter
Cheesecloth, pkg/5 yd	1	12/The Stuff of Life
Chicken wing	2	2/Evidence for Change Across Time
Chlorophytum "spider" plant, live, ea	8	3/Adaptation, Diversity, and Evolution
Clamp, stoddard test tube, pkg/6	6	7/What Is in the Food You Eat?
Clay, blue modeling, pkg/1 lb	1	11/Understanding Inherited Patterns
Clay, red modeling, pkg/1 lb	1	13/A Start in Development; 11/Understanding Inherited Patterns
Clothespin, large wooden	7	2/Modeling the Earth's History
Coins	15	11/Game of Chance
Coleus plant, living, ea	8	3/Adaptation, Diversity, and Evolution
Color plate, or spot plate	15	7/You Are What You Eat
Compost starter & energizer, ea	5	9/Generating Some Heat
Container for drawing numbers	1	6/What's the Risk?
Container, opaque	1	11/Patterns of Inheritance
Container, sterile calib. 250 mL, ea	1	16/Optional Activity: The Sun and Life (or Death?)
Containers with water	10	8/Keep on Running!
Containers, clear, various sizes	12	15/Optional Activity: A Jar Full of Interactions; 9/Exploring the Cycling of Matter in Communities
Containers, various sizes	1	15/Optional Activity: A Jar Full of Interactions
Corks, size 2, pkg/100	16	4/Cells in Action; 3/Adaptation, Diversity, and Evolution
Corks, size 20, bag/20	1	8/Keep on Running!
Corn syrup, light, btl/16 oz	3	4/Cells in Action
Coverslips, 22mm plastic, bx/100	2	4/Cells in Action; 11/Yeast Protocol; 8/Energy in Matter; 9/Exploring the Cycling of Matter in Communities; 3/Adaptation, Diversity, and Evolution
Crayons, assorted colors, bx/12	1	12/Gene Expression
Crushed ice		5/What's Your Temperature Now?
Crytomium leaflet & sorus slide, ea	8	3/Adaptation, Diversity, and Evolution
Cup, plastic with lid, 9 oz, pkg/25	2	9/Exploring the Cycling of Matter in Communities
Daphnia magna, cul/100	2	16/Tri-Lakes: The Investigation
Daphnia magna culture-immature	1	15/Optional Activity: A Jar Full of Interactions
Detergent, Woolite or Dawn	1	12/The Stuff of Life
Dialysis tubing, 15.9mm diameter, rl/10 ft	3	4/A Cell Model

Item	Qty.	Chapter/Activity
Diaper pins	6	5/Stepping Up the Pace
Dice, doubling	15	Engage/Optional Activity: Thinking; 15/Optional Activity: On the Double
Dice, traditional	15	15/Optional Activity: On the Double
Dip net, 3", ea	3	15/Optional Activity: A Jar Full of Interactions
Dissecting tray & tools	2	2/Evidence for Change Across Time
Duct tape		8/Keep on Running!
Earthworms (*Lumbricus*), living, pkg/10	4–6	9/Exploring the Cycling of Matter in Communities
Egg, raw	24	4/Cells in Action
Elastic, 1", 1 yd	6	5/Stepping Up the Pace
Elodea (*Anacharis*), living, pkg/10	3	15/Optional Activity: A Jar Full of Interactions; 9/Exploring the Cycling of Matter in Communities; 8/Using Light Energy to Build Matter
Erlenmeyer flask, graduated 125 mL, ea	15	8/Energy in Matter
Erlenmeyer flask, graduated 250 mL, ea	10	8/Using Light Energy to Build Matter; 8/Keep on Running!
Ethyl alcohol, 95%, denatured, btl/500 mL	1	12/The Stuff of Life
Fabric pieces	8	2/Modeling Natural Selection
Fats, oil, and sweets, sample	2	7/What Is in the Food You Eat?
Field guide to the insects, ea	1	9/Optional Activity: Field Observation
Filter paper, medium grade, pkg/100	1	4/Cells in Action
First-aid tape, roll	8	5/What's Your Temperature Now?
First guide to birds, softcover, ea	1	9/Optional Activity: Field Observation
First guide to wildflowers, book, ea	1	9/Optional Activity: Field Observation
Fish food, tropical, 2.25 oz, ea	1	15/Optional Activity: A Jar Full of Interactions
Flip chart paper	1	1/How Different Are We?
Folders with 5 sheets of paper	30	3/First Encounter with the Critter
Food coloring, red, btl/100 mL	1	4/A Cell Model
Food samples		8/Keep on Running!
Forceps, dissecting, medium, ea	30	3/Adaptation, Diversity, and Evolution; 4/Cells in Action; 9/Exploring the Cycling of Matter in Communities; 8/Keep on Running!; 2/Modeling Natural Selection; 5/On a Scale of 0 to 14; 1/Primates Exploring Primates; 8/Using Light Energy to Build Matter; 16/Tri-Lakes: The
Fruit samples	2	7/What Is in the Food You Eat?
Funnel, analytical 60 degree angle, ea	1	12/The Stuff of Life
Garbage bags, transparent	4	9/A Matter of Trash
Garbage (banana peels or similar)	1	9/A Matter of Trash
Gelatin LABgr, btl/100 g	1	7/What Is in the Food You Eat?
Genetic yeast culture, set/2	1	11/Yeast Protocol
Glass	1	9/A Matter of Trash
Glue, bottle	15	Explain/Science All Around You; 1/Portraying Humankind; 10/Cultural Influences on Human Mating Behavior
Gloves, disposable, medium, bx/100	3	9/Generating Some Heat; 7/What Is in the Food You Eat?; 4/Optional Activity: Cell Size and Diffusion
Gloves, heat defier kelnit cotton, pr	30	8/Keep on Running!
Glucose (dextrose), anhydrous, btl/500 g	1	4/A Cell Model
Glucose solution 15%, btl/250 mL	2	4/A Cell Model; 7/What Is In The Food You Eat?
Glucose test strip, vl/100	3	7/You Are What You Eat; 4/A Cell Model
Goldfish, comet living, pkg/12	1	15/Optional Activity: A Jar Full of Interactions
Graduated cylinder, 10 mL PP, ea	30	8/Energy in Matter; 7/What Is in the Food You Eat?; 7/You Are What You Eat; 16/Tri-Lakes: The Investigation
Graduated cylinder, 50 mL PP, ea	15	5/On a Scale of 0 to 14; 12/The Stuff of Life; 6/What's the Risk?

Item	Qty.	Chapter/Activity
Graduated cylinder, 100 mL PP, ea	10	8/Keep on Running!
Graduated cylinder, 250 mL PP, ea	10	8/Using Light Energy to Build Matter
Grain sample	2	7/What Is in the Food You Eat?
Graph paper, 5 squares/inch, pkg/100	3	5/On a Scale of 0 to 14; 15/Optional Activity: On the Double; 7/Optional Activity: Of Cannibals and Calories; 15/Optional Activity: Reindeer on St. Paul Island; 5/Stepping Up the Pace; 5/What's Your Temperature Now?; 2/Modeling Natural Selection
Grass clippings, 5 gallon	1	9/Generating Some Heat
Gumdrops, assorted colors	500	8/Energy in Matter
Hammer	15	1/Primates Exploring Primates
Highlighters	15	7/Optional Activity: Of Cannibals and Calories
Hot plate (700W) single burner, ea	6	7/What Is in the Food You Eat?; 12/The Stuff of Life
Humus in soil test kit, ea	1	9/Exploring the Cycling of Matter in Communities
Hydrochloric acid 1 N, volumetric, btl/150 mL	1	8/Energy in Matter
Hydrochloric acid, 0.1 M sol., btl/1 L	1	5/On a Scale of 0 to 14
Ice bucket	3	12/The Stuff of Life
Index cards, colored	30	11/The Genetic Basis of Human Variation
Index cards, unlined 3 × 5", pk/100	3	3/A Look at Diversity; 6/Self Defense!; 11/The Genetic Basis of Human Variation; 3/Strange Encounters
Indophenol solution, 0.1%, btl/500 mL	1	7/What Is in the Food You Eat?
Iodine, potassium iodide solution, btl/100mL	1	7/You Are What You Eat
Isopropyl alcohol, 99%, 2-propanol, btl/ 500 mL	1	7/What Is in the Food You Eat?
Jar cap, 58 mm, ea	16	16/Tri-Lakes: The Investigation
Jar cap, white metal, 53 mm, ea	15	1/Primates Exploring Primates
Jar, clear polystyrene, 2 oz, 53 mm, ea	15	5/On a Scale of 0 to 14; 1/Primates Exploring Primates
Jars for storing pH probes	8	9/Exploring the Cycling of Matter in Communities; 8/Using Light Energy to Build Matter
Kidney bean seed, pkg/1 lb	1	11/Patterns of Inheritance
Knife, plastic, ea	8	4/Optional Activity: Cell Size and Diffusion
Laboratory scoop, blade only, ea	15	7/What Is in the Food You Eat?; 8/Energy in Matter
Lamp, clamp, with reflector, ea	8	9/Exploring the Cycling of Matter in Communities; 8/Using Light Energy to Build Matter
Lilium young flower bud slide, ea	8	3/Adaptation, Diversity, and Evolution
Lima bean seed, large, pkg/1 lb	1	12/The Stuff of Life
Liver homogenate		5/On a Scale of 0 to 14
Liverwort, 3 × 4" portion, living, por	8	3/Adaptation, Diversity, and Evolution
Lugol's iodine solution, btl/500 mL	1	7/What Is in the Food You Eat?; 7/You Are What You Eat; 4/A Cell Model
Magazines		1/Portraying Humankind
Magnesium metal ribbon, .006 × .125", spl/25 g	1	8/Energy in Matter
Magnifier, dual 3× & 6×, ea	15	4/Cells in Action; 8/Energy in Matter 9/Exploring the Cycling of Matter in Communities; 11/Yeast Protocol; 3/Adaptation, Diversity, and Evolution
Maltose powder (malt sugar), btl/50 g	1	7/You Are What You Eat
Manila envelopes, letter size	3	2/Evidence for Change Across Time

Item	Qty.	Chapter/Activity
Markers, 4 color set, set/4	8	3/A Look at Diversity; 15/Optional Activity: Changing Ecosystems; 2/Evidence for Change across Time; 12/Gene Expression; 9/Generating Some Heat; 14/Growing Up—What Does That Mean?; 15/Critters and Interdependence; 1/Portraying Humankind; 3/Using Unity to Organize Diversity; 1/How Different Are We?; 3/Adaptation, Diversity, and Evolution; 3/Describing Life; 3/First Encounter with the Critter; 4/Regulating the Internal Environment; 10/A Reproductive Strategy for Your Critter; 10/Making Sense of Reproductive Strategies
Markers, black transparency, pkg/12	1	6/What's the Risk?; 6/ Self Defense!
Marking pen, black permanent, ea	30	2/Modeling the Earth's History
Marking pen, red permanent, ea	1	2/Modeling the Earth's History
Matches, wooden safety, pkg/320	1	8/Keep on Running!
Materials to design food labels		8/Keep on Running!
Measuring cup, 2 1/2 cup, ea	8	9/Generating Some Heat
Meat samples	2	7/What Is in the Food You Eat?
Meat tenderizer, 3g	1	12/The Stuff of Life
Metal objects	1	9/A Matter of Trash
Meter stick, maple, ea	1	2/Modeling the Earth's History
Microscope, compound, ea	15	3/Adaptation, Diversity, and Evolution; 4/Cells in Action; 8/Energy in Matter; 9/Exploring the Cycling of Matter in Communities; 11/Yeast Protocol
Microscope slide, qual. precleaned, pkg/72	3	4/Cells in Action; 8/Energy in Matter; 9/Exploring the Cycling of Matter in Communities; 11/Yeast Protocol; 3/Adaptation, Diversity, and Evolution
Milk of Magnesia, 1 bottle	1	5/On a Scale of 0 to 14
Milk sample	2	7/What Is in the Food You Eat?
Mixed pollen (WM) QS slide, ea	8	3/Adaptation, Diversity, and Evolution
Mulch, shredded leaves, 5 gallon	1	9/Generating Some Heat
Musical instruments		1/Portraying Humankind
Newspaper	1	9/Generating Some Heat; Explain/Science All Around You; 1/Tony's Brain
Newsprint, plain sheets	8	9/Generating Some Heat
Nonliving objects	1	3/Using Unity to Organize Diversity
Norfolk island pine, living, ea	8	3/Adaptation, Diversity, and Evolution
Onions	2	4/Cells in Action; 12/The Stuff of Life
Organic waste		9/Exploring the Cycling of Matter in Communities
Organism cards	1	3/Using Unity to Organize Diversity
Padlock with keys	15	1/Primates Exploring Primates
Pail, plastic utility, 5 qt, ea	15	12/Transferring Information; 1/Primates Exploring Primates
Pail, polyethylene 11 qt, ea	5	15/Optional Activity: A Jar Full of Interactions; 7/What Is in the Food You Eat?
Paintbrush (small)	15	Engage/Thinking as a Scientist Thinks
Palmolive dish soap, 1 bottle	1	12/The Stuff of Life
Paper	30	Engage/Thinking as a Scientist Thinks; 11/Understanding Inherited Patterns; 15/Critters and Interdependence; 10/A Reproductive Strategy for Your Critter; 13/A Start in Development; 10/Cultural Influences on Human Mating Behavior; 10/Making Sense of Reproductive Strategies; 12/Transferring Information; 3/Using Unity to Organize Diversity; 3/Describing Life
Paper bag, 5 × 10 1/2 × 3", pkg/50	3	7/What Is in the Food You Eat?
Paper clips, 8 colors, pkg/800	1	12/Genetic Technology

Item	Qty.	Chapter/Activity
Paper products	1	9/A Matter of Trash
Paper punch, one hole, ea	1	2/Modeling Natural Selection
Paper towel, 100 sheet 2-ply roll, ea	4	4/Optional Activity: Cell Size and Diffusion; 4/Cells in Action; 9/Exploring the Cycling of Matter in Communities; 7/Structures and Functions; 5/What's Your Temperature Now?
Paper, assorted construction, pkg/50	1	12/Gene Expression; 2/Modeling Natural Selection
Paper, squares	9	11/The Genetic Basis of Human Variation
Pen, black wax marker for glass, ea	16	12/The Stuff of Life; 16/Optional Activity: The Sun and Life (or Death?); 8/Using Light Energy to Build Matter; 7/What Is in the Food You Eat?; 6/What's the Risk?; 11/Yeast Protocol; 7/You Are What You Eat; 4/A Cell Model
Pencils, colored, pkg/12	3	15/Critters and Interdependence; 9/Spinning the Web of Life; 2/Modeling Natural Selection; 2/Evidence for Change Across Time
Pencils, ticonderoga #2, bx/12	3	11/The Genetic Basis of Human Variation
Pens, colored, set	15	Engage/Thinking as a Scientist Thinks
Petri dish, disposable 100 × 15 mm, pkg/20	3	4/A Cell Model; 9/Exploring the Cycling of Matter in Communities; 5/On a Scale of 0 to 14; 8/Using Light Energy to Build Matter; 16/Tri-Lakes: The Investigation; 2/Modeling Natural Selection
pH comparison strip 3.0–6.0, pkg/50	1	8/Using Light Energy to Build Matter
pH comparison strip 5.0–9.0, pkg/50	1	8/Using Light Energy to Build Matter; 16/Tri-Lakes: The Investigation
pH comparison strip 7.0–10.0, pkg/50	1	8/Using Light Energy to Build Matter
pH comparison strip 10.0–13.0, pkg/50	1	8/Using Light Energy to Build Matter
pH comparison strip 1.0–14.0, pkg/50	1	9/Exploring the Cycling of Matter in Communities
pH tester, pocket 1–15 pH, ea	10	5/On a Scale of 0 to 14
Phenolphthalein agar 1%, btl/800 mL	1	4/Optional Activity: Cell Size and Diffusion
Photographs, old		1/Portraying Humankind
Ping pong balls, pkg/6	3	1/Primates Exploring Primates
Pipet, glass, dropping 3", pkg/12	3	4/Cells in Action; 8/Energy in Matter; 7/What Is in the Food You Eat?; 6/What's the Risk?; 11/Yeast Protocol; 7/You Are What You Eat; 16/Tri-Lakes: The Investigation
Pipet, non-sterile 6", pkg/500	1	4/A Cell Model; 15/Optional Activity: A Jar Full of Interactions; 5/On a Scale of 0 to 14; 16/Optional Activity: The Sun and Life (or Death?); 8/Using Light Energy to Build Matter; 4/Cells in Action
Plastic milk container	8	9/Generating Some Heat
Plastic products	1	9/A Matter of Trash
Plastic wrap, 12" wide, rl/100 ft	1	4/Cells in Action
Plastic wrap, colored		15/Optional Activity: A Jar Full of Interactions
Pliers, 6", general purpose, ea	1	8/Keep on Running!
Polyethylene, expanded insulation, rl/2 lb	8	9/Generating Some Heat
Polystyrene foam	1	9/A Matter of Trash
Pond snails, living, pkg/25	2	9/Exploring the Cycling of Matter in Communities; 15/Optional Activity: A Jar Full of Interactions
Pop beads, black 10 cm, pkg/300	1	12/Modeling DNA
Pop beads, green 10 cm, pkg/300	1	12/Modeling DNA

Item	Qty.	Chapter/Activity
Pop beads, red 10 cm, pkg/300	1	12/Modeling DNA
Pop beads, white 10 cm, pkg/300	1	12/Modeling DNA
Poster board, white, 22 × 28", pkg/5; or butcher paper	1	15/Optional Activity: Changing Ecosystems; 12/Gene Expression; 14/Growing Up—What Does That Mean?; 11/Patterns of Inheritance; 4/Regulating the Internal Environment; 1/Portraying Humankind; 2/Evidence for Change Across Time; 2/Explaining Evolution; 3/A Look at Diversity; 3/Adaptation, Diversity, and Evolution; 6/What's the Risk?; 12/The Stuff of Life
Potato homogenate		5/On a Scale of 0 to 14
Projector, overhead, ea	1	4/A Cell Model; 11/Game of Chance; 11/Patterns of Inheritance; 6/What's the Risk?; 1/Tony's Brain; 12/Modeling DNA; 6/Self Defense!
Protractor, ea	1	2/Evidence for Change Across Time
Rope (clothesline) 5/32", pkg/96 ft	1	2/Modeling the Earth's History
Rubber bands, $\frac{1}{4}$ lb	30	7/Structures and Functions
Rubber bands, assorted, pkg/.25 lb	1	12/Modeling DNA
Rubber stoppers for 18 × 150mm test tubes	114	7/You Are What You Eat
Ruler, 6" white vinylite, ea	30	4/Optional Activity: Cell Size and Diffusion; 9/Generating Some Heat; 15/Optional Activity: Reindeer on St. Paul Island; 8/Using Light Energy to Build Matter; 2/Evidence for Change across Time
Saacharomyces, UV sensitive, culture	1	16/Optional Activity: The Sun and Life (or Death?)
Safety goggles, SG34 regular, ea	30	4/A Cell Model; 4/Optional Activity: Cell Size and Diffusion; 8/Energy in Matter; 8/Keep on Running!; 5/On a Scale of 0 to 14; 12/The Stuff of Life; 16/Optional Activity: The Sun and Life (or Death?); 7/What Is in the Food You Eat?; 7/You Are What You Eat; 4/Cells in Action; 16/Tri-Lakes: The Investigation
Sand, coarse white, bag/5 kg	2	15/Optional Activity: A Jar Full of Interactions; 2/Evidence for Change Across Time
Sandpaper, 3 cm pieces	10	8/Keep on Running!
Scalpel, economy $1\frac{1}{2}$" blade, ea	15	4/Cells in Action; 3/Adaptation, Diversity, and Evolution
Scissors, student econ. dissecting, ea	30	4/Cells in Action; 10/Cultural Influences on Human Mating Behavior; 12/Gene Expression; Explain/Science All Around You; 7/Structures and Functions; 11/Understanding Inherited Patterns; 1/Primates Exploring Primates
Sectioned rectangular tray, ea	8	5/What's Your Temperature Now?
Sheep brain, freeze-dried, ea	10	1/Primates Exploring Primates
Sheep brain: basic guide book, ea	1	1/Primates Exploring Primates
Slotted spoon	8	4/Cells in Action
Sodium chloride, 5%, makes 1 L	1	4/Cells in Action
Sodium chloride, lab grade, btl/500 g	1	4/A Cell Model
Sodium chloride, non iodized, 1.5g	1	12/The Stuff of Life
Sodium hydroxide for 0.4% solution, pkg/11	1	5/On a Scale of 0 to 14
Sodium hydroxide, SCIgr., flakes, btl/500 g	1	4/Optional Activity: Cell Size and Diffusion
Soil, garden potting, bag/8 lb	5	9/Generating Some Heat; 9/Exploring the Cycling of Matter in Communities
Spirogyra culture, cul	1	3/Adaptation, Diversity, and Evolution

Item	Qty.	Chapter/Activity
Spoons, plastic, pkg/100	1	8/Energy in Matter; 9/Exploring the Cycling of Matter in Communities; 4/Optional Activity: Cell Size and Diffusion
Stapler, ea	1	Explain/Science All Around You
Starch solution (1%), btl/250	2	4/A Cell Model
Starch, soluble, btl/100 g	1	7/You Are What You Eat; 7/What Is in the Food You Eat?
Step stool, ea	6	5/Stepping Up the Pace
Stereomicrosoope, widefield, ea	8	9/Exploring the Cycling of Matter in Communities; 16/Tri-Lakes: The Investigation
Stir rods, 6" glass, 150 × 5 mm, pkg/10	3	12/The Stuff of Life
Stopwatch, digital, ea	15	15/Optional Activity: A Jar Full of Interactions; 4/Optional Activity: Cell Size and Diffusion; 7/Optional Activity: Muscle Fatigue; 5/Stepping Up the Pace; 5/What's Your Temperature Now?; 1/Primates Exploring Primates
Straws, plastic wrapped, pkg/500	1	8/Using Light Energy to Build Matter
String, pkg/.5 lb	1	7/Structures and Functions; 4/A Cell Model
Sucrose, reagent, btl/100 g	1	7/What Is in the Food You Eat?
Sunflower seeds, pkg/.5 lb	1	15/Optional Activity: On the Double
Sunglasses, UV-absorbing	1	16/Optional Activity: The Sun and Life (or Death?)
Sunglasses, UV-nonabsorbing	1	16/Optional Activity: The Sun and Life (or Death?)
Sunscreen lotions SPF 4–30		16/Optional Activity: The Sun and Life (or Death?)
Stress coat, 8 oz	1	15/Optional Activity: A Jar Full of Interactions
Tape, masking ¾" × 60 yd roll, pkg/3	1	9/Generating Some Heat; 8/Keep on Running!; 11/The Genetic Basis of Human Variation; 1/Primates Exploring Primates; 8/Using Light Energy to Build Matter
Tape, transparent w/dispenser, ea	15	12/Gene Expression; Explain/Science All Around You; 7/Structures and Functions; 16/Optional Activity: The Sun and Life (or Death?); 10/Cultural Influences on Human Mating Behavior; 1/How Different Are We?
Teasing needle, wood handle, ea	16	3/Adaptation, Diversity, and Evolution; 4/Cells in Action
Termites: **must be genus *Reticulitermes*** Available from Carolina Biological Supply Co. (some states require a permit)		Engage/Thinking as a Scientist
Test tube multi-rack, economy, ea	18	9/Exploring the Cycling of Matter in Communities; 7/You Are What You Eat; 7/What Is in the Food You Eat?; 8/Energy in Matter
Test tube rack, 25 mm tubes, ea	15	12/The Stuff of Life
Test tube rack, white plastic, 40, ea	1	6/What's the Risk?
Test tube with rim, 10 × 75 mm Pyrex, ea	15	8/Energy in Matter
Test tube with rim, 18 × 150 mm Pyrex, ea	114	7/What Is in the Food You Eat?; 7/You Are What You Eat; 6/What's the Risk?
Test tube with rim, 25 × 150 mm Pyrex, ea	30	12/The Stuff of Life
Test tube with rim, 25 × 200 mm Pyrex, ea	16	9/Exploring the Cycling of Matter in Communities; 8/Using Light Energy to Build Matter
Thermometer, aquarium, hanging, ea	4	15/Optional Activity: A Jar Full of Interactions
Thermometer, non-roll, 6", ea	24	9/Generating Some Heat; 12/The Stuff of Life; 16/Tri-Lakes: The Investigation; 8/Using Light Energy to Build Matter; 5/What's Your Temperature Now?; 8/Keep on Running!
Thread, white cotton 300 yd/spool, pkg/3	1	12/Modeling DNA

Item	Qty.	Chapter/Activity
Tilia, 3-year-old stem (CS)QS slide, ea	8	3/Adaptation, Diversity, and Evolution
Timer clock, oakton, ea	1	15/Optional Activity: On the Double
Tin snips		8/Keep on Running!
Toothpicks, flat, bx/750	1	4/A Cell Model; 16/Optional Activity: The Sun and Life (or Death?); 11/Yeast Protocol; 16/Tri-Lakes: The Investigation; 8/Energy in Matter
Tote box, polyethylene 21 × 12 × 6", ea	2	15/Optional Activity: A Jar Full of Interactions
Transparency film, clear, ea	1	4/A Cell Model; 4/Cells in Action; 11/Game of Chance; 8/Keep on Running!; 11/Patterns of Inheritance; 6/Self-Defense!; 9/Spinning the Web of Life; 7/What Determines Fitness?; 6/What's the Risk?; 16/Optional Activity: Where Do We Go from Here?; 1/Tony's Brain
Trash bags, 4 gallon	8	9/Generating Some Heat
Tray, disposable Styrofoam™, pkg/10	3	9/Exploring the Cycling of Matter in Communities
Trowel, metal, ea	8	9/Generating Some Heat
Twist ties, ¼", rl/200 ft	24	12/Modeling DNA
Urea, reagent, prill, btl/500 g	1	8/Energy in Matter
Vegetable oil, btl/500 mL, lab grade 0	6	4/A Cell Model; 7/What Is in the Food You Eat?
Vegetable samples	2	7/What Is in the Food You Eat?
Video camera, 8 mm, ea	1	1/Portraying Humankind
Video cassette recorder, 4-head, ea	1	14/A View of Life; 10/Making Sense of Human Reproduction; 1/What Does It Mean to Be Human?
Vinegar, white, btl/1 pt	5	4/Cells in Action; 5/On a Scale of 0 to 14; 6/What's the Risk?; 16/Tri-Lakes: The Investigation
Vitamin C (ascorbic acid) pkt, 1% makes 1 liter	1	7/What Is in the Food You Eat?
Wall clock, 7 inch diameter, ea	1	2/Modeling Natural Selection
Watch glass	8	16/Tri-Lakes: The Investigation
Water, distilled, btl/1 gal	4	4/A Cell Model; 9/Exploring the Cycling of Matter in Communities; 8/Using Light Energy to Build Matter; 6/What's the Risk?; 11/Yeast Protocol; 7/You Are What You Eat; 4/Cells in Action; 5/On a Scale of 0 to 14; 12/The Stuff of Life
Water, sterile, btl/100 mL	1	16/Optional Activity: The Sun and Life (or Death?)
Wax paper, 12" wide, rl/75 ft	1	12/The Stuff of Life
White bean seed, pkg/1 lb	1	11/Patterns of Inheritance
Wire, bare copper magnet, spl/1 lb	1	12/Modeling DNA
Wood objects	1	9/A Matter of Trash
Yeast culture, strain HAR, cul	1	11/Yeast Protocol
Yeast culture, strain HBT, cul	1	11/Yeast Protocol
YM agar-media/box culture, pkg/4	15	11/Yeast Protocol

ACTIVITY MATERIALS LIST

Item	Qty.	Chapter/Activity
Dice, traditional	15	Engage/Optional Activity: Thinking
Dice, doubling	15	Engage/Optional Activity: Thinking
Paintbrush (small)	15	Engage/Thinking as a Scientist Thinks
Paper	15	Engage/Thinking as a Scientist Thinks
Pens, colored, set (specific see Teacher Guide)	30	Engage/Thinking as a Scientist Thinks
Termites: must be genus *Reticulitermes*	15 sets	Engage/Thinking as a Scientist Thinks
Flip chart paper	1	1/How Different Are We?
Markers, 4 color set, set/4	8	1/How Different Are We?
Tape, masking ³/₄" × 60 yd. roll	1	1/How Different Are We?
Ball, Styrofoam™ 2"	15	1/Primates Exploring Primates
Ball, Styrofoam™ 3"	15	1/Primates Exploring Primates
Ball, Styrofoam™ 6"	15	1/Primates Exploring Primates
Buttons	15	1/Primates Exploring Primates
Forceps, dissecting, medium, ea	30	1/Primates Exploring Primates
Hammer	15	1/Primates Exploring Primates
Jar cap, white metal 53mm, ea	15	1/Primates Exploring Primates
Jar, clear polystyrene, 2oz, 53mm, ea	15	1/Primates Exploring Primates
Padlock with keys	15	1/Primates Exploring Primates
Pail, plastic utility, 5 Quart, ea	15	1/Primates Exploring Primates
Ping pong balls	15	1/Primates Exploring Primates
Scissors, student econ. dissecting, ea	30	1/Primates Exploring Primates
Sheep brain, freeze-dried, ea	10	1/Primates Exploring Primates
Sheep brain: basic guide, book, ea	1	1/Primates Exploring Primates
Stopwatch, digital, ea	15	1/Primates Exploring Primates
Tape, masking ³/₄" × 60 yd. roll	1	1/Primates Exploring Primates
Projector, overhead, ea	1	1/ Tony's Brain
Transparency film, clear, ea	1	1/ Tony's Brain
Cardboard boxes	optional	1/Portraying Humankind
Cassette player/recorder, mini, ea	1	1/Portraying Humankind
Glue	15 bottles	1/Portraying Humankind
Magazines	variety	1/Portraying Humankind
Markers, 4 color set	8	1/Portraying Humankind
Musical instruments	optional	1/Portraying Humankind
Photographs, old	optional	1/Portraying Humankind
Poster board, white, 22" × 28"	15	1/Portraying Humankind
Video camera, 8mm, ea	1	1/Portraying Humankind
Cassette player/recorder, mini, ea	1	1/What Does It Mean to Be Human?
Video cassette recorder, 4-head, ea	1	1/What Does It Mean to Be Human?
Clothespin, large wooden	80	2/Modeling the Earth's History
Marking pen, black permanent, ea	1	2/Modeling the Earth's History
Marking pen, red permanent, ea	1	2/Modeling the Earth's History
Meter stick, maple, ea	1	2/Modeling the Earth's History
Rope (clothesline) ⁵/₃₂"	1	2/Modeling the Earth's History
Chicken wing	2	2/Evidence for Change Across Time
Dirt, sand, gravel, various textures and colors		2/Evidence for Change Across Time
Dissecting tray and tools	2	2/Evidence for Change Across Time

Item	Qty.	Chapter/Activity
Manila envelopes, letter sized	3	2/Evidence for Change Across Time
Markers, 4 color set	8	2/Evidence for Change Across Time
Poster board/butcher paper	30	2/Evidence for Change Across Time
Pencils, colored, pkg/12	2	2/Evidence for Change Across Time
Protractor, ea	1	2/Evidence for Change Across Time
Ruler, 6: white vinylite	4	2/Evidence for Change Across Time
Poster board/butcher paper	15	2/Explaining Evolution
Bags, resealable zipper, 4 × 6"	100	2/Modeling Natural Selection
Fabric pieces	8	2/Modeling Natural Selection
Forceps, dissecting, medium	30	2/Modeling Natural Selection
Graph paper, 5 squares/inch	24 sheets	2/Modeling Natural Selection
Paper punch, one hole, ea	1	2/Modeling Natural Selection
Paper, assorted construction	24 sheets	2/Modeling Natural Selection
Pencils, colored, pkg/12	8	2/Modeling Natural Selection
Petri dish, disposable 100 × 15mm	12	2/Modeling Natural Selection
Wall clock,with second hand 7 inch diameter	1	2/Modeling Natural Selection
Index cards, unlined 3 × 5"	30	3/Strange Encounters
Markers, 4 color set	4	3/Describing Life
Poster board/butcher paper	30	3/Describing Life
Index cards, unlined 3 × 5"	30	3/A Look at Diversity
Markers, 4 color set	5	3/A Look at Diversity
Poster board/butcher paper	5	3/A Look at Diversity
Chlorophytum "spider" plant, live, ea	8	3/Adaptation, Diversity, and Evolution
Coleus plant, living, ea	8	3/Adaptation, Diversity, and Evolution
Corks, size 2	16	3/Adaptation, Diversity, and Evolution
Coverslips, 22mm plastic	8	3/Adaptation, Diversity, and Evolution
Crytomium leaflet & sorus slide, ea	8	3/Adaptation, Diversity, and Evolution
Forceps, dissecting, medium, ea	8	3/Adaptation, Diversity, and Evolution
Lilium young flower bud slide, ea	8	3/Adaptation, Diversity, and Evolution
Liverwort, 3 × 4" portion, living, por	8	3/Adaptation, Diversity, and Evolution
Magnifier, dual 3× & 6×, ea	8	3/Adaptation, Diversity, and Evolution
Markers, 4 color set	8	3/Adaptation, Diversity, and Evolution
Microscope slide, qual. precleaned	8	3/Adaptation, Diversity, and Evolution
Microscope, compound, ea	8	3/Adaptation, Diversity, and Evolution
Mixed pollen (WM) QS slide, ea	8	3/Adaptation, Diversity, and Evolution
Norfolk island pine, living, ea	1	3/Adaptation, Diversity, and Evolution
Poster board/butcher paper	8 sheets	3/Adaptation, Diversity, and Evolution
Scalpel, economy 1$\frac{1}{2}$" blade, ea	8	3/Adaptation, Diversity, and Evolution
Spirogyra culture, cul	1	3/Adaptation, Diversity, and Evolution
Teasing needle, wood handle, ea	16	3/Adaptation, Diversity, and Evolution
Tilia, 3-year old stem (CS)QS slide, ea	8	3/Adaptation, Diversity, and Evolution
Markers, 4 color set	8	3/Using Unity to Organize Diversity
Nonliving objects	8 sets	3/Using Unity to Organize Diversity
Poster board/butcher paper	8	3/Using Unity to Organize Diversity
Folders with 5 sheets of paper	8	3/First Encounter with the Critter
Markers, 4 color set	8	3/First Encounter with the Critter
Apron, disposable polyethylene	30	4/Cells in Action
Balance, triple beam, ea	8	4/Cells in Action
Beaker, low-form 1,000ml griffin, ea	8	4/Cells in Action
Beaker, low-form 600ml griffin, ea	24	4/Cells in Action
Corks, size 2	16	4/Cells in Action
Corn syrup, light	2.5L	4/Cells in Action

Item	Qty.	Chapter/Activity
Coverslips, 22mm plastic, bx/100	2	4/Cells in Action
Egg, raw	24	4/Cells in Action
Filter paper, medium grade	1	4/Cells in Action
Forceps, dissecting, medium, ea	15	4/Cells in Action
Microscope slide, qual. precleaned	15	4/Cells in Action
Microscope, compound, ea	15	4/Cells in Action
Onions	2	4/Cells in Action
Paper towel, 100 sheet 2-ply roll, ea	4	4/Cells in Action
Pipet, glass dropping 3"	15	4/Cells in Action
Pipet, non-sterile 6"	15	4/Cells in Action
Plastic wrap, 12" wide, rl/100 ft	1	4/Cells in Action
Safety goggles, SG34 regular, ea	30	4/Cells in Action
Scalpel, economy 1½" blade, ea	15	4/Cells in Action
Slotted spoon	8	4/Cells in Action
Sodium chloride, 5%	1L	4/Cells in Action
Teasing needle	15	4/Cells in Action
Transparency film, clear, ea	1	4/Cells in Action
Vinegar, white	5L	4/Cells in Action
Water, distilled	4L	4/Cells in Action
Apron, disposable polyethylene	30	4/A Cell Model
Beaker, low-form 250ml griffin, ea	32	4/A Cell Model
Dialysis tubing, 15.9mm diameter	48 pieces	4/A Cell Model
Food coloring, red	1	4/A Cell Model
Glucose (dextrose), anhydrous	500g	4/A Cell Model
Glucose solution 15%	1L	4/A Cell Model
Glucose test strip	32	4/A Cell Model
Lugol's iodine solution	500mL	4/A Cell Model
Pen, black wax marker for glass, ea	16	4/A Cell Model
Petri dish, disposable 100 × 15mm	3	4/A Cell Model
Pipet, non-sterile 6"	30	4/A Cell Model
Projector, overhead, ea	1	4/A Cell Model
Safety goggles, SG34 regular, ea	30	4/A Cell Model
Sodium chloride, lab grade	500g	4/A Cell Model
Starch solution (1%)	250mL	4/A Cell Model
String	96 pieces	4/A Cell Model
Toothpicks, flat	10	4/A Cell Model
Transparency film, clear, ea	1	4/A Cell Model
Vegetable oil	1L	4/A Cell Model
Water, distilled	1	4/A Cell Model
Art supplies, miscellaneous	variety	4/Regulating the Internal Envirnoment
Markers, 4 color set	8	4/Regulating the Internal Envirnoment
Poster board/butcher paper	30	4/Regulating the Internal Envirnoment
Apron, disposable polyethylene	30	4/Optional Activity: Cell Size and Diffusion
Beaker, low-form 250ml griffin, ea	8	4/Optional Activity: Cell Size and Diffusion
Gloves, disposable, medium	30 pair	4/Optional Activity: Cell Size and Diffusion
Knife, plastic, ea	8	4/Optional Activity: Cell Size and Diffusion
Paper towel, 100 sheet 2-ply roll, ea	4	4/Optional Activity: Cell Size and Diffusion
Phenolphthalein agar 1%	1L	4/Optional Activity: Cell Size and Diffusion
Sodium hydroxide, SCIgr., flakes	500g	4/Optional Activity: Cell Size and Diffusion
Spoons, plastic	8	4/Optional Activity: Cell Size and Diffusion

Item	Qty.	Chapter/Activity
Stopwatch, digital, ea	8	4/Optional Activity: Cell Size and Diffusion
Ruler, 6" white vinylite, ea	8	4/Optional Activity: Cell Size and Diffusion
Safety goggles, SG34 regular, ea	30	4/Optional Activity: Cell Size and Diffusion
Crushed ice	1 gal	5/What's Your Temperature Now?
First-aid tape, roll	8	5/What's Your Temperature Now?
Graph paper, 5 squares/inch	30 sheets	5/What's Your Temperature Now?
Paper towel, 100 sheet 2-ply roll, ea	4	5/What's Your Temperature Now?
Stopwatch, digital, ea	8	5/What's Your Temperature Now?
Thermometer, non-roll, 6", ea	24	5/What's Your Temperature Now?
Diaper pins	6	5/Stepping Up the Pace
Elastic, 1", 1 yd	6	5/Stepping Up the Pace
Graph paper, 5 squares/inch,	30 sheets	5/Stepping Up the Pace
Step stool, ea	6	5/Stepping Up the Pace
Stopwatch, digital, ea	6	5/Stepping Up the Pace
Ammonia, clear household	1	5/On a Scale of 0 to 14
Apron, disposable polyethylene	30	5/On a Scale of 0 to 14
Bags, resealable zipper, 4×6"	10	5/On a Scale of 0 to 14
Beaker, low-form 50ml griffin, ea	30	5/On a Scale of 0 to 14
Bleach, Clorox	1	5/On a Scale of 0 to 14
Blender	1	5/On a Scale of 0 to 14
Forceps, dissecting, medium, ea	10	5/On a Scale of 0 to 14
Graduated cylinder, 50ml PP, ea	10	5/On a Scale of 0 to 14
Graph paper, 5 squares/inch	30 sheets	5/On a Scale of 0 to 14
Hydrochloric acid, 0.1 M sol.	1L	5/On a Scale of 0 to 14
Jar, clear polystyrene, 2oz, 53mm, ea	10	5/On a Scale of 0 to 14
Liver homogenate	300 ml	5/On a Scale of 0 to 14
Milk of Magnesia	1 bottle	5/On a Scale of 0 to 14
Petri dish, disposable 100×15mm	5	5/On a Scale of 0 to 14
pH tester, pocket 1–15 pH, ea	10	5/On a Scale of 0 to 14
Pipet, non-sterile 6", pkg/500	1	5/On a Scale of 0 to 14
Potato homogenate	300 ml	5/On a Scale of 0 to 14
Safety goggles, SG34 regular, ea	30	5/On a Scale of 0 to 14
Sodium hydroxide for 0.4% solution	1	5/On a Scale of 0 to 14
Vinegar, white,	1	5/On a Scale of 0 to 14
Water, distilled	3L	5/On a Scale of 0 to 14
Index cards, unlined 3×5"	40	6/Self Defense!
Markers, transparency	1	6/Self Defense!
Transparency film, clear, ea	1	6/Self Defense!
Beaker, low-form 50ml griffin, ea	7	6/What's the Risk?
Bromothymol blue 0.1%, aqueous solution	200mL	6/What's the Risk?
Container for drawing numbers	1	6/What's the Risk?
Graduated cylinder, 50 ml PP, ea	15	6/What's the Risk?
Markers, transparency	8	6/What's the Risk?
Pen, black wax marker for glass, ea	16	6/What's the Risk?
Pipet, glass dropping 3"	6	6/What's the Risk?
Projector, overhead, ea	1	6/What's the Risk?
Test tube rack, white plastic, 40, ea	30	6/What's the Risk?
Test tube with rim, 18×150 mm Pyrex, ea	30	6/What's the Risk?

Item	Qty.	Chapter/Activity
Transparency film, clear, ea	1	6/What's the Risk?
Vinegar, white	1L	6/What's the Risk?
Water, distilled	1L	6/What's the Risk?
Transparency film, clear, ea	1	7/What Determines Fitness?
Apron, disposable polyethylene	30	7/What Is In The Food You Eat?
Beaker, low-form 600ml griffin, ea	12	7/What Is In The Food You Eat?
Beaker, low-form 100ml griffin, ea	36	7/What Is In The Food You Eat?
Benedict's solution, qualitative, btl/ 500 ml	500mL	7/What Is In The Food You Eat?
Biuret reagent, urea protein test, btl/ 100 ml	100mL	7/What Is In The Food You Eat?
Clamp, stoddard test tube, pkg/6	6	7/What Is In The Food You Eat?
Fats, oil and sweets, sample	2	7/What Is In The Food You Eat?
Fruit samples	2	7/What Is In The Food You Eat?
Gelatin LABgr	100g	7/What Is In The Food You Eat?
Gloves, disposable, medium	30 pairs	7/What Is In The Food You Eat?
Glucose solution	500mL	7/What Is In The Food You Eat?
Graduated cylinder, 10 ml PP, ea	30	7/What Is In The Food You Eat?
Grain sample	2	7/What Is In The Food You Eat?
Hot plate (700W) single burner, ea	6	7/What Is In The Food You Eat?
Indophenol solution, 0.1%	100mL	7/What Is In The Food You Eat?
Isopropyl alcohol, 99%, 2-propanol	200mL	7/What Is In The Food You Eat?
Laboratory scoop, blade only, ea	15	7/What Is In The Food You Eat?
Lugol's iodine solution	100mL	7/What Is In The Food You Eat?
Meat samples	2	7/What Is In The Food You Eat?
Milk sample	2	7/What Is In The Food You Eat?
Pail, polyethylene 11 qt, ea	2	7/What Is In The Food You Eat?
Paper bag, 5" × 10^1/$_2$" × 3"	6	7/What Is In The Food You Eat?
Pen, black wax marker for glass, ea	12	7/What Is In The Food You Eat?
Pipet, glass dropping 3"	12	7/What Is In The Food You Eat?
Safety goggles, SG34 regular, ea	30	7/What Is In The Food You Eat?
Starch, soluble	100g	7/What Is In The Food You Eat?
Sucrose, reagent	500mL	7/What Is In The Food You Eat?
Test tube multi-rack	18	7/What Is In The Food You Eat?
Test tube with rim, 18 × 150 mm Pyrex, ea	114	7/What Is In The Food You Eat?
Vegetable oil, lab grad 0	500mL	7/What Is In The Food You Eat?
Vegetable samples	2	7/What Is In The Food You Eat?
Vitamin C (ascorbic acid) 1%, 500mg tablets	6 tablets	7/What Is In The Food You Eat?
Alpha amylase, powder, btl/25 g	1	7/You are What You Eat
Apron, disposable polyethylene	30	7/You are What You Eat
Glucose test strip	multiple	7/You are What You Eat
Graduated cylinder, 10 ml PP, ea	30	7/You are What You Eat
Iodine, potassium iodide solution	1	7/You are What You Eat
Lugol's iodine solution	1	7/You are What You Eat
Maltose powder (malt sugar)	1	7/You are What You Eat
Pen, black wax marker for glass, ea	16	7/You are What You Eat
Pipet, glass dropping 3"	10	7/You are What You Eat
Rubber stoppers	114	7/You are What You Eat
Safety goggles, SG34 regular, ea	30	7/You are What You Eat
Spot plate	3	7/You are What You Eat
Starch, soluble	100g	7/You are What You Eat
Test tube multi-rack	18	7/You are What You Eat

Item	Qty.	Chapter/Activity
Test tube with rim, 18 × 150 mm		
Pyrex, ea	114	7/You are What You Eat
Water, distilled, btl/1 gal	4	7/You are What You Eat
Brass brads, $\frac{1}{2}$", box/100	1	7/Structures and Functions
Cardboard, thin	15	7/Structures and Functions
Paper towel, 100 sheet 2-ply roll, ea	4	7/Structures and Functions
Rubber bands, $\frac{1}{4}$ lb	30	7/Structures and Functions
Scissors, student econ. dissecting, ea	30	7/Structures and Functions
String, pkg/.5 lb	1	7/Structures and Functions
Tape, transparent w/dispenser, ea	15	7/Structures and Functions
Stopwatch, digital, ea	15	7/Optional Activity: Muscle Fatigue
Graph paper, 5 squares/inch	30 sheets	7/Optional Activity: Of Cannibals and Calories
Highlighters, 2 colors	15 each	7/Optional Activity: Of Cannibals and Calories

Item	Qty.	Chapter/Activity
Ammonium nitrate, crystals,		
LABgr.	75g	8/Energy in Matter
Apron, disposable polyethylene	30	8/Energy in Matter
Coverslips, 22mm plastic, bx/100	2	8/Energy in Matter
Erlenmeyer flask, graduated		
125ml, ea	15	8/Energy in Matter
Graduated cylinder, 10 ml PP, ea	15	8/Energy in Matter
Gumdrops, colored (optional)	500	8/Energy in Matter
Hydrochloric acid 1 N, volumetric	1L	8/Energy in Matter
Laboratory scoop, blade only, ea	15	8/Energy in Matter
Magnesium metal ribbon,		
.006 × .125"	30cm	8/Energy in Matter
Magnifier, dual 3× & 6×, ea	5	8/Energy in Matter
Microscope slide, qual. Precleaned	3	8/Energy in Matter
Microscope, compound, ea	15	8/Energy in Matter
Pipet, glass dropping 3"	15	8/Energy in Matter
Safety goggles, SG34 regular, ea	30	8/Energy in Matter
Spoons, plastic	15	8/Energy in Matter
Test tube with rim, 10 × 75mm		
Pyrex, ea	15	8/Energy in Matter
Test tube rack, ea	15	8/Energy in Matter
Toothpicks, flat (optional)	200	8/Energy in Matter
Urea, reagent, prill	50 mL	8/Energy in Matter
Aluminum foil roll, 12" wide	2	8/Keep on Running!
Apron, disposable polyethylene	30	8/Keep on Running!
Balance, triple beam, ea	10	8/Keep on Running!
Can, metal "soup" w/o lid,		
20 oz, ea	10	8/Keep on Running!
Containers with water	10	8/Keep on Running!
Corks, size 20	10	8/Keep on Running!
Duct tape	1 roll	8/Keep on Running!
Erlenmeyer flask, graduated		
250 mL	10	8/Keep on Running!
Food samples	variety	8/Keep on Running!
Forceps, dissecting, medium, ea	10	8/Keep on Running!
Gloves, heat defier kelnit		
cotton/pot holders	20	8/Keep on Running!
Graduated cylinder, 100 ml PP, ea	10	8/Keep on Running!
Matches, wooden safety	1 box	8/Keep on Running!
Materials to design food labels	variety	8/Keep on Running!
Pliers, 6", general purpose, ea	1	8/Keep on Running!
Safety goggles, SG34 regular, ea	30	8/Keep on Running!

Item	Qty.	Chapter/Activity
Sandpaper, 3 cm pieces	10	8/Keep on Running!
Tape, masking $^3/_4$" × 60 yd. roll	1	8/Keep on Running!
Thermometer, non-roll, 6", ea	10	8/Keep on Running!
Tin snips	1 pair	8/Keep on Running!
Transparency film, clear, ea	1	8/Keep on Running!
Aluminum foil roll, 12" wide	2	8/Using Light Energy to Build Matter
Beaker, 2,000ml Pyrex std. grade, ea	8	8/Using Light Energy to Build Matter
Beaker, low-form l00ml griffin, ea	8	8/Using Light Energy to Build Matter
Bromothymol blue, 0.04% aqueous solution	20mL	8/Using Light Energy to Build Matter
Bulb, floodlight 100W, ea	8	8/Using Light Energy to Build Matter
Cellophane sheet, blue 20 × 60", ea	1	8/Using Light Energy to Build Matter
Cellophane sheet, green 20 × 60", ea	1	8/Using Light Energy to Build Matter
Cellophane sheet, red 20 × 60", ea	1	8/Using Light Energy to Build Matter
Elodea (*Anacharis*), living	16 sprigs	8/Using Light Energy to Build Matter
Erlenmeyer flask, graduated 250ml, ea	8	8/Using Light Energy to Build Matter
Forceps, dissecting, medium, ea	8	8/Using Light Energy to Build Matter
Graduated cylinder, 250 ml PP, ea.	8	8/Using Light Energy to Build Matter
Jars for storing pH probes	8	8/Using Light Energy to Build Matter
Lamp, clamp, with reflector, ea	8	8/Using Light Energy to Build Matter
Pen, black wax marker for glass, ea	8	8/Using Light Energy to Build Matter
Petri dish, disposable 100 × 15mm	8	8/Using Light Energy to Build Matter
pH comparison strips 10.0–13.0	1	8/Using Light Energy to Build Matter
pH comparison strips 3.0–6.0	1	8/Using Light Energy to Build Matter
pH comparison strips 5.0–9.0	1	8/Using Light Energy to Build Matter
pH comparison strips 7.0–10.0	1	8/Using Light Energy to Build Matter
Pipet, non-sterile 6"	16	8/Using Light Energy to Build Matter
Ruler, 6": white vinylite, ea	8	8/Using Light Energy to Build Matter
Straws, plastic wrapped	8	8/Using Light Energy to Build Matter
Tape, masking $^3/_4$" × 60 yd. roll	1	8/Using Light Energy to Build Matter
Test tube with rim, 25 × 200mm Pyrex, ea	16	8/Using Light Energy to Build Matter
Thermometer, non-roll, 6", ea	8	8/Using Light Energy to Build Matter
Water, distilled	2 gal	8/Using Light Energy to Build Matter
Aluminum cans	4	9/A Matter of Trash
Garbage (banana peels or similar)	4	9/A Matter of Trash
Garbage bags, transparent	4	9/A Matter of Trash
Glass	4	9/A Matter of Trash
Metal objects	4	9/A Matter of Trash
Paper products	4	9/A Matter of Trash
Plastic products	4	9/A Matter of Trash
Polystyrene foam	4	9/A Matter of Trash
Wood objects	4	9/A Matter of Trash
Aluminum foil roll, 12" wide	2	9/Exploring the Cycling of Matter in Communities
Bromothymol blue, 0.04% aqueous solution	50mL	9/Exploring the Cycling of Matter in Communities
Coverslips, 22mm plastic	30	9/Exploring the Cycling of Matter in Communities
Cup, plastic with lid, 9 oz, pkg/25	2	9/Exploring the Cycling of Matter in Communities
Earthworms (*Lumbricus*), living	40–60	9/Exploring the Cycling of Matter in Communities
Elodea (*Anacharis*), living	30 sprigs	9/Exploring the Cycling of Matter in Communities
Forceps, dissecting, medium, ea	30	9/Exploring the Cycling of Matter in Communities
Humus in soil test kit, ea	1	9/Exploring the Cycling of Matter in Communities
Jars for storing pH probes	8	9/Exploring the Cycling of Matter in Communities
Lamp, clamp, with reflector, ea	8	9/Exploring the Cycling of Matter in Communities

Item	Qty.	Chapter/Activity
Magnifier, dual 3× & 6×, ea	15	9/Exploring the Cycling of Matter in Communities
Microscope slide, qual. precleaned	30	9/Exploring the Cycling of Matter in Communities
Microscope, compound, ea	15	9/Exploring the Cycling of Matter in Communities
Organic waste	200 to	9/Exploring the Cycling of Matter in Communities
Paper towel, 100 sheet 2-ply roll, ea	4	9/Exploring the Cycling of Matter in Communities
Petri dish, disposable 100 × 15mm	8	9/Exploring the Cycling of Matter in Communities
pH comparison strips 1.0–14.0	30	9/Exploring the Cycling of Matter in Communities
Plastic shoe-box sized containers	4	9/Exploring the Cycling of Matter in Communities
Pond snails, living	30	9/Exploring the Cycling of Matter in Communities
Soil, garden potting	1 large bag	9/Exploring the Cycling of Matter in Communities
Spoons, plastic	7	9/Exploring the Cycling of Matter in Communities
Stereomicroscope, widefield, ea	8	9/Exploring the Cycling of Matter in Communities
Test tube multi-rack, economy, ea	2	9/Exploring the Cycling of Matter in Communities
Test tube with rim, 25 × 200mm Pyrex, ea	8	9/Exploring the Cycling of Matter in Communities
Tray, disposable Styrofoam™	7	9/Exploring the Cycling of Matter in Communities
Water, distilled, btl/1 gal	4	9/Exploring the Cycling of Matter in Communities
Pencils, colored, pkg/12	30	9/Spinning the Web of Life
Transparency film, clear, ea	1	9/Spinning the Web of Life
Balance, triple beam, ea	10	9/Generating Some Heat
Compost starter & energizer, ea	5	9/Generating Some Heat
Gloves, disposable, medium	30 pair	9/Generating Some Heat
Grass clippings	5 gal	9/Generating Some Heat
Markers, 4 color set, set/4	8	9/Generating Some Heat
Measuring cup, 2½ cup, ea	8	9/Generating Some Heat
Mulch, shredded leaves	5 gal	9/Generating Some Heat
Newspapers	8 sheets	9/Generating Some Heat
Newsprint (blank)	8 sheets	9/Generating Some Heat
Plastic milk container	8	9/Generating Some Heat
Polyethylene, expanded insulation, rl/2lb	8	9/Generating Some Heat
Ruler, 6" white vinylite, ea	8	9/Generating Some Heat
Soil, garden potting	40 lb	9/Generating Some Heat
Tape, masking ¾" × 60 yd. roll	4	9/Generating Some Heat
Thermometer, non-roll, 6", ea	8	9/Generating Some Heat
Trash bag, 4 gallon	8	9/Generating Some Heat
Trowel, metal, ea	8	9/Generating Some Heat
Field guide to the insects, ea	1	9/Optional Activity: Field Observation
First guide to birds, softcover, ea	1	9/Optional Activity: Field Observation
First guide to wildflowers, book, ea	1	9/Optional Activity: Field Observation
Glue	5 bottles	Explain/Science All Around You
Newspapers	30	Explain/Science All Around You
Scissors, student econ. dissecting, ea	30	Explain/Science All Around You
Stapler, ea	1	Explain/Science All Around You
Tape, transparent w/dispenser, ea	15	Explain/Science All Around You
Marking pen, black permanent, ea	8	10/Making Sense of Reproductive Strategies
Poster board/butcher paper	15	10/Making Sense of Reproductive Strategies
Video cassette recorder, 4-head, ea	1	10/Making Sense of Human Reproduction
Poster board/butcher paper	10	10/Cultural Influences on Human Mating Behavior
Scissors, student econ. dissecting, ea	30	10/Cultural Influences on Human Mating Behavior
Glue	8 bottles	10/Cultural Influences on Human Mating Behavior
Tape, transparent w/dispenser, ea	15	10/Cultural Influences on Human Mating Behavior
Markers, 4 color set, set/4	8	10/A Reproductive Strategy for Your Critter
Poster board/butcher paper	30	10/A Reproductive Strategy for Your Critter

Item	Qty.	Chapter/Activity
Agar, (YEKAC) bottles	15	11/Yeast Protocol
Agar, complete MIN plates	15	11/Yeast Protocol
Bags, resealable zipper, 4 × 6"	90	11/Yeast Protocol
Biohazard bag, 12 × 24"	8	11/Yeast Protocol
Coverslips, 22mm plastic	15	11/Yeast Protocol
Genetic yeast culture, set/2	1	11/Yeast Protocol
Microscope slide, qual. Precleaned	15	11/Yeast Protocol
Microscope, compound, ea	15	11/Yeast Protocol
Pen, black wax marker for glass, ea	15	11/Yeast Protocol
Pipet, glass dropping 3"	15	11/Yeast Protocol
Toothpicks, flat	1 box	11/Yeast Protocol
Water, distilled, btl/1 gal	4	11/Yeast Protocol
Yeast culture, strain HAR, cul	1	11/Yeast Protocol
Yeast culture, strain HBT, cul	1	11/Yeast Protocol
YM agar-media/box culture, pkg/4	15	11/Yeast Protocol
Calculator, Slimline TI-1100 +, ea	15	11/Game of Chance
Coins	15	11/Game of Chance
Projector, overhead, ea	1	11/Game of Chance
Transparency film, clear, ea	1	11/Game of Chance
Container, opaque	1	11/Patterns of Inheritance
Kidney beans	50	11/Patterns of Inheritance
Poster board, white, 22" × 28"	1	11/Patterns of Inheritance
Projector, overhead, ea	1	11/Patterns of Inheritance
Transparency film, clear, ea	1	11/Patterns of Inheritance
White beans	50	11/Patterns of Inheritance
Clay, blue modeling	1 lb	11/Understanding Inherited Patterns
Clay, red modeling	1 lb	11/Understanding Inherited Patterns
Paper	15 sheets	11/Understanding Inherited Patterns
Scissors, student econ. dissecting, ea	15	11/Understanding Inherited Patterns
Index cards, colored	30	11/The Genetic Basis of Human Variation
Index cards, unlined 3 × 5"	30	11/The Genetic Basis of Human Variation
Paper, Squares	9	11/The Genetic Basis of Human Variation
Pencils, ticonderoga #2	30	11/The Genetic Basis of Human Variation
Tape, masking ³/₄" × 60 yd. roll	1	11/The Genetic Basis of Human Variation
Calculator, Slimline TI-1100 +, ea	15	11/Can You Sort It Out?

Item	Qty.	Chapter/Activity
Apron, disposable polyethylene	30	12/The Stuff of Life
Beaker, low-form 1,000ml griffin, ea	8	12/The Stuff of Life
Beaker, low-form 600ml griffin, ea	3	12/The Stuff of Life
Blender, laboratory mixer, ea	1	12/The Stuff of Life
Cheesecloth, pkg/5 yd	1	12/The Stuff of Life
Ethyl alcohol, 95%, denatured	150 mL	12/The Stuff of Life
Funnel, analytical 60 degree angle, ea	1	12/The Stuff of Life
Glass stirring rods	30	12/The Stuff of Life
Graduated cylinder, 50 ml PP, ea	15	12/The Stuff of Life
Hot plate (700W) single burner, ea	3	12/The Stuff of Life
Ice bucket	3	12/The Stuff of Life
Lima bean seed, large	1 lb	12/The Stuff of Life
Meat tenderizer	3g	12/The Stuff of Life
Onions, yellow	2	12/The Stuff of Life
Palmolive® dish soap	1	12/The Stuff of Life
Poster board/butcher paper	15	12/The Stuff of Life
Pen, black wax marker for glass, ea	7	12/The Stuff of Life
Safety goggles, SG34 regular, ea	30	12/The Stuff of Life
Salt, non-iodized	2g	12/The Stuff of Life
Test tube rack, 25 mm tubes, ea	15	12/The Stuff of Life
Test tube with rim, 25 × 150mm Pyrex, ea	30	12/The Stuff of Life

Item	Qty.	Chapter/Activity
Detergent, Woolite or Dawn	1	12/The Stuff of Life
Thermometer, non-roll, 6", ea	3	12/The Stuff of Life
Water, distilled	1	12/The Stuff of Life
Wax paper, 12" wide, rl/75 ft	1	12/The Stuff of Life
Pail, plastic utility, 5 quart, ea	4	12/Transferring Information
Paper, butcher	6 sheets	12/Transferring Information
Pop beads, black 10 cm	300	12/Modeling DNA
Pop beads, green 10 cm	300	12/Modeling DNA
Pop beads, red 10 cm	300	12/Modeling DNA
Pop beads, white 10 cm	300	12/Modeling DNA
Projector, overhead, ea	1	12/Modeling DNA
Rubber bands, assorted, pkg/.25 lb	1	12/Modeling DNA
Thread, white cotton	500m	12/Modeling DNA
Twist ties, $1/4$", rl/200 ft	24	12/Modeling DNA
Wire, bare copper magnet	1 lb	12/Modeling DNA
Crayons, assorted colors, bx/12	1	12/Gene Expression
Markers, 4 color set, set/4	8	12/Gene Expression
Paper, assorted construction, pkg/50	1	12/Gene Expression
Poster board, white, 22" × 28", pkg/5	1	12/Gene Expression
Scissors, student econ. dissecting, ea	30	12/Gene Expression
Tape, transparent w/dispenser, ea	15	12/Gene Expression
Paper clips, 8 colors	1 box	12/Genetic Technology
Clay, red modeling	1 lb	13/A Start in Development
Paper, butcher	6 sheets	13/A Start in Development
Cassette recorder, mini, ea	1	14/A View of Life
Video cassette recorder, 4-head, ea	1	14/A View of Life
Art supplies, miscellaneous	variety	14/Growing up- What does that mean?
Markers, 4 color set, set/4	8	14/Growing up- What does that mean?
Poster board, white, 22" × 28"	8	14/Growing up- What does that mean?
Markers, 4 color set, set/4	8	15/Critters and Interdependence
Paper	30	15/Critters and Interdependence
Pencils, colored, pkg/12	3	15/Critters and Interdependence
Brush, drosophila/camel hair, pkg/12	3	15/Optional Activity: On The Double
Calculator, Slimline TI-1100 +, ea	30	15/Optional Activity: On The Double
Dice, doubling	15 pair	15/Optional Activity: On The Double
Graph paper, 5 squares/inch, pkg/100	3	15/Optional Activity: On The Double
Timer clock, oakton, ea	1	15/Optional Activity: On The Double
Sunflower seeds, pkg/.5 lb	1	15/Optional Activity: On The Double
Aluminum foil roll, 12" wide	1	15/Optional Activity: A Jar Full of Interactions
Containers, clear, various sizes	12	15/Optional Activity: A Jar Full of Interactions
Containers, various sizes	5	15/Optional Activity: A Jar Full of Interactions
Daphnia magna culture-immature	1	15/Optional Activity: A Jar Full of Interactions
Dip net, 3", ea	3	15/Optional Activity: A Jar Full of Interactions
Elodea (Anacharis), living	20 sprigs	15/Optional Activity: A Jar Full of Interactions
Fish food, tropical 2.25 oz, ea	1	15/Optional Activity: A Jar Full of Interactions
Goldfish, comet living	12	15/Optional Activity: A Jar Full of Interactions
Pail, polyethylene 11 qt, ea	5	15/Optional Activity: A Jar Full of Interactions
Pipet, non-sterile 6"	10	15/Optional Activity: A Jar Full of Interactions
Plastic wrap, colored	1 roll	15/Optional Activity: A Jar Full of Interactions
Pond snails, living	12	15/Optional Activity: A Jar Full of Interactions
Sand, coarse white	20 lb	15/Optional Activity: A Jar Full of Interactions
Stopwatch, digital, ea	5	15/Optional Activity: A Jar Full of Interactions
Thermometer, aquarium, hanging, ea	4	15/Optional Activity: A Jar Full of Interactions

ENGAGE IMPLEMENTATION

	Instructional Flow			Classroom Support			
Activity/ Student Text pp. Teacher Guide pp.	GACD, TRCD, DVD, and CD-ROM Resources	Essays/ Student Text pp.	Estimated Time	Team Size/ Cooperative Learning Focus	Strategies and Tools	Assessment Opportunities	Special Considerations
ENGAGE Cooperating like a Scientist pp. 3–4 TG pp. 6–9			50 minutes	Team size: 4 Skill: Contributing to the team effort	Communication skills; teamwork	Social skills; self-confidence	Reduce team size to pairs if any students in the group require a translator to communicate. Assign the roles so that a student with a severe hearing impairment does not play the role of the "blind." If you have visually impaired students, guide the class to be sensitive about the game's role for the "blinds." Honor the visually impaired students' expertise by insisting that they play a helper role to give their partner experience working without vision. This can be accomplished smoothly by teaching the helper role ahead of time to any students with visual disabilities or assigning an aide to show them the helper's directions during class time.
EXPLORE Communicating like a Scientist pp. 5–8 TG pp. 9–15	Rubric: Journal Techniques	Appendix B, Technique 1 Journals pp. 696–698	50 minutes	Team size: 2 Skill: Listening to your teammates; encouraging participation	Observation techniques	Team assessment; following directions	Students who need assistance writing or drawing can describe and answer questions orally if you provide a tape recorder, or you may direct an aide to record for them. Specifically explain your expectations for inclusion to your class, and encourage teammates to help all students to participate.
EXPLAIN Thinking as a Scientist Thinks pp. 8–10 TG pp. 15–20			50 minutes	Team size: 2 Skill: Managing and organizing team tasks; contributing ideas; dealing with distractions while staying on task	Observation skills; wet lab; discussion	Team assessment	Some students may object to using live termites for an experiment. You may be able to encourage their participation by reminding students of the number of insects killed incidentally on car radiators or purposefully through extermination. If you have students with fine motor control difficulties, consider having those students observe while asking teammates to draw the patterns they would like to try with the termites.

	Instructional Flow				Classroom Support			
Activity/ Student Text pp. Teacher Guide pp.	GACD, TRCD, DVD, and CD-ROM Resources	Essays/ Student Text pp.	Estimated Time	Team Size/ Cooperative Learning Focus	Strategies and Tools	Assessment Opportunities	Special Considerations
ELABORATE *Recording Data in Your Scientific Journal* pp. 10–11 TG pp. 21–22		Appendix B, *Technique 2 Graphing* pp. 698–701	25–50 minutes	*Team size:* individuals	Reading; class discussion	Evaluate prior knowledge, graphing skills; data table constructions; organizational skills	Use this activity to establish strategies for modified journal techniques that can be used by students with disabilities throughout the program.
EVALUATE *You and the Science of Biology* pp. 11–13 TG pp. 22–24		Appendix A, *Laboratory Safety*	25–50 minutes	*Team size:* 2 or individuals *Skill:* Contributing to the team effort	Reading; team and class discussion; homework	Journal entries; class discussion	Enlarge print materials and/or read aloud if needed.

Being a Scientist

Opener Strategies

Begin the class by engaging the students in lighthearted discussion about scientific inquiry by asking a question such as, How many of you think like scientists? Provide a convenient mental transition for returning to school by asking if they encountered something during the summer that made them feel curious enough to try to figure it out, or by asking them to describe all the ways they used thinking skills to investigate a question during the summer.

After this brief discussion, ask the students to look at the scientists in the opening photograph of the Engage Section. The accompanying text directs the students to consider what they picture when they hear the term *scientist*. From the start, the students need to feel capable of doing science themselves. They also should begin to think about the processes of scientific thinking and the role that collaboration plays in scientific investigations.

Because this course emphasizes the processes of thinking, gathering information scientifically, and working cooperatively as well as understanding basic biology, it is important for students to develop strong communication and collaboration skills right away. This is also an appropriate place to call the students' attention to the instructional model (the 5Es) used in this curriculum. Every chapter opener will include a list of the activities and will identify the stage of the instructional model that each activity represents.

There is an optional activity involving dice and a thinking activity, titled *Thinking*, in the *Teacher Resource CD* (*TRCD*).

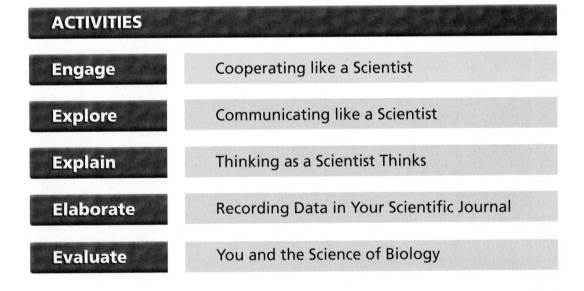

ACTIVITIES	
Engage	Cooperating like a Scientist
Explore	Communicating like a Scientist
Explain	Thinking as a Scientist Thinks
Elaborate	Recording Data in Your Scientific Journal
Evaluate	You and the Science of Biology

Prior Conceptions

Understanding the nature of science is central to *BSCS Biology: A Human Approach*, and it is a key component of the Engage Section. As the students progress further into the program, their opportunities to design and carry out scientific inquiries will become more and more sophisticated, so it is essential that they develop a solid grasp of the nature of science to conduct those inquiries well. This Engage Section provides you with a valuable opportunity to assess your students' current understanding of the nature of science and facilitate common experiences that can help students recognize the roles that evidence, reasoning, and investigation play in scientific inquiry.

The Project 2061 *Atlas of Science Literacy* notes that the primary middle school benchmark for understanding scientific investigations is central to nearly all aspects of students' understanding of the nature of science. That benchmark states, "Scientific investigations usually involve the collection of relevant evidence, the use of logical reasoning, and the application of imagination in devising hypotheses and explanations to make sense of the collected evidence." During the activity *Thinking as a Scientist Thinks*, you will have the opportunity to see your students involved in designing and conducting an inquiry, then drawing conclusions. Although it is reasonable to expect high school students to understand the general procedure for planning experiments with controlled variables, it is likely that they will have difficulty identifying all the important variables. Students are more likely to control those variables that they believe will affect the result (AAAS, 2001). Allow the students a lot of freedom to conduct their termite experiments as they choose. Then use the discussion that follows to call attention to the wide variety of variables present in the situation and the creativity each team exhibits.

Thinking as a Scientist Thinks also gives you a chance to observe your students as they draw conclusions from their experiments. High school students should be able to accept and develop logical conclusions based on evidence (AAAS, 2001), but some may still show the middle school tendency to base conclusions on personal experiences rather than on scientific evidence. Students may still believe that evidence selected from what is already known or from secondhand knowledge, rather than information produced by experimentation, provides a sound basis for scientific conclusions (AAAS, 2001). On the other hand, high school students may recognize the inadequacies in conclusions drawn from invalid or insufficient data, but they likely will need prompting and practice to state their reasoning clearly (AAAS, 2001).

Another valuable aspect of scientific inquiry that can be raised during this Engage Section, and particularly during the activity *Thinking as a Scientist Thinks*, is avoiding bias in science. As in other experiments they will conduct, students will tend to look for and accept evidence to explain their hypotheses that is consistent with their prior beliefs. They will tend to distort or fail to generate evidence that is not in keeping with their preconceived ideas (AAAS, 2001). High school students are developmentally ready to recognize and correct those tendencies with your guidance (AAAS, 2001). By showing the variety of data collected and conclusions drawn from the termite activity during the postexperimentation discussion, you can begin to facilitate students' understanding that scientific inquiry *strives* to avoid bias, but it may be unavoidable. Use this activity to set the tone in your classroom that all students should watch for bias with a critical eye.

Cooperating like a Scientist

Major Concepts Cooperative learning

Overview

This activity places learners in a situation in which the need for cooperation and communication becomes obvious and sets the stage for the use of cooperative learning throughout the program. It also provides an opportunity for students to get to know one another and to begin to build a community of science learners in your classroom.

Journals

Materials (per class of 30, teams of 4)

16 blindfolds   8 textbooks of any kind
8 rulers   8 pens or pencils

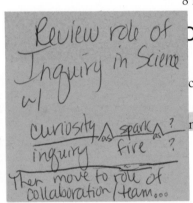

Review role of Inquiry in Science w/ curiosity ∧ spark ∧ ? inquiry ∧ fire ∧ ? Then move to role of collaboration/team...

Outcomes and Indicators of Success

The following indicators allow you to assess the students' level of success with the activity and to assess their process of learning.

By the end of this activity, the learners should become aware of the need for cooperation and communication when functioning as a team.

They will show their awareness by

a. expressing frustration at not being allowed to communicate,

b. having difficulty accomplishing a task without being able to communicate, and

c. discussing the cooperative efforts of some famous scientific teams.

Preparations

Create heterogeneous teams of two. These pairs will be the teams referred to throughout this chapter and Unit 1. Although not all teams will get along instantly, try to let them work out their differences rather than offering the easy solution of changing partners. Because you may not know your students well at the beginning of the school year, an occasional team assignment may be unworkable and need to be altered. Use this strategy as a last resort.

You will need two blindfolds for each team of students because each person wearing a blindfold will need a clean, unworn one. Two or 3 days before the activity, ask each student to bring in a clean scarf or handkerchief. Another option is to tear up one or two old, but clean, bedsheets into long blindfold-sized strips. Set used blindfolds aside in a pile separate from the unused ones.

Strategies for Guiding Learners

PROCESS AND PROCEDURES

As a class, read orally or silently all introductory materials for the activity and the Process and Procedures to help students build connections between concepts and activities. Use the time spent reading to bring the students' attention into focus.

1. Write a paragraph in response to this question: How do we do science?

   The students likely will provide answers that describe the use of microscopes and other technological advances, or they will mention the use of experimentation and data collection. Have the students share their paragraphs and discuss the differences among the ideas. Take this opportunity to get to know your students' preconceptions about scientific inquiry. For example, students may not know the difference between explanations for natural phenomena that are based on pseudoscience and those based on scientific inquiry.

2. Your teacher will assign lab partners randomly. Exchange paragraphs with your lab partner and discuss the differences among your ideas.

   Decide on the pairs you will use in the Engage Section. Then combine two pairs to form the teams of four in which the students will work during the first unit of the program. Make the selection process as random as possible to ensure that your teams are heterogeneous. (See *Strategies for Cooperative Learning Teams* in the *TRCD* for suggestions about forming teams.)

3. Join another pair of lab partners as directed by your teacher so that you have a team of 4 together at 1 table to play the radar game.

   After the students have settled into their teams, preferably around lab tables or four desks pushed together to form a table, ask them to clear their work space completely by putting their books and bags under their table.

4. Choose 2 people to be "blinds" (persons wearing blindfolds) and 2 people to be "helpers." The people who are blinds will stay blindfolded and remain seated for this entire activity.

   Direct each team to choose their "blinds" and "helpers." Be sure the learners understand that the blinds will be blindfolded for the duration of the activity. If you have some teams of three, have two students be the blinds and one student be the helper.

5. Have the 2 students who will be the blinds sit on the same side of the table. Helpers sit on the opposite side of the table. Blinds must stay seated.

6. From this point on, you must follow these rules:

   Read aloud and explain the rules in the need to know box.

   a. Helpers may not touch any materials or the blinds. (If a blind drops something, however, helpers may retrieve the material and give it back to the blinds.)

   b. Helpers may not talk. They may not talk to the teacher, their blinds, or other helpers or blinds from other teams. Helpers may not speak to answer a question even if a blind asks. Helpers pretend that they are completely mute.

   c. Helpers and blinds may not use any materials other than those your teacher instructed you to get after the blindfolds were in place.

   d. Blinds *may* talk. They may talk to each other, to the teacher, to their helpers, and to helpers and blinds from other teams.

   e. Blinds may touch the materials.

7. Obtain a clean blindfold from your teacher. Now, helpers blindfold their blinds. Your teacher will give instructions to the helpers as soon as all the blinds in the class are blindfolded.

Pass out two clean blindfolds to every team, and have the helpers blindfold the blinds. From this point on, for safety reasons, do not allow the blinds to leave their chairs.

8. Follow the instructions given by your teacher.

Once the students understand the rules, arrange the book, the pencil or pen, and the ruler into a formation such as one of those illustrated in Figure TG En.1.

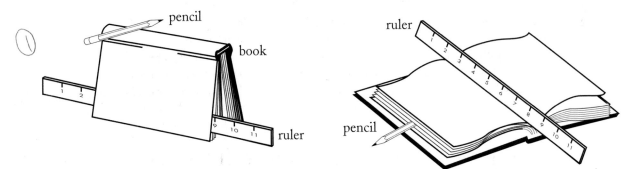

Figure TG En.1 Possible placements of ruler, book, and pencil

Now tell the helpers to help the blinds arrange their materials in the same formation.

Expect the students to be completely stymied by your request. They will challenge the rules immediately. They will want to know if there is any way around the rules. Some will express extreme frustration and say that completing the task is impossible. Circulate from team to team offering advice and encouragement. You can say something like, It is within your power to do this task. Who can talk here? The blinds? Okay, blinds, start talking. Don't ask questions of your helpers. They can't answer. Tell your helpers something. Tell them anything. Tell them how they can help you.

A few of the groups will never get much further than they were when they started. They will simply watch the blinds playing with the materials. Most of the teams, however, after much frustration, probably will come up with a code of some sort, usually using knocks on the table or clapping of hands by the helpers. For example, the blinds might eventually tell their helpers that one knock means yes and two means no. The blinds then will proceed to manipulate the materials saying, Is this right? Do we put the ruler in here? Do we open the book? Are we close? Then, for each question, the helpers will knock in response.

It is critical that the teams determine their own solutions to the problem. It also is critical that the teams become frustrated and want to talk to each other. You should allow about 10 minutes or so, depending on the success rate of most of the teams in your class, before calling a halt to the activity and asking the blinds to remove their blindfolds. Then follow immediately with a discussion.

9. Participate in a class discussion of your success rate with the radar activity. Answer the following questions:

   a. How did you do?

   > The teams will tell you how close they came or if, indeed, they accomplished the task.

   b. How did you feel?

   > The students will tell you how frustrated they were.

   c. Why did you feel the way you did?

   > The students will tell you that you did not allow them to communicate.

   d. If you could change the rules of the radar game, how would you change them?

   > Allow the students to change the rules without restriction. Many will say that in their version of the game, they would be allowed to talk.
   >
   > In response to those who wanted to communicate, probe for deeper understanding: "I saw some of you accomplishing the task, though. How did you do that?" The students will share the type of code, if any, that they managed to devise. Probe further by asking the students if their codes were forms of communication. At this point, the students should discuss what falls under the definition of communication.
   >
   > Next, ask the students, "What is so important about communicating that you had to figure out a way to do it without talking or touching?" The students probably will mention that they can't do what you asked them to do without communicating. If they do not, then mention this idea.

   e. How does this game relate to the work that scientists do?

   > Scientists often work in teams and accomplish remarkable things that way. Famous teams that you can give as examples include the Curies or Watson and Crick.
   >
   > Conclude this discussion by informing the learners that they also will work in teams this year in science. Mention that each time they work as a team, they will need to communicate. Some students may not want to work with or even know a particular person, but this should not keep them from accomplishing their task.

10. Look back at the paragraph you wrote in step 1. Write another short paragraph that explains the role that communication plays in doing science.

    > Look for students to mention that science is a collaborative enterprise and that we do science by working in teams, sharing ideas, and communicating.

Communicating like a Scientist

Explore

Major Concepts The methods of science

Overview

This activity introduces the learners to science journal techniques they will use throughout the program. In Part A, students will work as a class with you to explore the features that make a science journal communicate data, observations, and analyses effectively. In Part B, students explore techniques for recording observations by drawing. This activity provides an opportunity for you to emphasize the important role that journals will play in your class.

Materials   (per student)

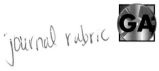
journal rubric

1 copy of the *Journal Techniques* rubric	soft pencil (#2)
textbook	2 unknown objects
spiral notebook	ruler
blank drawing paper	brown paper bag

Outcomes and Indicators of Success

The following indicators allow you to assess the students' level of success with the activity and to assess their process of learning.

By the end of this activity, the learners should be able to

1. reflect on the roles that communication and observation play in the nature of science.

    They will demonstrate their reflection by

    a. listing key features necessary for effective communication in relation to
    - recording data,
    - responding to questions,
    - taking notes,
    - keeping track of questions,
    - keeping track of responsibilities, and
    - using journals during assessment;

    b. participating in a class discussion about journal techniques;

    c. answering a question about recognizing the value in drawings to record observations; and

    d. answering questions about the influence that prior knowledge and preconceptions have on scientific observations.

2. record observations by drawing observed objects.

    They will demonstrate their drawing skills by

    a. determining the identity of an unknown object based on an oral description, and

    b. creating a detailed sketch representing careful observations.

3. begin to recognize the detail and time required to record observations accurately through drawing.

    They will demonstrate their recognition by

    a. drawing the observable properties of an object to describe it sufficiently for a partner who cannot see it,

    b. noting the amount of time it takes to draw the outline of an object without being able to see it, and

    c. making a detailed drawing.

Preparations

Review the background about journals in Appendix B in the student book and in the front matter of this guide. Decide how you will implement this characteristic of the program in your classroom. You may want to modify the rubric before printing it to make it more closely aligned with your expectations of journal techniques.

Collect a variety of unknown objects for students to observe, identify, and draw. You will need one object for each student in Part B *Observing and Describing,* and one more object for each student in Part B *A Blind Drawing.* The objects can include such things as leaves, twigs, feathers, seashells, bones, fossils, crystals, or distinct rocks. Objects also can be humanmade. Whatever you choose should have an interesting texture and color and be reasonably simple to sketch.

Strategies for Guiding Learners

PROCESS AND PROCEDURES

As a class, read orally or silently all introductory materials for the activity and the Process and Procedures to help students build connections between concepts and activities. Use the time spent reading to bring the students' attention into focus.

PART A   *Your Scientific Journal: Recording Your Thoughts and Observations*

1. Read Appendix B, *Technique 1 Journals*, on page 690.

    This part of the assignment can be given the previous day as homework, or it can be completed in class as a silent reading or oral group activity.

2. From your reading, list the key points that you need to remember about

    Expect the students to find key points similar to those listed below for each point.

    a. recording data
        Record data in pen; keep records in diary form with the date at the beginning of each entry; keep each activity's records separate; be brief but to the point; use hard pencil for drawings, and include labels and units; record all data directly into the journal (not on separate pages); and keep track of the source of observations.

    b. responding to questions
        Record the date and activity title when answering discussion or analysis questions; number responses; indicate whether responses are your own or your team's; and write in complete sentences.

    c. taking notes
        Begin with the date; record the source of information; group related ideas together under broad headings; write more than you think is needed; take notes during team discussions and class discussions as well as during teacher presentations; and use information in your journal to prepare for discussions and assessment activities.

    d. keeping track of your questions
        Use the technique of recording questions or notes about any confusion to remember to ask about it when the opportunity arises.

    e. keeping track of your responsibilities
        Record class assignments and responsibilities in the journal, and write those reminders in the upper corner of the page in red or another color.

f. using your journal during assessment.

Keep complete and detailed journal entries to make it easy to be assessed.

3. Your teacher will provide you with a rubric to help you evaluate your journal techniques. Read and discuss the rubric with your partner. Record any questions you have about journal evaluation.

Each student should have a rubric to read and keep. This step in the instructions provides you with an important opportunity to set the protocols by which students will record data in their journals. If you articulate clear strategies for data entry that make it easier for you to quickly locate specific content for assessment, then grading journals will be significantly less cumbersome.

You may wish to have students glue the journal rubric inside their spiral notebook cover for easy reference. Collect the journals at the end of the first week, and evaluate the overall techniques being used according to the rubric. This will give you an opportunity to assess students' understanding of your expectations and to emphasize the strong role that journals will play throughout the program.

4. Participate in a class discussion about journal techniques. Think about the following questions:

a. What are the differences between keeping a science journal and writing a laboratory report?

Discussion should wrap up with an understanding that a science journal is a chronological record of notes, observations, data, and analyses, whereas a laboratory report is a summary written after completing a laboratory investigation.

b. What do you think sounds the most interesting about keeping a science journal?

Students may like the fact that a science journal is less rigid than the format typically required for a laboratory report. We do not expect a science journal to be as neat as a laboratory report (spills on pages are acceptable, for example), and the science journal will contain all of the students' science work in a single location.

c. What part of keeping a science journal sounds the most challenging?

Some students will find it challenging to keep up with assignments when you are not collecting them immediately. (Several assignments likely will be assessed at one time when using a science journal because students cannot be without them at inopportune times.) Some students also may have difficulty remembering to *always* bring their science journals to class.

PART B   Using Drawings to Record Observations

Observing and Describing

Read through and explain the steps for this activity with the students. Emphasize that the observer can *only* use the art terms (found in a need to know box in the student text) to describe the object.

1. You and your partner are going to work as a team. One person will be the observer, and the other will identify an object without seeing or touching it.

2. The observer will select an object in the room without showing it to his or her partner.

3. Sit back-to-back with your partner. The observer holds the selected object.

4. The observer will describe the object to his or her partner but can only describe the object with these art terms.*

- ◆ **Line:** This can be horizontal, vertical, diagonal, broken, wavy, and so forth. Length is the most important dimension of line.
- ◆ **Space:** The area between, around, above, below, or within.
- ◆ **Shape:** Shapes can be geometric or lack a specific form. Shape is the length and width of an object.
- ◆ **Form:** There are five fundamental forms in nature: sphere, cube, cone, pyramid, and cylinder.
- ◆ **Texture:** The surface quality of an object. This can either be a real texture that you can feel or a visible texture that you see. It is the look and feel of the surface of an object.
- ◆ **Value:** The relative lightness or darkness of areas.
- ◆ **Color:** Comprised of three distinct properties:
  - a. hue: the name of a color
  - b. value: the lightness (tint) or darkness (shade)
  - c. intensity: the quality of brightness or dullness

5. After the partner has correctly identified the object, switch roles and obtain a new, unknown object for the second observer to describe.

6. Record in your journal which 3 art terms you found most useful for describing the object. Explain which terms you found the most difficult to use.

The object being described may determine which property is most challenging to use.

A Blind Drawing

In this exercise, you will work by yourself to draw an object that you can touch, but cannot see.

1. Obtain a sheet of plain paper, a soft pencil (#2), and 1 brown paper bag that contains an object from your teacher. Do not look in the bag!

Store the objects in paper bags for this exercise so that students can simply pick a bag to take to their work space. The objects you select for this portion of the activity should be easy to trace with a finger, like a leaf or a seashell.

2. With 1 hand, create a line drawing of what you feel as you trace the outline of the object in your bag with your fingers. Carefully feel the edges of your object and draw its outline at the same time. Take your time and concentrate.

3. When your drawing is complete, compare it to the object in the bag. Make this comparison by explaining 3 ways that your drawing is like the object and 3 ways it is different.

Guide students to consider how accurately the drawing is scaled, if it is recognizable, and if it shows perspective. Differences between the object and the drawing may include those factors as well as differences such as color, texture, and three-dimensionality.

*Adapted from Stoops & Samuelson, 1983.

[handwritten margin note: Paper Bags / Drawing Paper / or in journal]

The design that students use for drawing lines and initially investigating termite behavior should be chosen to simply explore the termite's behavior. The example given is designed to encourage students to draw simple lines and use minimal variables. If the students begin drawing overly complex patterns, they may have difficulty detecting any behavioral patterns. If that happens, ask questions of those teams to probe their reasoning for the patterns they choose. For example, ask students, "What are you trying to see if the termite will respond to?" In this way, you can help teams refine their initial questions.

4. The first step in thinking scientifically is to identify the questions you are trying to answer. Begin this process by thinking about the questions that come to mind as you watch your termite on the diagram. Identify 3 questions and record them in your journal.

Individual

Students should complete step 4 individually, though their questions will likely grow out of their collaborative work. It is important for each student to individually commit to a few questions before he or she participates in cooperatively choosing which question to investigate further.

1 Q

5. Work with your partner to select 1 question about the termite's behavior that you think you might be able to answer through experimentation.

It is possible that partners may have difficulty agreeing upon one question as the basis of their inquiry. Remind the students that cooperation is a central part of this program, and encourage them to practice the skills of listening to and respecting others' ideas. In addition, it likely will be possible for teams to investigate more than one question in the time allowed.

Predict

6. In your journal, predict the answer to your question. Also, explain briefly why you think that your prediction may be reasonable.

As in the case of writing down the questions, it is important that each student commit to a prediction by recording it individually so that he or she will be fully engaged in the inquiry.

How do q record
(15-20 min)

7. Discuss with your partner how you will experiment and make observations to learn more about your question. Save all test diagrams that you use, and record your observations in your journal. Pay attention to the amount of time you are given to conduct your experiment.

Announce the amount of time students will have to conduct their investigation ahead of time. Fifteen to 20 minutes should be sufficient time for teams to conduct a series of tests before the termite becomes less responsive.

Circulate among the student teams while they work, and encourage them to think aloud about their ideas. Use probing questions to help the students recognize the variables they are testing. For example, if students are drawing a series of blue circles, you might ask, "What kind of behavior are you looking for?" If the students respond by stating a clear variable, such as whether the termite follows a particular color or shape of line, then they probably need little additional guidance. However, if their response is unclear, guide them gently by asking questions like, "Are you looking for whether the termite follows a circular pattern or a particular color?"

As students talk with each other, refine their tests, and answer your questions, note their levels of sophistication for developing testable questions and designing controlled experimental trials.

Announce the time periodically to keep the students focused and on task within your time frame.

Individual (HW?)

8. Use the information and observations that you gather to develop a possible explanation for what you observe and a possible answer to your question. Include any additional questions that come up while you are experimenting.

Students need to record their explanations and additional questions individually. Remind the teams that their explanations need not agree. If some teams gathered insufficient evidence to develop any explanation, have them focus on the additional questions they would need to answer to formulate an explanation.

9. Be prepared to report to the class what question you tested, the results of your experimentation, and your explanation or additional questions.

Analysis

1. Participate in a class discussion of the questions, experiments, and ideas about termites.
   Create a chart for all students to view as you record each team's findings. Poll each team orally in front of the class, and briefly summarize their findings on your chart. A chart with two columns labeled *Behavior* and *Cause* provides a concise way for the class to view all the teams' conclusions. Summarize findings in a few words. See Figure TG En.2 for a chart with some possible findings that students may report.

Put on SmartBoard

Behavior	Cause
Follows a line	Sees a *particular color* of ink **(record the color reported by the teams)**
Follows a line	Detects wet ink
Follows a line	Avoids white paper (or prefers dark)
Hides from light	Prefers dark
Follows a line	Likes a *particular brand* pen **(record the brand reported by the teams)**

Figure TG En. 2 Collect team ideas about termite behavior into a chart that all students can see.

After collecting all the teams' ideas and explanations about termite behavior, facilitate a discussion about the processes involved in scientific inquiry. In particular, this activity provides an excellent opportunity for you to highlight the value in collaboration and acquiring as much data as possible when making scientific conclusions.

While one or two teams may come to the conclusion that the termites are attracted to a substance in the ink and that some inks contain more of that substance than others, there are other possible explanations that are also valid. It is possible that every team will conclude entirely different explanations for the observed tracking behavior and have evidence to support their claims. Use that discrepancy to illustrate the need in scientific inquiry for the following:

◆ Creative questioning
◆ Collaboration
◆ Peer review
◆ Repeated trials with repeatable results

- ◆ Keen observations
- ◆ Accurate records
- ◆ Systematic investigation practices

Wait until the end of the discussion about scientific inquiry to explain the phenomenon of tracking pheromones. Some additional information about termites appears in the essay *The Importance of Being Children* on pages 98 – 102 in the student text.

2. Read the terms below and identify two additional terms that could be used to describe the way scientists think:

    explanation
    evidence
    prediction
    logic

Students will likely list terms they have learned in previous science classes in addition to ideas that came up during the discussion, such as measurement, hypothesis, observation, and conclusion. Answers to this question, in combination with the investigation and discussion held earlier, provide opportunities for you to assess the students' understanding of scientific inquiry. It also will help you to determine how well the learners can synthesize their work.

3. Write a paragraph in your journal to summarize the statement, *science is a way of knowing*. Include the four terms from question 2 and the two additional terms that you added.

Student paragraphs may include the following ideas:

Scientists observe the world and listen to the questions that come to mind about what they experience. They then develop predictions about what they think causes the observations they have made. When possible, scientists design experimental procedures to test their predictions, and those tests usually lead to more observations, questions, and predictions. Finally, the scientist conducting an inquiry tries to gather as much evidence as possible and uses that information to support a conclusion and additional questions that are based on reason and logic.

4. In your journal, explain whether you agree or disagree with each of the following statements:

- ◆ Scientists observe without making any judgments; scientific observations are objective and value free.

- ◆ If two scientists run the same experiment and have similar observations, they will develop the same explanation for the results.

    Neither statement is true, though both represent common misconceptions held by high school students. Science is not free from bias, nor is it completely objective, as many people assume. Humans conduct science and do so from their own perspectives. Which question is asked, which method is used, and how the results are analyzed all depend on the scientist doing the work.

Recording Data in Your Scientific Journal

Major Concepts Recording data

Overview

This activity gives students experience applying their knowledge of the important roles that recording observations and communicating information accurately play in scientific inquiry. The students will apply this understanding to another type of journal technique. In addition, it provides an opportunity for you to elaborate on your expectations for how students will use their journals and record their experiences in your class.

Outcomes and Indicators of Success

The following indicators allow you to assess the students' level of success with the activity and to assess their process of learning.

By the end of this activity, the learners should be able to explain multiple reasons why making data tables and graphs clear, as well as accurately reporting scientific results, is important.

They will indicate their understanding by

a. participating in a class discussion about reporting results accurately in tables and graphs, and

b. reading Appendix B, *Technique 2 Graphing*, and following the instructions to practice graphing.

Strategies for Guiding Learners

PROCESS AND PROCEDURES

As a class, read orally or silently all introductory materials for the activity and the Process and Procedures to help students build connections between concepts and activities. Use the time spent reading to bring the students' attention into focus.

1. In your journal, explain 3 steps that you think are most important when making a data table.

   Use the students' answers to this question to inform you about prior knowledge they may or may not have about creating data tables.

2. What do you find is the hardest decision that you have to make when you construct a data table? Why is it difficult to decide?

   Answers to this question should help you decide how to focus the class discussion that follows so that students understand the reasons why data tables are particularly effective for recording and presenting data.

3. Participate in a class discussion about how your class will make data tables to report results clearly and accurately to each other and to your teacher. Consider the following questions:

   a. What are the terms that you use to describe data?

   b. Why is it important for your class to agree to use the same terms when you describe data in tables, graphs, conclusions, analysis questions, and presentations?

   c. Why is it useful for scientists to have a particular format that is always used when making data tables and graphs? What is useful about having standard formats for data in a high school biology class?

   d. What table and graph formats will be standardized in your class.

   Actively involve the students in this process of setting your class's data recording standards. Guide the discussion so that you can both clarify the key features *you* want included in data and respect students' ideas. Participating in the process will increase the students' commitment to the agreed-upon format.

   The discussion should include such ideas as

   - **types of graphs, for example, line and bar (histogram);**

   - **graph labeling and use of units;**

   - **determining appropriate graphing scale;**

   - **selecting data table column and row categories;**

   - **using color to help clarify data in graphs and tables; and**

   - **using software to generate graphs and tables.**

4. Read Appendix B, *Technique 2 Graphing*, on page 690, and follow the instructions to practice graphing.

   Depending on the students' prior experiences with measurement techniques, you may want to have them read *Technique 3 Measurement*, on page 695 as well.

Evaluate # You and the Science of Biology

Major Concepts The relevance of science

Overview

The students will have an opportunity to express their understanding of the nature of science by reading a description of biology and discussing why and how biology is relevant to their lives. During this activity, you will have a chance to evaluate students' understanding about the nature of science.

Outcomes and Indicators of Success

The following indicators allow you to assess the students' level of success with the activity and to assess their process of learning.

By the end of this activity, the learners should

1. understand that many aspects of biology are relevant to their lives.

   They will demonstrate this understanding by identifying reasons why the study of biology is relevant now, in the future, and in this program.

2. recognize the social implications of scientific issues.

   They will demonstrate their recognition by

   a. identifying the role science has and will have in their lives,

   b. identifying how science can help them make decisions, and

   c. describing how decisions made today could influence future generations.

3. be able to identify issues in their communities that involve science.

   They will show their ability by identifying issues involving science that affect their community.

Strategies for Guiding Learners

PROCESS AND PROCEDURES

As a class, read orally or silently all introductory materials for the activity and the Process and Procedures to help students build connections between concepts and activities. Use the time spent reading to bring the students' attention into focus.

Read *A Human Approach to Biology* on page 12, and identify at least 1 reason why each of the following is relevant:

- The study of biology now
- The study of biology in the future

You can assign the story *A Human Approach to Biology* as homework prior to the discussion in the Analysis. Have the students record in their journals two reasons why the study of biology is relevant to them now, in the future, and in this program. Look for responses that indicate that the students have read the story, such as references to technology as a way of solving problems, the cultural and historical context within which science takes place, and ethical analysis as a way of making decisions.

Analysis

Use your experiences from the activities you have just completed and your general life experiences to answer the following questions in your journal. After each answer, leave room to revise your response following a class discussion of the questions.

- begin to develop an appreciation for the methods of science and begin to develop the ability to apply these methods to their work in the unit. In this unit, these methods include developing critical-thinking skills, making observations, asking questions, collecting data, recording and analyzing data, and using evidence and inference appropriately.

Prior Conceptions

Research into the *Benchmarks* for high school students regarding biological evolution suggests that understanding evolution is tied to the students' understanding of the nature of science and their general reasoning abilities (AAAS, 2001). The *Atlas of Science Literacy* notes further that students who have poor reasoning skills tend to hold on to nonscientific ideas such as "evolutionary change occurs as a result of need." Students need to use reasoning skills to examine the theory of evolution in light of the scientific evidence for the theory and its predicted consequences if they are to understand it (AAAS, 2001).

Natural selection is often misunderstood by middle and high school students who are confused by the different meanings and uses for the word "adaptation" (AAAS, 2001). Students must be able to distinguish between its everyday use in which individuals adapt deliberately, and the inadvertent adaptations that occur as populations change over generations (AAAS, 2001). In addition, the students need to recognize that a biological adaptation is a particular *inherited* trait that makes an organism better able to survive and reproduce, that an adaptation in one generation may turn out to be insignificant or maladaptive in a subsequent generation, and that *acquired* traits do not qualify as adaptations in terms of natural selection. Watch students closely for signs of misunderstandings about adaptations, for example, that they believe adaptations result from a conscious effort or overall purpose or design (AAAS, 2001).

The discussion of human characteristics, *Tony's Brain* (Chapter 1), likely will stimulate valuable discussion about the diagnosis and treatment of mental disorders. The students may have difficulty recognizing the roles that the conscious and subconscious processes play in daily life and the complexity of interactions that occur between the mind and brain (AAAS, 2001). This activity also provides a good opportunity for you to guide the class discussion to include acknowledgment that cultural differences in defining "disorders" affect both diagnoses and treatments (AAAS, 2001).

Overall, Unit 1 provides an opportunity for students to explore the widely accepted scientific explanation for the diversity of life on earth: evolution. As a science teacher, your role is to respect the widely varied beliefs that likely will occur in your class while presenting the scientific evidence that is the basis for the theory of evolution. Expect many students to have the misconception that "humans evolved from apes" and to picture modern apes as the common ancestor to which scientists refer. Students also will likely have difficulty comprehending the expanse of time involved in producing the biodiversity we see today. Illuminating the time span necessary for evolution to occur and the concept of common ancestry will be key for students to develop an understanding of evolution and natural selection.

Advance Preparation for the Unit

There are several video activities in this unit. To ensure that these activities go smoothly, reserve the equipment well ahead of time. Familiarize yourself with the DVD player arrangement you will be using before you begin this unit. You also should preview each video activity before using it in class so that you are familiar with the images and segments for that activity.

Several activities in each chapter will require that you prepare in advance. Review the Advance Preparation section of each chapter and the Preparations section of each activity before you begin the unit so that you are aware of the necessary preparations well in advance of the activity.

It is important that you plan ahead for Unit 2 as well. Several activities in Chapter 5 require that the students know how to use your probe ware system, if you will be using probes to make measurements. Probe ware systems are the basis for the microcomputer-based labs in this program. Those labs may be conducted with or without probes, but we recommend using probe ware if it is available to you. Depending on your schedule and students' prior experience with your probe ware, you may wish to plan for some training and practice time for students prior to Unit 2.

In estimating the time it takes to teach the activities in this program, we have assumed that students can read some of the material as homework. You are, of course, the best judge of what is appropriate for your students. Allow additional time to complete activities if you do not assign reading as homework.

The Human Animal

As Chapter 1 begins, the learners first explore the idea that humans, as animals, share many characteristics with other animals, especially other primates. The learners also consider a collection of characteristics that somehow distinguish humans from other organisms. Through video segments, experiments, and essays, the learners begin to construct an understanding of the range of characteristics that make us human.

The learners continue their study of human characteristics with an activity involving the relationship between the human brain and mind. Next, the students elaborate on their understanding by considering the importance of childhood for humans, as children learn language and learn about themselves. At the end of the chapter, the students present a project that represents their understanding of the central question, What does it mean to be human?

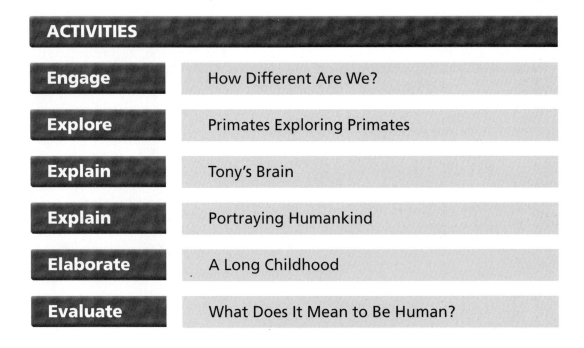

ACTIVITIES

Engage	How Different Are We?
Explore	Primates Exploring Primates
Explain	Tony's Brain
Explain	Portraying Humankind
Elaborate	A Long Childhood
Evaluate	What Does It Mean to Be Human?

CHAPTER 1 IMPLEMENTATION

	Instructional Flow			Classroom Support			
Activity/ Student Text pp. Teacher Guide pp.	GACD, TRCD, DVD, and CD-ROM Resources	Essays/ Student Text pp.	Estimated Time	Team Size/ Cooperative Learning Focus	Strategies and Tools	Assessment Opportunities	Special Considerations
ENGAGE How Different Are We? pp. 18–20 TG pp. 31–34		The Chimp Scientist pp. 84–86	40–50 minutes	Team size: 2–4 Skill: Contributing to the team effort	Engaging opening story	Prior knowledge of scientific work with primates and knowledge of primates in general; ability to articulate distinctions	Enlarge print materials and/or read opening story and essay aloud if needed.
EXPLORE Primates Exploring Primates pp. 20–27 TG pp. 35–42	DVD: Observing Primates and Comparing Brains	Do You Have a Grip on That? pp. 86–87; Mapping the Brain pp. 88–89; Brains and More Brains pp. 89–92	100–150 minutes	Team size: 2 Skill: Listening to your teammate	Experiments with humans as subjects; video	Ability to ask a testable question; ability to apply criteria	Enlarge essays and brain images if needed. You may wish to purchase additional preserved brains or brain models for students with severe visual disabilities to use to compare relative sizes and general structural differences.
EXPLAIN Tony's Brain pp. 27–29 TG pp. 42–47	Copymaster: Personal Interview with Tony; Copymaster: Some Disorders of the Mind and Brain; Copymaster: Results of the Doctors' Investigations of Tony's Behavior; DVD: Behavioral Disorders and the Brain		100 minutes	Team size: 4 Skill: Contributing to the team effort; listening to teammates		Ability to use evidence to propose an explanation; ability to use additional evidence to modify an explanation	Enlarge print materials and/or read aloud if needed.

continued

CHAPTER 1 IMPLEMENTATION (*continued*)

	Instructional Flow			Classroom Support			
Activity/ Student Text pp. Teacher Guide pp.	GACD, TRCD DVD, and CD-ROM Resources	Essays/ Student Text pp.	Estimated Time	Team Size/ Cooperative Learning Focus	Strategies and Tools	Assessment Opportunities	Special Considerations
EXPLAIN *Portraying Humankind* pp. 30–31 TG pp. 47–51	Rubric: *Portraying Humankind* presentation; DVD: *More About the Brain and Nervous System and Nerve Transmission*	*On Being Human* pp. 92–95; *Brains and a Lot of Nerve* pp. 95–98;	100 minutes	*Team size:* 2 or individuals *Skill:* Inviting others to talk		Ability to synthesize information in a meaningful way	The flexibility in types of presentations that students can produce makes selecting an appropriate format for individual students easy to accomplish. If you have students who will not be able to hear other students' presentations, emphasize the need for all students to include visual aids, provide eye contact, and speak clearly to help students who can read lips. In addition, visual aids should be described during the presentation for any students who are unable to see them.
ELABORATE *A Long Childhood* pp. 31–33 TG pp. 51–55		*The Importance of Being Children* pp. 98–102	50–100 minutes	*Team size:* individuals		Ability to make comparisons and draw conclusions from those comparisons	Enlarge print materials and/or read aloud if needed.
EVALUATE *What Does It Mean to Be Human?* p. 33 TG pp. 55–57	Rubric: *Portraying Humankind*		100 minutes	*Team size:* individuals		Ability to synthesize ideas and to present them effectively	All students should present their work in class. However, if you have a student with severe presentation anxiety, consider having him or her videotape the presentation while giving it to you, then show the videotape to the class.

Chapter Goals

By the end of this chapter, students should understand that

- humans are animals and share many characteristics with other animals;
- humans possess a combination of characteristics that distinguish them from other animals, but that no single characteristic distinguishes them; and
- the human capacity for language and learning is associated with large and complex brains.

The learners also will

- make observations,
- identify and ask testable questions,
- conduct experiments, and
- develop explanations.

Advance Preparation

Check Materials and Preparations for the activity *Primates Exploring Primates* so that you can begin to assemble the necessary materials. Preview the interactive DVD videos for the unit.

How Different Are We?

Engage

Major Concepts Characteristics of the human animal

Overview

Often learners do not take the time to reflect on exactly how they are similar to or different from other organisms. In this activity, the students will begin to do this, and they likely will come away with a few questions and perhaps a sense that we are not so different from other organisms after all.

Materials   (per class of 30)

flip chart paper
felt-tipped markers
masking tape

Outcomes and Indicators of Success

The following indicators allow you to assess the students' level of success with the activity and to assess their process of learning.

By the end of this activity, the learners should

1. be engaged in thinking about the extent to which humans are different from other animals.

They will show their interest by

    a. creating a list of the characteristics that may make humans different, and

    b. discussing ways that chimpanzees seem like humans and ways that they seem different.

2. be aware that observation and reflection are important aspects of science.

They will demonstrate their awareness by developing a set of questions that these observations of chimpanzees might generate.

Strategies for Guiding Learners

PROCESS AND PROCEDURES

As a class, read orally or silently all the introductory materials for the activity and the Process and Procedures to help students build connections between concepts and activities. Use the time spent reading to bring the students' attention into focus.

1. Your teacher will assign teams. With your teammates, conduct a brainstorming session to consider the question, What is it about humans that makes us unique? Imagine that you are describing a human to an alien in outer space. How would you describe humans so that the alien could tell them apart from other animals?

> **In this brainstorming session, accept all answers to the question. Expect that the learners first will mention things such as humans can communicate using language, humans are smarter, humans invent things, and humans build things. Encourage students to think of less-flattering examples as well, such as humans fight wars and humans abuse drugs.**

> **Be sure to have students write large enough in step 2 so that the rest of the class will be able to read their list.**

2. Write your team's responses on a large piece of paper and post it in the front of the room. Participate in a class discussion. What common ideas did all teams have? What ideas are unique to each team? What other animals show the same characteristics that you listed as being unique to humans?

> **Limit the amount of time spent creating the list, and have all the teams post their lists at the same time. During the discussion, remind students to challenge the ideas presented in the lists, not their classmates.**

> **The discussion will provide you with an opportunity to assess the learners' prior knowledge of these concepts.**

3. After the class discussion, choose at least 6 characteristics that all teams agree describe humans.

record in
journal ←

> **Record this list and leave it posted in your classroom (after all of your classes have finished with the activity) for the duration of this chapter or unit. Revisit those characteristics periodically as the students continue to look for unique and shared human characteristics.**

?, homework

4. Consider these human characteristics while you listen to or read the narrative that describes Jane Goodall's observations of a family of chimpanzees at the Gombe Stream Chimpanzee Reserve in Tanzania, Africa. Think about whether the chimpanzees that Dr. Goodall studied show some of those characteristics. (See *Chimps at Gombe*, page 19.)

Jane Goodall is a British scientist who began studying chimpanzees in the wild in the 1960s.

You may want to ask one student to read aloud the story *Chimps at Gombe* in the student book, or you may have the students read it individually.

5. With your classmates, discuss what thoughts crossed your mind as you listened to this account. Consider the following questions:

   a. Were you surprised by anything that Dr. Goodall observed? If so, what?

   b. Did you find yourself reflecting more on the similarities or on the differences between humans and chimps? Explain your response.

   c. If you had been Dr. Goodall observing this group of chimpanzees, what questions would you now have about these animals? Record in your journal at least 2 questions that you would like to research if you were Dr. Goodall. Use the essay *The Chimp Scientist* (page 84) as a resource for this discussion.

   Remind the learners to think about the role of observation in science as they discuss this story.

Analysis

1. For each characteristic you have listed, identify and describe a nonhuman animal that also displays that characteristic to some degree.

   Accept all reasonable answers, but emphasize the importance of justifying answers in science. For the characteristic "is able to communicate," the students might suggest that chimpanzees or dolphins communicate. For the characteristic "walks upright," the students might suggest that gorillas do this sometimes, too, or that birds do this.

2. Do you think there is any *one* characteristic that sets humans apart from all other animals? Explain your answer.

   The students may respond that "use of complex language" or "big brain" are single characteristics that make humans human. Or they may indicate that because other organisms show these characteristics to some extent, there is not one unique characteristic. This question previews the main chapter concept, and it will be addressed more thoroughly throughout the next activities.

Extensions

◆ You may find it a useful extension of this activity to ask the students to participate in a discussion of questions such as the following:

   1. How do other cultures explain the relationship between humans and other animals?

      Students may mention that in certain Native American cultures, nonhuman animals as well as humans have souls and a right to occupy the earth. In fact, in many tribes, the name assigned to a person is based on an animal, because that person is believed to possess the characteristics of that animal.

   2. How might you respond to the question, How are humans distinctive, from a perspective other than a biological one?

Students may bring up the ideas of culture, war, souls, art, or anything else that they consider to be a nonbiological distinguishing characteristic of humans. Depending on the line of discussion, you could ask the students to point out the advantage of different ways of knowing, or you could challenge their perception of what fits in the category of a scientific or biological study.

◆ If you have students who are interested in Jane Goodall's work in particular or in observational studies of primates in general, ask them to continue their own research. Suggest the following resources:

Goodall, J. (2001). *Beyond Innocence: An Autobiography in Letters The Later Years.* Boston: Houghton Mifflin Company.

Goodall, J. (2000). *Africa in My Blood: An Autobiography in Letters.* Boston: Houghton Mifflin Company.

Goodall, J. (2000). *A Reason for Hope: A Spiritual Journey.* Boston: Houghton Mifflin Company.

Goodall, J. (1990). *My Thirty Years with the Chimpanzees of Gombe.* Boston: Houghton Mifflin Company.

Goodall, J. (1988). *In the Shadow of Man,* Rev. ed. Boston: Houghton Mifflin Company.

◆ You may want to show the National Geographic Society's videotape on Jane Goodall's work, if your school district has it available. There is a segment that depicts the interactions described in Dr. Goodall's journal notes that appear in the scenario *Chimps at Gombe.*

◆ The National Geographic Society has produced a more recent videotape called *The New Chimpanzees* (1995), which examines both the more common chimp and the pygmy chimp.

◆ Watch the video *The First Signs of Washoe*, by Time-Life Video, from the NOVA series. This video documents one of the first extensive experiments conducted on two-way communication between people and chimpanzees. Alan and Tracy Gardener, professors at the University of Nevada, brought Washoe, a chimpanzee, to live at their home to teach and observe the transference of language from humans to chimpanzees. The Gardeners used American Sign Language to communicate with Washoe and filmed much of their progress through the years. The film also highlights experiments with other chimpanzees that have been trained to communicate by alternative methods.

◆ Suggest that the students read *Gorillas in the Mist*, by Dian Fossey (1983), published by Houghton Mifflin. This is the true story of Dian Fossey, an amateur ethologist, who went to Africa to study gorillas. She became so enthralled with the gorillas that she got involved in numerous power and political struggles. She eventually was murdered, and her murder was never solved.

◆ Explore the Gorilla Language Project on the Internet at www.Koko.org. Koko and Michael are two lowland gorillas who were taught American Sign Language. Koko, a female born in 1971, and Michael, a male born in 1973 (who died in 2000), use sign language and understand spoken English. Koko joined the study when she was 1 year old, and Michael was 3½. Dr. Penny Patterson and other scientists studied Koko and Michael's intellectual, physical, and linguistic development in the longest continuous interspecies communications project of its kind.

Primates Exploring Primates

Major Concepts Characteristics of the higher primates

Overview

Now that the learners have had an opportunity to read about and think about observations of primates that someone else has made, they can begin developing their own observational skills.

In Get a Grip! (Part A), students will observe how humans and other primates move about and use their hands and feet. Based on their observations, the students will develop a set of questions about their observations and then determine which of their questions are testable. To reinforce the importance of the testability of a question, the students will carry out an experiment to test a question.

In All Brains on Board (Part B), the students will continue to compare humans and other animals by observing the similarities and differences in the principal parts of the brains of humans and other animals. They then will reflect on additional questions that these new observations bring to mind.

Materials   (per class of 30, teams of 2)

15 sets of assorted objects to grip in different ways, for example:
  jar with lid
  different sizes and shapes of balls
  tweezers
  hammer
  scissors
  pail with handle
  button

15 stopwatches (optional)
masking tape (sections of stretch bandages, which can sometimes be obtained from your
  school's sports trainer, can be substituted for tape)
15 padlocks with keys
3–10 sheep brains
DVD
DVD player

Outcomes and Indicators of Success

The following indicators allow you to assess the students' level of success with the activity and to assess their process of learning.

By the end of this activity, the learners should

1. begin to appreciate that there are certain characteristics that humans share with other animals, but that the expression of those characteristics is somewhat different.

They will demonstrate their appreciation by

    a. comparing how humans and other primates move about and use their hands and feet, and

    b. comparing the size and shape of various regions of the human brain with those regions in other animals' brains.

2. begin to appreciate the role of observation in science.

    They will demonstrate their appreciation by

    a. making observations and then creating a list of questions about the way primates use their hands,

    b. referring back to notes of their own observations as they respond to questions, and

    c. using their experiences in this activity to describe why observation is important in scientific studies.

3. begin to understand what a testable question is.

    They will demonstrate their understanding by

    a. articulating both testable and untestable questions and using a set of criteria to identify the testable ones, and

    b. carrying out a protocol that seeks to answer a testable question.

Safety

As the learners manipulate objects in Part A of this activity, caution them not to swing, throw, or drop objects in a way that might harm their classmates.

Preparations

Collect objects that will require the students to use a range of grips to manipulate them. The essay *Do You Have a Grip on That?* shows human grips and examples of objects that require different grasps.

Order sheep brains for your students to examine. Order at least two or three for a class of 30. The brains will not be dissected, so they can be reused in all of your classes. Ward's carries both freeze-dried and preserved sheep brains. You also may want to order Ward's pictorial *The Sheep Brain: A Basic Guide*, which would be a helpful resource for Part B of this activity.

Plan for use of the interactive DVD library.

Strategies for Guiding Learners

PROCESS AND PROCEDURES

As a class, read orally or silently all the introductory materials for the activity and the Process and Procedures to help students build connections between concepts and activities. Use the time spent reading to bring the students' attention into focus.

PART A   Get a Grip!

homework

1. Spend 10 minutes observing how humans move from place to place. Make a record of these observations in your journal.

Take the time to notice such things as the different types of strides that are possible and the differences in the way humans use their arms, legs, and feet. You can record observations with words and drawings.

You may want students to make these observations as homework, or you may decide to have them complete this task during the first 10 minutes of class. You might ask for volunteers to move about the room doing a variety of activities. Remind the students that sometimes it is difficult to make careful observations of things with which they are extremely familiar.

2. Now work with a partner to observe how humans use their hands. Use the objects that your teacher provides to explore the different ways that humans hold and use objects. Record these observations in detail in your journal.

   As the students manipulate the objects, remind them to be careful with the objects and to make detailed observations of the range of ways in which humans hold and manipulate objects with their hands.

Caution

3. Watch the DVD segment "Observing Primates." Record your observations of how each primate moves about and uses its arms, legs, hands, and feet. Make the same type of observations for each primate as you made for humans. As you observe humans in this segment on the DVD, add any new observations to those that you made in steps 1 and 2.

   Primates are the group of animals that includes humans, apes, and monkeys, along with a few lesser-known animals. Record as much detail as you can and be sure to label your journal entries clearly so you can tell which observations go with each primate. Pay particular attention to how each primate uses its fingers and thumbs so you can compare those motions to the human grip observations you made earlier.

   Chart?

   The DVD segment "Observing Primates" shows primates (both human and nonhuman) as they move about using their hands and feet in various ways. Repeat this segment two or three times so that the students have an opportunity to add to their observations. Refer to the interactive DVD guide in the *Teacher Resource CD* for narration and notes.

4. With your partner, have a brainstorming session to create a list of all the questions that come to mind about how primates move about and use their hands. Record this list in your journal.

   Come up with at least 5 questions.

   As the students work together to generate a list of questions about how primates move, ask them to practice the working-relationship skill of being open to the ideas of another.

5. Science begins with observing and asking questions about the world around us. Then it moves to a stage in which we begin to answer those questions by using a combination of further observation and experimentation. Scientists often have many questions that they would like to answer, but usually they focus their efforts on those that are testable.

   Use the criteria in the need to know box titled Testable Questions to determine which of the questions on your list are testable. Mark these questions with a *T*. Continue to work with your partner.

While the students are working to determine which of their questions are testable, use this as an opportunity to assess whether they can successfully apply the criteria in the need to know box titled Testable Questions (page 22 in the student text) to their lists. If you find that they are having difficulty, take a sample question or two from a student's list and go through this process as a class.

6. To gain a clearer sense of the nature of a testable question, compare these 2 questions:

   a. What is the importance of an opposable thumb for the ways in which humans use their hands?

   b. Without using your thumbs, can you use a key to open a lock?

   With your partner, discuss which question is easier to test. Explain the reasons for your choice in your journal.

    Again, as the learners discuss which question is easier to test, you can walk around the room and listen to the discussions to assess which students understand the criteria and can apply them.

7. Read through the 5 questions that you recorded in your journal in step 4. Select 1 of your testable questions to use in an experiment, or select the question you chose as most testable in step 6. If you are choosing one of your own questions, have your teacher check your procedure.

   Steps a–k in the following protocol box help you investigate whether you can open a lock without using your thumbs. You may be able to modify this protocol to test 1 of your own questions.

   Use the following protocol to test your question.

   If you think that your students are sufficiently prepared for such a step, you may decide to have them carry out an experiment on one of their own questions that they determined was testable. If they do this, they may use the Protocol for Testing the Question on page 23 in the student book as a template.

   Before the learners work through the protocol or write their own procedures, ask them to think about how making observations of human hands might have led an observer to ask the question that they now will test. Read through the protocol as a class to ensure that the students understand what they are to do and why. Call on individuals to explain the importance of each step. As they discuss step i of the protocol, see whether any students understand why you would want to compile the data as a class, even if these are data from a variety of procedures.

 8. Read the essay *Do You Have a Grip on That?* on page 86, and with your partner, complete the following in your journal:

   As the students work through this step, again ask them to practice the skill of being open to each other's ideas. The answers they generate will depend on the class results.

   a. Use the class results to formulate an answer and an explanation to the question you tested.

    Expect that the students who explain the basic question tested with the given protocol will indicate that they are not successful (or at least not as successful) when trying to use a key to unlock a lock when they cannot use their thumbs. They may explain their answer in terms of the role their thumbs would play as

they use a key. For example, they might indicate that they need to use their thumbs to get a strong enough grip on the key to unlock the lock. Students who conduct other experiments about how humans use their hands should have similar findings about the role that the thumb plays.

b. In what ways do you think the thumb is important to the way humans use their hands?

   Expect the students to indicate that the human thumb is important for using tools like a key, for getting a firm grip on a ball, and in general for adding strength, stability, and precision to the rest of the hand. They may indicate that this has something to do with the thumb's position in relation to the other fingers.

c. Look back in your journal at the record of your observations of the way other primates use their hands.

   1) In what ways do they use their thumbs?

      The students may have recorded information about the gorilla that uses its thumbs to grab bunches of grass, the chimpanzee and orangutan that use their thumbs to hold a tool to remove food from a hole, and the gibbons whose thumbs tend to stay out of the way as they grasp with the rest of their hands.

   2) How are those ways different from what you just discovered about how humans use their thumbs?

      It seems that the gibbon does better without using its thumbs; this is not the case for humans. It also seems that humans use their thumbs in ways that are similar to, but may be more precise than, the ways chimpanzees, gorillas, and sometimes orangutans do.

d. Review the observations of posture and stride that you made for humans and other primates. How is human movement and posture different from that of other primates?

   When humans walk or run, we hold our bodies upright. Students will notice a distinct difference between the posture of humans and that of the other primates; nonhuman primates often use their arms and hands to support part of their bodies when walking.

PART B   All Brains on Board

1. Examine the sheep brain that your teacher provides. Be sure to wear gloves when handling the brain and to wash your hands thoroughly at the end of class.

   To allow students time to examine the sheep brains, divide your class into groups depending on how many sheep brains you were able to provide for your class. This experience will enrich their understanding of comparative brain structures. Remind students to wash their hands with soap when they are done handling the brain.

2. Use the drawing of the sheep brain (Figure 1.3) to study the 2 color-coded regions of the brain. Locate the same 2 regions on the sheep brain that you are examining.

3. As you continue to study the sheep brain, read the essay *Brains and More Brains* (page 89) to learn about the basic functions of these regions of the brain.

The drawing of the sheep brain will help guide students' observations of the sheep brain they have before them. The essay *Mapping the Brain* will provide the students with more information about various regions of the brain.

4. Compare the color-coded regions of the sheep brain to the color-coded brains of 6 additional organisms. Record your observations in your journal.

   Use the drawings in Figure 1.4 on pages 25 and 26 and the images of brains in the DVD segment "Comparing Brains" to make these comparisons.

As the learners study the brains, walk around the room and listen to each team's discussion. This will provide you with an opportunity to assess the learners' abilities to make comparisons. If any team seems to need direction, ask the members to focus on one region at a time and look at it across all images of the brains. Ask the students to identify the structures in the other nonhuman mammal brain and then make educated guesses about what mammal it might be. It is the brain of a cat, and students may guess cat or some other sure-footed mammal because of the large cerebellum, which is responsible for posture and balance.

After the students have compared the drawings of the brains, show the DVD segment "Comparing Brains" so that they can observe close-up images of some of the actual brains from which these drawings were made. As each image appears on the screen, have the learners study the drawing of that brain and then study the image on the screen. Following the plain images, there is a series of color-coded images to help the students make comparisons.

5. Create a table in your journal to record your observations so that you can make comparisons more easily. Compare the relative sizes, shapes, and textures of the different regions of the brains. Also, record any unique or distinguishing characteristics that you observe.

6. Using your observations of the various brains, participate in a class discussion of the following questions:

   a. Consider the sheep brain. Which brain of those that you have studied is most like the sheep brain?

      Expect that the students will indicate that the sheep brain belongs somewhere closer to the human brain than to the fish brain. Some students will place it near the chimpanzee brain, perhaps between the bird brain and the chimpanzee brain. They should explain their placement in terms of the relative size and shape of each part of the brain.

   b. Why are some brains similar? Use the information you collected in step 4. Make sure you can explain your choices.

      Expect some students to suggest that the more similar brains may be from animals that are more closely related, or that the animals that have similar life strategies may require similar brain capabilities.

   c. Consider the cerebrum of each animal. Do you observe anything about the human cerebrum that makes it distinctive from the others? If so, what?

      Expect that the students will indicate that the cerebrum of the human is larger, covers more of the lower parts of the brain, and has more folds in it.

d. What did you learn about the function of the cerebrum as you read the essay *Brains and More Brains* that helps you understand why the cerebrum makes humans distinctive?

> **The students should indicate that the cerebrum is the part of the brain that allows us to think and solve problems and to make conscious movements, and that humans are fairly sophisticated at all of this. The students may think of the Phineas Gage account and may mention some social behaviors as well.**

e. Consider the cerebellum of each animal. Which animals would you expect to have well-developed cerebellums and why?

> **Expect the students to give examples of animals that require good balance to survive, like a mountain goat or sheep, squirrel, or cat.**

f. Consider the other observations you made about the brains. What inferences might you make about an animal that has a brain that has very large optic lobes or olfactory bulbs?

> **Students should recognize that brains with very large optic lobes likely are found in animals with well-developed vision, and those with large olfactory bulbs likely have a well-developed sense of smell.**

Analysis

1. How might the differences that you notice in the behaviors of the animals you studied be related to the differences that you noticed in their brains? Explain your answer.

To answer this question, use what you know about the behavior of fish, amphibians, reptiles, birds, sheep, other nonhuman mammals, and humans. Think about what you have learned from the observations that you made during this activity.

> **In general, expect students to indicate that because the cerebrum is responsible for thought, symbolic communication, and voluntary movements, it would seem that the larger, more complex cerebrum in humans may have something to do with our sophisticated use of language and the intricate ways we use our hands. Students also may point out that there seems to be little difference, except in overall size, between the chimpanzee brain and the human brain. The students likely will infer that the sense of smell and the sense of sight seem to be quite important in certain organisms.**

2. List two additional questions that you have about the brain as a result of your observations and readings in this activity.

> **This directive encourages the students to express their own curiosities by recording questions that come to mind. Students may have questions about which organisms on earth have the largest brains, how much of the human brain is actually used (the idea that only 10 percent of the brain is actually used is false), and other widely varied topics. You may wish to record these questions, assign students to research the answers, and revisit them later in the chapter or unit.**

Further Challenges

1. If you want to learn more about the way humans use their hands, revisit the essay *Do You Have a Grip on That?* (page 86). When you have finished reading, review the DVD segment "Observing Primates" and see which grips you observe other primates using.

2. Visit a zoo and make detailed observations of the way various primates or other animals move. You could record your observations in writing, drawings, or video.

Students may want to visit a zoo and make detailed observations of the way primates or other animals move; specifically, encourage them to explore how various primates use their feet.

3. Develop an experiment designed to answer another one of your testable questions from this activity.

Have the students develop an experiment to answer another testable question that they came up with during this activity.

Explain **Tony's Brain**

Major Concepts
Relationship of the brain and the mind; effect of new information on inductive explanations; brain structure and function

Overview

Students will study human brain function through an inquiry-based investigation of the brain/mind connection. This activity uses evidence gathered from copymasters, essays, and the DVD, and it introduces inductive reasoning skills as tools that students can use to search for the cause of altered behavior in a teenager. They also will discover that the distinction between brain and mind is not straightforward.

Materials   (per class of 30, teams of 4)

overhead projector and transparency, sheet of newsprint, or chalkboard
DVD
DVD player

30 copies of the Copymaster *Personal Interview with Tony*
30 copies of the Copymaster *Some Disorders of the Mind and Brain*
30 copies of the Copymaster *Results of the Doctors' Investigations of Tony's Behavior*

Outcomes and Indicators of Success

The following indicators allow you to assess the students' level of success with the activity and to assess their process of learning.

By the end of this activity, the learners should

1. recognize a distinction between the human brain and the human mind.

    They will demonstrate their recognition by

    a. defining the terms *brain* and *mind* in their own words, and

    b. explaining how the brain and the mind are related.

2. propose evidence-based explanations for the change in behavior of an individual.

   They will demonstrate their ability by

   a. listing evidence that is related to the cause of the behavior,

   b. generating several alternative explanations that are based on the available evidence for the cause of the behavior, and

   c. suggesting a tentative diagnosis for Tony's condition.

3. understand that scientific explanations involve evidence and inference.

   They will demonstrate their understanding by

   a. explaining that explanations without evidence are not considered scientific,

   b. making inferences that are based on their observations and evidence, and

   c. analyzing their explanations, and revising them if necessary, in light of new information.

Strategies for Guiding Learners

PROCESS AND PROCEDURES

As a class, read orally or silently all the introductory materials for the activity and the Process and Procedures to help students build connections between concepts and activities. Use the time spent reading to bring the students' attention into focus.

PART A   Making Sense of Words

1. With your team of 4, consider the words *brain* and *mind*. Try to develop 1 consensus definition for each word. The definition should be acceptable to all members of your team. Record your definitions for both brain and mind in your journal.

   Ask the students to record their team's initial consensus definitions of the terms brain and mind. Tell the students that they have only 5 minutes to come up with their definitions.

2. Meet with another team to compare your definitions. Explain why your team defined brain and mind as it did.

   Assign each team to meet with a second team so that this larger group can compare their definitions of *brain* and *mind*. You might listen for their ideas as you walk around the room. This is an opportunity for students to express openly their current understanding of these terms. The students' impressions might range from uninformed ideas that are based on misconceptions and clichés to thoughtful insights that are based on personal experience. For example, the students might define the brain as "the lump of stuff that sits inside my skull," or as "an organ inside my skull that contains different parts such as the cerebellum, the brain stem, and cerebrum; each of these parts contains millions of nerve cells." Likewise, the students initially might define the mind as "a characteristic that distinguishes humans from other animals because humans can think, talk, create, and make decisions."

PART B   A Problem and Possible Explanations

1. Read the following scenario:

    (See the scenario box on page 28 of the student text.)

2. Think of explanations that might account for Tony's behavior and contribute them to a class list.

    Generate as many explanations as possible. At this point, do not discuss which explanations are better than others.

    Ask the students to read individually the information about the patient, Tony. When they have finished, encourage the class to generate a list of possible explanations to account for Tony's behavior. As they contribute their suggestions, construct a class list on an overhead transparency, a large piece of newsprint that all students can see easily, or the chalkboard. Keep this list posted or otherwise available so that students can refer to it later. Numerous explanations are possible, including that Tony was taking drugs, had an inherited genetic disorder, or was having problems with his family and his personal life. These explanations do not necessarily have to meet the criteria for scientific explanations. For example, the explanation that "Tony is losing it" is a perfectly valid explanation to include in the list. The explanations also should not be ranked in order of likelihood. Discourage the students from discussing the strengths and weaknesses of the different explanations at this point.

3. Discuss the following question with your team:

    Why would it be unscientific to strongly support 1 of these explanations over all the others?

    Each member of the team should take a turn giving his or her reasons.

    As the students work in their teams to answer this question, listen for answers that reflect the students' awareness that not enough evidence is available to strongly support one explanation over all the others. Don't let the students dwell too long on this; 5 minutes is long enough. If they think that it is appropriate to support one explanation despite having no evidence, then prompt them with a question such as, What reasons can you give to justify your selection?

4. Read the information on Copymaster *Personal Interview with Tony* to help you understand more about Tony's condition. Then, with your teammates, modify the list of explanations so it contains only those that are still reasonable in light of this new information.

    Where possible, support an explanation by including evidence that you found in the conversation.

    Distribute Copymaster *Personal Interview with Tony*, and let the students work in their teams to generate a revised list of explanations. Advise the students to listen to each team member's comments and to practice the skill of being a thoughtful contributor. The student lists may include most of the explanations displayed on the original list, but look for examples that demonstrate that the students are using evidence to support some of those possibilities. For example, as evidence to support the idea that Tony was injured, the students should list the comment that Tony made about hitting his head while playing soccer. Similarly, the students can use evidence from the story to eliminate some possible explanations. For example, the students should realize that Tony's behavior probably cannot be explained by drug or alcohol abuse because he tells his friend that he does not use drugs or alcohol. At this stage, the process of choosing explanations is becoming scientific because the students are using evidence to narrow their list of possible explanations.

5. With your class, watch the DVD segment "Behavioral Disorders and the Brain." Then, with your team, decide whether to revise your list again.

Information in Copymaster *Some Disorders of the Mind and Brain* may help you with this task. Use what you have learned to determine the part of Tony's brain that is most likely affected by the illness. You can draw a diagram of the brain or write an explanation on your worksheet, but be certain to include evidence that supports your decision.

Begin by showing the DVD segment "Behavioral Disorders and the Brain." This set of PET images shows the pattern of activity in the brain of a patient with manic depression disorder in a depressed state, in remission, and just before, during, and after a manic state. Point out the parts of the brain as they appear on these images. Emphasize to the students that magnetic resonance imaging (MRI) and positron emission tomography (PET) reveal different information about the brain. The MRI is a tool for examining the physical structure of the brain. The method often is used for detecting tumors, swelling, degeneration, and other lesions. PET images, on the other hand, detect brain activity and can distinguish normal levels of activity in specific parts of the brain from decreased and increased levels of activity. PET images are used for research and to confirm diagnoses obtained by other tests.

Distribute the Copymaster *Some Disorders of the Mind and Brain*, and encourage the students to compare the PET images shown in the DVD segment with the descriptions of PET test results given for several of the disorders listed in this table.

As the teams revise their lists based on this new information, remind them that scientific inquiry sometimes involves the revision of explanations based on new evidence. These revisions, however, generally do not require the replacement of entire theories; rather, they refine and improve our understanding of existing theories.

6. Read the additional information on Copymaster *Results of the Doctors' Investigations of Tony's Behavior*. Revise your list again by crossing out any explanations that are no longer consistent with the new evidence.

Provide the students with the Copymaster *Results of the Doctors' Investigations of Tony's Behavior*. Although this handout contains many new terms and concepts, do not provide definitions or explanations. The students should use the information as best they can to evaluate the quality of their explanations and to revise them as necessary. Encourage them to discuss their explanations in light of this new evidence.

7. With your team, draw a conclusion about which disorders from the table in *Some Disorders of the Mind and Brain* that Tony most likely suffers from. List 3 pieces of evidence that support your conclusion. On your team's worksheet, record your team's consensus conclusion.

8. Imagine that your team is the group of doctors treating Tony. Develop a plan to determine if your diagnosis is correct.

Ask the students to use all available information to make a tentative diagnosis and to indicate the evidence that supports their decision. Ask them what additional information would be helpful for confirming their diagnosis.

Analysis

Do in class w/ Fund.

1. It appears that Tony's mind was affected by his illness because his feelings and behaviors changed so dramatically. At the same time, there is medical evidence of physical changes in his brain. Based on your analysis of the brain/mind connection, explain whether or not you would now change your original definitions for brain and mind.

   The students may or may not choose to change their original definitions of brain and mind. Suitable definitions at this time should reveal an awareness that the brain is an organ, a physical structure, that directs our life functions, whereas the mind is a collection of mental activities that defines who we are as individuals. The definition of the mind still is debated actively by scientists and ethicists, so no single definition should be held as conclusive.

2. In this activity, you conducted an analysis using inductive reasoning. This means that you made observations and collected evidence in an effort to explain Tony's unusual behavior. How does new information affect the conclusions that people might draw through inductive reasoning? When can you be certain that you have arrived at the correct explanation for a problem like Tony's?

   It might help to consider where the mind and brain are located and what their relationship is. Also, consider these questions: Under what conditions does the brain cease to exist? Under what conditions does the mind cease to exist?

   Students' answers should reflect an understanding that they may change their explanations as they receive new or improved information. An explanation can be no better than the evidence one uses to support it, hence the importance in scientific inquiries for large amounts of accurate and reliable data. You never can be fully certain that you have the correct explanation, but as more and more evidence accumulates in support of a given explanation, the less likely it becomes that the general features of the explanation will be found incorrect.

   If there is time and interest, you could follow up this question by asking students for examples from recent school or news events in which additional information changed their understanding of a situation. This will underscore the importance of evidence in the analysis of life situations that do not involve science.

3. As humans age, the brain undergoes changes that, in some individuals, can affect a person's memory. Some people might also respond more slowly to certain things. These difficulties can be caused by a slight decrease in the number of neurons or in their connections in some areas of the brain. These changes are normal.

   In the brains of people who have Alzheimer's disease, however, more extensive changes take place. Changes that happen in the production of two proteins lead to the buildup of plaque and "tangles" that affect the neurons' ability to function. These neurons cannot communicate normally with other neurons' ability to function. These neurons cannot communicate normally with other neurons. As a result of this buildup, the neurons eventually die from impaired function. We see evidence of this neuron death as shrinkage of the cerebral hemispheres.

   Think about what you have learned about the brain and mind in the last two activities. Explain how the changes in the brain of a person with Alzheimer's disease relate to the changes in the function of the person's mind.

Discuss Alzheimer's disease briefly with the students to be certain they know about the symptoms of memory loss and the progressive decline of intellectual abilities in affected individuals. Students should recognize that the physical changes in an Alzheimer patient's brain result in a change in the functioning of the person's mind. Because the cerebral cortex is the region of the brain responsible for processing visual and spatial information, shrinkage has a large impact on the Alzheimer patient's daily brain function. Students also should recognize that neurotransmitters act as messengers that transmit signals across the gap between neurons, and that interconnectedness of neurons is required for the brain to function. Reducing the number of neurotransmitters present in the brain results in memory loss and difficulties with emotions and language.

Resources

The following references provide additional information about the relationship between the brain and the mind:

Fishbach, G.D. (1992, September). Mind and brain. *Scientific American*, 267(3), 48–59.

Gershon, E.S., & Rieder, R.O. (1992, September). Major disorders of mind and brain. *Scientific American*, 267(3), 126–133.

Klivington, K. (1989). *The science of mind*. Cambridge, MA: The MIT Press.

Konner, M. (1982). *The tangled wing: Biological constraints on the human spirit*. New York: Harper and Row.

Martin, R. (1986). *Matters gray and white*. New York: Henry Holt and Co., Inc.

The mind. PBS documentary television series. Available on videotape.

Restak, R.M. (1988). *The mind*. Toronto: Bantam Books.

The Scientific American Frontiers videos produced by PBS include several videos about brain and mind function, including Season VII: *Pieces of Mind* and Season XI: *Changing Your Mind*. PBS videos can be ordered from http://teacher.shop.pbs.org.

Portraying Humankind

Explain

Major Concepts
Characteristics of the human animal; brain function

Overview

In the previous activities, the learners have been making observations, reflecting, asking questions, and answering some questions about humans as animals. In this activity, they will begin a project to illustrate their understanding of a much larger question: What does it mean to be human? They will use their experiences from the previous activities as well as information from the essays and observations from the DVD segments to create this project.

Materials (per class of 30, individuals or teams of 2)

poster board

felt-tipped markers

glue

old photographs

musical instruments

video camera

tape recorder

magazines

cardboard boxes

other assorted materials that the
   students might find useful

DVD

DVD player

30 copies of the *Portraying Humankind* rubric

Outcomes and Indicators of Success

The following indicators allow you to assess the students' level of success with the activity and to assess their process of learning.

By the end of this activity, the learners should

1. develop a better understanding of what it means to be human.

    They will demonstrate their understanding by

    a. sharing their understanding of the following with a classmate:
        ◆ **How humans are structured to be bipedal.**
        ◆ **How the human hand is similar to and different from the hands of other primates.**
        ◆ **How different parts of the cerebrum are associated with various behaviors.**
        ◆ **How different parts of the human brain are similar to and different from the brains of other primates.**
        ◆ **How nerves transmit information.**
        ◆ **Why the human brain is responsible for complex human behavior.**

    b. listing concepts that illustrate their understanding, such as those mentioned in outcome 1a, in the description of their project.

2. begin to pull together concepts about the study of humans as animals.

    They will demonstrate this ability by writing a description of a project that pulls together concepts about humans to create a project that illustrates their understanding of what it means to be human.

3. be able to review criteria and apply them to a certain task.

    They will demonstrate this ability by providing a critique of a classmate's written description of his or her proposed project.

Preparations

You may want to begin collecting materials for these projects and ask that the students also contribute. Review the rubric for *Portraying Humankind* (on the *GACD*) and decide how many points you will assign to each category. Share this information with the students. If you want to fit all of the presentations into one class period, you will have to set limits on the length of each presentation. You may prefer to extend the activity for several days; in either case, include in your rubric how much time you will allot for presentations so that students can plan accordingly. You also may decide to team-teach this activity with an art teacher or a language arts teacher; if you do so, arrange for this ahead of time.

Strategies for Guiding Learners

PROCESS AND PROCEDURES

As a class, read orally or silently all the introductory materials for the activity and the Process and Procedures to help students build connections between concepts and activities. Use the time spent reading to bring the students' attention into focus.

To facilitate this activity, begin by making sure that each student understands what is expected of him or her and what qualifies as a successful project. The rubric criteria provide a structure for this discussion.

After the students understand their responsibility, you may wish to provide them with the option of working alone or with a partner. If you choose to allow students to work in teams, remind them that both members will earn the same score so it is incumbent on teammates to work together and to pull their own weight. Also, if learners work in pairs, ask them to practice the skill of including the ideas of others.

Provide one class period for students to think about and plan their projects. Explain that they will have more time in class and at home to work on the projects after they finish the activity *A Long Childhood*.

1. Think about designing a project to illustrate your understanding of what it means to be human.

   Think of an activity that you enjoy doing and consider what it is about being human that makes it possible for you to do this activity. Perhaps you can incorporate a demonstration or description of this activity into your project and presentation.

2. When you have a general idea in mind, share your idea with your partner.

   As students think about a project that they might design, it will be helpful to most students to share their ideas with a partner. If some students are struggling to come up with an idea, suggest that they talk with another student to generate some ideas.

3. Obtain a copy of the rubric that your teacher will use to evaluate your project. To meet the criteria for this project, be sure that you understand and can explain the following ideas to your partner:

   ◆ How humans are structured to be bipedal.

   ◆ How the human hand is similar to and different from the hands of other primates.

   ◆ How different parts of the cerebrum are associated with various behaviors.

   ◆ How different parts of the human brain are similar to and different from the brains of other primates.

   ◆ How nerves transmit information.

   ◆ Why the human brain is responsible for complex human behavior.

   The essays *On Being Human* (page 92) and *Brains and a Lot of Nerve* (page 95) and the DVD segment "More About the Brain" will help broaden your understanding of these ideas. As you watch the DVD segments, practice your observation skills. Record notes in your journal.

   You may want to divide the class into thirds for 15- to 20-minute intervals and have each group concentrate on one of the two essays or on the DVD segment

"More About the Brain." The DVD segment "Nervous System and Nerve Transmission" follows "More About the Brain" and would typically be shown with it. However, "Nervous System and Nerve Transmission" can be omitted if it is too complex for your students. Each group then can move on to the other essay or the DVD segment until all groups have completed each task. As each group completes its work, the learners can share their ideas and observations with their partner or another classmate who has finished. This strategy provides the learners with the opportunity to articulate the concepts for themselves and to listen to the concepts articulated in a slightly different way by someone else. Walk around the room and listen to the discussions. Use the indicators for outcome 1 as a way of assessing the learners' level of understanding.

The DVD segments "More About the Brain" and "Nervous System and Nerve Transmission" provide a resource of information about the brain and nervous system. Still images show structures and functions of the brain by using photographs, drawings, MRIs, and PET scans. A narrated sequence introduces the nervous system and includes animation of a nerve impulse and a reflex arc. More MRIs are available in the optional DVD segment titled "Brain Structure."

4. Write a short description of your project in your journal. List 4 or 5 concepts from the essays and the previous activities that you plan to incorporate into your project.

As the students write their project descriptions, walk around the room and read some of the descriptions to see that the projects are practical and meaningful. To assess each student's level of understanding, read the list of concepts that each student plans to include. If some of the students are not as focused as they need to be, redirect them to the criteria listed in the rubric.

Analysis

If the students are working with a partner for this project, then have each pair team up with another pair to complete this Analysis. To give you an idea of what to expect, review the following list of some of the projects from the field test and earlier editions of *BSCS Biology: A Human Approach*:

- ◆ Musical compositions with accompanying narration
- ◆ Poems, sonnets, and essays
- ◆ Newsletters with a range of articles
- ◆ Posters, both formal and animated
- ◆ Videotapes
- ◆ Skits and plays
- ◆ Presentations that involve the audience
- ◆ Computer or slide presentations

1. Meet with your partner and exchange written descriptions of your projects.

   a. Read your partner's description.

   b. If something about your partner's project is unclear to you, ask questions of him or her.

    c. Review the criteria for the project that are listed in the rubric provided by your teacher. Tell your partner how well you think his or her proposed project meets them.

    d. Make suggestions that you think would contribute to your partner's project.

        Even though the students may be working individually, they likely will benefit from discussing ideas with each other.

2. According to the feedback that you receive from your partner, revise or add to your description.

You will present your project to the class as the evaluate activity for this chapter.

Extensions

◆ If your students are interested in learning more about the brain, ask them to research a topic and present a short report to the class. One topic of interest recently has been the differences that exist between male and female brains.

A Long Childhood

Major Concepts Human capacity for culture and learning

Overview

In this activity, the learners will reflect on the human capacity for learning, language, and culture, and explore how these qualities might relate to the existence of a long childhood in humans. The students then reflect on how this situation is similar to and different from what takes place in other animals. They conclude the activity by deciding how to fold the ideas of culture and learning into their projects and by beginning to work on their projects.

Materials (per class of 30)

resources that will have information about maturation in animals

Outcomes and Indicators of Success

The following indicators allow you to assess the students' level of success with the activity and to assess their process of learning.

By the end of this activity, the learners should

1. understand that humans have a longer period of dependency as they mature than most other animals.

They will demonstrate their understanding by pointing out this trend as they compare and contrast the maturation characteristics of a range of animals, including humans.

2. appreciate how a long childhood in humans is connected to our capacity for learning, our capacity for language, and our capacity for culture.

They will demonstrate this appreciation by stating that having a long period of dependency gives us time to learn language and to learn how to behave within our culture.

3. appreciate the existence of learning, communication, and culture in other animals.

   They will demonstrate this appreciation by providing examples of other animals, such as chimpanzees, gorillas, and dolphins, that have a certain capacity for learning, communication, and culture.

Preparations

Begin to collect resources students can use to find the necessary data on humans and other animals. For example, the segment "The Young Ones" from the Public Broadcasting Service series *Nature* is an excellent resource. Many encyclopedias also include this type of information about animals. You may want to alert the school librarian that your students will be coming to the library in search of specific information on how various animals mature. Placing books on reserve will ensure that all students have access to these resources. In addition, you and your students may enjoy the segment "The Long Childhood" from *The Ascent of Man*, a British Broadcasting Corporation series.

Strategies for Guiding Learners

PROCESS AND PROCEDURES

As a class, read orally or silently all the introductory materials for the activity and the Process and Procedures to help students build connections between concepts and activities. Use the time spent reading to bring the students' attention into focus.

1. Participate in a class discussion and answer the following questions as they apply to humans:

   This class discussion of the questions about humans should be brief and to the point. This information is likely to be common knowledge for students, so the information will not stand out until they begin to compare it with similar information for other animals. Expect answers similar to the following:

   a. What is the length of pregnancy?
      Nine months. (Note: The terms *gestation* and *incubation* likely will come up when students research other animals. Take this opportunity to define and discuss their meanings.)

   b. At what age do the young stop nursing or are able to get food on their own?
      Generally, children stop nursing anywhere from 6 months to 2–4 years. If children had to acquire food on their own, this might be difficult even for 6- or 7-year-olds.

   c. At what age are the young completely and independently mobile?
      Children begin to walk at about 1 year, but are not sophisticated at moving around until 5–6 years.

   d. At what age do individuals become sexually mature?
      Between 10 and 16. This range will vary depending on whether we are defining "sexually mature" in terms of biology or in terms of culture and

psychology. Also, there is a difference between being able to become pregnant and being able to deliver a live baby, which seems to require a more mature body.

2. Record the answers to those questions in your journal.

You also will collect this information for other animals, so create a table in which to organize and record all of the information. You may want to arrange the questions across the top and list the animals in the left column as in Figure 1.5.

3. Select another animal and answer the questions in step 1 for that animal.

Use the resources that your teacher provides or resources from the library.

You may want to go around the room and ask each student to choose an animal to research. It is acceptable that two students choose the same animal, but if a third student chooses the same one, suggest an alternative. Instead, you may want to present students with a list of animals and have them sign up for the ones you list.

You can give the students time to complete this work in class or assign this as homework.

4. Contribute your answers to a class data table.

Record the class data in your own data table.

Have each student contribute to the class data table the information about the animal that he or she researched. If two students researched the same animal, have them record their data in the same row.

5. With your classmates, discuss what patterns emerge as you compare the data for humans with those of the other animals.

Use the data to identify the animals that have long "childhoods."

Ask the students to compare the answers for one question at a time. Then ask them to discuss anything they notice as they make these comparisons. A general pattern that may emerge is that the smaller the animal, the shorter the pregnancy and the sooner the animal is independent and reaches adulthood. There will be exceptions to this pattern, of course. Also, the students should see a striking difference between the data for humans and the data for other animals. Humans have an unusually long period of dependency. This step provides you with the opportunity to assess the learners' critical-thinking skills that are associated with comparing data.

6. With a partner, discuss the question, What are some of the things that happen as the result of a long childhood in humans? Record your ideas in your journal.

Use the essay *The Importance of Being Children* (page 98) as a resource.

The students most likely will think about learning of various types, including the learning of language, of survival skills, and of cultural norms. The students also may associate this learning with the continuation of brain development. The essay *The Importance of Being Children* will be a valuable resource for the students.

Analysis

Think about how you will fold your ideas developed in this activity into the project you began in the activity *Portraying Humankind*.

1. To help you do this, discuss the following questions with a classmate:

   a. How does a long childhood help humans develop complex culture?

   Expect students to indicate that a long childhood provides children with time to learn and to experience intricate aspects of their culture, for example, what behaviors are considered appropriate or inappropriate in various settings.

   b. How does our language ability help us develop complex culture?

   Expect students to realize that language is one of the ways that humans transmit information and consequently is one of the ways that humans learn. Because written language allows humans to store information, the type of information can be quite complex.

   c. How does our ability to learn help us develop complex culture?

   Expect students to realize that the human capacity for learning is a characteristic that enhances the idea of shared, complex cultures that are different from each other.

   d. Give three examples of different ways that humans learn. How do you learn best?

   Students might indicate that humans learn by imitation and doing, by listening to others, by reading, and by teaching something to others.

   e. Give two examples of other animals that exhibit a certain capacity for learning, language, and culture.

   Students might mention other primates such as chimpanzees, gorillas, and gibbons; dolphins; or wolves.

   f. How different are humans and other animals? How alike are they? Support your answers with new information that you have learned in this activity.

   Expect that students will say that humans are in many ways like other animals but that they have a certain collection of characteristics that is more complex than in other animals. The fact that humans, unlike most other animals, have such a long childhood gives them time to learn complex behaviors and then, in turn, to teach these behaviors to their offspring.

2. Decide how you will fold some of these expanded ideas into your project. Then add this information to your written description for the project.

3. Have your teacher approve your completed plan for the project.

   Use this opportunity to check that all students have committed to a project at this point and that it is a worthwhile project to pursue. You may wish to meet individually with students for 1 or 2 minutes to discuss projects so that you can identify any special needs that may need consideration.

4. Work on your project as your teacher directs.

   Tell students whether there will be additional class time to work on projects or if they are to be completed as homework.

Further Challenges

1. Together with other interested classmates, find out about the existence of culture and society in other animals.

   Some of your students may want to explore the existence of culture in other animals, for example, chimpanzees or dolphins.

2. Do further library research on the learning abilities of other primates or dolphins.

   The *Scientific American Frontiers* video from Season IX: *Animal Einstein*, Episode 3, is an excellent source of information about research into intelligence in nonhuman animals.

3. Learn more about your own learning style. Your teacher may have some resources to get you started.

   Your learning style is the way you prefer to learn. There are questionnaires you can take to find out more about how your brain works best for learning new information.

   If you have the time and the students are interested, you might want to do a learning style inventory with them to increase their appreciation for the range of ways in which people learn. The Myers-Briggs type indicator or the Gregorc learning style inventory are both popular. If you are not certified to administer and score the inventories, arrange for someone in your school district to do this for you. You can obtain these inventories from the following locations:

   Myers-Briggs Type Indicator (NBTI)
   Center for Applications of Psychological Type, Inc.
   2815 NW 13th Street, Suite 401
   Gainesville, FL 32609
   or call: 800-777-CAPT (Order Form G)

   Gregorc Model
   Gregorc Associates
   15 Doubleday Road
   Columbia, CT 06237
   or call: 203-228-0093

What Does It Mean to Be Human?

Evaluate

Major Concepts   Overall characteristics of humans

Overview

In this activity, the learners will present the project they began thinking about in the activity *Portraying Humankind* that will illustrate their understanding of the concepts in this chapter. In addition to presenting their projects, the students will evaluate themselves and their peers.

Materials   (per class of 30)

VCR and monitor (optional)
cassette tape player (optional)
computer and projector (optional)
30 copies of the *Portraying Humankind* rubric
    (or reuse the rubrics given out in the explain activity)

Outcomes and Indicators of Success

The following indicators allow you to assess the students' ability to evaluate their current understanding of what it means to be human.

By the end of this activity, the learners should be able to evaluate their understanding of the main concepts of this chapter as indicated in the chapter goals.

They will demonstrate their ability by

a. presenting a project that visually, orally, or in writing expresses the main ideas of this chapter,

b. identifying the three strongest projects in the class and justifying those choices, and

c. assessing their own project and presentation according to the stated criteria.

Preparations

Ask the students whether they need special equipment for their presentations so that you can arrange to have it in the classroom. You also may wish to have a stopwatch to time presentations.

Strategies for Guiding Learners

PROCESS AND PROCEDURES

As a class, read orally or silently all the introductory materials for the activity and the Process and Procedures to help students build connections between concepts and activities. Use the time spent reading to bring the students' attention into focus.

1. Present the project that you began in the activity *Portraying Humankind* to your classmates according to your teacher's directions.

    If the majority of students do a visual or three-dimensional project, you may want to set up a project fair. If you decide to fit all the presentations into one class period, you will have to set limits on the length of each presentation and time the presentations so that they do not last too long. You may prefer to extend this phase of the activity into another class period.

     If you choose, you may evaluate the students' presentations as they are given. This is most easily accomplished by highlighting and recording comments directly on the rubric while the students present. Have students write their names on their rubrics and hand them to you prior to presenting. You need not total the scores or hand back rubrics until you have the chance to look more closely at the visual aids or products included in the presentations.

Remind the students also to recall the rubric for *Portraying Humankind* as they listen to and view the projects. You may wish to provide an extra copy of the rubric for students to keep as they listen to the presentations. Students should base their selections of the three strongest projects on the rubric criteria. You can use the project and the presentation combined with the students' analyses of other projects to assess each student's understanding of the chapter.

2. Using the criteria given to you by your teacher, identify what you think are the 3 strongest projects in your class. List these in your journal and justify your choices.

The students may identify any three projects as the strongest. It is likely that some students may focus on their friends' work.

The task to justify their choices sets apart the students who are supporting their friends from the students who can analyze the projects they have seen. The students' justifications for their selections should include a description of how each project demonstrates the key concepts of the chapter, identifies three distinguishing characteristics of humans, is creative, makes references to other activities, and includes a strong presentation.

Analysis

Use the same criteria to rate your own project and presentation. Explain your rating in your journal.

Assign the self-evaluation of projects as homework or provide time after the students have evaluated the three strongest projects. Check their journals to assess their evaluations and to provide feedback.

CHAPTER 2 IMPLEMENTATION (continued)

Instructional Flow				Classroom Support			
Activity/ Student Text pp. Teacher Guide pp.	GACD, TRCD, DVD, and CD-ROM Resources	Essays/ Student Text pp.	Estimated Time	Team Size/ Cooperative Learning Focus	Strategies and Tools	Assessment Opportunities	Special Considerations
EXPLAIN Explaining Evolution pp. 50–51 TG pp. 81–85	Copymaster: DNA Comparison; Copymaster: Primate Comparisons; Copymaster: Fossil Finds; Rubric: Fossil Find; DVD: Embryology, Hominid Skulls, and Continental Drift	Darwin Proposes Descent with Modification pp. 111–113; Evolution by Natural Selection pp. 113–118; Just a Theory? pp. 119–120	50 minutes	Team size: 2 Skill: Taking responsibility	Newspaper story; charts; rebuttals	Current level of understanding; ability to articulate understanding	Enlarge print materials and/or read aloud if needed. Some students may be better able to show their understanding if they write their stories during class time, use a word processor, and/or present their stories orally.
ELABORATE Modeling Natural Selection pp. 52–55 TG pp. 85–92	Copymaster: Natural Selection Record Sheet		150 minutes	Team size: 4 Skill: Taking responsibility	Simulation; lab; journal entries; graphing	Ability to apply knowledge to new setting	Preview the roles that students are assigned for the modeling activity, and preselect roles for students with challenges that might hinder participation in a particular role. Encourage teamwork that facilitates participation by all.
ELABORATE A Cold Hard Look at Culture pp. 55–58 TG pp. 92–96	DVD: A Glimpse of the Iceman, X-rays of the Iceman, and Artifacts		75–150 minutes	Team size: 4 Skill: Encouraging participation	DVD; journal entries; discussion	Critical-thinking skills; ability to justify responses	Enlarge print materials and/or read aloud if needed. Some students may be better able to explain their ideas to you orally.
EVALUATE Evolution in Action pp. 58–61 TG pp. 96–99	Rubric: Evolution in Action		50 minutes	Team size: individuals	Scenarios; journal entries	Current level of understanding; critical-thinking skills; ability to justify responses	Enlarge print materials and/or read aloud if needed. Some students may be better able to show their understanding if they write their answers during class time, use a word processor, and/or present their answers to you orally.

Chapter Goals

By the end of this chapter, students should understand that

◆ populations of organisms change across time;

◆ evolution is a scientific explanation for the diversity of life on earth;

◆ billions of years were required for the evolutionary process to produce the great diversity of life on earth;

◆ evidence for biological evolution exists in the fossil record and in biological characteristics such as embryological development and genetics;

◆ natural selection is a major mechanism of biological evolution; and

◆ humans are both a product and a driving force of biological evolution.

The learners also will

◆ make observations,

◆ collect evidence and data,

◆ make comparisons,

◆ draw graphs,

◆ develop explanations,

◆ make inferences,

◆ evaluate evidence, and

◆ use models.

Advance Preparation

Both the explore activity, *Modeling the Earth's History*, and the elaborate activity *Modeling Natural Selection* require that you prepare materials beforehand. See Materials and Preparations in these activities for details.

Lucy

Engage

Major Concepts Change in humanlike organisms

Overview

This activity engages the learners as they think about the concept of change across time. We ask the learners to look at the specific example of the fossil hominid Lucy. The students later will learn that, in biology, change often is a synonym for evolution. But because this is an engage activity, it is not necessary at this point to describe the change in hominids as evolution. Rather, the students should begin to think about the idea that living things do change across a long period of time.

Outcomes and Indicators of Success

The following indicators allow you to assess the students' level of success with the activity and to assess their process of learning.

By the end of this activity, the learners should become aware that the fossil Lucy helps build a case for ideas about how hominids have changed across time.

They will show their awareness by

a. describing how Lucy may have looked and behaved,

b. speculating on how Lucy might bridge the gap between modern humans and early nonhuman primates,

c. participating in a discussion comparing early hominids to modern humans, and

d. identifying the role of evidence and inference in formulating their discussions.

Preparations

You may find it useful to review human evolution in a general sense as well as Lucy's place in the picture. Campbell and Loy's book, *Humankind Emerging,* Concise Edition, (2001, Boston: Allyn and Bacon), provides a well-rounded discussion of human evolution and presents various scientific points of view. The Public Broadcasting System's special on evolution is another good source of background information for both teachers and students. There is a set of videos and an accompanying Web site at http://www.pbs.org/wgbh/evolution.

Strategies for Guiding Learners

PROCESS AND PROCEDURES

As a class, read orally or silently all the introductory materials for the activity and the Process and Procedures to help students build connections between concepts and activities. Use the time spent reading to bring the students' attention into focus.

1. Describe in your journal how Lucy may have looked. Explain 3 things she might have done during a typical day and how she would have gone about doing them.

   Use the photograph of the fossil skeleton in the opening photo to this chapter and your notes from Chapter 1 to help you develop your description. Pay particular attention to Lucy's hands, feet, posture, and way of moving. Try to describe how she may have communicated with family members and others living in her group.

   Encourage students to use the photograph of Lucy and the story to complete their journal entries. They should develop descriptions that indicate what Lucy might have looked like and how she might have behaved. This is another good opportunity for students to use their drawing skills to express their ideas. If they are including only physical characteristics, ask the learners to consider other types of characteristics as well, such as whether they imagine that early hominids lived in naturally occurring or constructed shelters. Students should consider daily activities such as gathering food, interacting with family, and carrying supplies. Encourage the students to build on the concepts from Chapter 1 about the distinguishing characteristics of humans.

2. Consider the following question and record your answer in your journal:
What evidence from the Lucy find could help scientists develop an explanation about the gap between modern humans and early nonhuman primates?

As the students consider the question, expect them to describe characteristics and capabilities that represent something in between modern humans and what they think early nonhuman primates might have looked like. The students may say that Lucy may have been taller than some of the early primates, or that Lucy's brain might have been larger, her thumb more opposable, and her feet better suited to walking bipedally. If the students begin using modern apes as a model for early nonhuman primates, remind them that modern apes are the product of evolution across the same period of time as modern humans are, and consequently, modern apes might be quite distinctive from the early nonhuman primates that were the common ancestor of both modern humans and modern apes.

If the students are interested in learning more about the fossil record with respect to these early primates, Bernard Campbell's book, mentioned earlier, and the many articles on human evolution found in *National Geographic* (for example, *The First Pioneer?*, by Rick Gore, in the August 2002 issue) would be good resources with which to begin.

Analysis

Use the information from your description to answer the following questions as part of a class discussion:

1. Compare hominids from Lucy's lifetime to your own. Do you think there have been more changes in physical characteristics of the body (such as hands, feet, head, posture) or more changes in how hominids lived (types of shelter, ways of getting around, ways of gathering food)?

Accept all responses from the students at this point in the learning cycle. Encourage them to defend their opinions and responses. Students with more understanding of geologic time may argue that the biological changes have been more significant. Those who view technological progress as significant may argue that the changes in lifestyle are greater.

2. Use the information in the need to know box to help you answer these questions:
   a. Which aspects of your descriptions did you base on evidence?
   b. Which aspects of your descriptions were inferences related to evidence?
   c. Which aspects of your descriptions were guesses?
   With the information available, the only direct evidence the students have is the shape and size of the skeleton and the place where the fossil was found. The important focus of this question is helping students to distinguish between evidence and inference.

Extensions

The students may want to read more about Lucy and other hominid finds. The following two books are good beginning resources:

Johanson, D.C., & Edey, M.A. (1981). *Lucy: The beginning of humankind*. New York: Simon & Schuster.

Leakey, R.E. (1994). *The origin of humankind*. New York: Basic Books.

Modeling the Earth's History

Major Concepts Earth's history (sequence and placement of events); geologic time

Overview

This activity lets the students explore the relationship between significant biological and geological events. They will explore these ideas by constructing a timeline that models the earth's history. This activity should give the students an appreciation of the vastness of geological time, which is important to their understanding of how a diversity of life could have arisen through evolution.

Materials   (per class of 30, teams of 4)

80 clothespins or large paper clips
30 copies of the Copymaster *Major Events in the Earth's History*
1 copy of the Copymaster *Event Cards* (see Preparations)

For making the timeline:
red and black permanent, broad felt-tipped markers
25–50 m clothesline (see Preparations)
metric tape measure or meterstick

Outcomes and Indicators of Success

The following indicators allow you to assess the students' level of success with the activity and to assess their process of learning.

By the end of this activity, the learners should

1. appreciate the sequence of biological and geological events in the earth's history.

    They will indicate their appreciation by

    a. estimating when certain events occurred and placing them accordingly on a timeline,

    b. identifying relationships among various events, and

    c. developing explanations for those relationships.

2. begin to understand the usefulness of models.

    They will demonstrate their understanding by using the timeline to identify patterns and relationships between events.

3. appreciate the enormous expanse of time since the formation of the earth.

    They will show their appreciation by discussing the amount of time that is visually modeled on the timeline.

Preparations

In this activity, the students use a clothesline to create a timeline. The model is more powerful if the clothesline is 25–50 meters long. Depending on your students and the space available, you may want to conduct this activity in an area longer than a classroom—perhaps a hallway, gymnasium, cafeteria, or outside. As a last resort, run the timeline around the perimeter of your classroom. After you have determined the location, purchase the appropriate length of clothesline. If possible, attach the ends of the clothesline to something solid. If this is not possible, have students hold each end.

After subtracting the amount of clothesline needed to attach each end, divide the clothesline into five equal sections, each representing 1 billion years. Mark the ends of the clothesline and each division with the red markers. Next, divide each billion-year segment into 10 equal sections, each representing 100 million years; mark these divisions in black.

Make 30 copies of Copymaster *Major Events in the Earth's History*. Make one copy of the event cards, then cut the cards apart on the dotted lines. To make the relationships between the geological and biological events more obvious, copy the respective events onto two different colors of paper.

Background

One of the most powerful techniques in scientific inquiry is modeling. A model system accounts for observations and allows for predictions of the real system, but the model system generally is much simpler. Modeling has widespread applications in science. For example, the application of mathematical models to scientific investigation involves using abstract symbols with well-defined rules of deduction to model or describe the behavior of some phenomenon. The mathematical manipulations mirror the physical behavior of the real system. This parallelism allows us to use the model to make predictions about the real system. The quality of a model is determined by how easy it is to manipulate and how well it mimics the real system.

Many disciplines use models. Anatomical models may consist of a physical reconstruction of a body plan or a computer-generated image of some aspect of an organism's structure. Many scientists use computers extensively for abstract modeling of biological phenomena, such as growth patterns in plants, evolution of species, and behavior in insects. Many of these phenomena are sufficiently complex and have enough variables to make them inaccessible by other means. In the most basic sense, all biological experiments done *in vitro* (in glass) are models of the biological systems under study. When a scientist carries out an enzymatic reaction in a test tube, for example, she or he is modeling the analogous reaction that occurs inside cells.

Strategies for Guiding Learners

PROCESS AND PROCEDURES

As a class, read orally or silently all the introductory materials for the activity and the Process and Procedures to help students build connections between concepts and activities. Use the time spent reading to bring the students' attention into focus.

1. Discuss the following question with your teammates:

   How long ago do you think each of the following events took place and in what sequence?

   ◆ First dinosaurs

   ◆ Formation of Rocky Mountains

- First hominids
- First life (bacteria)
- First modern humans
- First oxygen in atmosphere
- First land plants

Combine two pairs of students to get teams of four. As the teams estimate times and a sequence for the events listed, encourage them to discuss their ideas about the events openly and creatively. They do not need to edit and critique the accuracy of their sequence and dating at this time.

If you want to add a working-relationship skill to this activity, have the students in each team concentrate on listening to and respecting each other's ideas. Make clear to the students that this is one goal of the activity. You might decide to write "Listen to your teammates" on the board as a reminder. As the activity proceeds, keep track of how well the students are listening to each other. If a team seems to be having trouble with one or two dominant individuals, model the types of questions and etiquette expected of the dominant individuals by asking another team member, What ideas do you have about how this event should be placed?

2. Make a list of the events in the order that your team thinks they happened.

List the most recent event first. Write large enough that the class will be able to read your list when you post it at the front of the class. Next to each event, record the number of years ago that your team thinks each event took place.

To keep this prediction phase of the lesson moving quickly, you may wish to write the seven events in large print on a piece of paper and copy one for each team. Then the students can cut the events apart and physically move them into various arrangements while discussing and coming to consensus about the order. Once teams have settled on a particular order, the events can be quickly taped to a page that can be posted. This method also will assure that the printing will be readable for the rest of the class.

3. Post your team's list of events at the front of the class as your teacher directs. Compare your team's estimated times and sequence with those of other teams. Discuss the questions below with your teammates.

   a. Consider your estimates. Explain whether they were guesses or logical conclusions based on evidence.

   b. Why did your team's estimates differ from those of other teams?
   As the teams compare their responses, listen for indications that they understand the difference between logical conclusions based on evidence (an inference) and wild guesses. This step connects directly to the Analysis of the previous activity.

4. Examine the table *Major Events in the Earth's History* that your teacher provides, and answer the following question in your journal:

Which times or sequences of occurrence surprised you?

Scientists use several tools to think about geologic time. One of these tools is the use of evidence and inference. This table is based on inferences from evidence that scientists have gathered about the history of the earth and its living organisms. It also is based on theories that geologists and paleontologists have developed about the time spans and patterns of change in the earth's history. For those reasons, the dates in this table are more accurate than guesses.

Distribute the Copymaster *Major Events in the Earth's History*. Many students are surprised by the distance between dinosaurs and humans, by the length of time between events for the majority of earth's history, or by the time when oxygen first occurred in significant amounts on earth. Encourage careful study of the table by using the question, Which times or sequences of occurrence surprised you?

5. Study the marked clothesline that your teacher has prepared. Discuss with your teammates how it might be used to represent the events listed in Copymaster *Major Events in the Earth's History*.

    Show the students the clothesline you have prepared as a model. Discuss with the students the concept of a model. Ask if they ever have built scale models or have other experiences with models that are representations of larger events or longer periods of time.

    Explain to the students that the distance between red marks represents 1 billion years and between black marks represents 100 million years. You may need to review the relationship between thousands, millions, and billions.

    After this discussion, ask the teams to consider how they could use this model to represent the events from the table they just studied.

6. Study the event cards that your teacher provides.

    Fold each card in half, crosswise, to form a tent.

    Distribute four or five event cards (a mix of biological and geological events) to each team. If your class is small, give each team more cards. You may wish to have students trim their folded cards to the narrowest possible width to make it easier to fit more recent events on the timeline.

7. Decide where on the timeline each event card should go, and place your cards in the appropriate locations.

    Use the information in the table of events to help you decide. Beneath the name of the event on each card, write the number of years ago that each event occurred. Carefully locate the correct time on the timeline. Fasten your event cards to the timeline as your teacher directs.

    Have students record on the event card the number of years ago that each event occurred so that their classmates can help them locate the right position on the timeline if they have difficulty. Next, have the students place their cards on the timeline in the appropriate location. Depending on the nature of your class, you can let them come up to the timeline at their own pace or you may want to call on students to control the pace of placing cards on the timeline. You may need to instruct students to clip event cards to the bottoms of other event cards if your timeline is so short that it makes some events coincide.

    After all the cards are placed on the timeline, the students will need time to survey the outcome to answer the analysis questions.

Analysis

Use the timeline that you just created to answer the following questions with your teammates, and then participate in a class discussion:

1. Look for and describe the following patterns on the timeline:

    a. Relationships between geological and biological events

    b. Relationships between plant and animal events

    c. One or two additional patterns that you see on the timeline

    Circulate among the teams as they work on the tasks in the Analysis. If some of the teams are struggling or fail to see the relationships, convene a short class discussion to clarify misconceptions and pull together the major concepts of the activity.

    Relationships that the students may note include the clustering of biological events at the more recent end of the timeline and the few and widespread events at the deep time end. If you use different colors for geological and biological events, the students may observe that certain geological events preceded biological events. For example, multicellular organisms developed after oxygen levels began to build up. (The buildup of oxygen levels is reflected by the appearance of iron oxides in rock layers.) Students also may observe that many plant events preceded animal events. For example, animals did not appear on land until after plants were established, as evidenced in the fossil record.

2. Is it likely that these patterns occurred separately, or do you think they might be related? Explain.

    The students might offer a variety of explanations for these relationships. Some students may focus on the fossil evidence. Make it clear that the fossil record is incomplete and that scientists do not have complete evidence for every major biological event that has occurred. Also, the designation of major events depends on our perspective as humans. In this activity, major events are those events that directly influence us. Finally, changes may require a great deal of time, and the large gaps account for this phenomenon.

3. Are the patterns that you chose to describe evidence, or were there inferences involved in finding and describing the patterns?

    This question revisits the students' understandings of evidence and inference. The patterns themselves are observed directly from the evidence presented by the model. The timeline model is based on the evidence that was gathered by scientists who determined the timing of the events. The exact timing given for the events are inferences that are based on collections of evidence.

4. What did the timeline (a model) help you understand about the earth's history?

    This question encourages the students to think about their own notions of time and the relative occurrence of events. The students should be able to describe something they learned during this activity, such as the immensity of the time scale for the earth's history or the relative rapidity with which recent biological events occurred.

Evidence for Change across Time

Major Concepts Evidence for change

Overview

This activity provides an opportunity for the students to pull together different types of evidence for change and begin to construct an explanation for biological change across time. We have developed this activity as a jigsaw in which the teams depend on each member for information that will contribute in a unique way to the students' understanding of the concepts. In the introduction, the students read about change. Then they work in jigsaw groups of specialists to collect evidence for change. The specialists return to their original teams and share their information with their teammates. Together they create a story that shows how these different scientific disciplines contribute to the collection of data that provides evidence for change across time.

Materials (students divided into 4 different teams of specialists; each team requires its own materials)

For the paleontologists:
Copymaster *Interview with a Paleontologist* (1 for each pair of paleontologists)
strata model and extra materials for constructing duplicate strata models (see Preparations)
3 letter-sized manila envelopes covered with different-colored paper to match markers used in the strata model (1 set for each pair of paleontologists—see Preparations)
Copymasters: *Hyracotherium, Merychippus,* and *Equus* (1 set for each pair of paleontologists)
Copymaster *Fossils in Strata* (1 for the group of paleontologists)
DVD
DVD player

For the evolutionary biologists:
Copymaster *Interview with an Evolutionary Biologist* (1 for each pair of evolutionary biologists)
dissecting tray and tools (1 for each pair of evolutionary biologists)
chicken wing (1 wing for each pair of evolutionary biologists—see Preparations)
Copymaster *Animal Limbs* showing anatomy diagrams of bird wing, bat wing, and human hand (1 for each pair of evolutionary biologists)
colored pencils
Copymasters *Human Vestigial Structures* and *Whale and Snake Vestigial Structures* in an envelope (1 for each pair of evolutionary biologists)

For the developmental biologists:
Copymaster *Interview with a Developmental Biologist* (1 for each pair of developmental biologists)
2 copies of Copymaster *Embryo Puzzle* (1 set for each pair of developmental biologists—see Preparations)
Copymaster *DNA Comparison* (1 set for each pair of developmental biologists)
DVD
DVD player

anthropologists. If you have access to human skull models, display them, along with calipers for measuring. Practice making measurements yourself from the pictures of skulls on the monitor. You may need to provide instruction for using protractors or calipers before leaving the physical anthropologists to work unassisted.

Make copies of the Copymasters *Primate Comparisons—Human*, *Primate Comparisons—Chimpanzee*, and *Primate Comparisons—Mystery*. You will need one set for each pair of physical anthropologists. Place each set of copymasters in an envelope.

For the wrap-up:

Before making copies of the rubric for the *Fossil Find* story, review the criteria and modify them as appropriate for your class. Decide ahead if you want to have students present their stories or hand in written assignments.

Strategies for Guiding Learners

PROCESS AND PROCEDURES

As a class, read orally or silently all the introductory materials for the activity and the Process and Procedures to help students build connections between concepts and activities. Use the time spent reading to bring the students' attention into focus.

This is a jigsaw activity where the teams depend on each member for information that uniquely contributes to the students' understanding of the concepts. During this activity, ask the students to concentrate on the working-relationship skill of communicating their knowledge to others.

Ask the students to first read their specialist instructions individually, and then join their teams of four.

1. Each member of your team will take on a different job. You will each become a specialist and learn about a different field of science.

   Each team member from your group will join team members from other groups who are studying the same field of science. After everyone has had time to study his or her special field of science, your original team will get back together so that you can teach each other what you have learned.

2. With your team, decide who will become each specialist:
   - Paleontologist: The scientist who investigates biological change by studying fossils and the history of the earth.
   - Evolutionary biologist: The scientist who studies the origins and relatedness of living organisms.
   - Developmental biologist: The scientist who studies how the processes of growth and development occur and change over time.
   - Physical anthropologist: The scientist who studies the biological evolution of humans.
     Make sure the teams have decided which member will assume each specialist role. In some cases, you may wish to assign roles where students have special needs or to make more heterogeneous groups.

3. Meet with the members of other teams who have assumed the same role that you have, and together read and study the information assigned to your role. As you work

with your team, make certain that everyone contributes ideas. *Then go to the procedural section that follows step 7.*

You will be responsible for sharing the information with your original teammates.

Direct the specialists to meet in different areas of the room. Students will begin their work as specialists by turning to the pages in their books that have the specific directions for their new group. Have the students work as groups on the questions embedded in their specialists' procedures, and have them record their answers in their journals. They are responsible for sharing this information with their original teammates. Monitor the specialist groups to see that everyone is contributing ideas. If necessary, ask the groups what they might do to encourage everyone to contribute.

4. When you complete your specialist work, return to your team and begin step 5.

5. Share your information with your original team. Discuss how each set of information represents evidence that supports the concept of change across time. Also, discuss how the collection of evidence is stronger than any of the separate pieces.

   When the specialist groups have completed their work, ask the students to return to their original teams and share the information that they have collected with other team members.

   Monitor the teams to see that everyone is contributing ideas. If a question comes up that a specialist cannot answer, suggest that the specialist consult with another member of his or her specialist group. After each specialist has updated the home team, the team should consider the strength of the collection of evidence in comparison to each separate piece.

6. Create a data table or diagram, like the one shown in Figure 2.3, to help you keep track of this collection of information.

   Make certain that you learn all about the scientific evidence for evolution that is contributed by each type of scientist.

   As the specialists describe their evidence, the students should create a table to organize the information they are collecting.

7. After all team members have taught their teams about their scientific specialty, you will write a short story about a fossil find. In the story that you write, you will show what you have learned in this activity by explaining the evidence that a paleontologist, evolutionary biologist, developmental biologist, and physical anthropologist would gain from such a fossil find.

   The stories provide you with an opportunity to assess the students' understanding and their performance. Give each team member one copy of the Copymaster *Fossil Finds* that their team will "find" and a copy of the rubric for the *Fossil Find* story. The copymaster pictures two Neanderthal discoveries. Either assign a fossil find or allow teams to choose. As the students begin to work on their stories, make certain that they understand the criteria that you will use to assess them. We provide a scoring rubric on the *GACD* that you may preview and modify in advance.

   The story can be written as a team project by having each student write about how one of the scientific disciplines would work with the fossil find. You may want to add the requirement that the specialist may not write about his or her own evidence. This strategy will ensure that the students convey their information to their teammates and that they are able to learn from each other.

When evaluating the *Fossil Find* stories, keep in mind that the students may or may not discuss the specific characteristics noted by scientists in the Neanderthal finds. The goal of the story is to provide an opportunity for the students to show what they understand about the types of work done and the kinds of evidence for evolution that the four scientific fields collected in this activity.

After completing the *Fossil Find*, you may decide to convene a short class discussion to address misconceptions and to invite the students to now ask, How does change across time happen? Because students differ in the amount of time and number of experiences it takes for them to build their understanding of major concepts, do not expect all of them to have a full grasp of evolution at this point. Explain to the students that as scientists accumulate evidence that supports a certain explanation, there may be gaps in their evidence. Emphasize the necessity for a body of evidence from which they can make observations, and if possible, construct testable hypotheses for developing a more complete scientific explanation.

Procedures for the Specialists

Paleontologists

1. Read the Copymaster *Interview with a Paleontologist*. Think about how you will explain the job of a paleontologist to your teammates.

2. Complete the following activities with the other paleontologists in your group.

   Geologists use an indirect method of dating rocks and fossils called stratigraphy. Stratigraphy is the study of strata on earth. Strata are layers. For this task, you will study a model of earth's strata.

   a. Observe the beaker of strata provided by your teacher. Work with 1 other team member to make an exact copy of the strata and its markers in your own beaker.

      Look closely at the layers. Make your beaker's layers match as closely as possible.

      Students will stay on task better if this work is done in teams of two, though it may be done in teams of three or four.

   b. Answer the following questions about your beaker and its strata:
      1) Which layer of materials is the oldest (has been in the beaker the longest)?
         The first layer placed in the beaker is the oldest.
      2) If these strata were layers in the earth's surface, what inferences might you make about the relationship between the depth of the layer and the amount of time that has passed?
         The deeper the layer is, the more time has passed (this assumes the layers have been undisturbed).

   c. Consider the locations of the 3 colored markers that you placed in the strata. If you found these colored markers in earth's strata, which would you infer to be oldest?
      The marker placed in the earliest layer formed would be the oldest.

   d. Obtain 3 colored envelopes from your teacher. Each envelope corresponds to 1 of the colored markers in your strata.
      Place sets of the colored envelopes somewhere in your classroom where you can easily direct teams to get their own materials after they build their strata models.

e. Imagine that each envelope represents a fossil discovery. Which "fossil" would be the oldest? Which would have formed most recently?

The colored envelope that matches the colored marker in the bottom-most layer of the strata model would be the oldest. The envelope that matches the marker in the upper-most layer of the strata model would have been formed most recently.

f. Open the envelopes and carefully observe the fossil pictures in each.

g. In your journal, compare each fossil with each of the others and with modern-day organisms. What similarities and differences do you observe?

Hint: Consider how the fossils look and their relative ages.

Expect students to notice that the youngest fossil most closely resembles the modern horse, that all fossils show similarities inferring common ancestry, and that the differences in the fossils show evidence that horses have changed over time.

3. Work with another paleontologist to create a poster that you can use to explain to your classmates how fossils form and how they can be dated.

Use the essays *Fossils: Traces of Life Gone By* (page 102) and *Technologies That Strengthen Fossil Evidence* (page 104) as resources.

The posters will be a visual aid that the students will use to teach their original team members about paleontology. The partners who create the poster together should teach their groups about their specialty at different times so they can share the poster.

4. When the DVD player becomes available, watch the DVD about plate tectonics (formerly thought of as continental drift) and think about the changes that the continents have undergone over time.

a. In your journal, explain how the movement and separation of continents affected the organisms living on land in earth's distant past.

Students should describe that over long periods of time, movement and separation caused populations of organisms to become isolated and also changed the climate and environmental conditions in which populations lived.

b. Add information to your poster about how the evidence for plate tectonics contributes to the theory of evolution.

5. Check that you have completed all the steps for the paleontologists. Finish preparing your poster to use as a visual aid when you teach your original team about paleontology. Return to step 5 in the general procedure.

Evolutionary Biologists

1. Read the Copymaster *Interview with an Evolutionary Biologist*. Think about how you will explain the job of an evolutionary biologist to your teammates.

2. Complete the following activities with the other evolutionary biologists in your group:

a. Work with a partner from your group to dissect a chicken wing carefully.

As you complete the dissection, compare the bones that you find with the chicken wing anatomy diagram provided by your teacher.

b. Locate the bones listed in the bird wing anatomy diagram, and color them in using the colored pencils.

Color-code the diagram so that each of the underlined bones is a different color.

If you have other skeletons or skeleton models available that students can observe, supplement the copymasters on homologous structures by having students compare their chicken wing to other limbs.

c. Wash your hands with soap. Next, obtain 1 bat wing diagram and 1 human hand diagram and their keys.

Remind students to wash their hands thoroughly with warm water and soap after this activity. There is always a risk of salmonella when handling raw or undercooked chicken.

d. With your partner, color the bones of the bat wing and human hand with the same color coding that you used on the chicken wing diagram.

While students color their diagrams, check to see that they have correctly identified the bones and use the same color coding to identify homologous bones.

e. In your journal, explain the similarities that you found between a human hand, a bat wing, and a chicken wing.

The similarities are the result of shared common ancestry.

f. Mount your diagrams on a poster board to share with to your classmates.

3. Read about homologous structures and vestigial structures in the essay *Modern Life: Evidence for Evolutionary Change*, on page 107.

a. On the diagram that you colored, are the parts of the animal limbs homologous or vestigial? Why do you think so?

Students should recognize the limb bones as homologous structures.

b. Title your poster with the correct term (homologous or vestigial structures), and write a definition for the term in your own words beneath the title.

The essay defines a homology as a characteristic that is similar among different organisms because they evolved from a common ancestor.

4. Obtain an envelope containing examples of vestigial structures. Study the structures inside.

a. On the handout showing human vestigial structures, write a brief, logical explanation about why each of the structures is considered vestigial.

b. On the handout showing vestigial hind limbs in whales and snakes, write a brief, logical explanation for why these hind limb bones are considered vestigial.

Use the information in the essay *Modern Life: Evidence for Evolutionary Change* on page 107 to help you write your explanations.

The essay defines vestigial structures as similar features shared by seemingly unrelated organisms that are functional in some species, but seemingly useless in others.

5. Make a poster about vestigial structures on the back of your poster about homologous structures.

6. Check over your posters. You will use your posters to teach your original team about the evidence contributed by evolutionary biologists to the theory of evolution. Return to step 5 in the general procedure.

The posters will be a visual aid that the students will use to teach their original team members about evolutionary biology. The partners who create the poster

together should teach their groups about their specialty at different times so they can share the poster.

Developmental Biologists

1. Read the Copymaster *Interview with a Developmental Biologist.* Think about how you will explain the job of a developmental biologist to your teammates.

2. Complete these activities with the other developmental biologists in your group.

   a. Read the information in the need to know box in your group.

   Background information about embryology is included in the need to know box on page 46 of the student text.

   b. Study the individual drawings of embryos that your teacher provides. Try to arrange all of the embryonic stages in a developmental order for each animal. When you have finished, your arrangement should show 3 stages of embryonic development for a fish, a frog, a chicken, a calf, and a human.

   These drawings depict various embryonic stages of 5 different vertebrates. These stages are relative. They do not represent the same point in time, but rather the same relative amount of development.

   c. Compare your arrangement with the illustration that your teacher provides.

   Let the developmental biologists try to arrange the embryo cutouts according to both development stage and animal. After they have assembled the puzzle, give them the entire figure and let them compare their efforts with the actual sequences.

   d. Discuss the following questions in your group, and record your answers in your journal:

   1) In general, which organisms have embryonic stages that are the most similar? the least similar? Explain your answers.

   As the students consider the embryos in the drawings, they may begin to see that certain characteristics relate all vertebrates and that in the most basic stage of embryonic development, the embryos of different species are quite similar.

   2) What do you think these similarities and differences tell scientists about how these organisms have changed across time and how they are related?

   Consider whether you expect related organisms to look similar or not. Would you also expect related organisms to go through similar stages of development? Consider the later stages of development. Do the more closely related organisms look more or less similar?

   As each embryo develops, the special adaptations that distinguish frogs from mammals, for example, become more apparent. These differences support the idea that frogs and mammals split off from a common ancestor a very long time ago. The differences between the human embryo and the calf embryo, both of which are mammals, are more subtle. These differences become clear only in the highly developed embryo of each species. Their similarities support the idea that they split off from a common ancestor more recently.

   At this point, the students only may be beginning to develop ideas about evolutionary relationships. Expect a range of ideas in response to the questions and be sensitive to a variety of views, some that may not have a thorough grounding in science.

e. Study the segment "Embryology" on the DVD. Compare the images to the ones you have assembled by answering the following questions:

1) Do the images on the DVD help you to see other similarities and differences that are not apparent in the drawings? Record your observations in your journal.

See the DVD guide on the *Teacher Resource CD* about specific strategies for the segment "Embryology." That segment presents evidence for evolution by showing side-by-side images of frog and human eggs and various embryonic stages followed by images of early and later embryos of human, mouse, chick, frog, and fish. Help the students to see that embryology provides a portion of a larger body of evidence for the relatedness of all animal forms.

2) Work with 1 other developmental biologist from your team to make a poster that you will use to teach your original team about embryology.

Your poster should show the embryo stages that you studied. It also should include a summary of how comparing the development of embryos contributes to scientists' understandings of how populations of species have changed over time.

3. Read the essay *Modern Life: Evidence for Evolutionary Change* on page 107.

a. In your journal, explain where DNA is located and what its purpose is.

Expect that the students will have widely varied prior knowledge about DNA. At this point, students need only understand that DNA is found inside organisms' cells and contains the information necessary for passing traits from one generation to the next.

b. Obtain a handout from your teacher that shows a comparison of the DNA that codes for the α and β hemoglobin proteins that are found in primate blood.

Compare the DNA from the different primate species. Determine which primates are most similar and which are most different.

c. Discuss this information with your partner and summarize your understanding of this evidence in your journal.

Use the information in the essay *Modern Life: Evidence for Evolutionary Change* on page 107 to help you interpret the DNA handout.

Students should recognize that the chimpanzee and human are most similar. This is significant because it shows that those two primates are closely related.

d. Add to your poster the DNA handout and a brief summary about how DNA analysis contributes evidence to the theory of evolution.

The posters will be a visual aid that the students will use to teach their original team members about developmental biology. The partners who create the poster together should teach their groups about their specialty at different times so they can share the poster.

4. Review your poster and your journal notes. You will use this information to teach your original team about how developmental biologists contribute to understanding evolution. Return to step 5 in the general procedure.

Physical Anthropologists

1. Read the Copymaster *Interview with a Physical Anthropologist.* Think about how you will explain the job of an anthropologist to your teammates.

2. Complete the following activities with the other physical anthropologists in your group:

   a. Obtain an envelope that contains pictures of selected human, chimpanzee, and mystery bones for yourself and 1 partner.

      1) Carefully observe the human and chimpanzee bones for similarities and differences.

      2) Compare each of the mystery bones to the human and chimpanzee bones. Make a table in your journal. List each mystery bone as either more like human bones, more like chimpanzee bones, or not like either human or chimpanzee bones.

      3) Based on your observations, write a feasible explanation in your journal for how the mystery fossil bones might be related to humans and chimpanzees.

      The mystery fossil bones are drawn from an *Australopithecine* skeleton. In some ways, they are more similar to the chimpanzee, and in other ways, they are more similar to the human. Expect that students likely will recognize that those bones represent an ancient ancestor that chimpanzees and humans share in common.

   b. When available, view the image sequence on the DVD "Hominid Skulls" and make observations. As you compare the skulls, focus on the features listed below, make measurements where appropriate, and record the information in your journal.

      ◆ Size of lower jaw

      ◆ Prominence of brow ridges

      ◆ Slope of face

      ◆ Width of face

      ◆ Size of forehead

      ◆ Size of brain case

      ◆ Size of molars

      Use the sketches of skulls in Figure 2.4 to help you determine which measurements to make. Create a data table like the one in Figure 2.5 to record your results. Review the sequence of skulls or individual frames as many times as necessary to make your comparisons.

      See the DVD guide on the *Teacher Resource CD* for specific strategies for the DVD segment "Hominid Skulls." In that segment, students study and take measurements from photographs of five hominid skulls.

   c. Read the essay *Primates Show Change across Time* (page 110), and discuss the following questions in your group. Record your ideas in your journal.

      1) What evidence did you find in the essay and in your observations of the hominid skulls that indicates change between early and modern hominids?

         Expect that students will describe the differences in skull sizes and shapes from their observations and list changes in posture and overall body sizes from the reading.

2) What evidence indicates relatedness between early and modern hominids?

The strong similarities in the skulls indicate relatedness (as does DNA evidence not studied by this group).

d. Summarize the pattern of changes that you observe in the hominid skulls from *Australopithecus afarensis* to *Homo sapiens.*

Students should describe how hominid skulls show changes over time that include increased brain capacity, less prominent brow ridges, lighter jawbones, less-projected mouths, smaller foreheads, and smaller molars.

e. Use the evidence that you have examined to draw an inference about the ancestors of modern humans and modern primates.

Students will likely make inferences about how modern humans and modern primates shared a common ancestor at this point.

f. Work with your partner to make a poster. You will use this information to teach your original team about the evidence that physical anthropologists contribute to our understanding of how species change over time.

g. Glue the human, chimpanzee, and mystery bones onto a poster board. Add a summary, in your own words, for how humans have changed over time.

The posters will be a visual aid that the students will use to teach their original team members about physical anthropology. The partners who create the poster together should teach their groups about their specialty at different times so they can share the poster.

3. Return to step 5 in the general procedure.

Further Challenges

If you have the students complete these challenges, make available the DVD segment "Plate Tectonics." This segment shows changes in the continents across time as a series of dissolves. It provides a helpful resource for students trying to complete these tasks.

1. Propose a place of origin and a migration route for marsupial mammals.

Mammals are animals characterized, in part, by hair, sweat glands, and the nursing of young with milk secreted by mammary glands. Marsupials are mammals that produce embryos that spend only a short time in the mother's uterus. At birth, the immature infants must crawl into the mother's pouch, where they continue to mature while nursing from the mother.

From the age of the oldest fossils, it appears that marsupial mammals originated in North America, migrated to South America and then to Europe and Antarctica, and eventually reached Australia.

2. Consider what the fossil record indicates about ancient distributions of marsupial mammals. Then propose an explanation for the present marsupial mammal distribution.

Because many marsupial fossils are found on landmasses that today are separated by large oceans, it is likely that the ancient continents were much closer together and/or that ice ages reduced the volume of the ocean creating land bridges. The oldest fossils are found only in North America, which suggests that these first marsupials migrated to other continents from one central origin.

Explaining Evolution

Major Concepts
The theory of evolution; natural selection; and the nature of science

Overview

In this activity, the students will work with a partner to develop a newspaper story about Darwin and the theory of evolution. They also will define and defend the importance of theories in science.

Materials   (per class of 30, teams of 2)

15 large pieces of butcher paper

Outcomes and Indicators of Success

The following indicators allow you to assess the students' level of success with the activity and to assess their process of learning.

By the end of this activity, the learners should

1. be able to articulate and explain the theory of evolution from a historical perspective.

   They will demonstrate their ability by

   a. developing questions about who, what, when, where, how, and why regarding Darwin and evolution;

   b. answering the questions they develop; and

   c. sharing the summary of their work with their classmates.

2. understand that scientists use the term *theory* in a manner different from the way most people use it in ordinary speech.

   They will demonstrate their understanding by

   a. developing a rebuttal to the criticism that Darwin's theory is conjecture, and

   b. including in the rebuttal an explanation of the proper scientific use of the term *theory*.

Preparations

You might consider making available copies of Darwin's books as well as other books and articles that explain the power and elegance of evolution. This also would be an appropriate time in the chapter to consider arranging for a panel of guest speakers who can elaborate on the evidence that supports the theory of evolution. Each community reacts differently to this potentially controversial subject, so consider your local area when deciding what extras to add to this chapter. Consider reviewing the differences in ways of knowing. Evolution is a scientific way of explaining biological change across time; creationism (even misnamed as creation science or intelligent design theory) is not scientific because it seeks to fit available data to a predetermined outcome. Evolution is not an affront to religion, which offers other ways of knowing the world.

After the students have surveyed their peers' work, conduct a class discussion. Ask the students what they learned about Darwin, how they would explain the mechanism for evolution, or any other interesting ideas they learned.

Analysis

Your editor is impressed with your work but doubts whether the story is important enough to print. "After all," the editor argues, "we refer to it as the 'theory' of evolution. If it's just a theory, it means that we aren't sure about it. Why should we pay attention to it? What makes Darwin's theory any more convincing than a theory that you or I might suggest?" You, of course, are horrified at the editor's lack of understanding about the nature of scientific theories.

1. Work with your partner to prepare a rebuttal to the editor's criticism. Your response should include:

   a. a definition of a scientific theory that demonstrates the error in the editor's argument, and

   b. an explanation of the importance of the theory of evolution to modern biology.

   Information in the essay *Just a Theory?* on page 119 will help you develop your response.

   Students' responses should reflect the difference in the way scientists, compared with the general public, use the word *theory*. For instance, students should note that explanations in science are not considered theories until there is a variety of strong observations, evidence, and tests supporting the explanation. In addition, a strong theory predicts new data and relationships that scientists may not have seen yet.

   Students should connect this activity to the previous one by noting that the theory of evolution is supported by evidence from the fields of geology, biology, and anthropology.

   b. **This theory is important to modern biology because it is the foundation for many other ideas. The key ideas in areas such as development, reproduction, genetics, and taxonomy are based in the theory of evolution. Students may not have enough experience with biological studies to recognize these links, so accept other answers that are logical and based on their experiences and knowledge base.**

   A question like this one is likely to spark the evolution/creationism debate in your classroom. You can defuse this debate quickly if you get the students to focus on the nature of scientific explanations as being different from the nature of religious (or other) explanations.

2. Choose one member of your team to offer the rebuttal orally to your editor (your teacher). Although one person should present the team's response, both members should be prepared to answer further questions about the issue if your editor is not convinced by your initial comments.

   You may consider this question optional or offer it for extra credit. If you have taken advantage of all of the class presentation options in this chapter, consider having students give their rebuttal to you at your desk while other students work on something else. Or students could rebut in writing and turn in their journals to you.

Further Challenges

To create a real journalism article, take the summary of your story and craft it into a smooth, informative article that answers the important questions about evolution.

Modeling Natural Selection

Major Concepts   Natural selection; adaptation

Overview

Students have examined multiple lines of evidence for biological change across time and the nature of the theory of evolution. In this activity, the students experience the mechanism for evolution through a simulation game that models the principles of natural selection and helps answer the question, How might biological change have occurred and been reinforced over time?

Materials   (per class of 30, teams of 4)

8 copies of the Copymaster *Natural Selection Record Sheet*
24 petri dish halves
8 36 × 44-in. pieces of fabric, 4 each of 2 different patterns
24 sheets of graph paper
8 sets of colored pencils with colors similar to the paper dot colors (see Preparations)
48 zip plastic sandwich bags, each containing 120 paper dots, 20 each of 6 colors, labeled
     Starting Population (see Preparations)
48 zip plastic sandwich bags of spare paper dots (see Preparations)
watch or clock with second hand
computer with spreadsheet/graphing software program (optional)
24 forceps (optional)

To create the paper dots:
24 8 × 11-in. sheets of construction paper, 4 each of 6 different colors
3-hole or regular paper punch

Outcomes and Indicators of Success

The following indicators allow you to assess the students' level of success with the activity and their process of learning.

By the end of this activity, the learners should

1. better understand predator/prey relationships.

   They will demonstrate their understanding by

   a. appropriately completing an assigned task,

   b. recording data from the predator/prey simulation, and

   c. creating a graphic representation of the activity.

2. recognize that various factors are involved in the survival and reproductive success of individual members of a species.

They will show their recognition by developing their own explanations for the reproductive success of certain colors of paper dots after several rounds of hunting.

3. be able to use the idea of natural selection to explain the reproductive success of certain members of a hunted species.

They will demonstrate their ability by

a. describing the details of the mechanism at work in the simulation. These details should include variation, reproductive potential, and differential survival;

b. listing two ways that Darwin's explanation of evolution helps explain the results of the simulation; and

c. explaining why change would proceed very slowly if there were little variation within a population.

4. understand that the process of natural selection helps explain the body of evidence that their team collected in the activity *Evidence for Change across Time*.

They will demonstrate their understanding by writing a paragraph that describes this connection.

Preparations

Make copies of the Copymaster *Natural Selection Record Sheet*—one for each team. Preview the rules and steps for the activity, and plan how you will manage the logistics so that the "hunt" can be completed within one class period.

Obtain fabric from a local fabric supply store or from the home economics teacher. Choose fabric patterns that simulate natural environments, such as floral, leaf, or fruit prints. The patterns should have several colors and an intricate design; small prints work better than large blocky prints. Select two designs, each with a different predominant color. Label one design *fabric A* and the other *fabric B*. The use of two designs enables the students to demonstrate the evolution of different color types from the same starting population.

Use the paper punch to punch out 1/4-inch paper dots from construction paper, 1,000 each of six different colors. Punch out all four sheets of a color at once or fold each sheet into four thicknesses. Use a wide variety of colors, such as red, orange, purple, green, blue, yellow, brown, grey, black, or white. Select two light colors (including white) and two dark colors so that they will compete against each other. Include at least two colors that blend well with the fabrics. For each color, put 100 dots into each of eight zip plastic sandwich bags. Put 20 dots of each color (for a total of 120 dots of six colors) into each of eight additional bags. Label these bags *Starting Population*. Save any extra dots for replacement dots or additional supplies. Enlist student aides or ask for student volunteers to punch dots, or stuff bags at home or after school.

Note: Instead of using bags to store and organize the paper dots, you can purchase plastic, daily pill containers that have seven separate compartments. You will need one pill container per team. Label one compartment "S" for starting population, which will contain 20 dots of each of six colors. Label the other six compartments one color each, and place the extra "offspring" dots (100 dots) in each separate color compartment. Label the compartments containing single-color dots by gluing or taping one of the colored dots to the lid. The advantage of the pill container is that each separate compartment can be opened individually so that dots can be added or removed without mixing the colors.

As an alternative to paper dots, you might try colored aquarium gravel, colored rice, or different kinds of beans that are similarly sized. Both are heavier than paper dots and are less likely to blow around the room. However, they will be easier for the hunters to pick up. You could color the rice grains with food dyes according to the criteria that we specified above for the dots. You also might use gift-wrapping paper instead of the pieces of fabric. You also can experiment with wrinkling the fabric instead of spreading it out flat, which will make it harder to find and pick up the "prey."

Strategies for Guiding Learners

PROCESS AND PROCEDURES

As a class, read orally or silently all the introductory materials for the activity and the Process and Procedures to help students build connections between concepts and activities. Use the time spent reading to bring the students' attention into focus.

This activity requires that students work in teams of four. If your class does not divide evenly, use teams of five. The activity calls for a jigsaw strategy with half of the teams using fabric A and half of the teams using fabric B.

Before the students begin the activity, review the procedure with them. Also, make sure your students are familiar with the concept of predator/prey relationships.

1. Decide which team member will be the game warden and which team members will be the predators.

   Three members of your team will play the role of predators. As predators, each will hunt paper dots (the prey) in their habitat (the piece of fabric). The 4th member will be the game warden, who will keep track of the hunting.

   Be sure everyone understands that the dots are the prey. Remind students that when they have completed the activity, the bags of dots must be returned to exactly the way they received them. You may want to add a lighthearted penalty for any dots that are found on the floor.

2. Examine the paper dots in the bag labeled *Starting Population*. Record the number of individuals (dots) of each color.

   The colored dots represent individuals of a particular species. The individuals of this species can be 1 of 6 colors.

   The game warden should record the starting population as the *Hunt 1 Starting Population* on the record sheet that your teacher provides.

   Make sure the game warden records the number of individuals of each color in the starting population.

3. Spread out the piece of fabric on a desk or tabletop. Tape the corners of the fabric to the table.

    Half of the teams will have pieces of fabric A, and half will have pieces of fabric B.

    Make certain that half of the teams use fabric A and half use fabric B. The procedures remain the same for both groups.

4. Read the information in the need to know box to learn the rules the predators must follow. Set up the model as follows:

    Predators: Obtain a petri dish half. Turn to face away from the habitat.

    Game warden: Obtain a petri dish half. Pour the dots from the bag labeled *Starting Population* into your petri dish. When the predators turn their backs, spread the *Hunt 1 Starting Population* throughout the habitat.

    Spread the dots over the fabric as uniformly as possible so that no dots stick together or cover other dots.

5. Put the model into action as follows:

    Game warden: Direct the predators to face the habitat and begin picking up dots (prey); say "stop" after 20 seconds.

    The predators must turn away from the habitats until the game wardens tell them to turn around, and then they must stop hunting when the game warden says, "stop." The predators must pick the dots up one at a time, with one hand. You also can provide forceps and require the predators to use them to pick up the dots.

6. Finish round 1 of predation in your model as follows:

    Predators: Sort the paper dots you collected by color, and record the number of each color that you "ate."

    Game warden: Subtract the total number of each color that was "eaten" from the *Hunt 1 Starting Population* to determine how many survivors remain in the "habitat." Record the number of survivors for each color of the paper dots. Label this *Hunt 1 Surviving Population*.

    Make sure the predators carefully count the dots that they picked up during the hunt and sort them by color. Review the procedure for calculating how many dots survived (and are still on the fabric habitat). Remind the game wardens that they are responsible for recording these data.

7. Prepare for round 2 of predation in your model as follows:

    Predators: Simulate reproduction among the survivors. For every colored dot remaining on the fabric, add 3 dots of the same color to the warden's petri dish. In this model, we are saying that each survivor has 3 offspring before the next hunting season.

    The 3 paper dots of each color represent offspring. Obtain these offspring from the bags containing single colors of dots.

    Game warden: Record the total number of each color of paper dot that will now be in the habitat as *Hunt 2 Starting Population*.

    Explain to the students that as they complete this step, they are simulating reproduction in the surviving population. Review the procedure for calculating how many offspring to add and what the new starting population is for each dot color. Remind the wardens that they are responsible for recording these data.

8. *Predators*: Again, turn away from the habitat.

Game warden: When the predators turn their backs, spread the "offspring" from the *Hunt 1 Surviving Population* throughout the habitat and mix them in with their "parents." (The offspring are the dots that were added to your petri dish in step 7.)

Spread the dots as uniformly as possible so that no dots stick together or cover other dots.

9. Repeat steps 5 and 6 for round 2 of predation.

   As the students repeat the predation, make sure that they are calculating the correct number of offspring to add and recording the number of dots in each starting population.

10. *Do not* repeat steps 4 through 6 for a 3rd round of predation. Calculate the number of each color of paper dot by assuming that each surviving paper dot would produce 3 offspring. Add the number of survivors (parents) to the number of offspring for each color. Record this information as *Hunt 4 Starting Population*.

    Each team member should record this information in his or her journal.

    Explain to the students that they do not have to simulate reproduction as they did before, but rather calculate the number of individuals that would be in the third generation starting population.

11. As a team, use colored pencils and graph paper to prepare bar graphs that show the number of each color of paper dots in each of the 4 starting populations (see Figure 2.8).

    Use colored pencils that correspond to the colors of the paper dots. You should have 4 bar graphs when you are finished with this step. If you need help making bar graphs, refer to Appendix B, *Technique 2 Graphing*.

    The construction and analysis of the bar graphs is a critical and time-consuming part of this activity. If your students need help making bar graphs, refer them to *Techniques*, Appendix B in the student book. If you have ready access to computers and spreadsheet programs, you could incorporate the use of a spreadsheet during this step. Either print the resulting bar graphs in color or print blank bar graphs that students can color to match the dots. When completed, the students' graphs are visual representations of the changing color trends in the two populations.

12. Study the bar graphs of each starting population (or generation). With your teammates, consider the following questions and record your team's responses in your journal.

    Use the questions in this step for the class discussion. Also, ask the students what physical or behavioral characteristics (besides camouflage) might be the basis of evolution by natural selection. This will help students generalize from the example of camouflage to other factors that contribute to reproductive success (for example, better night vision, ability to move quickly, ability to survive with little water). Some students may advance alternative explanations for the unity and diversity of life that are based on other ways of knowing. Acknowledge the obvious wide range of opinions that students might hold, but help them make a distinction between explanations that are scientifically derived (that is, those based on observation and testable hypotheses) and those based in whole or in part on other criteria.

Look for responses such as the following:

a. Which, if any, colors of paper dots had a better survival rate than other dots in the 2nd-, 3rd-, and 4th-generation starting populations.

> Answers will depend on the color of the fabric that the students used. The starting populations for the second and third generations should include more dots that are similar in color to the fabric and fewer colored dots that stand out. The change between the first and third generations should be more dramatic than the change between the first and second generations.

b. What might be the reason that predators did not select these colors as often as they did other colors?

> Some colors were better camouflaged than others were; they blended into the environment.

c. What effect did capturing a particular color dot have on the numbers of that color in the following generations?

> When an individual is removed from a population and dies, in this case through predation, that individual no longer reproduces. The students should realize that heavy predation leads to a decrease in both the size of the population and the size of the gene pool.

13. Now that your predator/prey investigation is complete, clean up by sorting the colored dots into their respective plastic bags as you found them.

> Allow the students enough time to re-sort the colored dots into the appropriate bags. The dots tend to stick to clothing and fly away easily. Be sure the students re-count the dots in each bag and replace missing dots. Have a three-hole punch and construction paper on hand to replace lost dots.

Analysis

At the location that your teacher indicates, post your team's bar graph for the *Hunt 4 Starting Population* beside the fabric that you used. Compare the bar graphs of teams who used fabric A with the bar graphs of teams who used fabric B. Complete the following tasks as a team. Record your team's responses in your journal.

This Analysis provides you with an opportunity to assess the learners' understanding of evolution and the mechanisms by which it occurs. Before the students begin to work on these tasks, display a piece of fabric A and of fabric B and ask the learners to post their third-generation bar graphs beside the fabric that they used. The learners now will benefit by comparing their own results with those from other teams that used the same fabric as well as with those from teams that used a different fabric. These comparisons will give them more data with which to construct explanations for the results that they see.

1. How well do the class data support your team's conclusions in step 12?

> Students need to be able to analyze the relationship between their response in step 12 and the cumulative data. The specific response is not important as long as it addresses the relationship between the team data and the class data.

2. Imagine one real-life predator/prey relationship (for example, wolves and rabbits).

   a. Record in your journal the predator/prey relationship that you select as your example.

   b. Write a paragraph that describes how one characteristic of the prey population might change because of natural selection.

   c. Write a second paragraph that explains how one characteristic of the predator population might change because of natural selection.

   Base your explanations on what you have learned in this model of natural selection by predation.

   Within the context of their chosen predator/prey relationship, the students should explain that variation exists in populations. Individuals with certain characteristics are better adapted to their environment than other individuals are, and consequently survive to produce offspring; less well-adapted individuals do not. The offspring, in turn, possess characteristics similar to those of their parents, and that makes them better adapted to the environment as well. These two concepts are the basis of natural selection, and they explain how populations evolve.

   Students should give specific examples for how a prey population might change in response to the pressure that predators place on it. For example, if a population of rabbits has a variety of colors, but the wolf predators can see and hunt the white rabbits most easily, then the white rabbits will not survive to reproduce. Over time, the rabbit population would have fewer and fewer white individuals.

   Similarly, changes in the prey population put pressures on the predator population. For example, if some rabbits have a trait that makes them better able to hold very still and hide when they are threatened, that trait might become more prevalent over time. The population of rabbits might become larger because they are harder to catch. In turn, the wolves with a trait that made them better able to find the rabbit prey would be best suited to survive and reproduce. For example, if some wolves had an exceptional sense of smell that made it possible to detect hiding rabbits without using vision, they might get the most food and survive to pass on their exceptional ability. Over time, the wolf population would have a better sense of smell.

3. When you and your classmates studied paleontologists, evolutionary biologists, developmental biologists, and physical anthropologists, you learned about the evidence and inference that each of these sciences contributes to the theory of evolution. Understanding the process of natural selection also adds to the collection of evidence and inference that helps scientists interpret change over time.

   Write a paragraph that explains why knowing about the process of natural selection adds more evidence and inference to support the theory of evolution.

Expect students to describe that in a population of organisms, variation exists among characteristics that parents pass on to their offspring. Individuals with certain characteristics may have a slight advantage over other individuals and thus live longer and reproduce more. If this advantage remains, the difference would be more noticeable across time. These changes could eventually lead to new species. This process of natural selection, then, provides an explanation both for the relatedness of organisms and for biological change across time. In this way, natural selection explains the mechanism for the change that is central to the theory of evolution.

4. Explain what *biological evolution* means. Use terms and ideas that you have learned from this chapter, including the following:

adaptation	natural selection	species
population	variation	mutation

    Use the students' answers to this question as a way to check for misconceptions about the concepts studied so far in this unit. In particular, look for explanations showing that students think adaptations are made purposefully by organisms choosing to compensate for changes in their environment. Students should explain that biological evolution takes place in populations, not at the level of the individual. Also, watch for students to show an understanding (or misunderstanding) about the vast amount of time required for evolution to take place through natural selection.

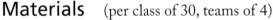

Elaborate | # A Cold Hard Look at Culture

Major Concepts Cultural and biological evidence for evolution; inference

Overview

In this activity, the students examine information about the well-preserved remains of a man who was found in 1991 in the Italian Alps. The students review a table that describes the artifacts that were recovered with this "Iceman." They then consider the evidence and make inferences about the Iceman's life and culture. The students also have the opportunity to consider the differences between biological and cultural evolution.

Materials (per class of 30, teams of 4)

DVD
DVD player

Outcomes and Indicators of Success

The following indicators allow you to assess the students' level of success with the activity and to assess their process of learning.

By the end of this activity, the learners should

1. understand some of the differences between cultural and biological evolution.

They will demonstrate their understanding by

    a. comparing the physical and cultural evolution of humans during the past 5,000 years, and

    b. describing some of the differences between cultural and biological evolution.

2. be able to distinguish between evidence based on direct observations and inference based on evidence.

They will demonstrate their ability by

    a. indicating that the artifacts that were with the Iceman represent evidence, and

    b. indicating that as they discuss possible uses for the artifacts and possible interpretations of the evidence, they are making inferences.

Preparations

You may find it useful to read some of the reports of the discovery and scientific study of this 1991 archaeological find (for example, *National Geographic*, June 1993, pp. 36–67). Scientific studies continue today, and there are Internet sites that post the latest findings (see SciLink human 3E56). There also is a NOVA videotape that chronicles the discovery and the early research on the Iceman (*Iceman*, 1993). Your school district may have this video available.

Background

The Iceman possessed a tool of remarkable construction for his time: a well-formed copper axe. This tool is significant because at first the scientists assumed it was made of bronze (the Bronze Age is more recent than the Copper Age). But when they realized that it was pure copper, they began to realize that the man and his artifacts were even older than they had first imagined.

Copper metallurgy first appeared in Europe about 6,000 years ago and lasted until the onset of the Bronze Age. The working of copper required a fairly specialized technical knowledge, including the ability to produce fires that were hot enough to melt copper ore to extract the copper. Copper melts at 1,082.8°C (1,981°F).

The first evidence of bronze working—the alloying of copper with tin—is dated about 4,400 years ago. The Copper Age lasted only a few thousand years. In contrast, the earlier stone technology lasted for about 2.5 million years.

The most remarkable aspect of the Iceman discovery is the preservation of soft materials such as human tissue, leather, fur, wood, and grass; artifacts of these types normally do not preserve well. This evidence supports many of the previous inferences that scientists have made about human life in Europe 5,000 years ago, while adding some new insights as well.

Strategies for Guiding Learners

PROCESS AND PROCEDURES

As a class, read orally or silently all the introductory materials for the activity and the Process and Procedures to help students build connections between concepts and activities. Use the time spent reading to bring the students' attention into focus.

If you use the NOVA videotape, have the students complete the reading in step 1 before you show the introductory footage that leads up to the discovery of the body. At this point, do not show any video segments that begin to present explanations or inferences. After step 2, you may want to fast-forward to some of the images of the artifacts so that the students can see what they looked like.

If you do this, turn the volume down so that the students cannot hear any ideas about or explanations of the artifacts. Then show the complete video after step 5.

1. Read the following paragraphs by yourself:

    Students should read the short section about the Iceman (in the student text, pages 56–57) **to themselves. Consider assigning this step as homework.**

2. Examine the table in Figure 2.9. This table lists many of the artifacts that authorities and scientists found with the Iceman and gives a general description of his body.

    This list will help you get a general idea of the types of clothing and tools the Iceman had.

    Encourage students to speculate about the purpose of each artifact in the table, especially those without comments.

3. Do the artifacts listed in Figure 2.9 represent evidence or inference? Explain your answer in your journal.

    This step reinforces the theme of evidence/inference that has been emphasized throughout the chapter. Students should be able to recognize that the artifacts themselves are evidence, while speculation about their use is inference or guessing.

4. Watch the DVD segment "A Glimpse of the Iceman."

    Show the DVD segment "A Glimpse of the Iceman." This segment shows images of the Iceman and his actual artifacts and parallels the list of artifacts that the students have (Figure 2.9). Refer to the interactive DVD guide in the *TRCD* for additional information about the artifacts.

5. With your team of 4, discuss what each artifact is and how the Iceman might have used it. Select 3 artifacts that you find most interesting. Record your ideas about their possible uses in a table in your journal.

    Provide time for the students to work with their team members and create a table in their journals of the possible uses for each artifact. If you want to shorten the amount of class time spent on this activity, students could draft the table for homework and then revise their responses based on discussions with their teammates.

6. Consider the artifacts, and select 2 of the following questions to answer in your journal:

    Look for responses such as the following:

    a. What might the bow and the finished and unfinished arrows and arrowheads indicate about his way of life?

        The students may suggest that the Iceman was a hunter, or because the bow was unstrung and some of the arrows were unfinished, that the Iceman was a person who made bows and arrows for others. This evidence might suggest that the Iceman was in the mountains hunting for animals when he died or perhaps he was a trader on his way to other settlements when he died. Have the students consider that he was above tree line when he was found and that most hunting for animals would take place below this elevation.

b. What might the copper-bladed axe with the wooden handle indicate about his culture?

>   The students might indicate that the use of copper in tools is a more sophisticated technology than the use of stone tools. They may or may not know that the presence of this axe indicates that members of his culture were aware of techniques that increase the temperature of a fire so that it would be hot enough (1,981°F) to melt the copper out of copper ore. These techniques include structuring devices so that more air (oxygen) would reach the base of the fire and gradually increase its temperature.

c. What can you tell from the bits of wheat and wheat pollen present?

>   The students might say that this indicates that people in the Iceman's community probably ate foods made from wheat, that they gathered wheat, or perhaps that they were farmers and grew wheat as a crop. Because this type of wheat grew only at low altitudes, students might say that this supports the idea that he lived in or visited the lowlands. Also, because this type of wheat is different from modern wheat, this evidence supports the idea of biological evolution through time.

d. What might the different markings on his body indicate?

>   Refer back to the descriptive paragraphs in step 1 and to Figure 2.9 if you wish.

>   The students might indicate that perhaps the markings identified the Iceman as a member of a particular group within his society, perhaps as a healer (the evidence of the thong of mushrooms supports this), or a spiritual person, or as a participant in a ceremony similar to a rite of passage.

7. How did you use evidence or make inferences to answer the questions in step 6? Explain.

>   Students should recognize that when they speculate about the Iceman's way of life based on the evidence, they are making inferences.

8. Did your personal opinions and previous experiences influence how you interpreted the evidence? Explain whether you think that happens when scientists examine evidence. How might such influences affect their work?

>   Students should recognize that prior knowledge and experiences influence the way that we interpret what we see. Scientists try to be aware of those biases, but they also are influenced by their prior knowledge and experiences.

9. If you could have 3 more pieces of evidence or 3 more bits of information to help you complete your understanding of the Iceman, what would they be? Explain.

>   The students may come up with any number of ideas for this question. They might suggest that they would like more information about (a) the markings on the body (this might help determine something about the Iceman's status in his society and provide information about his culture and some of the cultural practices); (b) what he was doing up in the mountains at the time of his death (this would help determine whether it was his job to be up in the mountains or whether he was traveling somewhere); (c) the sophisticated copper tools (this would provide more information about the level of the technology in his society); or (d) some written documents (this would help link him to a particular linguistic group in addition to providing information about him or his society in the document).

Analysis

1. What particular physical features of the Iceman would you compare with modern humans if you were looking for evidence of biological evolution? Explain.

   Expect the students to mention the areas that have been the focus of much of the discussion about human evolution. They likely would say that they would like to look at the skull, in particular the size of the lower jaw and the molars, the size of the brain case, the slope of the face, and the position of the point of articulation with the spine. They also may suggest looking at the hands and feet or the pelvis, for example.

2. What artifacts from the Iceman would you compare with artifacts from modern humans as evidence of cultural evolution?

   Students could pick just about any artifact from the table and compare it with its modern equivalent to demonstrate evidence of cultural evolution. The wheat might be difficult to justify as evidence of cultural evolution unless the students have a background in agriculture and realize that advances in seed crops are a combination of biological and cultural evolution.

3. Do you think there have been greater changes in humans physically or culturally in the last 5,000 years? Explain your answer.

   Expect the students to indicate that the greater changes in the last 5,000 years have been cultural. They most likely will base their choice on the simple artifacts that the Iceman possessed compared with the sophisticated technology of today, together with the observation that the Iceman did not appear significantly different from humans today. They may recall from the sequence of hominid skulls on the DVD that they viewed in the activity *Evidence for Change across Time*, that modern humans date back as far as 45,000 years ago and the Iceman is considered to be only 5,300 years old.

Evaluate   # Evolution in Action

Major Concepts   Evolution; evaluation of evidence

Overview

   In this activity, the students have a chance to evaluate their knowledge of the concept of evolution by considering an example of recent evolutionary change. They read a scenario about a girl who contracts an infection during an operation. Then they consider three different outcomes in different decades of the 20th century. By developing an explanation for the different outcomes, the students will demonstrate their understanding of the concept of evolution.

Materials   (per class of 30)

1 copy of the *Evolution in Action* rubric

Outcomes and Indicators of Success

The following indicators allow you to assess the students' level of success with the chapter and to assess their process of learning.

By the end of this activity, the learners should

1. be able to demonstrate their understanding of evolution as biological change across time.

   They will demonstrate their understanding by

   a. describing an evolutionary change that occurs in a particular strain of a common bacteria,

   b. identifying the factor that exerts a selective pressure on bacteria,

   c. explaining the role of variation in characteristics in the evolution of resistant populations, and

   d. explaining how differences in reproductive success affect the evolution of populations of bacteria.

2. recognize that cultural evolution is a factor in the advancement of medical science.

   They will demonstrate their understanding by describing the significant role that technological advancements play in the way medicine is practiced.

Strategies for Guiding Learners

PROCESS AND PROCEDURES

As a class, read orally or silently all the introductory materials for the activity and the Process and Procedures to help students build connections between concepts and activities. Use the time spent reading to bring the students' attention into focus.

1. Read the background information on antibiotics in the need to know box. Study the graph in Figure 2.10. Decide why the outcomes for the 3 scenarios are different.

   You can complete this activity in class or assign it as a take-home examination to help assess the students' understanding of evolution. Be sure to direct students to study the background information before they begin writing their responses.

2. For each outcome, write 1 paragraph that explains why that outcome is possible at that time in history.

   Base your explanations on your experiences in this chapter. Give a basic overview of how these scenarios could have happened.

   As the students write their responses to explain why the outcome for the patient was different in each time period, look for evidence that they understand the advent of the use of antibiotics. Penicillin and other antibiotics were not available in 1925. (Penicillin was discovered in the late 1920s and was available for common use in the 1940s.) So doctors had no effective way to treat a staph infection at that time. In the 1945 scenario, the patient has the same infection but is treated with penicillin, which kills the bacteria. By 1965, penicillin had been used so often that some resistant bacteria strains had evolved. Although the classic treatment is administered, the patient does not survive because the bacteria are different and do not respond to penicillin.

Describing Life

Major Concepts
Living organisms share characteristics that together enable us to describe and recognize life

Overview

This activity is designed to help students recognize the fundamental characteristics that are shared by all living organisms and to see that a description of these characteristics (as summarized in the unifying principles of biology) is, in fact, a description of life. Students also should see that the unifying principles provide criteria by which we can recognize life, even in unusual forms and conditions. The learners explore these ideas through a study of the experiments of 1976, 1997, and 2004 that were designed to search for evidence of life on Mars.

By focusing on the characteristics that are common to all living systems, this activity also establishes a critical foundation for the learners' study of biodiversity in subsequent activities.

Materials   (per class of 30, teams of 4)

8 large sheets of paper
15 felt-tipped markers

Outcomes and Indicators of Success

The following indicators allow you to assess the students' level of success with the activity and to assess their process of learning.

By the end of this activity, the learners should understand that

1. shared characteristics enable us to describe and recognize life.

    They will show their understanding by

    a. generating a list of characteristics that are common to life, based on their prior understanding;

    b. evaluating this list in light of their reading and discussion; and

    c. describing the similarities and the differences between how we recognize life in our everyday experience and how the scientists involved in the Mars project attempted to recognize life.

2. our preconceived notions about an issue may affect the questions that we ask and the ways in which we are prepared to interpret the data we collect.

    They will demonstrate their understanding by using the example of the Mars experiments to illustrate a case in which this inevitably occurred.

3. the unifying principles of biology summarize the shared characteristics of living systems, and therefore, constitute a valid description of life.

    They will show their understanding by justifying the design of *BSCS Biology: A Human Approach* around the unifying principles.

Strategies for Guiding Learners

PROCESS AND PROCEDURES

As a class, read orally or silently all the introductory materials for the activity and the Process and Procedures to help students build connections between concepts and activities. Use the time spent reading to bring the students' attention into focus.

1. Work with your team to develop a comprehensive list of characteristics that you think are common to all living organisms on earth. Record your list on a large sheet of paper.

   Refer to the scenario from the previous activity for ideas to get you started.

    Listen to each team as it develops its list of characteristics that are common to all living systems on earth. Because each team's list will be based on prior knowledge, this step provides you with an opportunity to assess the learners' present understanding of these characteristics.

2. With your team, identify the 1 characteristic from your list that you think would be easiest to look for if you were to mount a search for life on another planet. Mark this characteristic with a check mark, and be prepared to explain why your team selected it.

   The list that you have created is really a description of living systems as you understand them now. Notice, however, that you also can use your description as a checklist to try to determine whether some unknown object is or is not alive.

   As you circulate around the room, ask each team to explain its selection of the easiest characteristic. You may wish to challenge them with the related question, Which characteristic might be *best* to look for? In fact, if life is defined by the presence of all of these characteristics, then no one characteristic is most revealing.

   If students do not see this point, help by asking whether it is enough that an object display only one or two of the unifying principles. You also might prompt them by asking if they know of any nonliving thing that also exhibits this characteristic. For example, if students point to the ability of an organism to use energy to move, ask them if this characteristic also applies to cars and other motor vehicles. If students mention the ability of a living system to grow, ask them if this means that crystals are alive. Remind learners that a characteristic that would be helpful in identifying life must be common to *all* life. Thinking, for example, is characteristic only of some forms of life; likewise, photosynthesis and sexual reproduction and the ability to breathe (as we commonly use the term) are characteristics that are found only in some forms of life. These discussions should help learners see that the task of identifying truly *common* characteristics of life may be more challenging than it first appears.

3. Follow your teacher's instructions for displaying your team's list so other class members can see it.

   Provide a place where teams can display their lists. Suggest a strategy whereby students can view and compare these lists with their own in step 4b.

4. Scientists actually have searched for evidence of life on Mars. Prior to the 1976 and 2004 robotic surface explorations on Mars, scientists had to decide on a method for trying to detect the presence of life, whatever form it might have there.

Suggest that the learners read the essay *Describing Life: An Impossible Challenge?* before answering the questions in this step. Their responses will depend in part on the lists they generated in step 1, but should demonstrate the understandings indicated below.

Work with your team to learn about the Mars experiments and to answer the questions below. Record your answers in your journal. The essay *Describing Life: An Impossible Challenge?* on page 121 includes information about the Mars experiments that will help you answer these questions:

a. How do scientists describe life? (That is, what list of characteristics do scientists associate with life?)

Students should list the unifying principles from the need to know box on page 67, or some variation of them. Because the students likely have minimal background knowledge about *homeostasis*, you may wish to explain briefly what is meant by "maintaining internal balance."

b. How does the list of characteristics that scientists associate with life compare with your list and the lists developed by other teams?

Responses will depend on the lists that students generated in step 1. Look for indications that learners have recognized new characteristics that they did not include on their original lists. For example, students may not have mentioned evolution, homeostasis, or interaction and interdependence as fundamental characteristics of life. Look also for evidence that learners have recognized that scientists describe certain characteristics in broader terms and in more general language than the teams may have used. For example, many teams may have mentioned the use of energy in their lists. Learners should understand, however, that a scientific description of life does not stop at the simple fact of using energy (even steam engines use energy). Instead, a scientist relates an organism's use of energy with its ability to maintain a complex organization. Likewise, although many student lists may have included the notion of growth, scientists refer to that characteristic in terms of the more encompassing idea of development. (It is, in fact, not just growth, but growth *as part* of the process of development that helps to distinguish living from nonliving things.)

c. What were 2 difficulties your group faced in making your list of characteristics? For example, how would you classify something like a feather found on the ground or pieces of loose hair?

Students likely had difficulties finding characteristics that *only* living organisms display. Another difficulty in creating a list of characteristics that living things hold in common is that some things do not fit well into the two living and nonliving categories. In the examples of the feather or loose hair, they pose special difficulties because rather than being *living* or *nonliving*, they fall in the category of *once living*.

d. What specific characteristics of life did the scientists involved in the Mars mission look for?

Scientists involved with the Mars experiments decided to look for evidence of the use of matter and energy from the environment and for evidence that any exchange of matter and energy that they might see was associated with the development or maintenance of a complex organization.

e. Why do you think that they chose these characteristics and not others?

Expect students to answer that the characteristics that scientists selected were ones about which they could obtain evidence in a short time. Students also may point out that it likely would be easier to detect exchanges of matter and energy with the environment than it would be to detect any of the other characteristics. How, for example, would one go about trying to detect the reproduction of an unknown, unrecognized object, much less the evolution of these objects or their interaction with other, equally unknown living systems?

Although these were undoubtedly some of the reasons for the scientists' choices, other, more positive reasons also informed the actual design of the experiments. In particular, the characteristics chosen were those that are easily observed in microorganisms on earth. This was important because microorganisms could conceivably be detected using very small amounts of Martian soil, and practical constraints on the size and weight of the equipment involved required that the experiments be accomplished with very tiny samples. This also was important because microorganisms were probably the first organisms on earth, and today, they survive in environments in which no other organisms are found. Scientists reasoned that if any life at all exists on Mars, it presumably would include microbial life. Do not expect your students to offer this additional explanation.

f. How did their choice of searchable characteristics compare with the choice that you and your teammates made in step 2?

Depending on the students' original responses, they may feel that their chosen characteristic was similar to or different from those used by scientists.

g. If you were trying to solve Katrina's question (page 65), what would you do to determine whether or not the object was living?

Expect that students should describe methods similar to those used by scientists looking for life on Mars if they could not easily detect movement.

Analysis

1. Evaluate each of the following statements as either true or false. Support your thinking with a short explanation and an example drawn from this or the previous activity.

a. We usually can recognize life on earth because our experience of life has taught us that living things possess certain characteristics that things that are not alive do not have.

Learners likely will identify this statement as true, but do not accept just an affirmative answer. Instead, check that the learners have supported their answers with reasoned explanations and examples. For example, learners may refer back to the preceding activity and point out that Katrina's initial confusion resulted from the fact that the characteristics she first observed in the unknown object seemed to be an unusual mix of characteristics that she associated with life (for example, a scaly surface) and characteristics that she did not associate with life (for example, a geometric shape). Learners also may refer to the Mars experiments and note that a search for life on another planet can be based only on our experience—in this case, on the characteristics that we associate with life on earth.

b. The way in which scientists tried to recognize life on Mars was very similar to the way in which we recognize life, but it was more systematic.

True. For example, both Katrina and the scientists involved in the Mars search based their efforts to recognize life on their preexisting understanding of what life is. The scientists, however, likely went about their search in a more careful, more systematic fashion. Learners should recognize that scientific thinking is often just a more systematic form of the same type of thinking that most of us do daily.

c. Our preconceived notions about an issue may affect the questions that we ask and the ways in which we are prepared to interpret the data that we collect.

Your students may have difficulty responding to this statement. Because the issue is important to your students' growing understanding of the nature of science, you may wish to spend some class time discussing their answers to this question.

The understandings we bring to any scientific problem inevitably influence the types of questions we ask and the ways we interpret data. For example, at the most basic level, our description of life depends on our experience of life. (We have no way to describe life otherwise.) The questions that Katrina asked about the unknown object were based on her previous experience. Similarly, the questions that scientists asked about the samples of Martian soil were framed in light of what they knew about life on earth. Thus, they designed their experiments to recognize certain fundamental characteristics of life as we know it (note that earth soil gave a positive response), and they made certain assumptions about the types of earth life that might survive the harsh Martian conditions.

Likewise, we tend to interpret results according to the knowledge that we bring to the situation. In the early days of interpreting the data collected from the Mars experiments, many scientists thought it was possible that they found evidence of life. This early enthusiasm was related to some positive results that at that time could not be explained by any known chemical (as opposed to *biological*) mechanism. Good scientists, however, recognize that their knowledge of any system always is limited and that they must be particularly cautious in interpreting surprising results. The Martian experiments illustrate this type of careful thinking. Despite their early optimism, the scientists involved realized that they had to be careful not to interpret their results based simply on what they already knew about earth's soils. (They recognized that although a positive response on earth means life, a positive response on Mars may or may not.) It was possible, for example, that the Martian soil had demonstrated some yet unknown chemical processes that might yield results similar to those that would be associated with life on earth. Subsequent work that duplicated or came close to duplicating the Mars results using only completely abiotic systems highlighted the value of such careful and conservative analysis.

2. Examine the following list of unifying principles. What justification can you offer for organizing a biology course around these principles?

Students' justification should reflect the idea that because these principles describe life, a course organized around them encompasses the major concepts of biology, the study of life.

A Look at Diversity

Major Concepts Diverse forms of life express the unifying principles in a diversity of ways

Overview

This activity provides learners with an opportunity to examine life's diversity in some detail. Learners view the DVD segment "A Diversity of Organisms," which shows examples of organisms in each of the five kingdoms. This examination of diversity is not restricted to showing how organisms that are classified in one of the five kingdoms are *different* from those classified in other kingdoms. Rather, the learners see the diversity of life in light of its underlying unity. This objective is accomplished through a jigsaw arrangement in which each group tracks how different types of organisms express one of the unifying principles. The learners then return to their original teams of six and create a summary diagram, table, or drawing that illustrates how each of the five major groups of organisms expresses each of the six unifying principles.

These experiences introduce students to biodiversity and to the traditional classification of organisms into five kingdoms. An underlying purpose of the activity is to help learners see that patterns exist in the diverse characteristics that different life-forms display. Although the explanation for these patterns is not explicitly addressed until the next activity (*Adaptation, Diversity, and Evolution*), learners should begin to understand that these (and other) unifying patterns provide a starting point for asking how such remarkable diversity has evolved.

Materials (per class of 30, teams of 6)

5 large sheets of paper
5 sets of colored felt-tipped markers
5 sets of *Unifying Principle Cards* (see Preparations)
DVD
DVD player

Outcomes and Indicators of Success

The following indicators allow you to assess the students' level of success with the activity and to assess their process of learning.

By the end of this activity, the learners should understand that

1. diverse organisms express the common characteristics of life in a variety of ways.

    They will demonstrate their understanding by

    a. identifying ways in which each of the five major types of organisms displays one of the unifying principles;

    b. creating a summary diagram, table, or drawing that illustrates how each of the groups expresses each of the six unifying principles; and

    c. describing interesting structural, behavioral, or environmental features of examples from each of the five types of organisms.

2. the ability to categorize organisms into five large groups points to both the similarities and the differences that exist among living systems.

They will demonstrate their understanding by explaining how the five-kingdom classification pattern illustrates both the unity and the diversity of life.

Preparations

Make five copies of Copymaster *Unifying Principle Cards*. Cut apart the principles and the accompanying guiding questions and mount them on 3 × 5-inch cards. Assemble the cards into five sets; each set should contain one card for each of the six unifying principles.

Preview the DVD segment "A Diversity of Organisms" to prepare for its use. Decide ahead of time how many class periods you likely will use to view the DVD, and share your time expectations with students before showing the video.

Strategies for Guiding Learners

PROCESS AND PROCEDURES

As a class, read orally or silently all the introductory materials for the activity and the Process and Procedures to help students build connections between concepts and activities. Use the time spent reading to bring the students' attention into focus.

This activity depends on a jigsaw approach in which one member of each team becomes an "expert" about how organisms express one of the unifying principles of biology, and then shares that information so that the team can construct a summary diagram, table, or drawing. A good working-relationship skill for this activity might be accountability to the team. Remind the students to evaluate their use of this skill at the end of the activity.

1. Your teacher will give you a unifying principle to consider for this activity. Join the other members of your team. Each of you will have a different unifying principle.

   Take turns reading your unifying principles aloud. Then discuss them with the other members of your team.

   You will study each of these principles in detail later. For now, work with your team members to summarize the big idea for your assigned unifying principles.

   These questions may help to guide your team's discussion. How would you explain this characteristic of life to someone in middle school? What examples would you use to illustrate its importance to humans? to other organisms? Record your ideas in your journal.

   The essay *Describing Life: An Impossible Challenge?* on page 121 may help you think about your principle.

   Distribute one set of unifying principle cards to each team of six. Circulate among the teams as they discuss the principles and listen to their explanations. Remind the learners to use the guiding questions on their cards to help initiate their discussions. Keep this step fairly short.

2. Now, meet with the other members of your class who received the same unifying principle. Compare your summaries about the big idea for your principle. Add any new ideas that this discussion raises to the notes in your journal.

   Make sure that you all share the same understanding of your assigned principle. Refer to your teacher any questions that your group cannot answer.

3. Select a spokesperson to summarize your group's understanding of its unifying principle to your teacher.

   Your teacher will want to hear examples of how some living organisms that you are familiar with show your unifying principle.

   As the learners assemble in groups to discuss each unifying principle, monitor their discussions to assess their common understanding of the principle. Provide clarification when needed.

4. List the following 5 types of organisms down the left column of a table in your journal. Provide plenty of space to make notes about how different types of organisms display the principle. Use your unifying principle as the title to your table.

   ◆ bacteria

   ◆ protoctists

   ◆ fungi

   ◆ plants

   ◆ animals

   As the students create tables in their journals to track their unifying principle, check to see that they have left sufficient space to record notes during the DVD presentation.

5. Watch the DVD segment "A Diversity of Organisms." Complete the following tasks:

   a. In the note section of your table, begin describing how different types of organisms display the principle that you are tracking.

      Avoid taking notes on all of the specific examples and details that the segment provides. Instead, concentrate on understanding in general how each major type of organism displays the principle. Say, for example, you are tracking the principle of interaction and interdependence. You might record the fact that plants supply the oxygen to the air that both plants and animals require for life. You likely would not record the name of the specific places in the world where you would find each type of plant.

      Do not be concerned if you are unable to complete your table from the information presented in the DVD segment. Some principles are easier to observe in such images than others are. Step 6 offers another opportunity to complete your table.

   b. List 1 organism from each group that you find particularly interesting or surprising with respect to the principle that you are tracking. Be prepared to explain why you chose each organism.

      Ask the learners to remain in their unifying principle groups as they take notes during the DVD segment "A Diversity of Organisms." Remind them to focus on understanding *in general* how each major type of organism displays the characteristic they are tracking, and caution them against getting bogged down in detail. You may want to stop the video between each kingdom to allow the groups to discuss their observations. If necessary, repeat the video segment.

This DVD segment is designed to provide a rich introduction to the diversity of life—one that students are unlikely to experience in real life. The segment presents a general background about the characteristics of each kingdom and a natural history framework that includes information about habitat, structures, size, range, and characteristics such as the role of fungi and bacteria as decomposers. The focus is not on classification but rather on similarities within these five large groups. See the interactive DVD guide on the *TRCD* for specific strategies for using the segment.

6. Your teacher will stop the DVD after each major type of organism. This will allow you to briefly discuss your notes for that group with your classmates who tracked the same unifying principle. Use this discussion to help you expand or modify the information in your notes. That way, you will be able to represent your principle more effectively when you rejoin your original team.

The essay *Five Kingdoms* on page 127 contains information that may help you complete your table.

Monitor the groups as they refine the information they have collected about expression of their unifying principle. You may wish to supplement the information that the groups have available by providing access to a variety of high school and college-level biology textbooks. Encourage the group members to distribute their work efficiently. (For example, each member of the group might focus on refining his or her understanding of the assigned principle in a different kingdom.) But also remind them to discuss all of the information that the group collects. The goal is for all group members to provide thoughtful and well-organized descriptions of how each kingdom expresses the assigned principle when they rejoin their original teams.

7. Join the members of your original team, and take turns sharing the information that each of you has gathered.

8. Construct a summary diagram, table, or drawing that illustrates how each of the 5 major groups of organisms expresses or has expressed each of the 6 unifying principles of life.

Do all 5 major groups of organisms exhibit all of the principles? What does this tell you about the principles?

As the teams rejoin to share information, check that teammates are demonstrating accountability. Encourage creativity as the teams develop their summary diagrams, tables, or drawings, and as they add interesting examples. Provide several colors of markers for each team.

9. Add to your diagram a few specific organisms in each kingdom. Identify 1 interesting fact about how each displays 1 of the 6 unifying principles of life.

Have the teams display their finished products and allow time for the students to observe the other teams' compositions. Use this time to conduct a summarizing discussion and to fill in missing information as needed. The students will use their compositions as they work through the Analysis.

Analysis

1. Which of the six unifying principles seems to have been most useful to biologists in grouping organisms into different large categories, or kingdoms? Explain your answer.

Think about (a) the major difference that distinguishes prokaryotes from all other organisms on earth; (b) how plants differ from both fungi and animals by the way they obtain the energy required for life; and (c) how organisms in each of the kingdoms reproduce.

Accept thoughtful and well-supported answers. Many learners may respond that a major distinguishing characteristic among the kingdoms appears to be the way organisms acquire and use matter and energy and the way they organize that matter into physical structures (the principle of matter, energy, and organization). For example, many students will see that prokaryotes and eukaryotes are categorized separately in relation to a major structural difference (the presence or absence of a membrane-enclosed nucleus). Further, students likely may see that differences among the organisms represented in the four eukaryotic kingdoms relate not only to the way each organism acquires energy (photosynthetic organisms, decomposers, organisms that ingest food) but also to differences in cell structure (presence or absence of a complex, multicellular organization; presence or absence of cell walls; presence or absence of chloroplasts).

Some learners may note that organisms in different kingdoms differ in the way they express other principles. For example, organisms in different kingdoms vary in the way they interact in the environment (the principle of interaction and interdependence), in the way they maintain homeostasis, and in the way they reproduce. Each of these principles, of course, also is related to that of matter, energy, and organization.

2. How do these large categories by which biologists organize their thinking about life illustrate both its unity and diversity? Explain your answer.

The process of classifying organisms into taxonomic categories involves recognizing both differences and similarities among organisms. Organisms that differ in certain fundamental characteristics are categorized into separate kingdoms. This separation of living systems into five kingdoms reflects life's diversity. By definition, however, members of a particular kingdom share certain characteristics with other members of that kingdom. In addition, organisms in all of the five kingdoms share certain common characteristics, and this aspect of classification emphasizes life's unity.

Further Challenges

Read these observations about a virus, called a *bacteriophage* (see Figure 3.4), that infects bacteria.

A bacteriophage

◆ contains genetic material,

◆ reproduces only when inside another organism,

◆ has an outer case made of protein,

- injects genetic material into a bacterial cell, and
- uses the energy and the structure of the bacterial cell to make parts that assemble into copies of itself (and often kills the bacterial cell).

You may have noticed that neither the DVD segment nor the essay contained any reference to viruses. Yet, we often think about viruses in relation to life. For example, have you ever heard someone complain about being *attacked* by a virus?

1. Use your knowledge of the unifying principles of life to construct a well-reasoned argument to answer the question, Is the bacteriophage alive?

2. For a moment, assume that scientists have decided that a virus *should* be considered alive. Select one of the five kingdoms in which scientists would likely categorize viruses. Support your answer with specific references to the unifying principles and to the information about the bacteriophage listed above.

Some scientists think that viruses should be classified as living organisms and others think that they should not, largely because of the lack of cellular structure. Accept either answer from learners, as long as they support it by referring to the unifying principles. Learners may note that although viruses display many of the unifying principles, they do so in unusual and sometimes incomplete ways. For example, viruses reproduce but only within other living systems. Likewise, viruses do not have their own mechanisms for acquiring or using energy and matter to build and maintain their complex organization. Nor do they appear to manifest homeostasis, as it is traditionally defined. On the other hand, viruses clearly interact with and are dependent on other forms of life. Although this information is not listed for learners, viruses also undergo evolution.

If viruses were considered alive, it is unlikely that they would be classified into any of the five kingdoms, again, largely because of their lack of cellular structure. However, students may give reasons why they might be considered for any of the kingdoms. The key is that students should give well-thought-out reasons and list evidence from the background information about viruses to support their ideas.

Adaptation, Diversity, and Evolution

Major Concepts Adaptations lead to diversity; the utility of an adaptation depends on the organism's environment; adaptations arise through evolution

Overview

This activity is designed in three stages that help learners build an important conceptual link between their understanding of the *process* of evolution (Chapter 2) and their understanding of its diverse *products* (Chapter 3). In Part A, learners examine the biological diversity that occurs across a variety of spatially distinct marine environments. Using the information available, the students then explain in concrete terms what it means for an organism to be *well-adapted* to its environment. In Part B, learners examine further the nature of biological adaptation, considering adaptation in relation to environments that varied across time instead of space. Finally, in the Analysis, learners are challenged to use their accumulated knowledge from both Chapters 2 and 3 to propose a detailed explanation for the appearance of biological diversity on earth.

Materials   (per class of 30, teams of 4)

PART A

DVD

DVD player

30 copies of the Copymaster *Oceanic Life Zones*

30 copies of the Copymaster *Marine Organisms*

PART B

8 microscope slides and coverslips

8 compound microscopes

8 hand lenses

16 dissecting needles with corks on the tips

8 forceps

8 scalpels

8 large sheets of paper

30 felt-tipped markers

prepared slides showing vascular tissue, spores, pollen, microscopic parts of plants (optional)

8 sets of plant specimens (see Preparations) representing the following groups of organisms:

- Green algae (*Spirogyra*, *Oedogonium*, or *Ulothrix*)

- Moss or liverwort

- Conifer (pine, spruce, or fir)

- Flowering plant (monocots: lily, gladiolus, spider plant, wandering Jew; dicots: begonia, coleus, geranium, beans, peas)

Outcomes and Indicators of Success

The following indicators allow you to assess the students' level of success with the activity and to assess their process of learning.

By the end of this activity, the learners should understand that

1. adaptations may be structural, functional, or behavioral.

   They will demonstrate their understanding by listing examples of structural, functional, and behavioral adaptations of marine organisms.

2. adaptations are inherited characteristics that enhance survival.

   They will demonstrate their understanding by

   a. evaluating whether most marine organisms appear well-suited to their environments,

   b. describing characteristics that enhance survival of marine organisms, and

   c. offering examples of inherited characteristics that are not adaptations.

3. the usefulness of an adaptation depends on the organism's environment.

   They will demonstrate their understanding by

   a. comparing specific adaptations in marine organisms with the organism's particular habitat in the ocean, and

   b. naming a characteristic that is an adaptation in one environment but would not be in another environment.

4. evolution produces adaptations.

They will demonstrate their understanding by relating adaptations in plants to major steps in their evolution.

5. the appearance of different adaptations across time produces diversity.

They will demonstrate their understanding by proposing a general explanation for the appearance of biological diversity on earth.

Preparations

Collect the plant specimens listed in Materials. Fresh specimens are preferable to preserved. Because the students should observe with as little help as possible, the plants should exhibit the appropriate characteristics. For example, all groups (except the algae) should include stems. In addition, mosses and ferns should bear spore cases, conifers should have cones with seeds, and flowering plant specimens should include flowers. You can collect moss outdoors at almost any time of year and maintain it in a terrarium. Depending on what part of the country you live in, you may be able to collect many of the other organisms in the autumn. Flowering plants usually are available from local florists. Ideally, all teams should have their own plants to work with, but if sufficient specimens are not available, devise a plan for rotation among teams.

If available, provide prepared slides of tissues from any of the specimens.

Strategies for Guiding Learners

PROCESS AND PROCEDURES

As a class, read orally or silently all the introductory materials for the activity and the Process and Procedures to help students build connections between concepts and activities. Use the time spent reading to bring the students' attention into focus.

PART A   Diversity and Adaptation in a Marine Environment

1. Observe the DVD segment "Marine Life."

   a. Pay particular attention to the conditions that are present in each of the different environments described. Indicate these conditions in a few words at the appropriate places on Copymaster *Oceanic Life Zones.*

   Distribute a copy of Copymaster *Oceanic Life Zones* to each student and begin the DVD segment "Marine Life." If necessary, pause after each life zone so that the learners can record the relevant conditions.

   b. Work with the other members of your team to write on your copymaster the names of several organisms that live in each life zone.

    This video segment is a tour through several life zones and describes some of each habitat's physical characteristics. This information helps clarify adaptations such as feeding mechanisms and relationships between environmental challenges and adaptations. For specific strategies, see the interactive DVD guide on the *TRCD.*

2. For each species, briefly describe 1 adaptation that appears to make it better able to survive in the particular environment where it is usually found.

Adaptations may be structural, functional, behavioral, or a combination of these. Examples of adaptations that you might use include lungs, gills, internal skeleton, external skeleton, structural protections against predation, behavioral protections against predation, and feeding habits.

The information on Copymaster *Marine Organisms* will help you complete this task.

As the learners view the DVD segment "Marine Life" again, allow time for them to record on their copymaster the names of several organisms that live in each life zone. Encourage the learners to note and record examples of adaptations. Take this opportunity to review the definition of a biological adaptation—remind students that an adaptation must be inheritable and make the organisms that possess it better able to survive and reproduce. Listen for the common misconceptions that organisms *choose* to adapt to their environments, that acquired traits can be passed down to offspring, or that biological evolution takes place in a single generation.

After students have viewed the video segment, distribute a copy of Copymaster *Marine Organisms* to each student for additional reference.

3. Work with the other members of your team to answer the following questions. Record your responses in your journal.

Circulate among the teams as they discuss the questions. Look for responses such as the following:

a. In general, do most of these marine organisms appear to be well-suited to survival in their environments? Support your answer with specific examples.

Yes. Learners should provide examples such as the shape and protective coloration of the flatfish, the holdfast that anchors the kelp, the streamlined shape and modification of limbs into flippers of the aquatic mammals such as dolphins and seals, the stinging tentacles of the anemone, and the burrowing of the rock crab.

b. Are all inherited characteristics adaptations? Explain your answer, and support it with specific examples.

No. For example, lungs are not an adaptation in an aquatic environment any more than gills are an adaptation in a gaseous environment. As learners saw in Chapter 2, one type of coloration may be an adaptation against one type of background (that is, in one environment) but not against another. Different environments provide different challenges to survival (that is, different sets of selective forces). One outcome of the differences in selective forces from one environment to another is the survival and persistence of different types of adaptations.

Learners may offer many different examples to illustrate this point. The specific examples that they choose are not as important as the clear indication that they understand that all inherited characteristics are not adaptations. Instead, adaptations are recognized and defined in relation to the environment in which they occur. Characteristics that may enhance survival in one environment may not in another.

(Learners examine this question in a slightly different manner in the activity *Explaining the Zebra's Stripes.* In Part B of that activity, which is designed to help students develop further their understanding of the nature and methods of science, learners consider whether all inherited characteristics can be explained as the result of adaptive change. Learners examine several possible explanations for the appearance and persistence of the striped patterns that characterize the coloration of various species of zebras. As a way to understand the tentative and cumulative nature of scientific explanations, students discuss the difficulty that scientists sometimes face in developing immediate and complete explanations for every aspect of life's diversity.)

    c. Name a characteristic that is an adaptation in 1 environment but would not be an adaptation in another environment.

> Learners should use examples such as the following: lungs are adaptive for gas exchange on land but not in water.

    d. What explanation can you offer for the presence of characteristics that may not be particularly adaptive for a modern organism in its current environment?

> Learners should use examples such as the following: the presence of lungs in aquatic mammals supports the evolutionary origin of dolphins as terrestrial mammals that adapted secondarily to an aquatic environment.

PART B Diversity and Adaptation across Time

You may wish to have students read and conduct the exercises in Appendix B, *Technique 4 The Compound Microscope* before beginning this part of the activity.

    1. Work with the members of your team to examine the plant specimens that your teacher has provided.

Manipulate, dissect, or otherwise examine the specimens to gather as much information as possible.

    2. Record your plant observations in your journal. Use your sketching skills to record the observations that are best recorded through drawings.

> If there are not enough plants for all teams to have individual sets to examine, arrange the plants in such a way that all teams can rotate past stations while making their observations of plant names and characteristics. Alternatively, use a jigsaw technique with each team responsible for sharing information about one of the plants. Encourage the learners to manipulate the specimens to learn as much as possible about each one and to see structures that might be adaptations. Provide microscopes, hand lenses, dissecting tools, and prepared slides to further these manipulations. It is important for students to see the structure of the algae and the multicellular organization of the plants, chloroplasts, and vascular tissue.

    3. Respond to the following items. Record your answers in your journal.

> Based on students' examinations of the specimens, expect answers to the questions such as the following:

    a. Identify at least 1 characteristic that all of these organisms share.

> All are green, contain chlorophyll and thus can carry out photosynthesis. All except the algae are multicellular, and the algae are filamentous. All except the algae are terrestrial, and all of the plants except the mosses have vascular tissue.

b. Are these organisms as diverse as those in the DVD segment "Marine Life," or are they more similar to each other? Explain your answer.

> Superficially, these organisms may seem less diverse because all are photosynthetic. Their diversity is perhaps more subtle than that among the marine organisms, but it is just as distinct. All the plants are adapted to life on land, although mosses are much less well-adapted than the other plants; their means of reproduction are diverse; the protection provided for seeds is diverse; and so on. Use this opportunity to expand your students' appreciation for the diversity of these organisms.

4. Read the essay *From Cell to Seed* on page 134 for a short description of the evolution of modern plants. In your journal, make a list of the major adaptations that took place during the evolution of modern plants.

> As the teams begin their lists, check to determine whether the learners have understood the key evolutionary changes in plants as described in the essay *From Cell to Seed*. Their list of changes will help indicate the level of their understanding and also will guide their observations of the living organisms. Encourage students to reexamine their specimens to relate their adaptations to the evolutionary changes. Some key changes that students might list in their journals are the following:

> - ◆ Development of photosynthetic ability
> - ◆ Release of oxygen in the process of photosynthesis
> - ◆ Development of multicellularity
> - ◆ Adaptations that prevent water loss
> - ◆ Origin of a vascular system
> - ◆ Origin of seeds and flowers

5. For each plant specimen that you observed, use your list of adaptations from step 4 to help you identify at least 1 characteristic that biologists might use to distinguish that plant from all of the others. Record these characteristics in your journal.

> As students begin to identify characteristics that separate each organism from all others, look for items such as the following: algae are aquatic, the plants are terrestrial; moss lack vascular tissue, the other plants have it; ferns lack seeds, the other plants have them; conifers bear seeds in open cones, flowering plants bear seeds in enclosed structures.

6. Arrange your plant specimens in groups that represent those that are most closely related. Discuss and identify at least 1 characteristic that each group shares.

> Expect that students may identify characteristics such as the following:

> - ◆ Green algae—are aquatic
> - ◆ Moss or liverwort—are multicellular but tiny (or relatively simple)
> - ◆ Conifers—have seeds in cones
> - ◆ Flowering plants—have seeds that develop from flowers

7. Study the branching diagram in Figure 3.5. This diagram shows the relatedness of some vertebrates.

The points where branches separate represent where new lineages evolved from a common ancestor.

8. What do scientists call the characteristics that enable organisms to function better in their environment?

   Adaptations.

9. As a team, create a branching pattern on your large sheet of paper that organizes your plant specimens. Think as a biologist would and classify them according to their evolutionary divergence, or separation from an ancestral form.

   Be sure that someone who is not in your team would understand your diagram.

10. Label your diagram with the names of the plant specimens. Include a short statement that identifies the major distinguishing characteristic that caused you to place it at that point in the diagram.

Learners are likely to find it difficult to relate adaptations to evolutionary changes and to create a branching diagram. Thus, this portion of the activity will be the most challenging to teach. Resist the impulse to answer student questions directly, but provide input when the learners are not progressing in their explanations. Try to focus their thinking in the appropriate direction with suggestions or questions that help them make the connection between evolutionary changes and characteristics of modern plant groups. If difficulties persist, suggest the use of a dichotomous system in which succeeding branches consist of a single basic distinction between members of a group. Figure T3.1 provides sample diagrams of the evolutionary relationships that could be drawn from the essay. Do not expect all teams to produce the same diagram, but look for patterns that capture the essence of this figure.

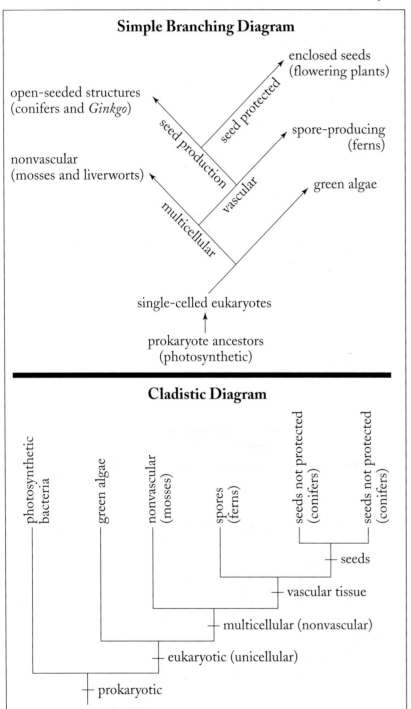

Figure T3.1 Sample diagrams of plant evolution

11. Post your diagram in your classroom as your teacher directs. Be prepared to share your ideas in a class discussion.

After the learners have completed their branching diagrams, conduct a brief, summarizing discussion. Direct the teams to post their diagrams at the front of the room. With these as visual aids, point out the similarities and the differences in the diagrams. Reinforce your learners' understanding that good explanations are based on evidence and sound reasoning by asking teams to explain why they represented certain characteristics and groups as they did. Use this discussion to help the class move toward a consensus view of plant evolution, acknowledging as you do so that there are a variety of ways in which this same evolutionary sequence might be represented visually.

Because this exercise focuses your learners' attention on a series of evolutionary changes that occurred across time, some students may develop the misconception that each major adaptation (or set of adaptations) that appears during an evolutionary sequence replaces those adaptations that occurred before it. For example, some learners may think that the vascular plants, because of their ability to grow in drier environments, *replaced* the nonvascular plants. Help students examine this notion critically. For example, you might ask the class what direct evidence they have that this has *not* been the case. (The fact that they have before them examples of all of the major types of plants suggests that earlier forms were not replaced or rendered extinct by the appearance of new forms.) To help learners move away from a replacement view of evolution, ask them to articulate a statement that is consistent with their experience of life and that might be an alternative to the replacement model.

Thoughtful learners will see that many different forms of life coexist on earth. They may propose that major adaptive modifications often persist, not because they allow organisms to compete more effectively than species that already are successful in the niches in which they occur, but because such adaptations allow these organisms to colonize new environments or new niches within which the earlier forms could not have survived.

Analysis

1. What are adaptations? Illustrate your answer using examples drawn from the organisms that you studied in Part A and Part B.

Adaptations are inherited structural, functional, or behavioral characteristics that enhance an organism's ability to survive in its environment. For example, fish such as the silversides swim in large schools that apparently confuse potential predators; sea otters use stones as tools to break open mollusks and gain access to the soft meat inside; kelp anchor to the seafloor by means of specialized structures called holdfasts; and fish use swim bladders to help adjust the pressure inside their bodies to the depth of the water. Most land plants are covered with a waxy cuticle that reduces water loss from their surface; vascular plants have specialized transport structures that enable them to reach sizes as large as the giant sequoia; and flowering plants produce seeds in enclosed structures that are modified in various ways that ensure wide distribution.

2. How is the diversity of organisms on earth related to the diversity of environments in which organisms live? Illustrate your answer using examples drawn from the organisms that you studied in Part A and Part B.

Adaptations suit organisms to particular habitats within each environment. The selective pressures within each habitat differ, and these selective pressures determine which characteristics survive. For example, adaptations that anchor organisms to the ocean floor enable them to survive along a rocky seacoast, and the buoyancy of jellies enables them to float in the surface waters. Desert organisms display a variety of structural and behavioral adaptations that enable them to survive in that harsh environment: burrowing, moving from shade to sun to adjust internal temperatures, activity during the night rather than during the day, spines instead of leaves on cacti, and either shallow root systems that can absorb rainwater before it percolates down in the sandy soil or very deep taproots that may reach the water table.

3. If a mutation occurs in a population, it can result in the appearance of a new adaptation. How might this relate to the ability of organisms to colonize new environments? Illustrate your answer using examples drawn from your work in Part B.

If certain characteristics increase survival in a changed environment, the organisms that display them are more likely to perpetuate their characteristics than other organisms. For example, multicellular algae could resist drying better than unicellular algae, and this characteristic gave them an advantage on land. We recognize these characteristics as adaptations that suit specific organisms to specific habitats.

4. Explain biological diversity.

Biological diversity refers to the wide variety of life-forms that occur on earth.

5. Propose a general explanation for the appearance of biological diversity on earth.

Refer to the essay *Mutations Are a Source of Variation* on page 139 for background information that may help you answer this question.

Although their language likely will be less sophisticated than this language, learners should articulate the following basic ideas:

♦ Some characteristics are *adaptive;* they give the organisms that possess them a selective advantage over other organisms in the same or a new environment.

♦ Inherited characteristics that enhance the survival of an organism in an environment (that is, true *adaptations*) will be perpetuated unless that environment changes in such a way that the characteristic no longer is advantageous.

♦ The processes of random genetic change and natural selection occurring across a tremendous expanse of geologic time and in a variety of different physical environments have produced an enormous variety of different types of organisms, each type displaying a distinct set of characteristics that suits it to the environment in which it lives.

- Different types of organisms that have evolved from a common ancestor will share certain fundamental traits and will vary in others. For example, all plants, because they evolved from a common ancestor, share certain basic characteristics. Nevertheless, random genetic change, coupled with selective pressures that changed as the environment changed, have led to the appearance of hundreds of thousands of different types of plants, each with its own unique set of distinguishing characteristics (adaptations). Thus, evolution explains both the unity and the diversity of life.

Extensions

To explore phylogeny and natural selection, have the students complete *Phylogeny and the Evolution of Darwin's Finches* in Appendix C of the student text. This material can also be found on the *TRCD*, Appendix 4 of Section 7: Supplementary Materials. We have included a chapter on the evolution of plants from *BSCS Biology: An Ecological Approach* in Appendix C of the Student Edition and on the *TRCD*.

Using Unity to Organize Diversity

skip?

Elaborate

Major Concepts
Classification schemes reflect the criteria used; biological classification schemes are hierarchical and reflect evolutionary relationships

Overview

In this activity, learners examine the process of biological classification, not as an end in itself but as a tool that scientists use to help them describe and understand biological diversity. In Part A, learners classify a set of objects, discovering that different classification schemes (schemes that use different classification criteria) emphasize different sets of similarities and differences among the objects classified. In Part B, students learn that biologists create classification schemes based on the criterion of evolutionary relatedness and that shared characteristics sometimes provide a clue about the degree of relatedness between two species. As learners classify a set of biological specimens, they explore the hierarchical nature of biological classification and they recognize and articulate the power of such schemes to illustrate current thinking about evolutionary relationships.

Materials   (per class of 30, teams of 4)

8 sets of nonliving objects
30 copies of the Copymaster *Biological Classification*
8 sets of the Copymasters *Organism Cards* (see Preparations)
8 large sheets of paper
8 sets of colored felt-tipped markers

Outcomes and Indicators of Success

The following indicators allow you to assess the students' level of success with the activity and to assess their process of learning.

By the end of this activity, the learners should understand that

1. classification systems are based on criteria that humans select for various purposes.

   They will demonstrate their understanding by

   a. establishing criteria to classify a set of objects, and

   b. explaining the importance of criteria to the process of classification.

2. biological classification schemes are hierarchical.

   They will demonstrate their understanding by

   a. classifying a set of biological specimens into a hierarchy, and

   b. using their classification scheme to illustrate the hierarchical nature of biological classification.

3. biological classification is based on evolutionary criteria.

   They will demonstrate their understanding by explaining what their classification scheme suggests about the evolutionary history of the organisms represented.

Safety

Make sure that each nonliving object has no sharp edges or points, no breakable parts, and includes no filled containers. Do not use objects longer than 30 centimeters, greater in mass than 500 grams, or personal-use items. Emphasize that students should feel free to examine the objects carefully by using all of their senses—**except their sense of taste**.

Preparations

PART A. Assemble a set of 10–15 objects for each team of students; select objects that are interesting to examine. For example, a wide variety of sea shells, unusual arthropods that are glued into small, plastic magnifying boxes, or unusual seeds make interesting subjects for this activity. Alternatively, the objects can include a mix of such things as matchbooks, buttons, writing implements, nails, screws, hooks, keys, playing cards, scraps of fabric, bottle caps, or objects that have no apparent function, such as a piece of an electronic appliance. The sets should include a variety of objects that share enough common characteristics that they can be classified in many ways. The sets for each team also should be identical, or at least similar, so that teams can compare their classification systems.

PART B. Prepare a set of organism cards for each team from the Copymasters *Organism Cards*. Laminate the cards if possible.

Strategies for Guiding Learners

PROCESS AND PROCEDURES

As a class, read orally or silently all the introductory materials for the activity and the Process and Procedures to help students build connections between concepts and activities. Use the time spent reading to bring the students' attention into focus.

PART A Classification as a Tool

As the students begin this part of the activity, remind them that we frequently organize information or objects by developing classification systems. The rules, or *criteria*, that we use to group objects determine how many categories we have and how we assign objects to each category.

1. Work with your team to examine the set of nonliving objects. What, if anything, do all of these objects share in common? What characteristics do some objects possess that others do not? Record your observations in your journal.

   As the teams examine the set of objects, monitor their progress to see that they are looking for both common characteristics and differences.

2. Sort the objects in your set into 4 different categories.

   When you sort your objects into categories, you are classifying them. The system that you use to sort your objects is called a classification scheme.

   Your students will not be able to sort these objects in any meaningful way unless they first recognize properties that some objects share and other objects do not. It is important, however, that the learners recognize that this type of thinking precedes and is part of the act of establishing categories and assigning objects to those categories. This procedural step makes explicit the thinking aspect of the process of classification.

3. Write your team's classification scheme on a card. Leave the card facedown on the table with the sorted objects.

4. When directed by your teacher, go to another team's table and try to guess what their classification scheme is. Compare your classification scheme with that of the other team. Are the categories the same? Could you easily recognize their categories?

   Expect that learners used criteria such as shape, color, composition (metal, wood, plastic), or function (use) to sort the objects. Encourage the teams to discuss with each other the criteria that they used to classify the objects. To make this part of the activity more fun, have each team try first to *figure out* the criteria that the other team used to classify its objects before turning over the card that explains the criteria. Emphasize that there are many ways to classify these objects and that the purpose of this portion of the activity is not to develop the right scheme or even the best scheme, but simply to see that classification is a relatively straightforward process. The categories that one ends up with depend on the criteria one has chosen as a basis for the sorting decisions.

5. Answer the following questions in your journal:

   Look for responses such as the following:

   a. Your team and the other team probably used a different basis for the classification schemes. Nevertheless, each team used some basis. That is, each team used some general criteria to determine what groups they would include in their scheme and what objects would go into each group. Is it possible to classify without establishing such criteria? Support your answer with a different example of classification drawn from your life experience.

It should be clear that without criteria, classification is impossible. Learners should explain that classification is a way to sort a set of objects. Sorting always involves separating some objects from others based on differences, or grouping some objects together based on common properties. Classification always involves establishing criteria.

Learners may illustrate this principle in a variety of ways. For example, they might point to the classification of students by grade level, to the classification of automobiles based on manufacturer and model, and even to the classification of foods into the basic food groups.

b. Consider the categories of objects that you created in your classification scheme. Could you further separate (or classify) the objects in any of these categories into smaller groups within the large category? Support your answer with specific references to the objects and the classification scheme that you developed.

Depending on the objects that you provide for classification and the criteria that the learners select, the groups may or may not be subdivided into smaller categories. In principle, objects can be sorted so that there is only one object in each category. It should be clear, however, that such subdivision is not always useful.

PART B   Biological Classification

1. Examine the data provided on your organism cards. Work with the other members of your team to create a simple hierarchical classification scheme for these organisms.

    Ask yourselves what broad category all of these organisms fit into. Then ask yourselves what criteria you could use to sort them into smaller categories. Continue creating smaller categories until each category contains only 1 type of organism.

    Distribute a set of organism cards to each team. Emphasize to the learners that the main purpose of this part of the activity is to examine the biological basis for classifying organisms. Although there may be a variety of criteria that students could use to classify these organisms (for example, color, size, first letter of the name of the organism), make it clear that their task is to create a hierarchical scheme based on biological criteria.

As students complete this step, circulate around the room to monitor their progress and to make sure that the schemes they develop actually are hierarchical. Point out when this is not the case, but resist the temptation to provide hints about how a team might modify its scheme to make it hierarchical. If learners appear to be struggling, recommend that they think carefully about the hints provided in the student procedures.

If some teams seem unable to get started, ask them what all of the organisms have in common. Then ask whether there are any characteristics that would enable them to separate one type of bird from all of the others. (At this point, they may find the behavioral characteristics most helpful.) Figure T3.2 provides information from which you can offer further hints, if necessary. Remind students who begin to use the organisms' names that naturalists first must classify an organism before they can assign a name. (The biological characteristics precede the name.)

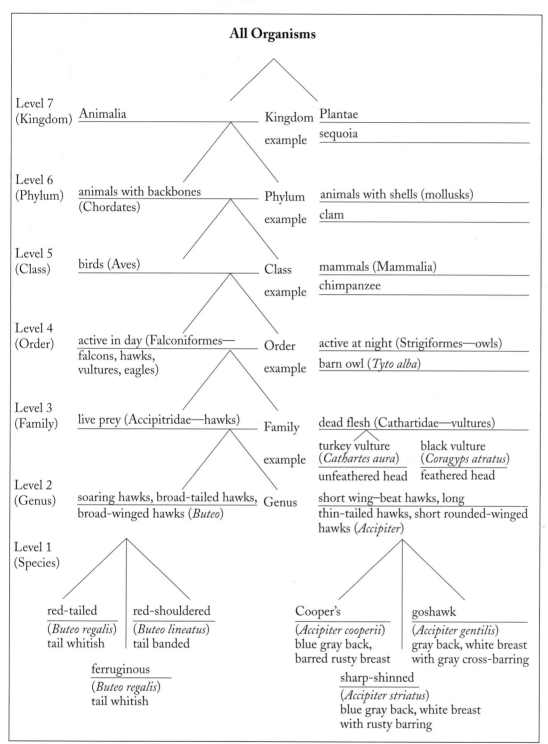

Figure T3.2 Completed biological classification table

The organisms described on the cards were selected to make dichotomous sorting into orders, families, and genera quite clear cut. Sufficient information was included to enable the students to sort the organisms in each genus into species, but at this point, dichotomous sorting is counterproductive. It should become evident that more specific information is necessary to sort organisms at each lower level of the classification scheme; this point might trigger a fruitful discussion.

2. Figure 3.6 illustrates the hierarchical classification scheme that most biologists use. Compare this classification scheme with the one that you have developed for your organisms. Which levels in Figure 3.6 represent levels in the scheme that you developed? Explain your answer.

If the students have classified their organisms so that their smallest categories contain only one type of organism (see the hint provided in step 1), then their schemes should show the species, genus, family, order, and class levels of classification. Students likely will express this idea in a variety of ways, but their answers should reflect an understanding that the smallest taxonomic category reflected in Figure 3.6 is that which corresponds to a single type of organism.

If the students are having difficulty comparing their scheme with the one in Figure 3.6, you might ask a question such as, What is an aviary? to help them relate birds to the class Aves.

3. Complete the classification diagram shown on Copymaster *Biological Classification*. Fill in the names of the organisms that you classified. Then add the names of other appropriate organisms to the remaining lines.

Students should have little difficulty completing the lowest levels of the hierarchical scheme shown on the copymaster. Be sure, however, that they add the names of other appropriate organisms up to and including those at the kingdom level (these organisms are not represented on their specimen cards). Completing the scheme in this fashion will place the specimens with which they have been working into the larger context of all living things and will provide a useful review of your students' knowledge of the five kingdoms. You may want to suggest that the students read the essay *Organizing Diversity* at this point.

4. Answer the following questions in your journal:

Look for responses similar to the following:

a. Which group in a hierarchical classification scheme contains

◆ the most organisms?

◆ the fewest organisms?

◆ the most different types of organisms (the greatest diversity)?

◆ the fewest different types of organisms (the least diversity)?

It should be apparent to learners that the largest category (kingdom) contains the most organisms and the greatest diversity, and that the smallest category (species) contains the fewest organisms and the least diversity. Clarify this fundamental aspect of hierarchical classification for any students who are having difficulty.

b. What does this classification scheme suggest about evolutionary relationships that exist among these organisms? Explain your answer.

Information in the essay *Organizing Diversity* on page 141 may help you with this step.

Biologists use classification schemes to display their understanding of structural and behavioral similarities and differences among organisms. These similarities and differences often reflect the multiplicity of changes in species that have occurred during evolution. In general, shared structural and behavioral characteristics usually are interpreted as evidence of a close evolutionary relationship. Because the students had structural and behavioral characteristics on which to base the classification of their organisms, their completed schemes should illustrate not only a set of structural and behavioral relationships among organisms but also a set of evolutionary relationships. In particular, species that appear close together on the scheme are likely to be more closely related in an evolutionary sense than are species that appear farther apart.

Analysis

1. Imagine that you are a member of a large publishing company that is writing a new textbook for high school biology classes. Your team has been assigned to write the chapter on the nature and importance of biological classification. Before you can begin to write, of course, you need to decide what the future students should learn about your topic.

   Identify the *three most important ideas* about biological classification that you think a scientifically literate citizen should understand. Summarize these ideas in three concise statements, and record them in your journal.

   The learners should include three of the following:
   A biological classification system

   - ◆ **reflects evolutionary relationships,**
   - ◆ **is hierarchical,**
   - ◆ **is based on shared structural and behavioral characteristics,**
   - ◆ **involves identification of similarities and differences among organisms, and**
   - ◆ **involves dichotomous sorting.**

2. Now, imagine that the editor-in-chief has decided that your team must reduce the size of the book and that there will be no chapter on biological classification. Instead, everything you want the students to learn about the topic has to fit on one page, preferably in the form of a diagram or a drawing (although this can include words or short statements). Luckily, you already have distilled your understanding about the topic into three clear statements (step 1).

   Create a one-page display that communicates and illustrates these ideas in an attractive and interesting manner.

   Before the learners begin to create their displays, evaluate their statements for level of understanding and ability to synthesize important ideas. Give the students the opportunity to revise their statements if they need to.

3. Follow your teacher's instructions and post your display for the class. If you were a textbook editor, which display would you choose to use in the book and why? Record your answer in your journal.

   Provide space for teams to post the displays they create. Allow time for the teams to evaluate each other's displays. You may wish to conclude the Analysis with a short summarizing discussion.

Extensions

For a look at classification from the perspective of another culture, try the optional elaborate activity *Looking at Diversity through a Different Lens* on the *TRCD*. Or have students complete investigations 2.1 and 2.3 in Appendix C of the student text. These investigations can also be found in Appendix 2 of Section 7 on the *TRCD*. Here they can study specimens, collect organisms, and use and create dichotomous keys.

Elaborate

Explaining the Zebra's Stripes

Major Concepts   Diversity, variation, and adaptation; the dynamic nature of science

Overview

This activity affords the students an opportunity to elaborate on the concepts of biological species, diversity, variation, and adaptation. It also reminds students that science is an active, dynamic endeavor, in which legitimate controversy and differences of opinion can occur, and in which answers to certain questions sometimes must wait until new information or new techniques are available. The students first will investigate patterns of differences and similarities in the physical and behavioral characteristics and ranges of four zebras. Using these patterns, the students will infer relationships among the zebras, some of which are members of the same species and others of which are members of different species. Then the students will investigate two explanations that address the question, How might zebra stripes enhance the survival or reproduction of zebras? Through their evaluations, the students will see that there are different explanations for the patterns they observe in nature, including the patterns of zebra stripes.

Materials   (per class of 30, teams of 4)

30 copies of the Copymaster *African Zebras*
30 copies of the Copymaster *Ideas about the Zebra's Stripes*
DVD
DVD player

Outcomes and Indicators of Success

The following indicators allow you to assess the students' level of success with the activity and to assess their process of learning.

By the end of this activity, the learners should

1. analyze how differences among zebras represent diversity among related species and variation within a species.

    They will demonstrate their ability by

    a. comparing the physical characteristics and geographic ranges of four different members of the genus *Equus*,

b. categorizing the four zebra populations into different species, and

c. evaluating additional comparative information to refine their categorization.

2. evaluate explanations about the adaptive significance of zebra stripes.

They will demonstrate their ability by

a. analyzing two explanations about the adaptive significance of zebra stripes,

b. identifying with their teammates the evidence and inferences that support and contradict each explanation,

c. discussing the strengths and weaknesses of the evidence and inferences for each of the explanations, and

d. evaluating and defending the explanation that they think the data best support.

3. understand that explanations in science have limitations.

They will demonstrate their understanding by

a. comparing their evaluation of the explanations with those of other students,

b. proposing observations or experiments that might provide additional data to test explanations about the zebra's stripes,

c. critiquing statements that indicate a misunderstanding of science, and

d. illustrating how the process of science is open to change and modification.

Strategies for Guiding Learners

PROCESS AND PROCEDURES

As a class, read orally or silently all the introductory materials for the activity and the Process and Procedures to help students build connections between concepts and activities. Use the time spent reading to bring the students' attention into focus.

PART A Looking Closely at the Concept of Species

1. Work with the other members of your team to compare the physical characteristics of the 4 zebras shown in the DVD segment "Zebras" and in Figure 3.7.

   These zebras represent 4 populations that live in Africa; each population has a different common name. Record your observations about these animals in your journal in a table similar to the one in Figure 3.8.

2. Examine the map in Figure 3.9. Compare the ranges of each of these 4 populations of zebras. Add this information to the observations that you recorded in step 1.

   As the teams of four work together to gather data and compare and discuss the characteristics of the zebras in Figure 3.7, show the DVD segment "Zebras." The segment shows three of the zebras in their natural habitat; the mountain zebras were filmed at a zoo. There are stills of each type and a final screen that shows all four together to help students make comparisons.

Figure 3.7 contains examples of three species: the Grevy's zebra (*Equus grevyi*), the plains or Burchell's zebra (*Equus burchelli böhmi*), and the mountain zebra (*Equus zebra*). The plains zebra includes both of the subspecies, Chapman's zebra (*Equus burchelli antiquorum*) and Grant's zebra (*Equus burchelli*). Do not reveal this information to the students at any point during the activity. Rather, allow them to form their own explanations and opinions. Even if students express misconceptions about species or other concepts, do not correct their errors outright. Instead, guide them toward a more accurate and complete understanding by asking questions such as, How do you know? How can you be sure? or How might you test your idea? You also might suggest that the students review the essays if they appear to have problems with the concepts of species and diversity.

Direct the students to record the data they collected from step 1 in a data table such as the one shown in Figure 3.8. Students should add the information they gather in step 2 to this data table.

3. Discuss with your teammates how you might categorize the 4 zebras into species. Record your answer in your journal.

The fundamental question here is whether each of these populations of zebras represents a separate species or whether some of them are members of the same species. Develop and support your answer using the information that you collected in steps 1 and 2.

Encourage the students to categorize the zebras by describing patterns of similarities and differences in the physical and behavioral characteristics and ranges of the zebras. Their initial descriptions might include the following:

◆ Some of the zebras are very different from the others.

◆ The zebras are similar except in the places they live.

◆ The zebras look like horses (or mules or donkeys) with stripes.

◆ The more you look, the more patterns you see.

◆ Grant's and Chapman's zebras share many of the same stripes, and they also share parts of the same range.

As the teams discuss how they might divide the zebras into different species, expect the students to express a range of explanations for the patterns in the data. For example, the range map shows that there is overlap in the ranges of Grant's zebras and Chapman's zebras—zebras that share many common characteristics—and in the ranges of Grant's zebras and Grevy's zebras. This might lead some students to conclude that these zebras are closely related.

4. Examine the additional information on Copymaster *African Zebras* to make further comparisons among the 4 populations of zebras. How might you categorize these zebras? Support your answer using all of the information you have available to you. Record your answer in your journal.

The information provided in the table on Copymaster *African Zebras* should help the students form a clear sense of the species' distinctions among these organisms. For example, as the data show, Grevy's zebras do not interbreed with other zebras. Many students likely will recognize that the ability to interbreed defines the biological species for certain sexually reproducing animals.

5. Contribute your ideas to a class discussion about the zebras and about the difficulties involved in assigning species distinctions.

Conduct a short (10-minute) class discussion to allow teams to share their conclusions. The students should weigh the similarities and differences that they observe among the zebras and their ranges. Although the four groups of animals share characteristics such as their overall body shape and their striped color pattern, each group has a unique combination of characteristics not shared by the others. These unique characteristics include the following:

- Grevy's zebras have larger bodies, narrower stripes, larger, hairy ears, and longer, narrower snouts than all of the other zebras.
- Grant's and Chapman's zebras have smaller bodies and shorter ears than the other zebras.
- Chapman's zebras have faint "shadow" stripes on their hindquarters.
- Mountain zebras have more stripes, narrower ears, and whiter bellies than Grant's or Chapman's zebras.

The students also might cite specific differences in the patterns of stripes, including the absence of stripes above the rump and on the bellies of Grevy's zebras, the presence of faint stripes in Chapman's zebras, or the transverse stripes along the rump of mountain zebras. In addition, differences in the lifestyle or environments of the zebras include the following:

- Grevy's zebras exist in desert regions.
- Mountain zebras exist in the hills and mountains.
- Chapman's and Grant's zebras exist in the plains and grassy woodlands.

The students should recognize that the factor that determines the boundary between biological species of certain sexually reproducing animals is the ability to interbreed. In this respect, members of different populations that can interbreed also can be considered members of the same species (for example, Grant's zebras and Chapman's zebras). Nonetheless, students should realize that the biological species concept can be problematical: species boundaries can exist despite occasional hybrids or interbreeding. Therefore, although some students might look for definitive answers to the question of zebra species, they should see that natural populations do not always behave in clear-cut and simple ways.

PART B Explaining the Adaptive Significance of Structural Characteristics

1. Hold a brainstorming session with the other members of your team about the significance of a zebra's stripes. How might these stripes be adaptations? List your ideas in your journal.

Encourage the students to think broadly about the potential adaptive significance of zebra stripes. The students may suggest that the stripes play several roles, such as roles in camouflage, mating, and/or temperature control. Monitor their discussions and listen carefully for evidence that the students are offering explanations that are rooted soundly in evolutionary theory (for example, explanations that reflect an understanding of the roles of variation and differential reproduction in evolution). Challenge students to modify explanations that do not reflect an appropriate application of concepts learned from this chapter.

2. Read the 2 explanations on Copymaster *Ideas about the Zebra's Stripes* for the appearance and perpetuation of the zebra's stripes.

   Distribute Copymaster *Ideas about the Zebra's Stripes.*

3. Work with the other members of your team to analyze the data that relate to each explanation.

   As you read and discuss each explanation, identify and record each bit of evidence, each inference, and all of the assumptions that you recognize. Then decide whether each piece of information supports, does not support, or contradicts each explanation. Take notes in your journal about the results of your discussion. View the DVD segment again if you think it will help you.

4. Discuss the strengths and weaknesses of each of the 2 explanations. Summarize this discussion with a list of the evidence that supports, or fails to support, each explanation.

5. Work with the other members of your team to determine which explanation best accounts for the data presented. Record your answer in your journal.

   Weigh the data that you have collected by asking yourself questions such as, What pieces of information are most relevant to each explanation? What are the most serious flaws of each explanation? Might there be more than 1 explanation to account for the stripes?

    Encourage the teams to view the DVD segment "Zebras" again. Allow the students adequate time to analyze their explanations for how stripes might enhance the survival and reproduction of zebras. You might assign the analysis of these explanations as homework.

6. Participate in a discussion and evaluation of the explanations.

   Encourage students to take turns describing the explanations and then discussing the balance of data that support and do not support each explanation. Try to keep the discussion focused on evaluations based on the data. Make sure that everyone participates and considers all opinions, even contradictory ones. Use the students' discussions to demonstrate the nature of science: debates and disagreements are valuable processes that help us refine our understandings and improve our explanations. You also might indicate that the explanations in the student materials are not the only ones that have been suggested by scientists. Two more possible explanations are provided below. Use them at your discretion as time permits.

Additional Explanations

Explanation 3: Stripes act as a visual defense against the zebra's predators, allowing zebras to avoid or thwart attacks by the predators.

Some scientists have proposed the explanation that the stripes act as a visual defense—not to camouflage the zebras but rather to confuse their predators once an attack is underway. Zebras' main predator is the lion. Individual lions or small groups of lions hunt zebras by stealthily approaching a herd and then charging the zebras. As the zebra herd flees, the lions single out an individual and bring it down, using blows from their large forelimbs. According to this explanation, zebra stripes act to confuse the lions or make them unable to single out individual zebras. For example, the lions might not be able to distinguish the outline of the individual and therefore may not know where to attack or strike a blow.

Some scientists have suggested, however, that lions appear to be confident in their ability to kill zebras; they do not appear hesitant or confused during their attacks. In addition, scientists have studied records of zebra mortalities (deaths) and shown that zebras are killed roughly in proportion to their relative abundance. The pattern of deaths suggests that zebras in larger groups are better able to avoid predators than are zebras in smaller groups.

Explanation 4: Zebra stripes provide chemical and visual defense against pests such as the tsetse fly.

Some scientists have proposed that zebra stripes act to deter pests that carry harmful diseases. In Africa, large grazing animals such as the zebra are the target of many different pests. The tsetse fly is one example. Tsetse flies require large quantities of blood that they obtain from host animals such as zebras or even humans. When the fly bites its host, it transmits a microorganism into the host's bloodstream. This microorganism causes a disease that can be fatal. (In humans, this disease is known as sleeping sickness.) This explanation proposes that zebra stripes decrease the degree to which the tsetse flies are attracted to zebras and thereby decrease the mortality rate among zebras.

Scientists have conducted experiments to test whether visual signals might deter the tsetse fly. In one experiment, for example, scientists constructed several different types of zebra models—some with stripes, some all white, and some black. They then towed these models for a short distance across the African savannah, in a region occupied by tsetse flies. Results showed that all-black and all-white zebra models attracted more flies than the striped models. These tests do not, however, reveal the mechanisms that might cause the flies to react differently to the different models. For example, the scientists do not know whether the flies distinguish between visual patterns in the different models or whether they are reacting to patterns that are less apparent to human observers (for example, differences in the temperature of the hide caused by differences in color patterns).

Analysis

1. Do new species appear on earth because two individuals from separate species mate and their offspring is a new and different species? Explain your answer.

   No. If two individuals are from different species, they cannot interbreed in nature. The process by which different species evolve is called speciation.

2. Have you ever heard people say, "I don't pay much attention to reports about new scientific findings? After all, scientists say one thing about *x*, *y*, or *z* this year. But they said something else last year, and something different the year before. It's clear that they don't know what's going on"?

   Analyze those statements in light of what you have learned in this activity about the nature of science. In your answer, refer to your experiences in both Part A and Part B of this activity. Record your critique in your journal. Be prepared to share it as your teacher directs.

   Student answers should reflect an understanding that scientific knowledge is at the same time both durable (in the sense of forming a lasting foundation of knowledge and understanding) and also subject to change as new information is uncovered and as investigators reexamine preexisting data in light of new questions and new hypotheses. Therein lies one of the great strengths of science as a method of searching

for explanations of the world around us. Its durability means that we do not have to rediscover knowledge each generation, but can build on preexisting understandings. Its ability to be modified by new results acts as a constant verification/refinement mechanism that helps us reexamine and reformulate earlier explanations to bring them into better conformity with a constantly growing database.

Students should point out that science's ability—and tendency—to constantly self-edit to accommodate new information is not a weakness but a strength. Thus, as new information becomes available about the zebras shown in Part A, good scientists modify their hypotheses about species relationships. Likewise, as Part B illustrates, scientists entertain several different explanations for the presence of stripes, preferring to keep the question open to discussion until more data are available rather than arbitrarily or prematurely cutting dialogue short.

3. In the essay *Five Kingdoms,* you read about the history of the classification scheme that biologists use to group all living systems into five large kingdoms.

a. How does that history illustrate this statement: Classification is not an end in itself, but is a means, or a tool, that biologists use to express their understanding about biological diversity?

   The history of these classification schemes reveals that scientists have proposed new schemes as new information about organisms has been uncovered. Often that new information has suggested that shifts needed to be made in the proposed relationship among different types of organisms. In a sense, one can think of classification schemes both as a representation of current understandings of these relationships and as a tool for helping scientists consider how consistent these relationships are with emerging data.

b. How does it illustrate this statement: Science is characterized by its openness to change and modification?

   The fact that scientists never say that a particular classification scheme is the final, correct representation of such relationships illustrates the open, iterative nature of science. Scientists may be content to say, for example, that a particular scheme is consistent with knowledge at a particular point in time, but they generally do not insist that their understanding cannot or will not be modified and refined by new findings.

c. What role does the discovery or development of new evidence play in the modification of scientific ideas?

   This question provides you with an opportunity to assess the students' understanding of two central benchmarks from the scientific inquiry standards (AAAS, 2001):

   "In science, the testing, revising, and occasional discarding of theories, new and old, never ends. This ongoing process leads to an increasingly better understanding of how things work in the world but not to absolute truth." And "From time to time, major shifts occur in the scientific view of how the world works. More often, however, the changes that take place in the body of scientific knowledge are small modifications of prior knowledge. Change and continuity are persistent features of science."

First Encounter with the Critter

Major Concepts Common properties of living systems; adaptation; evolutionary relatedness of all living systems

Overview

This activity, the first in a series of six (one per unit), offers students an ongoing opportunity for personal involvement and creativity. In this activity, students are challenged to describe a new organism that they discover in their work as part of a field team studying life-forms in a particular habitat. In subsequent activities, students will expand their initial descriptions to reflect their growing understanding of the unifying principles of biology.

Materials (per class of 30, individuals)

30 folders, each with 5 sheets of plain paper *do in journal
30 copies of the *First Encounter with the Critter* rubric
30 felt-tipped markers
5 copies each of 6 Copymaster *Habitat Cards* (see Preparations)
DVD
DVD player

Outcomes and Indicators of Success

The following indicators allow you to assess the students' level of success with the activity and to assess their process of learning.

By the end of this activity, the learners should be able to

1. apply their understanding of the unity and diversity of life to a previously undescribed life-form in a given habitat.

   They will demonstrate their ability by

   a. writing a description of the organism that explains how it is similar to all other forms of life, and

   b. drawing a detailed diagram of this organism and labeling its distinctive structures.

2. explain the relationship that exists among an organism's evolutionary history, its adaptations, and the environment in which it lives.

   They will demonstrate their ability by

   a. describing how the organism is adapted to the habitat in which it was discovered, and

   b. identifying the organism's closest relation(s) and describing the evidence on which these relationships were identified.

Preparations

Make five copies of each habitat card from Copymaster *Habitat Cards*. If possible, laminate the cards. Preview the *First Encounter with the Critter* rubric found on the *GACD*, and modify it if you wish to meet your own specifications.

Background

The power of this activity, and the others that follow in each unit of the program, is that it provides students with an open-ended project in which they have control of the task. There is no "right answer," so students do not have to outguess the teacher. The combination of a focusing goal and a great deal of freedom of expression should empower your learners to tackle this project with enthusiasm and interest.

The series of activities offers rich opportunities to assess the learners' understanding of the large concepts in biology through their ability to apply these concepts to the task of describing their novel organism. In this first activity, for example, the students' descriptions should reflect an underlying understanding of the unifying principles of biology, a recognition that organisms show specific adaptations to the environments in which they exist, and the understanding that all organisms are related through evolution. Throughout the rest of the course, learners will display their growing knowledge of biology by expanding and modifying their descriptions of these organisms in light of their further study of each principle. Figure T3.3 lists the activities in this series and identifies the unifying principle and the students' task that is associated with each.

Chapter	Activity	Unifying principle	Task
3	*First Encounter with the Critter*	Evolution: Patterns and Products of Change in Living Systems	Students describe a novel organism that they have discovered and provide it with adaptations that suit it to life in a specific habitat.
5	*Homeostasis in Your Critter*	Homeostasis: Maintaining Dynamic Equilibrium in Living Systems	Students describe how their organisms maintain homeostasis in light of specific environmental stress factors.
8	*Building Living Systems; Part B Energy and Matter for Your Critter*	Energy, Matter, and Organization: Relationships in Living Systems	Students describe how their organism uses matter and energy to maintain its organization.
10	*A Reproductive Strategy for Your Critter*	Continuity: Reproduction and Inheritance in Living Systems	Students describe how their organism reproduces and compare it with human reproduction.
13	*Evaluating Where We Stand*	Development: Growth and Differentiation in Living Systems.	Students create a description of a developmental pattern for their organism and draw its developmental stages.
15	*Critters and Interdependence*	Ecology: Interaction and Interdependence in Living Systems	Students write a story that describes interactions and interdependence between their organism and those of other students with the same habitat. They also consider adaptations that might evoke ecological changes that might occur and how humans from different cultures might interact with the organisms in this habitat.

Figure T3.3
Activities that involve your critter

A challenge in this first activity and throughout the study of evolution is to help students avoid thinking and speaking in a teleological manner. (*Teleology* is the use of purpose or design to explain how things are or how they evolve.) It is difficult for the learner to make the subtle distinction between (1) a randomly arising characteristic that comes to predominate through the pressures of natural selection (the evolutionary process), and (2) the development of a characteristic toward a planned goal (a teleological view). Nevertheless, this distinction is critical if we are to help students internalize their understanding of the process of evolution. Because we often examine the products of evolution in hindsight, it may *appear* that "birds got wings so they could fly" (implying that they "wanted" to fly), but it is essential to an understanding of evolution that students see the error in this statement. They need to see that wings *enable* birds to fly, and that this new access to the air offered some advantages in protection and hunting. Thus, most (but not all) birds fly.

This activity has been designed with these considerations in mind. Notice that the activity emphasizes the importance of adaptation to a particular habitat. Although students may freely exercise their imaginations to describe organisms that no one has ever seen, the learners must correlate the organisms to their habitats. Furthermore, the learners must recognize that all living things, including their "discoveries," no matter how outlandish they may be, are related. This point is highlighted as the students are challenged to offer plausible suggestions for how their inventions may have arisen from existing life-forms. At the end of the course, the students who "discovered" organisms in each specific habitat will form a team charged with the task of combining all of their organisms into this habitat, explaining the ways in which these organisms interact and evaluating the resulting community's relative potential for survival.

post colored cut out of all critters.

Strategies for Guiding Learners

PROCESS AND PROCEDURES

As a class, read orally or silently all the introductory materials for the activity and the Process and Procedures to help students build connections between concepts and activities. Use the time spent reading to bring the students' attention into focus.

1. Study the habitat card that describes where you are going. Mount the card on a page in your folder as a permanent record of the environment in which you will work for the next few weeks.

   Use the habitat cards provided or develop your own descriptions of the habitats to be explored. As you hand out the cards to students, try to distribute each habitat evenly throughout the room. This technique will avoid having clusters of students working on organisms adapted to the same habitat and may help stimulate independent thinking. Make sure that you have enough students receiving each habitat so that there will be a sufficient number of different organisms in that environment in the final stage of the project (Unit 6).

   The first six ecosystems in the DVD segment "Ecosystems of the Earth" correspond to the habitat cards. Use them to supplement the cards and to set the scene for the learners. The segment includes 10 other ecosystems that could provide alternative habitats, as well as information about climatic and other limiting factors for each ecosystem. See the interactive DVD guide in the *TRCD* for narration text.

2. Describe your organism by drawing 1 or more diagrams of it. Include labels with brief descriptions of its distinctive structures.

Invent an organism, or critter. Use your imagination. The organism that you discover may resemble others found in this habitat or another habitat. Or you might create something quite different from any real species.

Remember, your critter invention is the evidence that your teacher will use to evaluate what you have learned about evolution, biological diversity, and the unity of life.

Make it clear to the students that this project will continue throughout the course. We suggest that you handle the project as a folder that remains in the classroom, available for students to consult and to make changes and additions as appropriate. It is important that the students keep this work separate from their journals and that they understand that it is an ongoing project that will take clearer shape as they move through the course.

Give students some freedom and time to think of an organism, but be sensitive to the student who feels daunted or frustrated by the blank page. In such a case, ask the student specific questions such as: What size is the organism that you discovered? What colors or patterns does your organism have? Where does your organism spend most of its time? and Why is this environment a good place for your organism to be?

3. Write a paragraph about the adaptations you labeled on your critter drawing. Select 1 adaptation as an example to explain your understanding of how adaptations arise in a population and how they can lead to new species.

Emphasize to students that an evaluate activity is the equivalent of a traditional test, so their examples and explanations need to reflect the knowledge and experience gained throughout the last unit.

4. Write a 2nd paragraph that explains what kingdom you would assign your critter to and why. Include an explanation for your critter's placement in a kingdom based on its common ancestry with other organisms in the same kingdom. Explain how your critter's species originated.

When you describe the most closely related organisms to your critter, your explanation for the relatedness must provide evidence that you understand how new species evolve.

Ask students to classify their organisms according to the traditional five-kingdom classification system and/or to describe which of these large taxonomic groups their organisms are most closely related to and why.

5. Obtain a rubric from your teacher that explains the grading criteria for your critter. Read the rubric carefully. Use it as a checklist to be certain that you describe your newly discovered critter effectively.

You will know that you have generated a good description if it meets the following criteria:

◆ It describes how your organism resembles all known forms of life.

◆ It describes how your organism is adapted to the habitat in which you found it.

◆ It identifies the known species to which your new organism is most closely related, and it describes the evidence on which you base your answer.

Encourage students to use their imaginations when thinking about these organisms, but be certain that they understand that their goal always is to see and to illustrate in their organism the biological concepts under study. For example, the way in which their organisms display the common properties of life, specific adaptations in relation to habitat, and evolutionary history are more important than the specific characteristics that the organism may possess.

6. One of the most exciting privileges granted to the individual who discovers a new form of life is the honor of naming it. Complete your initial description of this new species by giving it both a common name and a scientific name. (Remember, the scientific name must indicate the organism's relatedness to other organisms.) Add an appropriate caption to each diagram that you have drawn, and record the organism's names in your folder.

Refer to the essay *Organizing Diversity* on page 141 for information about how scientists name new species.

Analysis

The analysis focuses students on the difference between a scientific and a teleological view of evolution.

Which of the following two statements is most consistent with scientists' understanding of the process of evolution, and why? What is wrong with the other statement? Record your response in your folder.

Statement 1: The habitat that I worked in is very wet and salty. The organism that I discovered evolved a rubberlike skin to keep from shriveling up.

Statement 2: The habitat that I worked in is very wet and salty. The organism that I discovered has a rubberlike skin that may have evolved because it offered protection from the harmful effects of all that salt.

Statement 2 is most consistent with a proper understanding of evolution because it recognizes the possible selective advantage of a rubberlike skin without suggesting that the organism evolved such a surface to protect itself from salt damage. Statement 1 is teleological; it improperly suggests a purposefulness (a deliberate movement toward an identified goal) to the evolution of a rubberlike skin in this organism.

Extensions

For an in-depth study of the plant kingdom, including the evolution and adaptations of plants, see Appendix C of the student text or Section 7: Supplementary Materials, Appendix 2, *Eukaryotes: Plants* on the *TRCD*.

Unit Goals

By the end of this unit, the learners should

◆ understand that all organisms have an internal and external environment and are affected by interactions between these environments;

◆ understand that organisms must actively maintain a balance in their internal environment;

◆ understand that the interactions of systems that adjust the internal environment result in a dynamic balance called homeostasis;

◆ recognize that stresses may overwhelm the ability of organisms to maintain their internal environment;

◆ understand that individual and collective behavior may influence an individual's ability to maintain homeostasis; and

◆ continue to collect, analyze, and graph data; make and test predictions; construct and use models; and conduct ethical analyses.

Prior Conceptions

Most of the students' prior knowledge of the concept of homeostasis likely will be in the context of disease in which balance is disrupted. According to the research into the *Benchmarks*, upper elementary students may believe that germs cause all illnesses (AAAS, 2001). However, research also shows that as students grow older, their understanding and beliefs should grow to include the ideas that illness can be caused by malfunctioning internal organs and systems, poor health habits, and genetics (AAAS, 2001). These concepts are integrated extensively in Chapter 6, *Human Homeostasis: Health and Disease.* The challenge to students throughout Unit 2 is to understand the complexity of coordination and interactions involved in maintaining homeostasis from the cellular to the organismal level.

Advance Preparation for the Unit

Before you begin Unit 2, create new cooperative teams of four students. The students now should be comfortable in a group setting and be ready to practice their working-relationship skills with another group of students. During this unit, the students may work in teams of various sizes, but their core team should consist of four learners.

You may want to review the DVD segments and the activities that involve probe ware systems in the unit before you have the students do them in class. As you begin each chapter, look ahead to the specific strategies for each activity that uses probe ware.

Unit Extension

Because this unit focuses on human examples of homeostasis, you may want to add information on plants that is found in Appendix C in the student text and on the *TRCD*, Section 7: Supplementary Materials, Appendix 1, *Prokaryotes and Viruses* and Appendix 2, *Eukaryotes: Plants.*

[handwritten margin note: Next year— add stimate lab]

The Internal Environment of Organisms

Chapter 4 examines homeostasis and its importance as a unifying principle of biology. This first chapter in Unit 2 addresses the necessity of maintaining internal balance as a condition for life. The circulatory and urinary systems are the primary vehicles for introducing the concepts of regulation and feedback and the role these concepts play in homeostasis. (Chapter 5 presents detailed explanations of how internal conditions are maintained despite varying external conditions, and Chapter 6 presents disruptions of homeostasis.)

Students become engaged in this chapter by reading a story about a young man who creates an imbalance between the internal conditions of his body and the external environment. The students then explore the effect of cell boundaries in separating an internal cellular environment from an external environment. They do this by designing a controlled experiment using shell-less eggs. In the next activity, the learners use a model of a cell to help develop an explanation for how cells maintain an internal environment that differs from their external environment (for example, the selective permeability of biological membranes). Later in the chapter, the learners apply their understanding of compartments, membranes, and internal balance to the circulatory and urinary systems. Finally, the learners evaluate their understanding of the chapter's concepts by revisiting the opening story and analyzing the factors that led to the young man's dehydration.

ACTIVITIES

Engage	Can You Stand the Heat?
Explore	Cells in Action
Explain	A Cell Model
Explain **Elaborate**	Regulating the Internal Environment
Evaluate	Can You Stand the Heat—Again?

Instructional Flow | **Classroom Support**

Activity/ Student Text pp. Teacher Guide pp	GACD, TRCD, DVD, and CD-ROM Resources	Essays/ Student Text pp.	Estimated Time	Team Size/ Cooperative Learning Focus	Strategies and Tools	Assessment Opportunities	Special Considerations
ENGAGE *Can You Stand the Heat?* pp. 150–151 TG pp. 150–153			40 minutes	*Team size:* 2 *Skill:* Working with new team member	Team and class discussions	Prior knowledge of concepts: maintaining balance in the human body	Enlarge print materials and/or read aloud if needed.
EXPLORE *Cells in Action* pp. 150–160 TG pp. 153–161	DVD: *Blood Cells in Solution*	*Compartments* pp. 218–220	100–150 minutes	*Team size:* 4 and 2 *Skill:* Taking responsibility	Wet lab; DVD; journal entries	Misconceptions and current understanding of cells and membranes; using controls and variables	Prepare an appropriate number of solutions to choose from for Process and Procedures step 2 based on your students' prior experiences.
EXPLAIN *A Cell Model* pp. 161–163 TG pp. 161–167		*Membranes* pp. 220–221 *Molecular Movement* pp. 222–224	100–130 minutes	*Team size:* 2 *Skill:* Dealing with specific problems	Demonstration; wet lab; modeling lab report	Current understanding about using controls and variables; using data and models to construct explanations	Plan ahead for students who have difficulty with fine motor control or vision. Pair them with partners who can assist in building the cell models and preparing the wet-mount slides.
EXPLAIN/ ELABORATE *Regulating the Internal Environment* pp. 164–166 TG pp. 167–170	DVD: *The Circulatory System; Regulation in the Urinary System*	*Making Exchanges throughout the Body* pp. 224–226 *Disposing of Wastes* pp. 227–229	50–80 minutes	*Team size:* individuals, 2, 4	DVD; illustrations; discussion	Making connections between related ideas; applying understandings to new situations	Plan to include discussion time to describe the DVD segments while watching them. This will help students with visual or auditory challenges, as well as clarify content for all learners. Make simple outline drawings of the heart available for students who have difficulty taking notes. They can write on the outline while watching the video segments. Choose partners who will work well with students who may need help drawing the posters.

Instructional Flow

Classroom Support

Activity/ Student Text pp. Teacher Guide pp	GACD, TRCD, DVD, and CD-ROM Resources	Essays/ Student Text pp.	Estimated Time	Team Size/ Cooperative Learning Focus	Strategies and Tools	Assessment Opportunities	Special Considerations
EVALUATE Can You Stand the Heat—Again? pp. 166–169 TG pp. 170–173	Rubric: Can You Stand the Heat—Again?		30–40 minutes	Team size: individuals	Journal entries	Using data to construct explanations; synthesizing ideas	Enlarge print materials and/or read aloud if needed.

Chapter Goals

By the end of this chapter, students should

◆ understand the distinction between internal and external environments and the importance of boundaries in maintaining that distinction;

◆ understand that living organisms have different levels of compartmentalization;

◆ understand that the external environment can cause changes in the internal environment of living things;

◆ understand that living systems have mechanisms for restoring normal internal conditions;

◆ understand that systems within living organisms interact to adjust internal conditions; and

◆ recognize the role that the circulatory system and the urinary system play in maintaining balance.

The learners also will

◆ design a controlled experiment,

◆ collect and organize data using instrumentation, and

◆ develop a more complete understanding about how to conduct scientific inquiry.

Advance Preparation

Review Materials and Preparations, especially for the activities *Cells in Action* and *A Cell Model*. Both activities require substantial time to gather materials and to set up. You also will need a DVD player.

Engage

Can You Stand the Heat?

Major Concepts Conditions in the body can change in response to external conditions; various factors can affect internal conditions, including the individual's behavior

Overview

This activity engages the students in the reactions of a living system to specific stimuli from the environment. The students read a story about Josh, a recent college graduate, who comes home to help his parents clear some land that they recently purchased. His zeal turns into a case of dehydration. The students then participate in a discussion and try to suggest what is wrong with Josh. Through this reading and discussion, students become aware that living systems respond to specific environmental stimuli by regulating internal conditions. The activity focuses on the broad concept that living systems maintain balanced conditions; students will explore the specific mechanisms involved in balance later in this chapter.

Outcomes and Indicators of Success

The following indicators allow you to assess the students' level of success with the activity and to assess their process of learning.

By the end of this activity, the learners should

1. be aware that internal body conditions respond to external stimuli.

   They will demonstrate their awareness by discussing how Josh's body responded to specific external stresses.

2. realize that individual behavior can affect internal conditions.

   They will demonstrate this realization by describing how Josh's conscious behavior affected the way his body responded to the stresses.

Background

Energy drinks that contain caffeine can have a significant diuretic effect—that is, they can result in a person losing more fluid than he or she took in. In the scenario presented in this activity, such drinks easily exaggerated Josh's dehydration. For more information about diuretics, you might want to refer to the need to know box titled Additional Information in the activity *Can You Stand the Heat—Again?* in the student book. In addition, the September 1998 issue of the *American Family Physician* has an informative article on heat-related illnesses. You can access this article on-line at http://www.aafp.org/afp/980901ap/barrow.html.

Strategies for Guiding Learners

PROCESS AND PROCEDURES

As a class, read orally or silently all introductory materials for the activity and the Process and Procedures to help students build connections between concepts and activities. Use the time spent reading to bring the students' attention into focus.

1. Read the story *A Pause That Refreshes?* to yourself (page 151).

   Ask the learners to read the story *A Pause That Refreshes?* Expect that they will be able to relate to the scenario at some level.

2. After reading the scenario, work with your partner to develop an explanation for Josh's condition.

   Consider the evidence you have and what inferences you can make about how Josh's body responded to external stresses.

   Encourage the students to generalize about Josh's situation and how all living systems react in ways that alter internal conditions. For instance, you might ask, "What does a dog do when it is very hot? Does this help cool the dog?" As the learners begin their team discussions, visit each team and monitor their responses, prompting them as necessary.

   Josh's body obviously was under stress from the heat, lack of fluids, and the physical exertion of the work. As evidence of this, his body responded first by perspiration, dry mouth, and thirst. From these observations, one can infer that his body was becoming dehydrated. The additional symptoms exhibited later, such as the dizziness, nausea, vision changes, and headache, indicated the severity of Josh's condition.

Analysis

1. As a class, develop answers to the following questions:

   a. What stresses from the external environment was Josh's body (internal environment) having to balance?

   Josh was coping with hot, dry external conditions.

   b. How did the choices that Josh made affect the stresses placed on his body?

   Josh's determination to finish the job before his parents returned led him to ignore some of the signals his body gave. Also, he had not brought along enough fluids to drink. Perhaps he did not anticipate the effect that the hot, humid weather would have on him having just come from a northern climate. When he finally returned to the house to get something to drink, he drank three energy drinks. His decision did not take into consideration the additional stress that the drinks' caffeine, a diuretic, would place on his body. When he tried to resume his work, he had not effectively rehydrated his body.

   c. What symptoms did Maggie show that were evidence that her body (her internal environment) was under stress from the conditions outdoors (her external environment)?

   Maggie tried to find a spot of shade, and she lay on the ground panting. When they returned to the house, she rushed in to get a drink of water.

2. Work with your partner in a brainstorming session to develop a list of four terms and concepts that relate to homeostasis.

   Use this question as an opportunity to learn what your students' preconceptions are about homeostasis. Expect that they may list things like maintaining balance, equilibrium, and internal or external conditions. However, guide the discussion to probe for better signs of the students' understanding rather than stopping with the term from the brief summary of homeostasis that occurs in the book. If students have difficulty thinking of four terms or concepts, prompt them to think about times when the body's balance is disrupted; this may help them think of ideas related to maintaining balance. Listen for students to list conditions that must be kept in balance to stay healthy; some students may think of the need for water balance and may or may not have an idea *why* that is important.

3. Contribute your list to a class concept map that shows what you currently understand about homeostasis.

   Use the students' lists from step 2 to create a simple map with homeostasis as the central concept. Concept maps are a tremendous tool for guiding learners and assessing understanding. Current research on how people learn shows that students learn best when they see how the concepts they are learning fit into the bigger picture and into their lives. Concept maps can help to make that more clear to students. For more information about how to develop concept maps and use them in your classes, there are a number of good Internet sites. The Institute for Human and Machine Cognition at the University of West Florida has a Web site with good background information on concept mapping and free concept mapping software (for educational nonprofit use). You can access this site at http://cmap.ihmc.us/.

You might bring closure to the activity by asking the students to describe instances in which they may have experienced similar extremes in reaction to environmental stresses. Chances are that some students may have had heat-induced illness, dehydration, or altitude sickness. Many students will be eager to talk about their experiences. Gradually, change the focus of this discussion from the extreme to the common by drawing parallels between how the body feels and responds to unusual activities and how it feels and responds to everyday activities. For example, students with a late lunch period will be very familiar with the hunger pangs associated with waiting too long before eating. Similarly, all students have shivered at one time or another, but they may never have considered that shivering is the body's way of responding to cold. Other examples are pain and fatigue.

Cells in Action

Explore

Major Concepts   Containers and boundaries; internal and external environments

Overview

In this activity, the learners explore the role that cell boundaries play in separating the external environment from the internal cellular environment. They do this by designing a controlled experiment in which shell-less eggs are placed in different solutions. The students further explore these concepts by observing a DVD segment that shows the behavior of red blood cells in hypertonic, hypotonic, and isotonic solutions and by examining the effects of salt solutions on onion cells.

Materials   (per class of 30)

PART A   (teams of 4)

30 pairs of safety goggles
30 lab aprons
30 pairs of gloves
8 1-L beakers, or large
   (8 $\frac{1}{4}$-in diameter) glass specimen
   dishes with the base inset for stacking
24 500-mL beakers or jars
8 balances
plastic wrap
coffee filters

8 slotted spoons
paper towels
2.4 L of corn syrup solution
2.4 L of distilled water
4–5 L of distilled vinegar
24 shell-less eggs, 3 per beaker of
   vinegar (see Preparations)
raw egg with shell intact
clear overhead transparency (optional)

PART B   (teams of 2)

30 pairs of safety goggles
15 dropping pipets
15 microscope slides and coverslips
15 compound microscopes
15 forceps
15 scalpels

15 dissecting needles with corks on the tips
paper towels
8 dropping bottles of 5% salt solution
1–2 onions, cut into wedges
DVD
DVD player

Outcomes and Indicators of Success

The following indicators allow you to assess the students' level of success with the activity and to assess their process of learning.

By the end of this activity, the learners should be aware

1. of the relationships among internal environments, external environments, and boundaries.

   They will demonstrate their awareness by

   a. describing their observations of animal cells and plant cells that are placed in different environments, and

   b. suggesting explanations to account for their observations.

2. that the external environment can cause changes in the internal environment of living systems.

   They will demonstrate their awareness by describing how the eggs, animal cells, and plant cells responded to their different and unusual environments.

Safety

Safety Goggles   **Lab Apron**

Remind the students to put on their safety goggles, gloves, and lab aprons and to use the slotted spoons when handling the eggs. Students also should wash their hands with soap and water after the activity in case they had contact with any raw egg. Plan how you will have students dispose of their eggs after the experiment to minimize the chance of contact with raw egg. A liter beaker lined with a large, freezer-quality, zip-type bag into which students can pour their eggs after the experiment or during the setup (if one breaks) works well.

Preparations

PART A. At least 3 days before this activity, prepare 24 shell-less eggs. (You may want to prepare extras in case some break during setup or after soaking in vinegar.) In each 1-L beaker or large specimen dish, place three or four raw eggs that are still in their shells. Examine each carefully, and reject any that have cracked shells. Fill each beaker with vinegar, and cover the beaker with a piece of plastic wrap. Punch a few holes in the cover. If you use the specimen dishes, you can stack them four or five dishes high and cover only the top dish with plastic wrap. Leave the eggs in the vinegar for about 48 hours. At the beginning of the third day, pour off the used vinegar and replace with fresh vinegar. Allow the eggs to soak for another 24 hours or until their shells have dissolved. If you replace the vinegar after 24 hours, this process may take only 2 days. (Shell-less eggs should appear almost transparent, with no areas of opaque white remaining.) You can leave this setup at room temperature. The acid in the vinegar will dissolve the calcium carbonate in the shells; the reaction will release bubbles of carbon dioxide. If time permits, you can involve students in preparing the eggs. Dissolving the shells is a very interesting process, and having students take on some of the responsibility may be both a valuable experience for them and helpful to you.

Prepare the corn syrup solution by diluting corn syrup 1:1 with distilled water.

PART B. Prepare the salt solution by dissolving 5 g of NaCl in about 25 mL of warm distilled water. Then add enough distilled water to bring the volume to 100 mL. Dispense in dropping bottles labeled *5% NaCl.*

Strategies for Guiding Learners

PROCESS AND PROCEDURES

PART A An Eggs-periment

As a class, read orally or silently all introductory materials for the activity and the Process and Procedures to help students build connections between concepts and activities. Use the time spent reading to bring the students' attention into focus.

1. Start a new journal entry for your eggs-periment. Begin by working with your partner to describe the internal environment of an egg. How is it different from the external environment?

   To engage the learners in the activity, hold up a raw egg and ask, "Where's the inside of this egg? Where's the outside?" Let the students call out answers to you. Then show the shell-less eggs and explain that you soaked them in vinegar to dissolve the shells. Guide the students to realize that now only thin membranes hold the contents of the eggs together. Make it clear that the egg is a single large cell that has an unusual distribution of contents in the white and yolk. (The nucleus is microscopic and is not the same thing as the yolk.)

2. Write 3 questions about what might happen if you place the shell-less chicken egg in a different external environment. One way to change the egg's external environment is to place it in a beaker containing a solution.

   Your teacher will provide distilled water and corn syrup as solutions.

   Students should record their questions in their journals. This step is important to actively involve students and their curiosities in the investigation.

3. Choose the most interesting question that you wrote for your eggs-periment.

   Guide students to select a testable question from the three written in step 2 for which they are unsure of the answer. Model and encourage curiosity.

4. Work with your partner to develop a list of at least 3 results that you expect to observe. You will use these results to indicate whether the internal environment of the egg has changed after you conduct your experiment. Next to each result, record whether it will be a *quantitative* or *qualitative* observation.

   Quantitative observations involve results that can be measured with standard scales (mass in grams, or temperature in degrees Celsius, for example). Think of *quantity*—something that you measure—as part of quantitative.

   Qualitative observations involve verbal descriptions and results that can be measured with nonstandard scales (color, or temperature described as "warm" or "cold," for example). Think of *quality*—the nature of something that you observe—as part of qualitative.

   Students should record their ideas in their journals. Expect them to list observations such as the following:

   Qualitative: overall egg size, egg contents' appearance (color, texture, viscosity, etc.), appearance of the external environment substance (color, texture, viscosity, etc.)

Quantitative: mass, volume of the egg contents, circumference of the egg, chemistry of the egg contents (students will not have the equipment to test this)

 Circulate among the students as they are recording their ideas to check for understanding. Assist any teams who have difficulty thinking of quantitative observations by asking questions such as, How might you measure to see if some soda pop leaked out of its can? or How might you measure if someone ate some cereal from a box? Guide all groups to recognize that mass should be one of the quantitative observations used.

5. Read the eggs-periment protocol. Use it as a guide for designing a controlled experiment to gather information that answers your question.

   A controlled experiment is one in which you control all variables except one. See the need to know box on controlled experiments for more information.

   Your experiment should include a control and a record of the results. Review the available materials and safety guidelines before you plan your experiment.

   After the learners have read the background information, convene a brief class discussion to clarify the concepts of controls and variables and their importance in experiments. Guide students to decide on a control for their experiment. Typically, an egg left in an empty beaker covered with plastic wrap is used as a control. However, your students may have other ideas, such as wrapping the control egg in plastic wrap or submersing it in a beaten egg. Help students choose a reasonable procedure for setting up their control.

6. Predict how you think the eggs will react to the condition that you will vary in your experiment. Create a table in your journal similar to the one in Figure 4.2 to record your predictions.

   For students to invest themselves fully in their investigations, it is important for them to commit to a prediction by recording the idea in writing.

7. Have your teacher approve your design. Then conduct your experiment.

   Remember to record your experimental design and results in your journal.

   To track quantitative changes in their eggs, students should realize that they need to record initial masses of their eggs. If some learners overlook this, ask questions that help them realize why the egg mass is important, and then have them work in teams of four to determine the mass of their eggs. Remind them to rinse the vinegar-soaked eggs thoroughly. Coffee filters make handling the eggs more manageable. As the learners place the eggs in the solutions, check that they are using the techniques appropriate for your scales and that they have recorded the initial mass of each of the eggs. It is especially important that the eggs be dried carefully and thoroughly. The eggs must be left in solution for at least 30 minutes to get significant results. If they remain in solution for more than 4 hours, however, the initial results begin to slowly reverse as the eggs and solutions tend toward equilibrium. While the learners are waiting for the eggs to react to their external environments, you might have them move on to Part B and come back to the eggs later. This activity works best if the students have about 100 minutes of uninterrupted lab time or can return later in the day to measure the mass of the eggs that have been in the solutions. However, students will be able to collect meaningful data if the eggs must soak overnight, until the next class period.

8. When your experiment is complete, enter your results in the class data table.

Report your actual results; resist the temptation to change your results if they do not match your classmates' data.

On the chalkboard or a transparency, prepare a large data table in which all teams can enter their data. Convene a brief discussion about the results once they have all been reported. Facilitate the discussion to help those teams with contrary results consider the cause of their anomaly.

9. Discuss the following questions with your partner, and record your answers in your journal:

a. Why is it useful to combine data from the entire class?

A large sample size usually provides more accurate data. If the class data vary greatly, determine the average change in mass for each condition to help the learners see patterns.

b. What changes did you find, if any, in the internal environments of your eggs? Explain your answer by using specific evidence from your observations.

Ask the learners to think about how the eggs responded to changes in their external environment. They should use their observations, including change in mass of the eggs, to support their explanation.

c. How would you explain any differences that you noticed in the behavior of the 3 eggs under different external conditions?

The learners should infer that the decrease in mass of the eggs in corn syrup solution was due to fluid loss. The eggs in distilled water must have gained fluid because their mass increased. Other observations should support those inferences as well.

In two trials, we obtained the following data:

Condition	Original mass (g)		Mass after 1 hr. (g)		Mass after 4 hrs. (g)	
Trial #	1	2	1	2	1	2
Control	90.2	92.0	89.9	91.5	89.2	90.4
Corn syrup solution	96.3	102.3	81.2	85.9	69.7	72.9
Distilled water	94.3	103.0	98.3	106.9	97.7	106.1

Figure T4.1 Examples of egg mass changes

If students gather data contrary to the expected results, their answers should explain the possible cause of those results and show an understanding of why they were unexpected (in light of the data collected by the class).

d. What controls did you use in your experimental design? Why?

An empty, closed container with an egg provided the control, unless your class chose an alternate setup. A control is the group or subject that remains unchanged. In this case, the effects of the corn syrup solution and the distilled water on the shell-less eggs were the variables being tested if the protocol was used unchanged.

PART B Observing Cell Activity

1. View the DVD segment "Blood Cells in Solution," which illustrates the behavior of animal cells in different solutions. Before you watch this segment, create 3 columns in your journal. Label them *isotonic*, *hypertonic*, and *hypotonic*. Use these columns to record your observations about changes in the cells.

Ask the learners to read the introductory information about various types of solutions that scientists use. Check to be sure that the learners understand the difference between solutes and solvents. The video segment "Blood Cells in Solution" on the DVD demonstrates the response of red blood cells in isotonic, hypertonic, and hypotonic solutions. We provide this segment to avoid the safety concerns of using human blood in the classroom. The DVD guide on the *TRCD* provides you with explanations. Ask the students to record their observations in their journals.

2. To observe the responses of plant cells, prepare a wet mount of onion skin by following these steps:

   a. Remove 1 layer from your onion wedge.

   b. Snap the layer backward, as shown in Figure 4.5.

   This should expose the edges of several smaller layers.

   c. Use forceps to separate a piece of the transparent, tissue-thin layer from the outside of the original layer.

   d. Lay the piece flat on a clean microscope slide.

   e. As necessary, use the scalpel to trim the piece so that it will fit under a coverslip.

   f. Use the dissecting needle to smooth out any bubbles or wrinkles.

Caution

CAUTION: Scalpel blades and needles are sharp; handle with care. Replace cork on needle tip after use.

   g. Use the dropping pipet to add 1 or 2 drops of water to the slide. Then place a coverslip over the piece of onion skin.

   Have the learners work in teams of two to make wet mounts of onion skin. Monitor their techniques and offer advice when necessary or refer them to *Technique 4 The Compound Microscope*, in the student book appendix for background information about using microscopes and preparing a wet mount with a slide and coverslip. Remind the learners to use small pieces of only the thinnest outer layer of onion; they should discard the onion wedge after removing the piece they are to observe.

   Students may need help interpreting what they see. Identify structures in the cells as necessary to help the learners understand. If you have the equipment to project the image from a microscope, convene a brief discussion after students have completed the procedure, and prepare your own wet mount to point out structures for all to see.

3. Examine the onion skin under the low power of your microscope.

   Take turns observing the cells.

4. Switch to high power, and focus sharply on a few cells. Make a sketch of the cells in your journal. Then place a small piece of paper towel at 1 edge of the coverslip (see Figure 4.6).

5. Test the effects of changing the external environment of the cells you are viewing. To do this, place several drops of 5% salt solution against the edge of the coverslip opposite from the paper towel. Observe what happens, and record it in your journal.

   Take turns observing the cells. Compare your onion cells to the generalized plant cell illustrated in Figure 4.7.

6. Add more salt solution, if necessary, until you see changes in the cells. Record your observations in your journal by sketching the cells both before and after adding the salt solution.

   Be sure to record how much salt solution you added.

7. Dilute the salt solution on the slide by adding distilled water. Continue to add water until the cells return to their original condition. Make observations while you do this, and record them in your journal.

   To add water, use the same technique that you used to add the salt solution. Remember to record how much water you added.

   As the learners examine the onion cells, remind them to make careful observations and to record these in their journals. Use this opportunity to reinforce the value in recording observations with drawings. Also, check that the partners are switching places so that each student has an opportunity to observe the onion cells under the microscope.

   As the pairs observe the onion cells, make sure that they connect their observations to the events in Part A. If they are having difficulty making connections, use leading questions such as, What similarities do you see between the behavior of the onion cells and your eggs? If you were able to project a microscope image in step 2, you may wish to conclude the activity by demonstrating the events that students were observing while you facilitate a brief discussion about how the onion cell behavior relates to the eggs.

Analysis

When the students have completed Part B, ask them to analyze the concepts of internal environments, external environments, and boundaries by completing the Analysis. As they discuss the questions with their partner, circulate from pair to pair and listen as the students formulate ideas about how cells behave. When the students have completed the Analysis, collect their journals so that you can assess their responses. Possible responses to the questions include the following:

1. What evidence did you collect that indicates that the external environment affects the internal environment?

   The egg in corn syrup solution decreased in mass, whereas the egg in distilled water increased in mass. When the salt solution was added to the onion cell, its contents shrank away from the cell wall. Application of water restored the original condition.

2. In this activity, how did the egg serve as a model of how cells function as containers in living organisms?

The egg is a single, unusually large cell. Special treatment was required to dissolve the shell, but the tough membrane acted like a cell membrane in that it allowed water, but not corn syrup, to pass through it freely.

3. What do eggs, animal cells, plant cells, and the human body have in common?

Each is a container that has a boundary that separates the internal and external environments and allows the two environments to differ.

4. Based on your observations of cells, what might have been happening in Josh's body in the story *A Pause That Refreshes?* when he

a. first became hot and started to sweat

Sweating is a mechanism that removes heat from the body through evaporative cooling; in the process, fluids are lost.

b. became thirsty

As water was lost from Josh's cells and body fluids by sweating, several body systems interacted to produce the sensation of thirst to remind him that he needed to replace the lost water.

c. went to the house for refreshments

Josh's decision to seek refreshments to replace the lost body fluids was a good one, but he used poor judgment in drinking a caffeine-containing beverage, a diuretic, which only aggravated his dehydration.

d. returned to work?

Under the stress of dehydration, his decision to return to work without drinking more water resulted in additional stress, and more symptoms appeared.

Further Challenges

Caution

If time allows, encourage students to study cell structure firsthand by examining onion cells (and others that you have available) more carefully and sketching them. Provide Lugol's iodine solution in dropping bottles labeled *Warning: Poison if ingested/Strong irritant.* Staining with Lugol's solution will help visualize the location of starch storage in the cells.

Possible observations might include the following:

◆ There are compartments or cells of roughly equal size.

◆ Compartments contain a faint inner compartment, roughly located in the center of the cell.

◆ There are no colors in the cell.

◆ Compartments are packed tightly together.

◆ The boundaries are very symmetrical and even.

◆ The insides of the compartments are grainy.

◆ The Lugol's solution stains smaller compartments within the cells.

◆ There usually is only one stained compartment inside each cell.

Ask the learners to label all compartments and boundaries on their sketches. Explain that compartments should include cells, nuclei, and vacuoles. Boundaries should include the cell walls around the onion cells and the membranes and the vacuoles. Make histology texts available as additional reference material. Although students likely did not observe the membranes directly, they could have inferred their existence from the iodine stain and from damaged onion cells whose membranes have drawn back from the cell walls.

Encourage the learners to relate these observations to their work in Part B. They should recognize that iodine molecules must have moved through the boundaries of the cells; this phenomenon is similar to what the learners will observe in the next activity, which uses a dialysis tubing model (depending on how they design their system). Students also might explain that areas of blue indicate that there are starch particles present in the cells. The Lugol's iodine should make the nucleus more obvious, although some students might observe this compartment even without the stain. Explain to the students that the two nucleoli are not true compartments but simply areas of material that are denser than the rest of the nucleus.

A Cell Model

Major Concepts Characteristics of cell membranes; molecular movement; selective permeability of biological membranes; modeling compartments and boundaries

Overview

In this activity, the learners use a cell model to help develop an explanation for the selective permeability of biological membranes, a property of cells that is critical to their function. The learners model a cell using dialysis tubing, two solutions, and appropriate indicators. With background information about the materials and the essay *Membranes* as resources, learners develop testable questions and then design a simple experiment to test one of their questions.

Materials   (per class of 30, teams of 2)

For the optional demonstration:
petri dish halves
flat toothpicks
lipid solvent (vegetable oil, motor oil)
aqueous solvent (water, apple juice)
food coloring
solutes (salt, sugar)
overhead projector
clear overhead transparency

For the student experiments:

Exact materials will depend on the experimental models that the students design but should include at least the following:

30 pairs of safety goggles
30 lab aprons
32 250-mL beakers
16 glass-marking pencils
48 20-cm pieces of dialysis tubing
96 10-cm pieces of string
300 mL of soluble starch suspension
300 mL of concentrated glucose solution
16 dropping bottles of Lugol's iodine solution labeled *Warning:*
    Poison if ingested/Strong irritant
32 glucose test strips
distilled water

Outcomes and Indicators of Success

The following indicators allow you to assess the students' level of success with the activity and to assess their process of learning.

By the end of this activity, the learners should understand that selectively permeable membranes allow only certain particles to pass into and out of cells.

They will demonstrate their understanding by

a. designing an experiment to answer questions about how membranes affect the internal environment of a cell,

b. designing and building a model of a cell from dialysis tubing and comparing their model to a cell, and

c. citing evidence that molecules passed into or out of the models.

Safety

Safety Goggles   Lab Apron

Remind the students to wash their hands at the end of each period and to observe the safety precautions about Lugol's iodine solution. Remind the students to wear their safety goggles and lab aprons.

Preparations

For the student experiments, purchase ready-made Lugol's iodine solution, glucose test strips, and a 10-ft roll of 15.9-mm dialysis tubing. Cut the required number of pieces of dialysis tubing, each 20 cm long, soak in tap water for 1–2 minutes, and then separate the sides of each piece by rubbing the cut ends between the thumb and the forefinger. Leave the pieces in water until the students are ready to use them.

Prepare the starch suspension and the glucose solution as follows:

10% Starch Suspension

Dissolve 15 g of starch in enough distilled water to make 150 mL of suspension. Heat to promote the starch to go into suspension. (Or use liquid laundry starch; consider it to be 100% starch. To make a 10% suspension, add 10 mL of starch to 90 mL of distilled water.)

Concentrated Glucose Solution

Dissolve 100 g of glucose in 150 mL of distilled water.

If you decide to do the optional demonstration described in step 3 below, you will need to mix a drop or two of food coloring with the aqueous solvent and assemble the other materials.

Strategies for Guiding Learners

PROCESS AND PROCEDURES

As a class, read orally or silently all introductory materials for the activity and the Process and Procedures to help students build connections between concepts and activities. Use the time spent reading to bring the students' attention into focus.

1. Read steps 1–5, and review the protocol for making a cell model.

    Remind the learners that they need to read steps 1–5 before they generate their testable questions because the experiments that they design to answer these questions are limited by the materials you provide in step 4. Refer the learners to the essay *Membranes* for information that will help them think of testable questions.

2. Generate at least 2 testable questions about how membranes affect the internal environment of the cell and that meet the criteria in step 4.

3. With your partner, choose the testable question that you would like to investigate. Have your teacher approve your question.

    Consider the results that you found interesting from the eggs-periment. Choose a question that builds on your experiences in that investigation.

    Expect the learners to generate testable questions such as, Can starch (or glucose or Lugol's iodine solution) pass through a membrane? Does the size of the molecule affect how fast it passes through a membrane? Are the results the same if the solution is either inside or outside the dialysis tubing? Is dialysis tubing selectively permeable?

    As you check the question that each team selected, make sure that it lends itself to an experimental setup that uses the available materials. Redirect the students as necessary.

    If the learners' understanding of cell membranes as selective barriers is inadequate for generating testable questions, point out how the properties of the molecules that make up cell membranes help explain the behavior of the membrane in cell processes. This quick demonstration may be helpful.

    Using an overhead projector and petri dish halves, show what happens as various solutes (salt, sugar) come in contact with different classes of solvents (lipid versus aqueous).

    ◆ First show the difference in solubility properties by mixing vegetable oil and water.

◆ If you have more than one type of aqueous and lipid solvent, show what happens when you mix two aqueous solvents or two lipid solvents, to contrast with the immiscibility of oil and water.

◆ Try out the relative solubility of the solutes in each of the solvents by adding a small amount of salt to test tubes of lipid and aqueous solvents, stirring vigorously, and observing the differences in solubility.

◆ Tell the students that the oil is a lipid similar to that which composes cell membranes.

◆ Ask the students how a boundary made of lipids can help a cell keep its internal environment different from its external environment. (The lipids repel the water.)

◆ Ask the students how the observed difference in solubility can help a cell keep its internal environment different from its external environment. (Solutes that dissolve in an aqueous solvent may not dissolve in a lipid solvent.)

The goal of the demonstration is to help students conceptualize that the cell membrane boundary is hydrophobic and thus fats will pass through it more easily than ionic substances, which dissolve readily in water.

4. Design an experiment to test the question you chose. Your design must be safe, and it must use dialysis tubing and

◆ starch suspension,

◆ glucose solution, or a teacher-approved solution designed to help you answer your question, and

◆ appropriate indicators.

The background information in this need to know box may help you design your experiment.

Before the teams begin to design their experiments, you may want to demonstrate the indicator reactions by adding 1 mL of Lugol's iodine solution to 5 mL of starch solution in a test tube. Demonstrate the use of the glucose test strips in two test tubes. One tube contains a dilute glucose solution and the other contains a concentrated glucose solution. These demonstrations will show students what positive reactions look like. After the students have viewed these reactions, show them the materials they can use to construct a model of a cell. Then allow the partners to confer about how they should construct their cell models.

5. Create a data table in your journal to record a brief summary of your experimental design and your predictions. Use the table in Figure 4.10 as a model.

6. Predict what will happen when you conduct the experiment. Record this information in your journal.

7. Have your teacher check and approve your design.

Remember to identify the variables in your experiment, and plan to test only 1 variable at a time.

Reread the testable question that you wrote. Be sure that your designed experiment will generate results that will help you answer your question.

Safety Goggles   **Lab Apron**

SAFETY: Put on your safety goggles and lab apron.

Remind the learners to come to you when they feel that they have an acceptable design. When you are reviewing the designs, ensure that the designs will test the selected question. Help teams think through the process of cell modeling if the basic ideas seem unclear to them. Their designs should include some variation of starch solution on one side of the bag with Lugol's iodine solution on the other side, or glucose solution on one side of the bag with glucose test strips on both sides. Ask the learners to explain their controls to you.

After you have approved the students' designs, remind the teams to modify their data tables and predictions from steps 5 and 6 as needed (if their experimental design changed as a result of discussing it with you) before they begin to construct their cell models in step 8.

8. Set up and conduct your experiment. Create another data table similar to the example in Figure 4.10 to record your observations and results.

Make observations of your setup for as long as possible, and record all observations and results in your data table.

Remind the teams to make sure that the dialysis tubes are tied securely so that the contents do not leak out of the ends and to rinse the outside before placing the tubes in the beakers of solution.

Designate a place for the teams to store their setups overnight. Indicate that they will record final results the next day. Encourage the teams to observe their setups carefully during the remainder of the class period and during the next class session.

9. Wash your hands thoroughly before leaving the laboratory.

10. During the next class session, observe your setup again. Record your final observations and results in your data table.

The following generalizations will help you interpret the data that students may generate from their cell models:

- Starch is a molecule that is too large to pass through the pores.

- Any tubing containing starch will swell as water diffuses in because starch cannot diffuse out.

- Initially, any tubing containing glucose will swell because water diffuses in faster than glucose diffuses out. By the next day, however, the solutions inside and outside the tubing should begin to equalize.

- The iodine will diffuse rapidly (within 15 minutes) into tubing containing starch, causing the development of a blue black color, and by the second day, the water outside of the tubing may be quite clear.

11. Wash your hands thoroughly.

You may wish to assign the essays *Membranes* on page 220 and *Molecular Movement* on page 222 as homework.

12. With your partner, develop possible explanations for your experimental results. Record your explanations in your journal.

The essays *Membranes* on page 220 and *Molecular Movement* on page 222 provide useful information that may help with this step. Be certain that you pay attention to the concepts of *exchange*, *diffusion*, and *osmosis*.

The essay *Molecular Movement* will help learners develop explanations for their data. Their explanations might include the following:

◆ Iodine moved into the starch suspension and stained the suspension blue black.

◆ Water moved into the tubing containing starch and caused the tubing to swell.

◆ Glucose moved out of or into the dialysis tubing and caused a positive reaction to the test strip.

◆ Osmotic pressure caused water to move into or out of the models.

◆ The dialysis tubing is selectively permeable and allows the passage of everything but starch.

◆ Molecules move at different speeds through selectively permeable membranes.

Analysis

Work with your partner to make a lab report about your experiment. Your teacher will instruct you to make either a written report or an oral presentation. Your lab report should include the following:

◆ A statement of the question you tested and the results you predicted

◆ A description of your methods (how you performed the experiment), including the materials that you used

◆ A description of the results that you obtained, presented in a well-organized table or diagram

◆ An explanation of your experimental results that clearly explains how a cell membrane behaves as a barrier and how the dialysis tubing setup serves as a model of a cell

Because this is the first lab report in this program, we have suggested a somewhat abbreviated format.

Use the lab reports to assess the learners' understanding of compartments, boundaries, and the effects of the external environment on the internal environment. Consider the following criteria as you assess the lab reports. (Remember that the effectiveness of the models depends on their quality.) In a successful lab report, the learners

◆ demonstrate an understanding that cell membranes are selectively permeable and that dialysis tubing models this phenomenon;

◆ explain their experimental design in terms of substances moving or being unable to move across a selectively permeable barrier; and

◆ explain that the hydrophobic nature of the cell membrane means that aqueous solutions cannot flow freely in and out of a cell, that this feature largely is responsible for the selective permeability that permits the cell to regulate its internal environment, and that without selective permeability, substances would flow in and out of cells without regulation.

Extension

You can extend the concepts in this activity by having students think about how the rate of diffusion places a limit on the size of cells. Use the optional elaborate activity *Cell Size and Diffusion* to demonstrate this point in a dramatic and visible way.

Regulating the Internal Environment

Major Concepts Circulatory system and urinary system as compartments made of smaller compartments; the role of these systems in regulating the internal environment

Overview

This activity helps learners continue to construct their understanding of how the human body regulates its internal environment. The learners will apply their current understanding of various types of exchanges to the processes that take place in two specific systems—the circulatory system and the urinary system—as these systems work to help maintain a balanced internal environment.

Materials   (per class of 30, pairs and teams of 4)

miscellaneous art supplies
poster board or large sheets of butcher paper (1 per student)
felt-tipped markers
DVD
DVD player

Outcomes and Indicators of Success

The following indicators allow you to assess the students' level of success with the activity and to assess their process of learning.

By the end of this activity, the learners should understand

1. the role of the circulatory system in regulating the internal environment of the human body.

   They will demonstrate their understanding by

   a. describing the journey of a red blood cell as it travels through the body;

   b. describing how a red blood cell is involved in exchanges of materials in the tissues of the toe, the kidneys, the lungs, the liver, and the intestines;

   c. using an illustration to construct an explanation for how the circulatory system helps to regulate the internal environment; and

   d. discussing these concepts with their teammates.

2. the role of the urinary system in adjusting internal conditions in the human body. They will demonstrate their understanding by

a. answering questions about the urinary system during the video segments, and

b. using an illustration to develop an explanation for how the urinary system helps regulate the internal environment.

Strategies for Guiding Learners

PROCESS AND PROCEDURES

PART A Circulatory System

As a class, read orally or silently all introductory materials for the activity and the Process and Procedures to help students build connections between concepts and activities. Use the time spent reading to bring the students' attention into focus.

1. Watch the DVD segment "The Circulatory System" with your class. Take notes in your journal. Ask questions if you need clarification about the path your blood takes and the functions of structures in the circulatory system.

    As the learners view the DVD segment "The Circulatory System," encourage them to ask questions if they need clarification, and repeat portions as necessary for understanding. They should gain a basic knowledge of the structure and function of the circulatory system from this explanatory video segment. Specific strategies are included in the DVD guide on the *TRCD*. Remind students to use the essay *Making Exchanges throughout the Body* as a resource.

Consider using white boards...

(1 group on Smartboard)

2. Imagine that you are a red blood cell. What would be the path you might follow through a human's body as you traveled from the left little toe, through the heart, and on into the right big toe?

    a. Draw a large, simple outline of a human on your poster board or butcher paper.

    b. Draw a heart (including all the chambers) and enough vessels to trace the path of a red blood cell from the left little toe to the right big toe.

    c. Label your drawing, and create a legend next to your illustration that describes the path.

    You will know that you have described your journey adequately if you have included

    ◆ capillaries,

    ◆ veins,

    ◆ arteries,

    ◆ all four chambers of the heart, and

    ◆ the lungs.

    Learners should demonstrate their understanding of the path of circulation, including the chambers of the heart, pulmonary and systemic circulation, arteries, veins, and capillaries.

PART B Making Exchanges

1. Create a table in your journal to describe how you, as a red blood cell, are involved in exchanges in each of the places listed in Figure 4.13.

   Leave room to add to your table as you learn more in this chapter and the next.

   The DVD segment "The Circulatory System" and the essay *Making Exchanges throughout the Body* on page 224 will help you with these tasks.

   Based on the DVD and the essay, the learners should be able to provide some information about oxygen, carbon dioxide, wastes, and glucose exchanges in the tissues of the toe. We suggest that they start a table in their journals and complete it with information about exchanges in the other places in the body as they complete this chapter and the next.

2. To expand your understanding of how various systems help regulate the human body's internal environment, watch the DVD segment "Regulation in the Urinary System." Use this information and the essay *Disposing of Wastes* (page 227) as background resources.

   The learners should be familiar with the information in the essay *Disposing of Wastes* as background for working through the DVD segments. As you show the DVD segment "Regulation in the Urinary System," pause at the appropriate times to allow the students to take notes and record their responses to the questions in the video. This video segment provides a guided inquiry into the function of the kidneys in maintaining homeostasis. As an alternative to working individually, you might have the learners work in teams and discuss the concepts. Encourage them to use the essay as a resource. See the DVD guide on the *TRCD* for additional strategies.

Analysis

Work with your team of four to complete the following task. Divide your team into two pairs. Decide which pair will develop a response to question 1 and which pair will develop a response to question 2. As you answer your question, refer to the information that you developed in Parts A and B of Process and Procedures. Include a supporting illustration in your response. You may wish to use an illustration similar to portions of Figure 4.14. When both pairs are finished, present your responses to each other.

Visit each team periodically as it develops its responses to the questions. Offer poster board, markers, and any other art supplies you have as they construct supporting illustrations for their responses. Some of the students already may have illustrations from the Process and Procedures, but they should enhance or add to these. They may refer to any of the information that they developed earlier in this activity, but their final responses should indicate a synthesis of that information. Expect responses similar to the following:

1. How does the circulatory system help regulate the internal environment of the body? How does the urinary system influence the work of the circulatory system?

   Learners' responses and illustrations should reflect an understanding that the circulatory system provides a way to supply all the cells of the body with oxygen and nutrients and to carry carbon dioxide and other wastes from them. The urinary system excretes the wastes the blood carries from the cells and helps to maintain the volume and composition of the fluid portion of the blood.

2. How does the urinary system help regulate the internal environment of the body? How does the circulatory system influence the work of the urinary system?

The kidneys filter nitrogenous wastes and other undesirable materials from the blood and help to recover water and other useful materials. Kidney function depends on close links between the nephron and the bloodstream. Each day, large quantities of fluid are filtered at the glomeruli of the kidneys. Most of the water and solutes filtered are reabsorbed, but the excess is excreted as urine. The composition of urine depends on three processes:

◆ Blood is *filtered* at the glomerulus (blood pressure provides the force needed for filtration).

◆ Water and useful solutes move from the nephron tubules back into adjacent capillaries through *reabsorption* by active transport or because of the concentration gradient between the blood and the materials in the nephric tubules.

◆ Some excess ions move out of capillaries and into the nephron by secretion.

Extensions

As an extension of this activity, students can complete the *Biology Explorer* program *Cardiovascular System*. This software is published by Riverdeep Interactive Learning Limited and is available for Macintosh and IBM-compatible computers with Windows. *Cardiovascular System* simulates the human cardiovascular system and can be used for studying phenomena such as distribution of blood flow, cardiac fitness, high and low blood pressure, heart attack, and valve dysfunction.

Evaluate

Can You Stand the Heat—Again?

Major Concepts Internal and external environment; compartmentalization; boundaries and membranes

Overview

This activity evaluates the entire chapter, incorporating elements of each of the activities and providing a human example of the balance between the internal and external environment. The learners revisit the story about Josh, *A Pause That Refreshes?*, and test their knowledge of the major chapter concepts as they analyze factors leading to Josh's dehydration.

Outcomes and Indicators of Success

The following indicators allow you to assess the students' level of success with the activity and to assess their process of learning.

By the end of this activity, the learners should understand

1. the concepts of internal and external environments as they apply to a human system.

   They will demonstrate their understanding by

   a. identifying the disparities between Josh's internal and external environments;

   b. listing ways in which Josh's body attempted to bring the internal environment back into balance; and

   c. explaining how Josh, through his conscious behavior, could have achieved a better balance between his internal and external environments.

2. the role of the urinary system as a major factor in maintaining the human internal environment.

   They will demonstrate their understanding by

   a. citing ways in which the kidneys help achieve internal water balance;

   b. explaining how the circulatory system is involved, along with the kidneys, in the process of maintaining internal water balance;

   c. relating these mechanisms to the role of diuretics as they affect internal water balance; and

   d. relating these mechanisms to the role of boundaries and compartmentalization.

Strategies for Guiding Learners

PROCESS AND PROCEDURES

As a class, read orally or silently all introductory materials for the activity and the Process and Procedures to help students build connections between concepts and activities. Use the time spent reading to bring the students' attention into focus.

1. Look back at the class concept map that you and your classmates constructed at the start of this chapter. Consider all that you have studied throughout the chapter. Then make a new concept map that reflects your current understanding of homeostasis. Include the following concepts and any others that you have learned:

   ◆ Diffusion   ◆ Homeostasis

   ◆ Gas exchange   ◆ Water

   ◆ Compartment   ◆ Osmosis

   ◆ Waste removal   ◆ Concentration gradient

   ◆ Environment   ◆ Cell membrane

                              ◆ Internal conditions

   You may wish to convene a brief discussion about the students' concept maps and/or construct one large concept map as a class, after students have completed their own maps. Use this step as a review to prepare students to synthesize their experiences from the chapter and to give complete answers to the evaluate questions.

2. Read the following conclusion to Josh's story, *A Pause That Refreshes?*

   As the learners read the conclusion to Josh's story, ask them to reflect on the title, *A Pause That Refreshes?*

3. To learn more about Josh's condition, examine the data in Figures 4.15 and 4.16. Study the additional information in the need to know box.

   As the learners study these data, help them interpret the information as necessary to understand Josh's condition.

Analysis

As the learners respond to the questions, walk around the room and make sure that they are relating the facts of the story to the concepts of internal and external environment and the role of membranes and compartments in maintaining internal balance. When they have finished, collect their journals to assess their understanding.

1. What percentage of body mass did Josh lose in the form of fluids? Do you think this represents a serious condition? Explain your answer.

   Percentage body mass lost in fluids equals
   [(final mass − original mass) ÷ (original mass)] × 100.

   You might need to review with your students some basic arithmetic about percentages. To determine the percentage change in Josh's mass, subtract the original mass from the final mass, and then divide by the original mass (73.55 − 77.25 = −3.70; −3.70 ÷ 77.25 = −0.048). This will give a decimal figure of −0.048 (negative because mass was lost). When multiplied by 100 to yield the percentage figure, this represents a loss in mass of 4.8 percent. Anything above a 3 percent loss is considered serious unless the fluid is replaced within a short time.

2. In what ways was Josh's body attempting to maintain an internal balance in spite of the changing nature of his external environment?

   Josh's external environment was becoming increasingly hot, and he was not accustomed to this intensity of heat. He needed to keep his core body temperature at a range within homeostatic limits. He experienced symptoms (such as a dry mouth, blurred vision, headaches, and nausea) that indicated he should make changes that would help his body restore internal balance.

3. How did Josh become dehydrated even though he drank 1.9 liters of liquid?

   Josh's dehydration was caused by the diuretic effect of the caffeine in the energy drink. Diuretics make the tubule wall of the nephron more permeable to water so excessive amounts of water move from capillaries into the tubule. Although Josh drank a lot of fluid, the net result was an almost equivalent loss of fluid that put him back in the dehydration danger zone. Diuretics make the body register an excess of fluid when none exists; this situation results in a significant water loss. (Alcohol also is a common diuretic, and it also causes a rapid loss of body fluid through the kidneys.)

4. How could Josh's water loss have caused him to become dizzy?

> Students should be able to make the connection between loss of body fluid and blood volume. Lower blood volume would cause a drop in blood pressure that could result in dizziness.

5. Do you think that Josh would have been better off to replenish his fluids by drinking iced coffee or tea rather than the energy drink? Explain.

> Students should realize that the caffeine in tea, many cola beverages, and certain other soft drinks also would act as a diuretic.

> It would have been much more efficient for Josh to have rehydrated by drinking a nondiuretic liquid, such as water or beverages without caffeine. If Josh had consumed a nondiuretic liquid, he would have added back and retained the mass he had lost as sweat. His dehydrated state would have caused him to retain nearly all of that fluid, and he would have produced only a negligible amount of urine.

6. Use your knowledge of homeostasis to write a brief explanation about why a plant in the hot sun might wilt. Include the following terms in your answer, as well as any others that will show your level of understanding:

- Osmosis
- Balance
- Compartment
- Cell
- Water
- Permeability
- Membrane

> Expect students to include similar descriptions of the following concepts in their answers (using less sophisticated language):

> - Osmosis is the movement of water from a region of higher concentration to a region of lower concentration across a selectively permeable membrane.
> - Balance is a state of equilibrium that a living organism tries to maintain through homeostasis.
> - Compartments occur in living organisms from the cellular to the organismal levels and enable organisms to maintain internal conditions that are different from the external surroundings.
> - Cells are compartments that are surrounded by a selectively permeable membrane.
> - Water balance is important in living organisms. Water can move freely across a selectively permeable membrane. Water is often the solvent in solutions associated with living organisms.
> - Permeability is a measure of how easily a substance can diffuse through a selectively permeable membrane.
> - Membranes enclose cells (and organs and organ systems), making it possible for them to have an internal environment that is separate from the external environment.

Chapter 5

Maintaining Balance in Organisms

In this chapter, the learners deepen their understanding of homeostasis by investigating some of the mechanisms by which organisms maintain an internal balance despite changes in their external environment. We engage the students with a DVD segment that shows scenes of four human activities that elicit a different physiological response. The students are challenged to match descriptions of those responses to the video scenes. Next, the learners explore the maintenance of internal balance by designing an experiment that tests the effects on internal temperature when the external temperature is lowered. We provide a hypothesis and a procedural protocol to help the students learn about experimental design, which is the Science as Inquiry focus. The learners conduct a step test to help them build an explanation of how organ systems interact to maintain homeostasis. For this experiment, the learners develop a hypothesis and convert it into an if-then statement that they can test using a protocol. They identify the variables, decide on a control, and design their experiment.

Students elaborate on their understanding of physiological regulation by using models to investigate how living systems maintain internal pH conditions. They further elaborate on the concept of regulation by observing a DVD segment and then analyzing the behavioral mechanisms that several animals use to regulate body temperature. Finally, the learners evaluate their understanding of homeostasis by demonstrating, in the medium of their choice, how their critter from Chapter 3 maintains its internal environment.

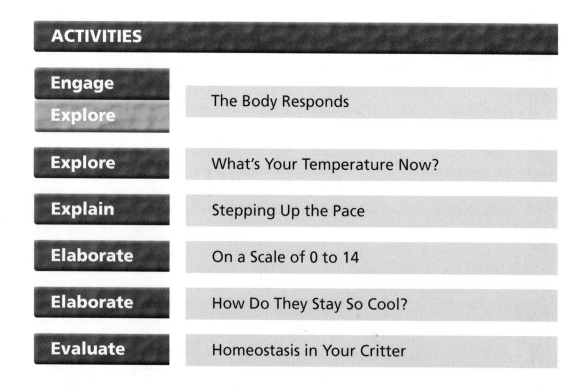

ACTIVITIES

Engage / **Explore**	The Body Responds
Explore	What's Your Temperature Now?
Explain	Stepping Up the Pace
Elaborate	On a Scale of 0 to 14
Elaborate	How Do They Stay So Cool?
Evaluate	Homeostasis in Your Critter

	Instructional Flow				Classroom Support		
Activity/ Student Text pp. Teacher Guide pp.	GACD, TRCD, DVD, and CD-ROM Resources	Essays/ Student Text pp.	Estimated Time	Team Size/ Cooperative Learning Focus	Strategies and Tools	Assessment Opportunities	Special Considerations
ENGAGE/ EXPLORE *The Body Responds* pp. 172–173 TG pp. 177–180	Copymaster: *Internal Events* DVD: *Just a Body Responding*		50 minutes	*Team size:* 4 *Skill:* Contributing ideas	DVD; discussion	Current understanding of the complexity of interactions involved in maintaining homeostasis	Plan to include discussion time to describe the video segments while watching them. This will help students with visual or auditory challenges, as well as clarify content for all learners.
EXPLORE *What's Your Temperature Now?* pp. 173–177 TG pp. 180–186		*Homeostasis* pp. 229–231	100 minutes	*Team size:* 4 *Skill:* Taking responsibility	Wet lab; probe ware system	Current understanding about using controls and variables; using data	Encourage teams to distribute responsibilities equitably and in ways that involve all members as participants.
EXPLAIN *Stepping Up the Pace* pp. 177–182 TG pp. 186–192		*Careful Coordination* pp. 231–236 *The Breath of Life* pp. 236–239	100 minutes	*Team size:* 5 *Skill:* Taking responsibility	Wet lab; probe ware system	Developing hypotheses and if-then statements; designing controlled experiments	Encourage teams to distribute responsibilities equitably and in ways that involve all members as participants.
ELABORATE *On a Scale of 0 to 14* pp. 182–188 TG pp. 193–199	Copymaster: *What Does pH Really Mean?*		100 minutes	*Team size:* 3 *Skill:* Managing and organizing team tasks	Wet lab; probe ware system	Current understanding of homeostasis; applying understandings to new situations	Encourage teams to distribute responsibilities equitably and in ways that involve all members as participants.
ELABORATE *How Do They Stay So Cool?* pp. 188–190 TG pp. 199–202	DVD: *Temperature Regulation in Animals*	*Behavior and Homeostasis* pp. 239–241	75 minutes	*Team size:* class	DVD	Current understanding of homeostasis; applying understandings to new situations	Plan to include discussion time to describe the video segments while watching them to help students with visual or auditory challenges.

continued

Instructional Flow

Classroom Support

Activity/ Student Text pp. Teacher Guide pp.	GACD, TRCD, DVD, and CD-ROM Resources	Essays/ Student Text pp.	Estimated Time	Team Size/ Cooperative Learning Focus	Strategies and Tools	Assessment Opportunities	Special Considerations
EVALUATE Homeostasis in Your Critter pp. 190–191 TG pp. 202–204	Rubric: Homeostasis in Your Critter		75 minutes	Team size: individuals	Folders of student critters	Applying understandings to new situations; expressing current understanding of homeostasis	Some students may be better able to show their understanding if they write about their critters during class time, use a word processor, and/or present their critters to you orally.

Chapter Goals

By the end of this chapter, students should

♦ understand that living systems must be able to detect and respond to changing conditions in order to maintain homeostasis;

♦ understand that humans have mechanisms for regulating internal conditions such as temperature and pH;

♦ understand that regulatory mechanisms may be physiological, behavioral, or a combination of both; and

♦ recognize that maintaining homeostasis requires the interaction of many organ systems, and recognize the role of pH and buffers in maintaining homeostasis.

The learners also will

♦ improve their ability to design and conduct controlled experiments,

♦ be able to develop hypotheses and if-then statements,

♦ become comfortable with using themselves as experimental subjects, and

♦ become adept at using technological tools to gather data.

Advance Preparation

For the three activities *What's Your Temperature Now?*, *Stepping Up the Pace*, and *On a Scale of 0 to 14*, it is preferable to use a probe ware system to collect data. If you have not done so already, allow time before beginning the first of these activities for your students to become familiar with your probes and any associated graphing software.

You will need a DVD player for the activities *The Body Responds* and *How Do They Stay So Cool?* Preview the video segments for those activities.

The Body Responds

Major Concepts The body responds to different external demands with different sets of internal changes; internal changes generally benefit the organism

Overview

This activity engages the learner in thinking about the variety of internal responses that take place as the human body encounters different external challenges. The students view a DVD segment that contains four short scenes depicting people involved in different types of activities, and teams are challenged with the task of matching each external activity or situation with its corresponding physiological description. The activity may help learners discover that the internal changes that their bodies experience are more complex than they realize. It also should help students begin to question how the body regulates and coordinates simultaneous changes in multiple systems.

Materials   (per class of 30, teams of 4)

1 copy of the Copymaster *Internal Events* (read aloud)
DVD
DVD player

Outcomes and Indicators of Success

The following indicators allow you to assess the students' level of success with the activity and to assess their process of learning.

By the end of this activity, the learners should

1. understand that the body undergoes specific internal changes in response to specific external conditions.

   They will demonstrate their understanding by matching scenes depicting several different human activities with the appropriate descriptions of the accompanying physiological changes.

2. understand that the ability to change internally in response to external conditions is beneficial (adaptive).

   They will demonstrate their understanding by developing short oral answers to questions about how the internal changes involved in each situation were beneficial to the person involved.

Strategies for Guiding Learners

PROCESS AND PROCEDURES

As a class, read orally or silently all introductory materials for the activity and the Process and Procedures to help students build connections between concepts and activities. Use the time spent reading to bring the students' attention into focus.

This activity may be done individually or in teams. Use the strategy that will work best for your class.

1. As you watch the DVD segment "Just a Body Responding," think about similar experiences that you have had. Your teacher will show the segment, stopping the DVD briefly after each scene to allow you to think of a short descriptive title for that scene. Record your titles in your journal.

   These titles can be funny or serious, as you choose. Make sure that each title is descriptive enough to help you remember what happened in each scene.

   Begin the activity by showing the DVD segment "Just a Body Responding," which shows four scenes: (1) a person shivering after a quick swim in a cold pool; (2) a stressed marathon runner near the end of a race; (3) people enjoying a rich meal and becoming relaxed and sleepy; and (4) a girl being stalked. We suggest that you show the segment straight through in this first step without offering any explanatory comments. You may wish to follow this first showing by asking what students saw on the segment and how it might relate to biology. Expect most of your learners to recognize only that the scenes showed several different people involved in different types of activities. You can use this answer to raise the important biological question of how the body can maintain an internal balance in each of the different types of activities.

Show the DVD segment again, but this time, stop after each scene to allow students to develop a descriptive title for that scene. This step gets students thinking about what is happening in each scene and also allows them time to create descriptive labels that identify each scene in preparation for the matching exercise that they will perform in step 2.

2. Listen while your teacher reads 4 descriptive paragraphs aloud. Each paragraph describes a set of events that might have gone on inside someone's body in response to 1 of the external situations from the DVD segment. While you listen, record the number of the paragraph that you think best matches each scene next to the scene titles in your journal.

Read aloud the Copymaster *Internal Events*, which describes some of the physiological events that occur in each scene.

3. Discuss the following questions with your partner:

a. Which DVD scene would you match to each description?

Move around the room and monitor the discussions as the teams try to match these descriptions with the scenes they observed on the video segment. We suggest that you do not offer students help in this matching process. If they seem to be struggling, suggest that they focus on creating matches for the easiest scenes to distinguish (likely the pool scene and the after-lunch scene) and then move on to the challenge of making the more difficult matches. The matches are as follows: A = scene 3; B = scene 1; C = scene 4; D = scene 2.

b. What information from the description is most helpful to you in determining a match?

Be sure the students identify the information that was most helpful to them as they made each match. This process will help them focus on using the information available to develop tentative answers and may reduce their tendency to guess without serious thought.

c. How did the internal responses benefit the people involved?

In many cases, the exact reason for the responses will be unclear to the students. In each case, however, there is at least one response that more obviously benefits the person involved. For example, in the people who just finished eating, the internal responses increased circulation to the digestive tract, thus facilitating digestion. Likewise, the swimmer was shivering, which generates heat that increases body temperature, and she wrapped herself in a towel, which would make her feel warmer. (Students may remember learning about goosebumps from Chapter 2.) Depending on the level of understanding of your learners, you also might ask how the internal responses could have harmed the people involved.

4. Participate in a class discussion about the questions.

> As you guide the discussion of these questions, encourage students to relate ideas from Chapter 4 to the scenes they studied here. This is a good opportunity for students to develop preliminary explanations about homeostasis that they will flesh out later in the chapter.

Analysis

Make a table in your journal. Identify three *behavioral* and three *physiological* types of responses from each of the four scenarios.

The word *physiological* refers to internal biological and chemical functions, like the actions of internal organs.

> **Students may note any of several behavioral and physiological responses. Curling up to minimize exposure is a behavioral response. Rhythmic muscle contractions and changes in blood flow are physiological responses.**

Explore

What's Your Temperature Now?

Major Concepts Regulation in the human body

Overview

In this activity, the learners explore the concept of homeostasis as they design and conduct an experiment to test the following hypothesis: If the human body can regulate its internal temperature automatically, then cooling the skin will result in a change in the internal temperature of less than 2°C. The activity is open-ended but includes defined parameters that should help learners design a successful investigation. The essay *Homeostasis* provides information about how the body regulates itself; the learners can use this information to help them interpret their experimental results.

Materials (per class of 30, teams of 4)

8 small plastic containers (margarine-tub size)
8 watches or a clock with a second hand
8 rolls of 1-in plastic first aid tape
paper towels
30 sheets of graph paper (optional)
crushed ice
24 thermistors and associated probe ware system
OR
24 6-in nonmercury, nonroll thermometers

Outcomes and Indicators of Success

The following indicators allow you to assess the students' level of success with the activity and to assess their process of learning.

By the end of this activity, the learners should

1. be able to design and conduct a successful experiment and collect, organize, and analyze data.

   They will demonstrate their ability by

   a. outlining an experimental design and carrying out their experiment;

   b. collecting data on core and surface temperatures of a test subject using an appropriate technological tool (thermometers or electronic thermistors);

   c. constructing a graph that shows how core and surface temperatures responded during the experiment; and

   d. answering questions that guide their analysis of experimental data.

2. understand that the human body can regulate temperature in response to cold.

   They will demonstrate their understanding by

   a. citing evidence that suggests that although body surface temperatures may change considerably in response to changes in environmental temperature, core temperature tends to remain relatively constant; and

   b. explaining whether their experimental results support or contradict the hypothesis that if the human body can regulate its internal temperature automatically, then this temperature will stay fairly constant when the skin is cooled.

3. understand that homeostatic processes adjust specific internal conditions automatically in response to external conditions and in a manner that benefits the organism.

   They will demonstrate their understanding by

   a. explaining how the changes in temperature regulation benefited the test subject and helped maintain homeostasis;

   b. naming two physiological processes, other than temperature control, that adjust automatically to external changes; and

   c. explaining that homeostatic regulation is a specific activity of the body.

Safety

See *Guidelines for Laboratory Safety* in this guide for safety requirements for using a computer in a laboratory if you have a probe ware system that involves a direct computer interface.

Instruct students to keep the ice bath at least 1 meter from the computer and to build a paper towel "dam" to safeguard the computer from spills. If you are not using a probe ware system, substitute the nonmercury thermometers for the thermistors; the general experimental design remains the same.

Warn learners not to place thermometers or thermistors in their mouths; this is unsanitary. Learners should remove their fingers from the ice bath if it becomes painful, although 30 seconds should not pose a problem for most students.

Preparations

The students should use water, the plastic containers, and crushed ice to make ice baths (crushed ice provides lower and more even temperatures than ice cubes). Although we have specified plastic first aid tape, you can substitute other high-stick, nonporous tape or transparent or masking tape (nonporous if possible) to fasten the thermistors.

If you are using probe ware, preview the experimental protocol and plan appropriately for the equipment and number of students in your class. Contact your probe ware manufacturer for specific assistance in designing laboratory settings for the associated graphing and data collection software.

Strategies for Guiding Learners

PROCESS AND PROCEDURES

As a class, read orally or silently all introductory materials for the activity and the Process and Procedures to help students build connections between concepts and activities. Use the time spent reading to bring the students' attention into focus.

This open-ended activity easily accommodates cooperative learning because the students must cooperate to design and execute a modest experiment. Have the learners work in teams of four. Because each team member has a distinct role, it is important that the learners focus on the working-relationship skill of shared responsibilities. If you are implementing cooperative learning explicitly in your classroom, discuss the working-relationship skill with the learners and create a T-chart. For information about T-charts, see the cooperative learning section on the *TRCD*.

1. Together with your teammates, begin designing an experiment to test the following hypothesis:

   If the human body can regulate its internal temperature automatically, then cooling the skin will result in a change in the internal temperature of less than 2°C.

   The Temperature Comparison Protocol will help you to design your experiment.

   Check that the learners understand the term *hypothesis*. A hypothesis is not a guess as students may have been taught; rather it is an informed *prediction* about what might happen. Usually, the students will conduct full inquiries and develop their own hypotheses, but in this activity, we provide a hypothesis because the Science as Inquiry focus is on actually designing the experiment.

   The steps for the Temperature Comparison Protocol are on page 174 of the student text.

   Protocol step 1. Students often have a difficult time progressing from a hypothesis to a structured experiment that is relevant to that hypothesis. The question in this step guides the students in making the transition from a hypothesis to the type of procedural question that will allow them to test the hypothesis.

   Protocol step 2. Emphasize that students will not use their mouths to sample core temperature.

Protocol step 3. This step offers guidelines to help the students plan for all essential elements of their experiment. As the teams use these guidelines to develop their experimental outlines, move from team to team and ask questions to assess whether the learners grasp the important features of this experiment's design. The emphasis here is on designing a good experiment so that the data the learners collect are reliable and meaningful.

Protocol step 4. Allow the learners to assign the roles that will be necessary to conduct a precise experiment. If you notice, however, that one student is assuming two or three roles, step in and explain that the team will gather more accurate data if each team member concentrates on only one role. (In addition, all team members must be involved in the role of data analysis.)

PROCESS AND PROCEDURES (*continued*)

2. In your journal, write your own prediction for how you think your test subject will respond to the environmental changes that you designed in your experiment.

   Mark your prediction clearly so that you and your teacher can easily refer to it when you analyze your results.

   If students follow some standard procedure for designating the location of key activity components recorded in the journals, it will be much easier for you to locate and assess their work.

3. Conduct your experiment.

   When the experiment is completed, each team member should obtain a complete set of data from the recorder and the observer and then copy these results into a data table in his or her journal.

   If the students are to collect accurate data, they must figure out how to arrange the thermistors (or thermometers) so that they can measure all three temperatures simultaneously. Figure T5.1 illustrates one way that the learners might set up their experiments. If you notice that they are not devising secure methods of fastening the thermometers or thermistors, suggest tape as one way to keep these devices fixed without affecting their readings. Good contact is essential for accurate readings. If time permits, encourage teams to repeat their experiments two or three times; this will help emphasize the role of repetition in producing reliable results. In the summarizing discussion, mention the importance of repetition in science.

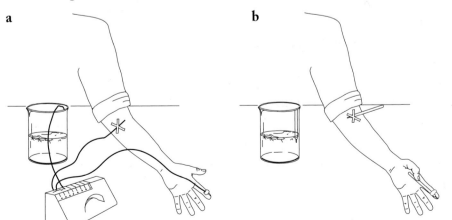

a   b

Figure T5.1
Possible experimental setup using
(a) thermistors or
(b) thermometers.

4. Construct a line graph that shows how the test subject's core and surface temperatures changed throughout the experiment.

Plot the temperature on the *y*-axis and the time on the *x*-axis. Use dashed and solid lines or different-colored lines for the core and surface temperature data. If you need assistance with graphing techniques, refer to Appendix B, *Technique 2, Graphing*.

You may need to help students determine which information goes on each axis of the graph or how to scale the axes.

5. Analyze your team's graph. Use any patterns that you see in your graph along with your data and observations to answer the following questions with your teammates. Record your answers in your journal.

Allow 10–15 minutes for the learners to complete the questions (or assign them as homework). Use this as an opportunity for embedded assessment by circulating around the room and monitoring their responses to these questions. This will allow you to assess the quality of their experimental designs and determine how well the learners understand temperature regulation in the human body.

a. How do the data from the temperature readings compare with observations made by the observer?

The temperature readings are quantitative; the observations and comments are qualitative. These qualitative observations provide a broad perspective to the measurements because they include such information as the color of skin and the behavior of the test subject. The test subject likely provided the most subjective information, including important clues about sensations such as a comfortable feeling of warmth. Such qualitative responses are important to maintaining homeostasis; humans sense when they are getting cold and take measures to get warm again.

b. What changes did you observe in the core and surface temperatures of the test subject?

Calculate the changes (increase or decrease) in temperatures (°C) for body core, body surface, and environment by subtracting the starting temperature from the final temperature.

Observations may include the following:

   ◆ **Initially the core and surface temperatures are slightly different.**
   ◆ **In the ice bath, the surface temperature decreases rapidly at first and then more slowly.**
   ◆ **The temperature of the finger does not decrease to the temperature of the ice water.**
   ◆ **Core temperature may not change in response to the ice bath until *after* the finger has been removed.**
   ◆ **After the ice bath, the surface temperature increases gradually but not steadily, depending on the subject.**
   ◆ **The surface temperature does not reach its former level before the test subject indicates the warmth has returned.**

In general, the core temperature changes very little (by 1°C or 2°C), whereas the surface temperature changes dramatically (by 13°C or 14°C).

c. Explain whether your experimental results support or disprove the hypothesis given at the start of the experiment and your own prediction for how the test subject would respond.

Refer specifically to both the hypothesis stated in step 1 and the prediction that you wrote in your journal after you designed your experiment.

If the students' results indicate that the internal (core) temperature stayed fairly constant despite a dramatic change in the external conditions (temperature), then the hypothesis was supported. The test subject did not do anything conscious or intentional to make this happen, thus it was an automatic regulation.

When the learners have completed step 5, convene a brief summarizing discussion by asking for volunteers from each team to present and explain their graphs to the class. Acknowledge the limited nature of the experiment (it showed temperature changes under only limited environmental conditions). Yet also emphasize that it illustrates patterns in the way that the body maintains its balance. In cases where experiments did not work well, ask the learners for suggestions about what went wrong and how they might change the experimental design if they were to repeat the experiment. Consider offering time after class to any teams that would like to conduct a redesigned experiment. Even if the teams obtained differing experimental data, it should be clear after this discussion that the human body responds automatically to changes in external conditions.

Complete this summarizing discussion by asking the learners to describe how technology enhanced their ability to collect and organize data. The enhancement will be especially apparent if your students have used a probe ware system, but thermometers also represent technology. Encourage students to think about the importance of technology in extending our ability to make observations beyond those which we could make through our senses alone (for example, simply touching the skin to evaluate its temperature as hot or cold).

Analysis

Complete the following tasks on your own, and record your answers in your journal:

Read the essay *Homeostasis* on page 229 for information that will help with these tasks.

Have the students complete the Analysis individually; if class time is limited, assign the Analysis as homework. Learners can use information in the essay *Homeostasis* to help them link the observed experimental results to feedback and regulation systems in the body.

1. How might the changes that you observed in the core and surface temperatures benefit the test subject and help to maintain homeostasis?

The organ systems vital for life are protected because the core temperature does not change with the external temperature. By constricting blood vessels in the extremity (finger), the body reacts in a way that prevents cold blood from being carried to the inside of the body, where it could cause a dangerous internal cooling. Although this response could result in damage or loss of extremity tissue, it helps to preserve the life of the organism.

2. Create a table like the one in Figure 5.4. Use it to identify stressors, behavioral responses, and physiological adjustments that help humans maintain homeostasis. In addition to temperature, name two other stressors that the human body might encounter and adjust to automatically. Give two examples each of the types of behavioral and physiological adjustments that the body makes in each case.

The darkening of skin is an automatic physiological change that occurs in response to external changes. In this case, an increased production of melanin pigment has the effect of protecting the body from the harmful effects of ultraviolet radiation, thus minimizing the stress and reducing the risk of skin damage. Reflexes, such as blinking when something rapidly approaches the eye, or retracting a hand when it encounters something sharp or hot, also are automatic physiological responses to external stresses. Vomiting is a physiological response to the presence of harmful substances in the body, such as excess alcohol, other poisons, or pathogens.

The observable responses brought about by internal processes involved in maintaining homeostasis qualify as behavioral responses. For example, wanting to step into the shade in response to the skin being exposed to bright sun, stepping out of harm's way after sensing that an object is hot or sharp, or feeling repulsed by a food that previously made an individual vomit are all behavioral responses. Students may suggest other responses.

3. Explain whether regulation to maintain homeostasis is a random or specific activity of the body.

Homeostatic regulation is specific and precise; that is, the responses that occur internally to correct for external changes occur in ways that return a normal balance or condition to only the relevant internal conditions. For example, your eyes do not reflexively blink when your finger is cold because the body does not sense a threat to normal vision homeostasis. Instead, the body senses a threat to core temperature and responds by constricting external blood vessels and preserving the temperature of the body's core.

4. Describe four qualities that you would expect to see in a highly respected scientist.

Expect students' answers to include qualities such as honesty, integrity, ability to plan and carry out plans, objectivity, well-developed reasoning and critical-thinking skills, and creativity. A brief discussion about students' answers to this question can provide an opportunity to highlight the skills you want your students to develop.

Explain # Stepping Up the Pace

Major Concepts Interaction of systems in maintaining homeostasis

Overview

In this activity, the learners design an experiment that uses a step test protocol to investigate the relationships between pulse rate and breathing rate at different levels of exercise. Their experimental results help them deepen their understanding of homeostasis by demonstrating the interaction of two systems during physical exercise. Learners can do the activity either with or without probe ware, but probe ware systems provide more accurate data. Learners apply the science process skills of proposing and testing hypotheses as they design and carry out their experiment.

Materials   (per class of 30, teams of 5)

probe ware systems and 4 respiration
    thermistors if available (see Preparations)
alcohol wipes (if using probe ware)
6 watches or a clock with second hand
6 stepping platforms

30 sheets of graph paper (optional)
6 1-yd pieces of 1-in-wide elastic
    (optional)
6 diaper pins (optional)

Outcomes and Indicators of Success

The following indicators allow you to assess the students' level of success with the activity and to assess their process of learning.

By the end of this activity, the learners should

1. understand that different homeostatic systems interact to adjust internal conditions.

    They will demonstrate their understanding by

    a. explaining how complex organisms react to changes in external environments to maintain homeostasis;

    b. describing the role of the endocrine and nervous systems in regulating homeostasis;

    c. explaining the mechanisms that the human body uses to adjust internal conditions;

    d. predicting how heart rate, breathing rate, and exercise are related;

    e. using the concepts of interacting systems to explain how atmospheric oxygen reaches cells deep within the body; and

    f. explaining how the acidity of blood controls breathing rate.

2. be able to develop hypotheses and test them using evidence gathered from experiments.

    They will demonstrate their ability by

    a. developing a testable hypothesis that proposes an explanation for the relationship among exercise, heart rate, and breathing rate;

    b. proposing an if-then statement to test their hypothesis;

    c. designing and conducting a step test experiment to test their hypothesis;

    d. constructing a graph that shows the results of their experiment;

    e. analyzing the results of a step test experiment; and

    f. developing a conclusion that describes the interaction between the circulatory and gas exchange systems during exercise.

Safety

See *Guidelines for Laboratory Safety* in this guide for safety requirements when using a computer in the laboratory.

Provide safe stepping equipment for all teams. The steps must be at least 8 inches high but no more than 14 inches high. Steps also must be wide and deep enough to allow for stable footing. If you use individual steps, make sure they are sturdy and firmly planted on the ground; steps should not tip, tilt, or move when used.

Allow at least 2 meters between teams, and make sure that other team members stand back from the test subject while he or she is exercising.

Do not allow students with medical conditions that prohibit strenuous exercise (such as asthma or heart problems) to be test subjects. Because students with such conditions sometimes overestimate their abilities, carefully monitor teams as they select test subjects and suggest changes as necessary. (Many disabilities do not prohibit strenuous exercise; students with such disabilities would be good candidates for test subjects. See Preparations.)

Test subjects should wear exercise shoes with nonslip treads and comfortable clothing. Clothing should not have long or flowing ends that might cause the person to trip. Test subjects should step calmly and purposefully at all times. If you see students becoming uncomfortable or exhausted, instruct them to stop the experiment.

Preparations

Give students advance notice about appropriate footwear and clothing for this activity.

Arrange a safe location for the step test (see Safety). If possible, borrow equipment such as stop watches, large timing clocks, or exercise steps from your physical education department. Two 8×8×16-inch cinder blocks placed side by side make a stable platform that is reasonable in cost.

Monitor teams as they select the test subjects (see Safety). Often volunteers tend to be athletes or athletically minded students. Encourage teams to select students who might normally shy away from such a role as test subject. A balance in the types of test subjects will ensure a broad range of experimental results.

If your class includes students with disabilities that do not prohibit strenuous exercise, such as students in wheelchairs, encourage them to be test subjects. In that case, design an exercise test equivalent to the step test. For example, a student in a wheelchair might push his or her chair back and forth a specified distance that requires the exertion equivalent to taking a single step.

Demonstrate the stepping procedure described in step 5 of the protocol so that all test subjects step the same way.

Familiarize yourself with your probe ware and any associated programs if you will be using them so that you can anticipate any problems or questions that students might have. If you are not using a probe ware system to detect respiration, you can make it easier for teammates to help detect breathing rate. As an alternative to having students count their own breathing rate, prepare strips of wide white elastic that can be fastened with diaper pins (for safety) around the test subject's chest. The elastic makes it easier for others to observe and count breathing rate.

Strategies for Guiding Learners

PROCESS AND PROCEDURES

As a class, read orally or silently all introductory materials for the activity and the Process and Procedures to help students build connections between concepts and activities. Use the time spent reading to bring the students' attention into focus.

1. Read the essay *Careful Coordination* on page 231.

2. Complete the following in your journal as you work individually:

   Use this step as a way of assessing the students' developing understanding of the concepts. The essay *Careful Coordination* will help the learners understand the regulatory interactions of homeostatic systems.

   The students' responses to the questions should include the following basic ideas:

   a. Why can maintaining homeostasis be particularly challenging for multicellular organisms?

   > To maintain an acceptable set of internal conditions, multicellular organisms require more complex systems. This is because most of their cells are buried deep inside their bodies, far from the external environment from which they must obtain oxygen and food as well as release wastes.

   b. How does the endocrine system compare to the nervous system in regulating homeostasis (see Figure 5.5)?

   > These two systems usually work together to regulate homeostasis. The responses of the endocrine system are slower, longer lasting, and more generalized than those of the nervous system, which tend to be rapid, short term, and very specific.

   c. Explain the role that sensors play in the maintenance of homeostasis in the human body.

   > Sensors throughout the body detect changes in the internal environment and communicate this information to organ systems that respond with actions that restore the internal balance. Sensors detect the restored internal balance and communicate this new information to the organ systems, a process known as feedback. The cycle of detection, response, and feedback enables the body to adjust internal conditions and maintain homeostasis.

   d. Describe a typical cycle that might take place as a body determines how to adjust internal conditions in response to change.

   The essay *Careful Coordination* (page 231) contains information that will help you understand and answer these questions.

   > The body first senses when changes have occurred in the external and internal environment, then it responds with appropriate adjustments. The process then repeats to maintain homeostasis.

3. Make a prediction about how heart rate, breathing rate, and exercise are related.

   Monitor the teams as they make predictions and develop hypotheses and if-then statements in steps 3–5 so that you can clarify any confusion about the difference between a prediction, a hypothesis, and an if-then statement.

4. As a team, examine the predictions that each of your teammates made in step 3. Then develop 1 testable hypothesis that you think offers the best explanation of the relationships between heart rate, breathing rate, and exercise. You will conduct an experiment to evaluate your hypothesis.

   Your hypothesis must be testable. In other words, your hypothesis will be an educated guess that provides a logical and possible answer to a testable question. Refer to the need to know box in Chapter 1 (page 22) to review the criteria for testable questions.

5. Rewrite your hypothesis as an if-then statement.

   In some cases, you can test a hypothesis by making a prediction and then collecting data to determine whether the prediction was accurate. For this, it is useful to express the hypotheses as an if-then statement such as, "If milk gets hotter than 80°C, then it will boil."

   Hypotheses and if-then statements might include the following:

Hypotheses	If-then statements
The heart has to work harder during exercise because it has to pump more blood to supply the muscles with oxygen and nutrients and remove wastes, such as carbon dioxide and lactic acid.	If the heart beats faster, then we should notice an increase in pulse rate from resting state to vigorous exercise.
During exercise, the gas exchange system must provide the blood cells with more oxygen and remove more waste gases such as carbon dioxide from the blood.	If the lungs have to provide more oxygen and remove more wastes from the bloodstream, then we should observe an increase in breathing rate from resting state to vigorous exercise.

6. As a team, read the Protocol for Conducting a Step Test. Discuss how you would use this exercise protocol to test your hypothesis.

   Monitor the teams as they discuss the step test protocol, the variables and controls, and the overall design of their experiments. If they have difficulty identifying controls, ask leading questions until they realize that the *resting state* represents the control. Likewise, lead the students as necessary to identify the different exercise rates as the variables.

   Remind the teams that they need to meet *all* of the criteria listed in step 9. Emphasize the safety issues. Monitor the teams as they select responsibilities, particularly the test subject (see Safety). Emphasize that the step test cannot succeed without the cooperation and support of all team members, whether performed with or without a probe ware system. See Protocol Strategies at the end of this activity for experimental procedures.

7. Construct a data table in your journal for the experiment.

   Include columns for each of the exercise rates and resting conditions that you decide to use. Make rows for pulse rate, breathing rate, and any other conditions. The exercise rate is the speed at which the test subject steps (or performs some other repetitive exercise).

8. Identify the variables in your experiment, and decide on an appropriate control. Record the variables and the control in your journal.

   Variables might include exercise rate, step height, and test subject's weight. Your control should allow you to test 1 variable at a time. You also may want to compare the responses of 2 or more test subjects.

   It is important that students recognize and isolate the variables as much as possible to design scientifically sound experimental procedures.

9. Design an experiment to test your hypothesis. Your experiment needs to meet all of the criteria listed below. Your experiment must

   ◆ be safe,

   ◆ be manageable in a classroom setting and appropriate for the length of the class period,

   ◆ use the materials available, and

   ◆ allow each team member to handle materials and record data.

10. Have your teacher approve your design; then begin your test.

    As you proceed with your test, you may need to modify the design of your experiment. If that happens, record the changes in your journal.

    Before you approve any of the designs and permit the teams to begin their experiments, review the safety cautions for the activity, the responsibilities of the team members, and the procedures for the step test so that students are familiar with the equipment and comfortable with the complexity of the experiment.

11. When you have completed your experiment, construct a graph that shows how pulse and breathing rates changed from the resting state through increasing rates of exercise. Copy the graph into your own journal.

12. After you have finished your graph, analyze your experiment. Develop a conclusion that describes the interaction between the circulatory and gas exchange systems during exercise.

    For a strong conclusion, analyze the data that you collected, including the graph, and relate those data to the hypotheses that you tested.

    When all teams have completed their experiments and shared the data they collected, ask them to graph their breathing rate and pulse rate results. Provide assistance with this skill as necessary and explain that the graphs should show the general patterns of the data but do not have to represent all data points. In developing a conclusion, teams should evaluate their hypotheses, and if necessary, they should restate or revise them in consideration of their experimental evidence. Expect their conclusions to indicate some version of the following pattern: pulse and breathing rates were lowest at rest, increased gradually for exercise of 1 step/5 seconds, then increased to a much higher rate as the rate of exercise increased. You would expect pulse and breathing rates to reach a plateau in most subjects during each specific exercise rate.

Analysis

Learners should use the essay *The Breath of Life* to help them with the Analysis. Collect their responses to assess their understanding of interacting systems.

Complete the following tasks individually. Write your explanations in your journal.

Use the information in the essay *The Breath of Life* on page 236 to develop well-reasoned answers. Consider the role of the respiratory system in your experiment (see Figure 5.7).

1. Use the concept of interacting systems to explain how oxygen from the atmosphere can reach cells deep within the body.

   Responses should include the basic ideas that gas exchange occurs in the lungs and that the circulatory system carries oxygen to all cells in the body. Learners should draw on information from the activity *Regulating the Internal Environment* in Chapter 4 to explain how the circulatory system performs its role.

2. Explain how the acidity of blood controls breathing rate.

   The learners' responses should include the following ideas. Carbon dioxide reacts with water in the blood to form carbonic acid, which increases the acidity of the blood. pH sensors in the brain detect the increased acidity and respond with messages that result in increased breathing rate. As the increased breathing rate removes carbon dioxide, the acidity of the blood decreases, the pH sensors detect the decrease, and breathing rate slows.

   The steps in the protocol allow you to assess the students' skills in conducting an experiment and in interpreting their data.

PROTOCOL

Protocol Strategies

- Monitor the teams to make sure that they have provided enough columns and rows to accommodate the data they plan to record.

- As the students set up their experiments, monitor teams to make sure that they set up the equipment properly and that all team members are participating. Emphasize the importance of involvement by all team members. Teams are free to suggest whatever exercise rates they decide on, keeping in mind safety factors and reasonable limits. We have suggested 1 step/5 seconds as a beginning, but do not require that they necessarily start with that rate.

- Make sure teams gather data on the resting state when the test subject is seated and resting quietly.

- As the teams perform the step test, help them coordinate their activities. Emphasize that breaks should be as brief as possible. Remind the test subjects to stop or rest if they feel uncomfortably tired and to adjust the breathing rate sensor if it becomes uncomfortable.

On a Scale of 0 to 14

Major Concepts Buffering; pH as part of homeostasis; chemistry of acids and bases

Overview

The level of acidity (pH) is an internal condition that must remain relatively constant in living systems. In this activity, the learners elaborate on their understanding of homeostasis by examining the role of buffers in the maintenance of a relatively constant internal pH. To provide a context for studying the role of buffers, the learners test the pH of several common substances. Then they perform a simple titration using water and potato or liver homogenate. Their results demonstrate that living systems have buffering capacity that helps them maintain a relatively constant pH. The activity also builds on students' understanding of models as they consider homogenate as a system for studying the homeostasis inside cells. Extensions offer a way for learners to examine the concepts of buffers, acids and bases, and solvents and solutes more closely.

Materials   (per class of 30, teams of 3)

30 pairs of safety goggles
30 lab aprons
10 50-mL beakers
10 50-mL graduated cylinders
10 petri dish halves
    (if pH paper is used)
10 pH probes or pH paper
10 forceps (if pH paper is used)
30 sheets of graph paper (optional)
10 pH meters or 5 rolls of wide-range
    pH paper (if probe ware systems
    are not available)
10 jars of tap water for storing pH probes
distilled water
10 dropping bottles of 0.1M HCl solution
    (100 mL total) labeled
    CAUTION: Mild irritant
10 dropping bottles of 0.1M NaOH solution
    (100 mL total) labeled
    CAUTION: Mild irritant

300 mL of potato homogenate
300 mL of liver homogenate
4 50-mL beakers containing a 50-fold
    dilution of household bleach labeled
    CAUTION: Irritant
4 50-mL beakers containing a
    50-fold dilution of household
    ammonia labeled
    CAUTION: Irritant
4 50-mL beakers containing
    vinegar labeled
    CAUTION: Mild irritant
4 50-mL beakers containing milk
    of magnesia
4 50-mL beakers containing
    0.1M NaOH labeled
    Dilute drain cleaner,
    CAUTION: Irritant
30 copies of the Copymaster *What Does pH*
    Really Mean? (Extensions)

Outcomes and Indicators of Success

The following indicators allow you to assess the students' level of success with the activity and to assess their process of learning.

By the end of this activity, the learners should

1. become aware that familiar solutions can be characterized in part by their pH.

    They will demonstrate their awareness by

    a. measuring the pH of several familiar solutions, and

    b. relating the pH values to the pH balance of their organ systems.

2. understand that a buffer maintains the pH of a solution within a narrow range of values.

    They will demonstrate their understanding by

    a. collecting data about the response of tap water and a homogenate of living cells to the addition of acid and base,

    b. plotting these data on a graph, and

    c. relating these data to the concept of buffers.

3. understand that living systems maintain pH within a narrow range of values and that maintenance of this range is important to homeostasis.

    They will demonstrate their understanding by

    a. explaining that living systems contain buffers, and

    b. explaining that a buffer helps maintain homeostasis by providing the specific pH conditions under which certain cell processes work best.

Safety

See *Guidelines for Laboratory Safety* in this guide for safety requirements for using a computer in a laboratory.

If the experiment spans more than 1 day, remind students at the break point to wash their hands before leaving and to observe safety precautions on the day class resumes. Warn students not to ingest any materials by inadvertently touching their hands to their mouths. Bleach, ammonia, and drain cleaner all are hazardous. Follow the manufacturer's precautions when using them, and be sure that the students are aware of the hazards.

Preparations

Dilute the bleach and ammonia 50-fold by adding 0.5 mL of each to 24.5 mL of water. (It is not necessary to dilute the vinegar or milk of magnesia.) Drain cleaner is too caustic to use in the laboratory; substitute $0.1M$ NaOH. Label the beakers appropriately when you have prepared the test solutions.

 Set up the probe ware system with two or three pH probes each if available. Prepare a small beaker each of bleach, ammonia, vinegar, milk of magnesia, and "drain cleaner." (You also can use other familiar liquids and blended foods such as tomatoes and grapes.)

Follow the manufacturer's directions for care and use of pH probes, and make preparations accordingly.

Although pH probes provide more accurate pH readings, both pH meters and wide-range pH paper work well. Consider having some teams use each of the technologies and then compare the results and discuss reasons for the differences if possible. Purchase ready-made 0.1M HCl (Ward's catalog #970V3307) and 0.1M NaOH (Ward's catalog #970V7806). Prepare the homogenates as follows:

Liver homogenate

In a household blender, blend 10 g fresh liver in 100 mL of distilled water. Use within 24 hours; keep refrigerated.

Potato homogenate

In a household blender, blend 10 g fresh potato in 100 mL of distilled water. Use within 24 hours; keep refrigerated.

Strategies for Guiding Learners

PROCESS AND PROCEDURES

PART A   pH Is Everywhere

As a class, read orally or silently all introductory materials for the activity and the Process and Procedures to help students build connections between concepts and activities. Use the time spent reading to bring the students' attention into focus.

1. If you compared 2 solutions, 1 with a pH of 6 and another with a pH of 5, what would be the difference? Read the background information about pH to find out.

   After the learners have read the information about pH, convene a brief discussion to consider the questions. Step 5 allows you to assess the learners' current understanding of pH and homeostasis.

2. Make a table in your journal. Include the name of each household solution that your teacher provides and 2 spaces. In the 1st space, you will make a prediction of what you think the pH will be. In the 2nd space, you will record the pH that you measure.

   This step is important for actively involving students' attention in the activity.

3. On your own, record your prediction for what you think the pH of the available solutions will be.

   Predictions should be made and recorded individually.

4. With your partner, determine the pH of the available solutions by using a pH probe or pH indicator strips. Record these pH readings in the data table in your journal.

5. Discuss the following questions with your class:

   a. Do any of the pH measurements differ from your predictions?

      Expect your students to be somewhat surprised at how acidic or basic these solutions are.

b. Which of the solutions that you tested could be harmful to the pH balance of your organ systems? Why?

Students should answer that all of these solutions could disrupt the pH balance of their organ systems.

PART B   Regulating pH

Safety Goggles   **Lab Apron**

SAFETY: Put on your safety goggles and lab apron.

1. To investigate how living cells regulate pH, you and your partner will compare how water and 1 type of cell homogenate respond to the addition of acids and bases. Water is not living. The homogenate, made from cells that were recently living, will model the internal environment of a living organism. Your job is to collect data that will allow you to compare the responses of a nonliving and "living" substance to the addition of an acid and then a base.

2. Read the protocol for changing the acidity of a liquid.

See the protocol box on page 185 of the student text.

As the learners work through Part B, make sure that each student actively participates in the experiment. Ask them to focus on distributed leadership during this part of the activity. For example, one student can add the drops of acid while another team member records the data, and then they can switch roles for adding the drops of base to each liquid. Each team member also should take a turn at operating the computer (or using pH paper or the pH meter).

Talk through the experimental procedure to be sure that your students understand the steps before they begin. For example, in step 8 of the protocol, they repeat steps 1–7 but add NaOH instead of HCl, and in step 9 they repeat steps 1–8 but use a homogenate instead of tap water. Have them read the CAUTION statements carefully, and remind them of the importance of mixing solutions thoroughly after adding each drop of acid or base. Be sure they understand that with each titration, they will have seven pH readings in their data tables.

3. Determine which homogenate your team will be using.

You will use either liver homogenate or potato homogenate. Your teacher made these homogenates by blending pieces of liver or potato at high speed to break open the cells and release their contents. Remember, these homogenates will act as models of the internal environment of living systems.

In step 9, provide half of the teams with potato homogenate and the other half with liver homogenate. (Other homogenates of living systems also work, for example, egg white, gelatin, corn, or apples. These homogenates might have a range of responses, however, so it is best to test them before using them with the students.) Remind the students that the homogenates serve as models of the conditions of pH in living systems. These models allow us to make valuable inferences about the importance of maintaining pH within a narrow range.

4. On your own, draw a graph that represents your prediction for how you think pH will change for both water and your homogenate when you add acid. Also, graph how you predict the pH will change for both when you add a base. Draw your predictions on a graph with the axes labeled like those in Figure 5.9.

Direct the students to record their predictions before beginning any of the protocol procedures.

5. Below your prediction graph, write a brief justification for your predictions.

✗ Expect students to predict a linear relationship between the number of drops of acid or base and pH. This step provides an opportunity for you to assess students' prior knowledge of the concept of pH. In addition, the graphs will show whether the students expect living organisms to behave differently than water when acid or base is added as a response to the external environment.

6. Divide the data collection jobs fairly among your team members. You need someone who will perform the acid tests, someone who will perform the base tests, and someone who will record pH levels in a data table. Change jobs after testing the water so that every team member takes a turn measuring the pH of a solution.

Use a table similar to the one labeled *pH Changes* in Figure 5.10 to record the data that you collect. After the experiment, all team members will copy the data from the experiment into their journals.

7. On graph paper or in your journal, draw a full-sized graph. Label the *x*- and *y*-axes the same as you did on the graph that you made for your predictions. Use the pH data that your team collected to make a line graph that shows 4 separate lines: 1 each for water plus acid, water plus base, homogenate plus acid, and homogenate plus base. Your graph should show the relationship between pH and the number of drops of acid or base.

Code your lines, using color or different line types. You will want to distinguish between the 4 conditions that you are graphing.

After they have washed their hands, make sure that the learners copy their team's data into their own data table before they prepare the graph of their results. Remind them to use different colors or a solid line for the acid and a dashed line for the base on the graph (see the sample student graph in Figure T5.2). If any of the learners need help with graphing, refer them to Appendix B.

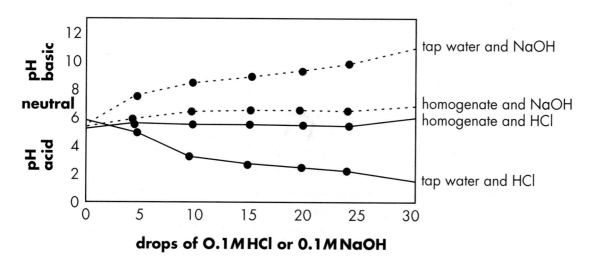

Figure T5.2 Sample graph of pH changes

8. Discuss the following question with your partner. Record an explanation in your journal based on the information portrayed on your graphs.

> When the learners have completed their graphs, ask them to discuss this question:
>
>> What similarities and differences do you see in the results of adding HCl or NaOH to water compared with a homogenate?
>
> Students should explain that the pH of tap water changed greatly with the addition of acid and base, but that the pH of the homogenate changed only slightly. They should be able to infer that something in the homogenate prevented significant change.

9. Join a team that tested the other homogenate. Compare data and explanations.

> Direct each team to join with a team that tested the other homogenate so that they can compare the results. They should observe only minor differences in the response of the two homogenates.

10. Discuss the following questions with your partner. Record the answers in your journal.

> The information on buffers in the need to know box may help you with your answers.

> Move around the room listening to the team discussions, and ask individual students for their responses. This feedback should give you an idea of how well the students understand the concept of buffering. If necessary, convene a brief class discussion to review the results. This may be particularly helpful if there are students whose experiments, for one reason or another, did not yield expected results. Expect to hear responses such as the following:

   a. Based on your results and using water as a comparison, do you think potato and liver cells are buffered? Explain your answer.

   > Students should respond that potato and liver cells are buffered because the pH of the homogenates changed only slightly when acid or base was added, whereas the pH of water changed greatly.

   b. Is it likely that all living systems contain buffers? Why or why not?

   > Yes, because living systems require closely controlled internal environments despite stress factors that would tend to change those conditions. One of the controlled conditions is pH, and buffers provide a way to maintain an appropriate pH environment within each type of cell or system.

   c. At what pH do you think living liver and potato cells function best? On what do you base this inference?

   > At a pH between 5 and 6 because that was the initial pH of both homogenates, and they changed only slightly during the course of the experiment.

Analysis

Use the Analysis to guide a summarizing class discussion. Consider providing interested students with extra class time to design an experiment to test the buffering capacity of hair care and health care products.

Answer the following questions in your journal. Be prepared to contribute your ideas to a class discussion.

1. Based on your data from the experiment in Part B, how might a buffer help maintain homeostasis? Explain your answer.

   Answers that reflect a thorough understanding should include some link between the ability to maintain internal pH conditions and the fact that different metabolic and chemical processes require specific pH values. A good response might be a buffer helps keep pH within a narrow range, and because certain processes in living organisms work best at certain pH values, a defined pH would allow those processes to be carried out efficiently.

2. Many manufacturers claim that their health care and hair care products are pH balanced or buffered. How would you test their claims?

   Such products could be tested using a procedure similar to the one in Part B. Acids and bases could be added to the product drop by drop (after diluting the product to the concentration at which it is normally used), and the buffering capacity could be compared with that of water.

Extensions

The Copymaster *What Does pH Really Mean?* includes a short reading about solvents, solutes, acids, bases, and buffers that should deepen your students' understanding of these concepts. The learners use the information in the reading to develop diagrams or short skits to explain how acids, bases, and buffers function in solution.

How Do They Stay So Cool?

Elaborate

Major Concepts Behavioral mechanisms that maintain homeostasis

Overview

In this activity, the students expand their understanding of homeostasis by working in their teams to observe the behavioral temperature regulation of reptiles and mammals. By applying their experiences from this chapter, students collect information and develop hypotheses about how these animals regulate their temperature and then develop explanations that account for the patterns that emerge. The students also synthesize their ideas by answering questions about the behavioral feedback and regulatory mechanisms that lizards, dogs, and an animal of their choice use to regulate temperature. They compare and contrast those with similar mechanisms that humans use.

Materials (per class of 30)

DVD
DVD player

Outcomes and Indicators of Success

The following indicators allow you to assess the students' level of success with the activity and to assess their process of learning.

By the end of this activity, the learners should demonstrate their ability to apply their understanding of homeostasis to behavioral situations.

They will demonstrate their ability by

a. making observations of behaviors that animals use to regulate temperature,

b. describing the behaviors humans and lizards share for regulating temperature,

c. comparing and contrasting the mechanisms that dogs use to adjust internal temperatures with the mechanisms that humans use, and

d. identifying at least two homeostatic processes besides body temperature that animals regulate behaviorally.

Preparations

Preview the DVD segment "Temperature Regulation in Animals" so that you can anticipate the students' questions or problems.

Strategies for Guiding Learners

PROCESS AND PROCEDURES

As a class, read orally or silently all introductory materials for the activity and the Process and Procedures to help students build connections between concepts and activities. Use the time spent reading to bring the students' attention into focus.

Use the question in the students' introduction—What methods of regulation have you experienced or observed so far in class or in the world around you?—to establish the common knowledge in the classroom. Ask who has seen a Gila monster or been to the desert.

1. Observe the DVD segment "Temperature Regulation in Animals." Record your observations in a data table that is similar to the one in Figure 5.13. Write your responses in your journal to the questions that the DVD segment poses.

   Provide time for students to construct a data table in their journals in which to record their observations of the animals in the video segment "Temperature Regulation in Animals" as well as information about the animal they will study in step 2. Then use the strategies in the DVD guide to guide the students through the DVD, which shows the behavioral responses of two lizards—the Gila monster *Heloderma suspectum* and the horned lizard *Phrynosoma cornutum*—and of dogs, hippos, bears, and humans to warm environmental temperatures. Give the students enough time to make complete observations and to respond to the questions in the segment. Make sure that they record their observations and interpretations in the data table and that they answer the questions as thoroughly as possible. This information will serve as a useful reference as they complete the Analysis. Some students may have more difficulty than others interpreting the graphs that show activity patterns of the Gila monster. If this seems to be a problem, consider discussing the first graph as a class; the graphs that follow are similar. After working through the video segment, ask whether any of the students need to see certain sections again. This step provides an opportunity to assess the learners' ability to make and interpret observations.

2. Add a column to your table, and record the behaviors of a living animal that you can observe directly.

Focus your observations on the behaviors that the animal exhibits to regulate its temperature or to respond to changes in the external temperature.

Use the information in the essay *Behavior and Homeostasis* (on page 239) and other available resources to describe an animal's behavioral responses to changes in external (environmental) temperature.

Assign the direct observation of behaviors of a living animal as homework unless you have several live animals in your classroom. Encourage the students to observe their pets, neighborhood animals (squirrels or birds), or local zoo animals at different times of the day so they can establish the typical behavioral responses to changes in temperature.

Analysis

Use your notes, observational data from the DVD, and the information in the essay *Behavior and Homeostasis* to answer the following questions. Write your responses in your journal.

The learners' responses provide an opportunity to assess their ability to synthesize information about behavior and homeostasis.

1. What similarities and differences do you see between the behaviors that lizards and humans use to help regulate temperature?

Students should recognize the behaviors these lizards employ to regulate temperature—changes in activity level in the Gila monster; panting and position changes in the horned lizard—and compare these with familiar behaviors that humans use to regulate temperature. For example, both lizards and humans can change location and activity level when it gets too hot or cold. Lizards can move into the shade or a burrow to cool off or into the sun to warm up; humans can move into the shade or sun or indoors or outdoors. Horned lizards and humans both use an open mouth and rapid breathing as an evaporative cooling technique. Horned lizards, however, use posture as a way of controlling heat absorbance and conductance. For example, if the air is cool and the ground is warm (just after sunset) horned lizards crouch close to the ground and use this warmth to keep their internal temperature high. By contrast, humans sweat to keep cool and shiver to keep warm. In general, humans have more options for staying warm or cool as a result of technology; we can change our environment. We use clothing, which creates a new external environment close to the skin, or we can heat and air condition our dwellings.

2. What similarities and differences do you see between the way dogs and humans regulate temperature?

Think about the physiology of a dog and of a human as each responds to temperature extremes.

Humans sweat and dogs pant to cool off; both shiver to warm up. Both move into or out of the sun, depending on their need to warm up or cool off. Dogs often curl up to reduce the surface area exposed to the environment if they are cold; humans achieve a similar effect by holding their arms tightly against the body. Some dogs can improve the insulating value of their coat by fluffing up their fur. In all mammals, a significant drop in environmental temperature can stimulate the vasoconstriction of blood vessels in the skin, which helps to conserve body heat.

3. Describe two homeostatic processes (aside from temperature regulation) that you or other animals regulate through behavior. For each process, identify the stimulus, feedback, and response. Record your responses in a table that is similar to Figure 5.14.

Examples students might use include the following:

Condition that is maintained through homeostasis	Stimulus	Feedback	Behavioral response
Water balance	Thirst	Brain signals thirst when sensors indicate that fluid levels in the body are low	Drinking
Water balance	High fluid levels	Brain signals kidneys when sensors indicate that fluid levels in the body are high	Urinating
Food/energy supply	Hunger	Brain signals hunger when sensors indicate that blood sugar or energy storage is low	Eating
Activity/rest cycle	Fatigue	Energy happens automatically, but humans and most animals have mechanisms to sense and prevent profound fatigue by sleeping at regular intervals; timing is determined by biological "clocks" in the brain	Sleeping
Well-being	Disease symptoms	Brain may signal status with fever, fatigue, nausea, or pain, which lead to specific responses	Resting; avoiding food; vomiting; seeking medical treatment

Evaluate

Homeostasis in Your Critter

Major Concepts Internal/external environment; interaction of systems to maintain homeostasis

Overview

This activity evaluates the learners' understanding of homeostasis by having them return to their description of the organism they "discovered" in Chapter 3. They are asked to apply what they have learned about how organisms maintain their internal environment to a novel organism living in a specific external environment and subjected to certain external stress factors.

Materials   (per class of 30, individuals)

descriptions and diagrams of students' critters from Chapter 3
30 copies of the rubric *Homeostasis in Your Critter*

Outcomes and Indicators of Success

The following indicators allow you to assess the students' level of success with the activity and to assess their process of learning.

By the end of this activity, the learners should be able to

1. demonstrate their understanding of the basic concept of homeostasis.

   They can indicate their ability by

   a. describing homeostasis, and

   b. citing reasons why it is important for living systems to maintain balanced conditions.

2. creatively apply their knowledge of homeostasis to a new situation.

   They can show their creativity in this area by describing interesting and logical ways that their critter maintains its internal environment in response to external stress factors.

Preparations

Make available the learners' folders from Chapter 3, or remind them several days in advance to bring their critter descriptions and diagrams to class on this day.

Strategies for Guiding Learners

PROCESS AND PROCEDURES

As a class, read orally or silently all introductory materials for the activity and the Process and Procedures to help students build connections between concepts and activities. Use the time spent reading to bring the students' attention into focus.

Circulate around the room as the students answer the questions in their journals. Look for responses such as the following:

1. Work individually to write a paragraph that answers each of the following questions. Include your paragraphs in your critter folder for evaluation.

   a. Based on what you have learned in this chapter and Chapter 4, how would you describe homeostasis?

      Homeostasis is commonly thought of as the dynamic balance that is achieved in an organism's internal environment. It is brought about by the interactions of various systems in response to external stress factors.

b. Why is it important for organisms to maintain homeostasis?

> **All organisms are affected by interactions between their internal and external environments. Internal conditions can change because of these interactions, and to survive, organisms must have mechanisms for restoring normal internal conditions.**

2. Recall your critter that you described in Chapter 3 and the environment in which it lives. List at least 5 specific environmental stress factors that your organism most likely would be subjected to in that environment. Include this list in your critter folder.

> **As the learners become reacquainted with their critter from Chapter 3, check that they are listing as many appropriate stress factors as possible for the environments in which their organism lives. As an example, an organism living in a desert environment would be subjected to dehydration. If the climate is hot much of the time as well, the problem of dehydration would be magnified, and heat stress is likely to be a significant factor. A freshwater environment, on the other hand, might subject an organism to solute imbalances.**

3. Use the medium of your choice to demonstrate a response to this question:

> **Encourage the learners to use a variety of media as they respond to the question.**

In what ways does your critter maintain its internal environment considering the external stress factors that you listed in step 2?

You will know that you have adequately addressed the question if your response includes an explanation, illustration, or demonstration of the following:

◆ How your critter regulates internal temperature in response to heat and cold

◆ How your critter regulates water balance

◆ How your critter deals with at least 2 other stresses caused by changes in the external environment that require a response by the internal environment

◆ How at least 2 key systems in your critter interact to adjust internal conditions

A medium is the method or materials you use to convey your response. You could write a response, draw or paint a picture or diagram, develop a collage, or use some other method that your teacher approves.

> **Provide each student with a copy of the rubric, and convene a brief discussion to be certain all students understand the criteria for the assignment. Check that the learners describe homeostatic mechanisms that are appropriate for the environment in which their critter lives.**

Analysis

 Evaluate your work according to the rubric that your teacher provides. Your teacher will use these guidelines to evaluate your work as well.

> **Emphasize that the experience of self-evaluation in the Analysis will help to reinforce the students' sense of responsibility for their own learning. Indicate how you will weigh their self-evaluation as part of your assessment. For example, you might count it as a percentage of their overall score.**

Human Homeostasis: Health and Disease

In this chapter, the students examine what happens when homeostasis is disrupted severely. We engage the students by presenting them with a story about canyon hikers who get themselves into a dangerous situation. The students then explore a number of emergency room triage cases, all of which involve disruptions of homeostasis. They interpret and evaluate emergency medical data and assign treatment priorities to the triage cases. This exercise lets students build an explanation of the connections between illness or injury and the systems that maintain homeostasis in humans.

The students participate in a simulation that helps them explain the immune system's role in preventing homeostatic disruptions. Next, the students assess some of their own behaviors and elaborate risks in their own lives that may reduce their ability to maintain homeostasis. Finally, the students evaluate their understanding of the chapter by using the knowledge that they have acquired to develop a proposal for a health care program. In this proposal, the students consider the biological ramifications, related health risks, and ethics of their proposed program.

ACTIVITIES

Engage	Pushing the Limits
Explore **Explain**	Hospital Triage
Explain	Self-Defense!
Explain **Elaborate**	What's the Risk?
Evaluate	Health Care Proposal

CHAPTER 6 IMPLEMENTATION

	Instructional Flow			Classroom Support			
Activity/ Student Text pp. Teacher Guide pp.	GACD, TRCD, DVD, and CD-ROM Resources	Essays/ Student Text pp.	Estimated Time	Team Size/ Cooperative Learning Focus	Strategies and Tools	Assessment Opportunities	Special Considerations
ENGAGE Pushing the Limits pp. 194–195 TG pp. 208–210		Beyond the Limits pp. 242–244	30 minutes	Team size: 2 Skill: Contributing ideas		Prior knowledge of homeostasis and human health concepts	Enlarge print materials and/or read aloud if needed.
EXPLORE/ EXPLAIN Hospital Triage pp. 196–202 TG pp. 210–216	Copymaster: Patients' Vital Signs—Preliminary Information; Copymaster: Triage Data Sheet; Copymaster: First Priority; and Copymaster: Additional Information	Coping with Disruptions: The Role of Medicine in Homeostasis pp. 244–246	100–150 minutes	Team size: 4 Skill: Taking responsibility; contributing ideas	Simulation	Analyzing information; using critical-thinking skills	Enlarge print materials and/or read aloud if needed. Some students may benefit from going over copymasters before class in preparation for the activity.
EXPLAIN Self-Defense! pp. 202–205 TG pp. 217–227	Copymaster: Test Subject Cards; Copymaster: Scenario Cards; Copymaster: Complete Scenario Information	Avoiding Disruptions: The Immune System pp. 246–250 Self and Nonself pp. 250–251 Immune System Memory pp. 251–252	100 minutes	Team size: 4 Skill: Reaching consensus	Simulation	Current understanding of disease and homeostasis; critical-thinking skills	Some students may benefit from having the steps of this activity explained ahead of time.
EXPLAIN/ ELABORATE What's the Risk? pp. 207–209 TG pp. 228–235	Copymaster: Risk Assessment Data; Copymaster: Taking Risks: A Self-Evaluation	Avoiding Disruptions: Behavior, Choices, and Risk pp. 253–254 Individual Behavior Can Affect Larger Groups pp. 255–256 Ethical Analysis pp. 256–257	150 minutes	Team size: 4 and individuals Skill: Managing and organizing team tasks; taking responsibility; reaching consensus	Active participation	Making connections between related ideas; self-assessment	Enlarge print materials and/or read aloud if needed.

Instructional Flow

Classroom Support

Activity/ Student Text pp. Teacher Guide pp.	GACD, TRCD, DVD, and CD-ROM Resources	Essays/ Student Text pp.	Estimated Time	Team Size/ Cooperative Learning Focus	Strategies and Tools	Assessment Opportunities	Special Considerations
EVALUATE *Health Care Proposal* pp. 209–217 TG pp. 235–239	Rubric: *Health Care Proposal*		100 minutes (in class)	*Team size:* 4, jigsaw and individuals *Skill:* Advocating a position	Project; outside resources (can include Internet research)	Applying understandings to new situations; making connections between related ideas	Plan research portion of this project to fit special needs if necessary. For example, if students will explore local resources for information, schedule opportunities that are appropriate for students with special challenges.

e. For each of your patients, list 1 or 2 emergency medical treatments that might help each restore homeostasis. Record this list in the 6th column as well. Use the back of the data sheet if you need more space to record your responses.

Ask the students to review briefly the information in Range of Vital Signs and General Triage Guidelines before they decide to divide up their responsibilities. The purpose of the triage data sheet handout is to help students understand their jobs and to keep the activity moving at a brisk pace. As the students begin completing the table, make certain they are working as a team. If they find this task difficult, remind them that particular medical answers are not required. Suitable answers are embedded in the triage guidelines.

As the students work to classify the patients, remind them that each team member needs to contribute his or her information.

 As the students fill in the last column of the chart, encourage them to review the information in Chapters 4 and 5 as needed. This step provides you with an opportunity to assess the students' ability to analyze information and use critical-thinking skills.

PART B   Let's Get More Information

   1. Obtain the Copymaster *First Priority* from your teacher. Discuss the importance of this new information with your teammates.

 Have the students review the Copymaster *First Priority*, which provides additional information about each patient. Explain to the students that their job is to extract the bigger homeostatic picture from the data that are presented. Again, you have an opportunity to assess the students' critical-thinking skills.

   2. Working as a team, reevaluate the order you should treat each patient. Record your order of priority in the 7th column of your team's triage data table. (This may be different from the order given in task 4c.)

Be prepared to show your ideas and your team's triage results in a class discussion.

As the students begin to revise their data tables, explain to them that this procedure is not designed to uncover a single, correct answer. Many reasonable orders are possible, and they may find that a simple subdivision of their previous categorization is sufficient.

   3. Obtain the Copymaster *Additional Information* from your teacher. Read the information to learn the consequences of your secondary triage decisions.

   4. In the 8th column, indicate any additional internal body systems (systems that were not identified as being disrupted in Part A) that your team thinks are disrupted. Base your decisions on the new information.

The information in the Copymaster *Additional Information* may provide additional clues about your patients' body systems.

This step gives the students an opportunity to make changes based on the new information at their disposal. Emphasize that changing a hypothesis is appropriate when new information supports such a change.

   5. With your team, discuss any additional factors that may have contributed to each patient's condition and to your priority choices. Write a brief explanation for your patients' final ranking in the 8th column of the triage data sheet.

These may include nonmedical factors, such as behavior and luck, which your team took into consideration.

As the students complete their tables, remind them that now they are providing justification for their decisions. Walk around the room and pay particular attention to any significant changes that the students may have made in assessing the patients' conditions. Students should focus on their reasons for ranking the patients in a particular way. Team prognoses probably will vary, but draw attention to the cases where partial or complete recovery seems possible. Emphasize that the human body has a tremendous capacity for recovery following injury, but it is not limitless. Boundaries exist beyond which recovery is not possible. This idea should be apparent from the cases where patients die.

6. As a team, discuss what the prognosis, or long-term outlook, is for each patient. Prepare to present your reasoning in a class discussion.

For instance, you might think that some patients will recover completely, others will recover slowly and may suffer long-lasting effects, and others may never recover and even die because of their injury or illness.

Encourage discussion about any interesting and reasonable prognoses that focus on how the illness or injury might affect a patient's behavior and lifestyle following recovery.

Analysis

When all the students are finished with their tables, ask them to work individually to complete the Analysis. Following are some potential responses:

1. Why are vital signs so valuable in assessing a patient's condition quickly?

Vital signs are direct indicators for the systems that are most critical for homeostasis, and they serve as sensitive indicators of human health. Vital signs are practical and reliable for use in emergencies (where patients are not always conscious) and can reveal aspects of a patient's health about which he or she may be unaware.

2. Explain how a head injury, such as the one Albert suffered when his motorcycle crashed, could affect so many internal body systems that are necessary to maintain homeostasis.

Answers should include statements indicating that the brain is the control center of the body. Students may mention specific parts of the brain that are involved in the control of feedback systems, such as the pituitary and hypothalamus.

3. How did a bacterial infection cause a higher-than-normal temperature in Maria?

Students should find this answer embedded in the description of lab results for Maria. Bacterial toxins can alter the set point of the hypothalamus and induce fever.

4. Monique and Nelson both had very high temperatures when they were brought into the emergency room. Why do you think Monique's heart rate was high and Nelson's heart rate was low?

The students may speculate that at high temperatures, the heart rate increases. In fact, for every 1°C elevation in body temperature, the heart rate increases approximately 10 beats per minute. This was the reason that Monique's heart rate was high. Beyond a certain temperature, however, the tissues begin to deteriorate irreversibly, which weakens the heart and causes it to beat slowly. Nelson's higher temperature weakened his heart muscle, causing the heart to pump less effectively. This weakening eventually progressed to the point of heart failure.

5. Why was Monique likely to survive if she received treatment in time but Nelson died in spite of the priority he was given?

   Students may make many suggestions, but accept only those that they can defend adequately on the basis of numerous or severe readings of vital signs. The link between vital signs and severity of condition should be relatively clear to the students by now.

6. What, if any, nonmedical considerations did you use to rank the patients? Explain your response.

   Several answers are possible; accept any that the students can support with well-reasoned arguments. The students almost certainly will take some nonmedical considerations into account, such as a patient's age and perhaps the role that a patient's behavior played in his or her circumstance. Explore their reasons and allow the discussion to move toward the potential ethical dilemmas, because later activities in this chapter deal with ethical dilemmas.

7. In one or two paragraphs, compare and contrast an illness or injury that the body can recover from on its own with one that requires medical intervention. Explain how the responses of internal body systems that are necessary to maintain homeostasis differ in the two situations.

   Expect that the students will be able to come up with a concrete example or examples to express these differences. For example, a student might describe the differences in homeostatic disruption that occur when a person falls down and cuts her knee and when a person is involved in an accident and suffers several severe lacerations. In the first instance, the blood loss is minimal and the risk of infection is minor. In the second instance, the blood loss could be great and the consequent lowering of blood pressure could cause the person to die if there were no medical intervention. Also in the second case, the risk of severe infection persists even after the bleeding has stopped.

Extensions

In this activity, the students are exploring the emergency health care services in an urban setting in the United States at the beginning of the 21st century. As an extension of this activity, your students might enjoy exploring health care or healing in another setting, another time, or another culture. These could be in the form of reports and presentations, the journal of an anthropologist, or the diary of a person who was injured and treated in another country. The PBS program *Bill Moyer's Journal* presents a six-part series titled *Healing and the Mind*. One part explores the differences between Western medicine and traditional Chinese medicine. Watching this part may be an interesting way to begin exploring medicine in another culture.

Self-Defense!

Major Concepts Mechanisms of immune function; how behavior affects immune function; role of vaccines

Overview

This activity provides a foundation for students to develop an explanation for the role of immune function in the human body as well as for some of the mechanisms by which it is carried out. In Part B, the students use this knowledge in an immune system puzzle. The teams work cooperatively to solve the puzzle that involves aspects of behavior, immune function, and the action of pathogens.

Materials   (per class of 30, teams of 4)

2 sets of the Copymaster *Test Subject Cards* (see Preparations)
1 set of the Copymaster *Scenario Cards* (see Preparations)
30 copies of the Copymaster *Complete Scenario Information*
large sheet of paper or overhead transparency
pens or pencils
container for test subject cards

Outcomes and Indicators of Success

The following indicators allow you to assess the students' level of success with the activity and to assess their process of learning.

By the end of this activity, the learners should

1. understand that the immune system's response depends on a number of factors such as the type of pathogen it encounters, the individual's medical history (vaccinations and previous exposures), and lifestyle factors (fatigue, stress, diet).

    They will demonstrate their understanding by using their knowledge to solve a pathogen identification puzzle.

2. understand that immune defense has mechanisms for both nonspecific and specific response.

    They will show their understanding by

    a. providing examples of a nonspecific response, and

    b. deducing the effects of vaccination or prior exposure on a given infection.

3. be able to distinguish some differences between bacterial and viral infections.

They will show this ability by correlating the effectiveness of antibiotic therapy on viral versus bacterial infections.

Preparations

PART B. Familiarize yourself with the suggested prognoses, which are described in the Strategies for Guiding Learners. Prepare two sets of test subject cards from that copymaster for step 1 and one set of scenario cards from that copymaster for step 5. You may want to cut out these cards and mount them on 3 × 5-inch cards or laminate them. Obtain a large sheet of paper or an overhead transparency on which to record the class data in Part B, step 3, or use the chalkboard. The students will need this information in Part B, step 7.

Strategies for Guiding Learners

PROCESS AND PROCEDURES

PART A   Natural Defenses

As a class, read orally or silently all introductory materials for the activity and the Process and Procedures to help students build connections between concepts and activities. Use the time spent reading to bring the students' attention into focus.

Suggest that the learners read all of the questions in this step first and record preliminary answers in their journals based on what they already know. Then have them use the essays as a resource to answer the questions more completely.

1. Respond to the following statements about how the immune system helps maintain homeostasis. Record your answers in your journal.

    Use the background information in the essays *Avoiding Disruptions: The Immune System* (page 246), *Self and Nonself* (page 250), and *Immune System Memory* (page 251) to help you with this task. The information in the Glossary of Immune System Components should also help.

    a. Why is it important for the body to distinguish material that is part of itself from nonself material? Explain what happens when the body fails to make that distinction.

    The immune system uses a network of defensive forces to eliminate invaders that threaten the body. When the immune system cannot distinguish between self and nonself, it attacks and may damage its own body tissues. Autoimmune diseases are the result of the body's failure to make this distinction. Rheumatoid arthritis, lupus, and multiple sclerosis are examples of autoimmune diseases.

    b. Provide 2 examples of the immune system's nonspecific defense mechanisms. Explain how nonspecific immunity differs from specific immunity.

    Expect that students give examples of nonspecific defense mechanisms such as the skin, tears, and macrophages. Students should point out that nonspecific defenses do not have to recognize the specific invader; they can defend against many types of invaders. Specific immunity involves specialized cells that recognize and attack certain invaders only.

c. Explain why viruses are unaffected by antibiotics such as penicillin and tetracycline.

   Expect students to explain that antibiotics kill invaders such as bacteria that are outside the cells. Because viruses live inside the cell and use these host cells as shields, antibiotics are not effective against viral infections. To kill viruses, a medication would have to kill the rest of the cell as well.

d. Describe how vaccination is a technological innovation that takes advantage of a basic property of the immune system.

   Vaccines are weakened or killed pathogens and are used in very small doses. Such doses are just sufficient to bring on an immune response but not sufficient to cause disease symptoms. As a result of the immune response, immunity to that pathogen develops. Subsequent exposures then trigger a major immune reaction.

2. Share your answers as part of a class discussion.

   Encourage students to share their answers; use this discussion as an opportunity to assess their current level of understanding. This step also provides you with an opportunity to clarify key points. Antibiotics are not effective treatments for viral infections, and thus penicillin would not kill the influenza virus.

PART B   Diagnosis: A Puzzle

1. Have 1 team member obtain a test subject card from the container that your teacher provides. Share the information on the card with the rest of the team.

   Give a test subject card (from the Copymaster *Test Subject Cards*) to one member of each team. Make sure that each of the four different test subjects is represented by at least one team and that at least three teams receive Test Subject 1, because this subject is used several times in the later scenarios. Explain to the students that they will keep this test subject identity for the remainder of the activity.

2. Assume that your subject has just been exposed to the influenza virus. Complete the following tasks with your team. Record in your journal the evidence and inferences that support your conclusions.

   a. Generate a prognosis for your subject.

      A prognosis is a prediction based on evidence and inference about whether a person will become ill, and if so, how soon he or she will recover.

   b. Discuss what effect penicillin would have if it were administered the 1st day that symptoms occur.

      Ask the students to complete the tasks that are listed, that is, to generate a prognosis and discuss the effect of penicillin. This is an opportunity to assess the students' current understanding of concepts.

3. As your teacher directs, share your team's prognosis for your test subject with your classmates.

   When the students have completed step 2, conduct a class discussion to solicit each team's prognosis. Post the prognoses on the chalkboard, a large sheet of paper, or an overhead transparency so that the students can refer to them. Also, post the characteristics of each test subject so that students can see the differences and can compare different subjects in the unknown pathogen part of this exercise. Use the following Suggested Prognoses for Subjects Exposed to Influenza Virus to guide the discussion.

CHAPTER 7 IMPLEMENTATION (continued)

	Instructional Flow			Classroom Support			
Activity/ Student Text pp. Teacher Guide pp.	*GACD, TRCD, DVD, and CD-ROM Resources*	*Essays/ Student Text pp.*	*Estimated Time*	*Team Size/ Cooperative Learning Focus*	*Strategies and Tools*	*Assessment Opportunities*	*Special Considerations*
EVALUATE *Marathon* pp. 278–285 TG pp. 272–279	Rubric: *Marathon;* DVD: *A Good Day for Running*	*Factors Influencing Performance* pp. 343–347	100 minutes	*Team size:* 4 *Skill:* Managing and organizing team tasks; sharing perspectives	Video; discussion	Assessing students' ability to synthesize and apply the chapter's concepts to a scenario about fitness	Enlarge print materials and/or read aloud if needed.

Optional activities:
• Elaborate: *Of Cannibals and Calories*—on TRCD, section 5

Chapter Goals

By the end of this chapter, the students should understand that

- human physical performance requires matter and energy,
- athletic fitness can be distinguished from fitness for life,
- an animal's ability to move is related to the organization of its muscles and skeleton,
- for humans, food is a critical source of both matter and energy, and
- an individual's fitness can be influenced by a variety of factors, including exercise and diet.

The learners also will

- design and conduct a controlled experiment,
- collect and analyze data,
- distinguish evidence from inference, and
- develop explanations.

Advance Preparation

Reserve a DVD player for *You Are What You Eat, Structures and Functions*, and *Marathon*. Check Materials and Preparations for *What Is in the Food You Eat?* and *Structures and Functions*, so that you can have the required materials available.

Thinking about Fitness

Major Concepts Fitness for life and athletic fitness

Overview

This short activity provides learners with an opportunity to think about their current understanding of the concept of fitness by offering their own definitions of fitness and by comparing athletic fitness with fitness for life.

Outcomes and Indicators of Success

The following indicators allow you to assess the students' level of success with the activity and to assess their process of learning.

By the end of this activity, the learners should begin to think about the meaning of fitness and that it has different meanings depending on one's point of view.

They will demonstrate their level of understanding by

a. suggesting their own definitions of fitness, and

b. using a diagram of athletic fitness and fitness for life to compare individuals with different levels of life fitness and athletic fitness.

ID PROCEDURES

...ally or silently all introductory materials for the activity and the
...es to help students build connections between concepts and activities.
...ding to bring the students' attention into focus.

...ler your answers to the questions below. Record your responses in your

...personal definition of fitness?

...most affect your level of fitness, as you defined it?

...cale diagrams shown in Figure 7.1 into your journal.

...ry *The Sky Awaits*, think about the fitness scales and what they mean.

...earners should work independently to respond to the questions and read the
scenario *The Sky Awaits*. Their answers should provide you with some insight to their
prior conceptions about fitness.

4. Refer to the fitness scales as you discuss and complete the following with the
members of your team:

   We suggest that the learners work in teams of four. Assign new cooperative teams of
   two for the unit, and select which pairs of teams should work together for those activities
   that require teams of four. As the teams discuss the questions, circulate around the room
   and note any misconceptions that you will need to address during the course of the
   chapter. Students often feel that athletic fitness is the only valid type of fitness.

   a. What does scale *a* represent? What physical and behavioral characteristics would
      you expect to find in an individual who scores very high on such a scale?

      Scale *a* represents athletic fitness. Individuals who score high on such a scale
      probably would be skilled in particular athletic activities and might have bodies
      that show evidence of specialized training appropriate to their athletic interests.
      (For example, runners might have strong legs and swimmers might have well-
      developed legs, shoulders, and backs.) Such individuals also probably would watch
      their diets closely, would not smoke, and would exercise and practice regularly.

   b. What does scale *b* represent? What characteristics would you expect to find in an
      individual who scores very high on this scale?

      Scale *b* represents the fitness-for-life scale. Individuals who score very high on
      this scale might or might not have specialized athletic skills. However, they would
      show evidence of general good health. They probably would be of moderate weight
      in relation to their height, and their muscles would be firm and well toned. Because
      they would have healthy systems for homeostatic regulation (such as circulatory and
      breathing systems), they would be at low risk for disease, especially heart disease,
      high blood pressure, and liver disease. Moreover, they probably would sleep well
      and feel energetic in their daily activities as a result of their fitness.

   c. Where on each scale would you place Sullivan and Yates? In your journal, mark
      and label where you would place Sullivan and Yates on each scale. Below the
      diagrams, write a sentence explaining why you placed Sullivan and Yates at those
      positions.

Learners may decide that Sullivan and Yates likely are very athletically fit, and because of the training and conditioning required for their jobs, also are very fit for life. This line of reasoning should lead the students to identify points somewhere in the upper portion of each scale. Some learners may decide that Yates and Sullivan fit elsewhere on the scales. Their explanations should support their decisions.

d. These separate scales represent athletic fitness and fitness for life. They suggest that it may be possible for a person to lack special athletic skills and still be very fit for life. Mark and label where you would place such an individual on each scale. What benefits do you think might be associated with a high level of fitness for life?

Though answers will be somewhat different, learners should mention benefits such as a long life, increased energy levels, restful sleep, and generally good health.

You might point out to your learners that it is possible that someone could be high on a scale of athletic fitness but not be particularly fit for life. For example, certain types of athletic performance do not require a high level of overall fitness but only a certain fitness required for a specific activity. Some sports, such as baseball, do not require sustained levels of activity for all positions on the team. Likewise, accuracy in sports such as golf, bowling, and target shooting is not necessarily related to overall physical fitness. Some athletes may train to the extreme and cause injuries to themselves or even compromise their immune function due to fatigue. Certain sports, such as gymnastics or football, may have debilitating effects on long-term health. Sometimes the behavior of individual athletes (for example, use of drugs, tobacco, or alcohol) may detract from overall fitness, even though they still may be able to perform well in their particular sport.

e. Where would you place yourself on the fitness-for-life scale? List several ways that you and the other members of your team could modify your lifestyles to improve your positions on this scale.

The learners already may be able to relate their exercise and dietary habits to fitness for life. Learners might suggest, for example, adding more vigorous activity or activities of longer duration to their weekly routines. They also might suggest dietary changes such as reducing intake of junk food and increasing their intake of fruits, vegetables, and grains.

What Determines Fitness?

Major Concepts Fitness as a function of activity level and diet

Overview

This activity provides learners with an opportunity to explore two factors that affect their level of fitness, activity level, and diet. Learners complete a brief analysis of their activity levels and dietary habits, compare themselves with highly trained jet pilots as well as with a profile of a "typical" classmate, and are challenged to suggest ways to improve their levels of fitness.

Materials (per class of 30, individuals)

30 copies of the Copymaster *Physical Activity Analysis*
30 copies of the Copymaster *Dietary Analysis*
1 copy of the Copymaster *Class Activity Level Profile*
overhead transparencies (optional)

Outcomes and Indicators of Success

The following indicators allow you to assess the students' level of success with the activity and to assess their process of learning.

By the end of this activity, the learners should begin to develop an understanding of how activity level and diet affect their level of fitness.

They will demonstrate their understanding by

a. using self-assessment surveys to determine their activity levels for 1 week and their dietary pattern for 1 day,

b. identifying resources their bodies need to sustain different levels of performance,

c. describing fitness in relation to the body's ability to mobilize matter and energy,

d. revising their earlier definitions of fitness to reflect the information encountered in the activity and in the essays, and

e. creating an advertisement to promote the reasons for maintaining or improving one's fitness for life.

Preparations

Make 1 copy each of *Physical Activity Analysis* and *Dietary Analysis* for each student. Study them carefully so you understand how the students are to use them. Do not require learners to share their results on either the activity level analysis or the dietary analysis; emphasize that most of the questions in the activity are for individual reflection, not for group comment.

Strategies for Guiding Learners

PROCESS AND PROCEDURES

As a class, read orally or silently all introductory materials for the activity and the Process and Procedures to help students build connections between concepts and activities. Use the time spent reading to bring the students' attention into focus.

PART A   Looking at Physical Activity

1. Work individually to complete the *Physical Activity Analysis* that your teacher provides.

Attach this analysis to your journal; you may need to refer to it during subsequent activities.

Work through one sample activity with the students to explain the steps in calculating the activity index for each session of exercise or activity conducted in the last week. The sum of the week's activity indices is the students' personal activity index from which they derive an activity level, using the chart under step 6 of the *Physical Activity Analysis*.

You may wish to instruct students to select a typical week rather than the last week if they were ill or had an unusual amount of activity for some reason during the past 7 days.

2. Answer the following questions individually. Record your answers in your journal. Base your responses on your activity level that you determined in step 1.

   a. How do you think your activity level compares with that of a typical student in your class?

   b. How do you think your activity level might compare with that of Yates and Sullivan from the story *The Sky Awaits*?

   As the learners work individually to complete the *Physical Activity Analysis* and answer the questions, be sure that they respect each other's privacy.

3. On the sheet that your teacher circulates, place a check mark (✓) next to your activity level, which you determined in step 1.

   Your teacher will use this information to create an activity level profile for the class.

4. Enter the activity level profile for the class in the appropriate spaces on the worksheet in the *Physical Activity Analysis*.

   Circulate the Copymaster *Class Activity Level Profile*, and ask each learner to place a check mark (✓) next to his or her activity level. When every learner has responded, record the class profile on the chalkboard or on an overhead transparency so that students can record the data in the table at the end of their *Physical Activity Analysis*.

PART B   Looking at Diet

1. Work individually to complete the *Dietary Analysis* that your teacher provides.

   Attach this analysis to your journal; you may need to refer to it in subsequent activities.

   Keep your classroom open to discussion during this step so that students can help each other determine the ingredients in more complex foods that must be broken down into several groups. For example, sausage and cheese pizza must be recorded in the milk, meat, and grain groups.

   If a student was sick or did not eat much the previous day for any reason, suggest she or he either select a different day or imagine a day with favorite foods for every meal.

2. Answer the following questions individually. Record your answers in your journal. Base your responses on the *Dietary Analysis* that you completed in step 1.

   a. How do you think your diet compares with that of a typical student in your class?

   b. How do you think your diet might compare with that of Yates and Sullivan?

   Have the learners work individually to complete the *Dietary Analysis* and answer the questions.

3. Work with your team to complete the following steps. The data you provide will help your teacher generate a dietary profile of a typical student in your class.

   a. Choose 1 of the food groups listed on the *Dietary Analysis*. Ask 4 students outside your team how many servings from that group they ate yesterday. Record their responses.

   Each member of your team should choose a different food group.

   b. Calculate the average number of daily servings (from the food group you chose) that you and the 4 students you polled ate yesterday.

   Average # of servings = (total # servings eaten in 1 day by you and 4 other students) ÷ 5.

   This will give you a rough approximation of how much a typical student in your class eats from that food group.

   c. Contribute your data to the dietary profile your teacher will compile on the chalkboard.

4. Enter the information for this typical student into the column titled Class Profile on the *Dietary Analysis* worksheet.

   As the learners collect data for a dietary profile, encourage them to complete their four interviews with people from different parts of the classroom. The interview process should not take more than a few minutes. As you poll the class, choose volunteers to report for each food group. Create a composite on the chalkboard or an overhead transparency to display what a "typical" learner from the class might eat in a day.

5. Participate in a class discussion of the following. Base your responses on the information that you collected in Parts A and B.

   As you lead the class discussion, pay special attention to question 5b. This question is particularly important because it focuses the students on the concept of validity of data.

   a. Are you surprised at the activity profile or dietary profile of your class? Are you surprised at how your own profiles compare to the class profiles? Explain your answers.

   Accept any thoughtful answer.

   b. Identify ways in which the class profiles do not accurately represent typical activity levels and dietary patterns in society.

   Answers will vary depending on whether learners think that a 1-week sample is likely to represent most of their classmates' normal levels of activity, and whether they think that a 1-day sample is likely to represent most of their classmates' eating habits. Activity levels and eating habits might vary with a number of factors, such as the season and the general health of the individual involved. If there are a large number of learners in the class, however, the results will tend to average out. Generally, a scientist would not use a 1-day or a 1-week sample as the basis for a detailed set of conclusions about a person's normal behavior, but probably would require a study that extends over a period of several weeks or even months.

c. Why do you think many people fail to sustain an adequate level of physical activity or fail to eat an appropriate number of servings from each food group?

Some learners may mention that America's infatuation with and dependency on the automobile has contributed to a sedentary lifestyle. Nonphysical forms of entertainment such as television and video games also contribute to lowered fitness. Technology has produced many laborsaving devices that reduce the demand for physical activity. Similarly, our "instant society" (fast-food restaurants, snack and beverage vending machines, frozen pizza) does not encourage good nutrition. Remind the learners to attach their completed activity level analyses and dietary analyses to their journals. They may wish to refer to both of these surveys during the course of the chapter, and they will need their dietary analysis to complete the next activity, *What Is in the Food You Eat?*

Analysis

Expect responses such as the following to the Analysis questions. Have your students use the essay *Human Performance: A Function of Fitness* (page 326) as a resource.

1. Work individually, and use all of the information in this activity to help you answer the following questions. Record your responses in your journal.

The essay *Human Performance: A Function of Fitness* (page 326) will be helpful.

a. What resources does your body require during extreme levels of physical performance?

Learners should list matter such as food and physical structures, and energy such as that needed for work, repair, and cellular processes.

b. What resources does your body require to sustain basic levels of nonathletic activity?

Learners again should list matter and energy as required resources. The resources necessary do not change from those listed in question 1a, only the particulars involved, such as the amount and/or frequency.

c. Refine and rewrite your personal definition of fitness from step 1 of the engage activity. Incorporate any new ideas that you have learned.

Look for evidence that the learners have included explicitly the importance of fitness for life in their definitions. Also, look for the sense that both moderate exercise and balanced nutrition are necessary requirements to maintain fitness. Athletic fitness need not be included.

2. Work with your partner to complete the following task. Then follow your teacher's instructions for posting your advertisement.

Imagine that you are the owner of a new health club in your neighborhood. Create a one-page newspaper advertisement for your club that would draw a reader's attention to the most compelling reasons you know for maintaining or improving one's fitness for life.

Designate a place where the learners can display their advertisements. Both the advertisement and the students' responses to the questions provide an opportunity for embedded assessment.

The advertisement should highlight *reasons* to invest effort (time and energy) into improving fitness. Expect learners to focus on having a longer, healthier life; looking and feeling better and consequently having an improved sense of well-being and self-esteem; having higher energy levels; and reducing stress as reasons to improve one's fitness for life. They also might suggest that fitness improves their ability to participate in recreations they enjoy.

Explain

What Is in the Food You Eat?

Major Concepts Food contains energy and several basic nutrients

Overview

In this activity, the learners examine the nutritional basis of performance. They test representative food samples for the presence of certain types of matter (nutrients) and relate these findings to the dietary analysis that they completed in the activity *What Determines Fitness?* The essay *Food: Our Body's Source of Energy and Structural Materials* explains how the body uses the major nutrients in food and considers the question of what constitutes a balanced diet.

This investigation allows the learners to discover some of the types of nutrients that occur in a variety of common foods. In the Analysis, they apply this information to the dietary analysis that they completed in *What Determines Fitness?* The learners test some common foods for the presence of several components that are nutritionally important.

Materials (per class of 30, teams of 4 or 5)

30 pairs of safety goggles
30 lab aprons
30 pairs of plastic gloves
6 dropping pipets
6 500-mL beakers
18 10-mL graduated cylinders
114 18 × 150-mm test tubes
2 2 ½-gal waste pails
6 test tube clamps
18 test tube racks
12 glass-marking pencils
6 hot plates
6 lunch-sized, brown paper bags
6 dropping bottles of Benedict's solution
    labeled *CAUTION: Irritant*
    (total 60 mL)

6 dropping bottles of Biuret solution
    labeled *WARNING: Strong irritant*
    (total 24 mL)
6 dropping bottles of indophenol solution
    labeled *CAUTION: Irritant*
    **(Note: Indophenol must be fresh.
    Keep it refrigerated between uses, and
    order a new supply each year.)**
    (total 24 mL)
6 screw-cap jars of isopropyl alcohol (99%)
    labeled *WARNING: Flammable liquid*
    (total 120 mL)
6 dropping bottles of Lugol's iodine
    solution labeled *WARNING: Poison if
    ingested, irritant*
    (total 24 mL)

50-mL food samples from each of the 6 food groups, such as

    fruits (apples, oranges, bananas)

    vegetables (potatoes, onions, broccoli stalks, squash, tomatoes)

    meats (egg whites, liver)

    milk (cheeses, milk)

    grains (breakfast cereals, fresh pasta, bread)

    fats, oils, and sweets (egg yolks, desserts, snack foods)

2 of each

12 samples

For positive controls (for a class of 30):

6 spatulas or dropping pipets

30 100-mL beakers

30 10-mL graduated cylinders

300 mL of 1% ascorbic acid (vitamin C)

6 pats of regular margarine or small bottles
    (dropping-bottle size) of vegetable oil

300 mL of a 6% suspension of gelatin

300 mL of a 10% solution of glucose

300 mL of a 10% solution of sucrose

300 mL of a 6% suspension of starch

For negative controls (for a class of 30):

6 100-mL beakers filled half-full with tap water

Outcomes and Indicators of Success

The following indicators allow you to assess the students' level of success with the activity and to assess their process of learning.

By the end of this activity, the learners should

1. be able to explore and develop an explanation for the nutrients in the foods they eat.

   They will show their ability by

   a. predicting results of food tests,

   b. conducting controlled food tests using protocols and their own organizational abilities,

   c. comparing their predicted results with their actual results,

   d. explaining the importance of positive and negative controls, and

   e. determining correlations between types of food and particular compounds.

2. know which common molecular compounds are found in which food.

   They will show their knowledge by listing the foods they tested that contained protein, glucose, sucrose, starch, lipids, or vitamin C.

Safety

Remind learners that alcohol is flammable and that its vapors can explode. Extinguish all flames before using any alcohol. Restrict the total amount of alcohol in the laboratory at any one time to 600 mL. Store it in bottles no larger than 100-mL capacity. Use screw-cap jars for storing isopropyl alcohol during the activity. Keep the hot plates in an area separate from where the tests are performed.

Caution

Preparations

To keep the quantities of materials to a minimum and still obtain meaningful results as a class, create 6 teams of 5 for this activity. Provide the class with samples of 2 foods from each food group so that the students will have data for all 6 food groups. For ease in handling the foods, grind them in a blender to a mushy consistency. You may need to add water to some foods to make them mushy. Frozen liver is easier to use than fresh liver. If you have students from a minority ethnic group in class, consider selecting a food to test that is common to their culture and uncommon in the majority culture.

Label the waste pails, and tell the students where they are located. Warn students of the health hazards and consequences of tasting the food samples (stomach pumping if indicators are involved).

Prepare the following solutions as positive controls, and place in labeled 100-mL beakers. Provide a graduated cylinder for each solution for each team. Also, place a beaker with 50 mL of tap water labeled *Water* at each lab table.

6% gelatin suspension

Add 18 g dry gelatin to 300 mL of distilled water. Heat to suspend; do not boil. Store it in a refrigerator if keeping it for more than a few hours. Dispense 50 mL to each of six 100-mL beakers, and label *Gelatin Suspension (Protein)*.

6% starch suspension

Add 18 g soluble starch or cornstarch to 300 mL of distilled water. Stirring constantly, heat until starch dissolves. If using cornstarch, filter. Dispense 50 mL to each of six 100-mL beakers, and label *Starch Suspension*.

10% glucose solution

Dissolve 30 g of glucose in 300 mL of distilled water. Dispense 50 mL to each of six 100-mL beakers, and label *Glucose Solution (Sugar)*.

10% sucrose solution

Dissolve 30 g of sucrose in 300 mL of distilled water. Dispense 50 mL to each of six 100-mL beakers, and label *Sucrose Solution (Sugar)*.

Vitamin C solution (1% ascorbic acid)

Note: Indophenol must be fresh. Refrigerate it when not in use, and order fresh indicator each year. Use the following positive control to test the indophenol before conducting the activity.

Crush six 500-mg tablets of vitamin C, and dissolve in 300 mL of distilled water. Filter if necessary. Dispense 50 mL to each of six 100-mL beakers, and label *Vitamin C Solution*.

Lipids

Place a small amount of margarine or vegetable oil at each lab table, and label *Lipids*. Provide a spatula or dropping pipet for each lab table.

Strategies for Guiding Learners

PROCESS AND PROCEDURES

As a class, read orally or silently all introductory materials for the activity and the Process and Procedures to help students build connections between concepts and activities. Use the time spent reading to bring the students' attention into focus.

1. Assemble in the teams of 4 that your teacher assigns. Obtain the 4 food samples that your team is to test.

Adjust the number of food samples tested by each team so that each team member tests a different food.

2. In your journal, create a table for recording the foods that the class will test, your predictions about what nutrients each food contains, and the actual test results.

Each team will test 4 foods. But your table should have space to record your predictions and the class results of 5 tests for each of 12 foods. Indicators are available to test for the following nutrients: starch, sugar (glucose and sucrose), vitamin C, fats and oils, and protein. *Indicators* are chemical or physical methods used to test for the presence of certain substances.

Have the learners assemble in teams of four or five. (If they are in teams of five, have them test five foods so that each student conducts all the tests for one food.) Move around the classroom, and make sure that the tables they create are suitable for recording the foods tested, their prediction for the nutrients each food contains, and the results of the tests. Students need to allow space for the 12 foods the class will test. The tables might look similar to Figure T7.1.

Foods	Glucose		Lipids		Protein	
	Prediction	Result	Prediction	Result	Prediction	Result
(name)						
(name)						
(name)						

Foods	Starch		Sucrose		Vitamin C	
	Prediction	Result	Prediction	Result	Prediction	Result
(name)						
(name)						
(name)						

Figure T7.1 Sample nutrient checklist

3. Begin to fill in your table. Enter your predictions about what nutrients you will find in each of the 12 foods that the class will test. Discuss your predictions with your other team members.

You may need to remind the students that some foods contain several nutrients.

4. Review the protocol for nutrient testing. Each member of your team will test 1 food for each of the 5 nutrients.

Be sure to use the correct indicator for each test. Follow the directions carefully for its use.

5. Read the information in the need to know box to help you understand the role of indicators in certain types of investigations.

(See the need to know box on page 269 of the student text.)

As the students decide what nutrients to test for and they read about indicators, ask questions to assess whether they understand what indicators are, as well as the importance of positive and negative controls. If they do not know, review the fundamental ideas.

6. As a team, make a complete set of positive and negative controls to be shared.

Be sure to label each test tube clearly with the nutrient that the indicator tests for. Use a plus sign (+) if it is the positive control, or a minus sign (−) if it is the negative control.

7. Complete your tests. Follow the instructions in Protocol for Nutrient Tests. Record a plus sign (+) in the results column of your table if the food contains a given nutrient. Use a minus sign (−) in the same column if it does not contain the nutrient. Also, record your observations about the color. Indicate how sure you were about your interpretation of each test result for later reference.

Remember, compare the appropriate negative and positive controls each time you test your food for a nutrient.

Pay particular attention to the warning/caution statements for each of the indicators.

As the learners perform their tests, remind them to follow the instructions in Protocol for Nutrient Tests on page 269 of the student textbook, and to heed all safety warnings. They should realize the need to test the same amount of positive and negative controls as they test for the food. For example, if they use 5 mL of ground-up food, they should use 5 mL of positive control and 5 mL of negative control. They must treat all samples the same when performing indicator tests.

8. Wash your hands thoroughly with soap and water.

Follow your teacher's instructions for disposing of all waste materials.

Instruct the learners to discard all food wastes in the waste pails when they have completed their tests. Take the waste to the school cafeteria for proper disposal.

9. Share your results with the other members of your team. Then enter their test results in your data table.

Be sure that you understand the results of each test.

10. In the class data table, list the foods that your team tested. Enter your test results.

11. Complete your data table by entering the class data.

Some foods may have been tested by more than 1 team. Enter all results in your table. Discuss any discrepancies in the results as a class.

Create a large data table in which teams can enter the foods they tested and the results for each nutrient test. This needs to be done as a class exercise, otherwise some teams will record incorrect information in the class data table without being asked to explain their reasons for their unusual results. You might lead off with a question such as, Which teams got a positive result for proteins when testing the hamburger? Some students may be inclined to change their results to match the majority; encourage discussion about anomalous results—they may reveal interesting secondary nutrients, contamination, or misunderstandings. For example, some liver has tested positive for vitamin C, apparently because of the role liver plays in vitamin C metabolism. Your class also may discover unexpected results that are not caused by errors. Remind the learners that each should have a complete data table.

12. Discuss the following questions with your teammates. Record your answers in your journal.

Walk around the room and listen as teams discuss the questions. The first question will reveal whether the learners had prior misconceptions about what types of nutrients would be found in particular foods. If a large number of learners had a similar misconception, you may wish to address predictions, results, and current conceptions in a brief class discussion.

a. How did the predictions that you made in step 3 compare with the test results? Which results were the most surprising? Why?

Predictions will depend on each learner's preconceptions and the variety of foods students test. Each team's answers should reflect the degree to which its predictions correlated with its experimental results.

b. How might the natural colors of the foods affect the results?

A blue result may give a green color on a yellow surface. The natural coloring of some materials, such as tomatoes, may mask the test results.

c. Why was it important to test each indicator using water as the negative control substance?

Water contains none of the nutrients being tested for. A negative control helps researchers interpret their results by illustrating what a negative test should look like. (An ideal negative control would be the same color and consistency as the food sample, without the nutrient of interest.)

d. Why was it important to test each indicator with a substance known to contain the nutrient in question?

These substances acted as positive controls. Positive controls help researchers interpret their results by illustrating what a positive test should look like.

Analysis

When the teams have completed their discussions, ask them to begin reading the essays *Food: Our Body's Source of Energy and Structural Materials* (page 328), and *Pioneers: The Changing Face of the Food Guide Pyramid* (page 333). They can complete the readings and the Analysis as homework. You may wish to collect their journals to assess their understanding of the concepts in this activity.

1. Examine the *Dietary Analysis* that you completed in the activity *What Determines Fitness?* Notice that the foods you tested in the laboratory included one from each of the six food groups in this analysis. If you assume that foods from the same food group contain many of the same nutrients, then you can use your test results to determine the actual nutrients that were likely present in the foods you listed on your dietary analysis. Based on your tests alone, identify which foods you ate that your body could use as a source of

a. protein,

b. sugar,

c. starch,

d. vitamin C, and

e. fats and oils.

The learners' answers will depend on the material they tested and on the foods they ate. In general, meats, dairy products, and legumes provide a source of protein;

fruits, honey, and desserts contain high levels of glucose and/or sucrose; foods made from grains (such as pasta or bread) and potatoes contain high levels of starch; citrus fruits are a source of vitamin C; butter, oils, and animal fats have high concentrations of lipids. Of course, most foods contain several nutrients.

2. Compare your test results with the information given in the essay *Food: Our Body's Source of Energy and Structural Materials*. What does the information in this essay suggest about the sensitivity and/or the accuracy of the tests you completed?

   Answers will depend on students' experience with question 1. The tests the learners completed are very simple, nonquantitative tests. Although they are adequate for the purposes intended here, they are not sensitive enough to detect very low levels of some nutrients. Learners also may have conducted some tests incorrectly or misinterpreted their results.

3. Which, if any, of the foods that you ate contained all of the nutrients for which you tested? What does this mean for eating a balanced diet?

   Very few of the tested foods are likely to contain all of the nutrients tested. This is why a variety of foods containing all nutrients, when eaten in combination—in other words, a balanced diet—is so important for good health. Calories for energy obviously are not the only reason for eating. The various nutrients that foods contain are used to build and maintain the various components of our bodies, and most foods tested do not contain every nutrient. This illustrates the importance of a diet that includes a variety of food types.

Further Challenges

Study the two graphs in Figure 7.5. These graphs represent the results of an experiment in which a cracker was placed in a test tube along with saliva. Points on the graphs were determined by using the same indicator tests for starch and sugar that you used in this activity. Use the results displayed in these graphs to explain the changes that the saliva caused.

◆ **If you assigned Further Challenges, look for responses stating that graph A shows that the amount of starch in the test tube decreased across time and graph B shows that the amount of glucose in the test tube increased across time. The logical conclusion is that digestive enzymes or some component in the saliva converted the starch in the cracker into glucose.**

◆ **The optional elaborate activity *Of Cannibals and Calories*, located on the *TRCD*, uses the tragic historical Donner Party incident to help learners understand how factors such as gender, age, and culture may be related to human physical performance in survival situations.**

◆ **Challenge your learners to examine the relationship between diet, culture, and fitness by relating the information in the essay *Pioneers: The Changing Face of the Food Guide Pyramid* (page 333) and other sources that describe how people of various cultures typically meet their nutritional needs. Locate morbidity and mortality figures that might indicate the particular advantages or disadvantages of some of these dietary traditions. The distinctive features of certain Asian cuisines, for example, provide a wealth of fitness hints, particularly when viewed against data that reveal that obesity and high blood cholesterol levels are relatively rare among some Asian cultures that eat traditional foods. Likewise, learners might enjoy studying** the dietary traditions associated with their own ethnic heritage. Based on the understanding gained in this activity, they should be able to suggest how to modify such diets to better promote fitness while still retaining their distinctive character.

◆ Learners also may enjoy investigating and analyzing a variety of unusual diets, including macrobiotics, vegetarian diets, and a variety of weight-loss diets.

You Are What You Eat

Explain

Major Concepts Releasing the energy stored in food; digestive system; enzyme function in starch digestion; experimental design; introduction to biosynthesis

Overview

This activity lets the learners investigate how the human digestive system releases the energy in food by breaking down a complex food molecule to a simpler molecule. Then after designing and conducting an experiment to test the effect of the enzyme amylase on starch, the learners are introduced to the concept of biosynthesis through a short video segment and brief discussion.

Materials   (per class of 30)

PART A   (teams of 4)

For student experiments:

Exact materials will depend on the experimental protocols that the students decide to use but should include the following:

30 pairs of safety goggles	test tube racks
30 lab aprons	rubber stoppers to fit test tubes
dropping pipets	glass-marking pencils
18 × 150-mm test tubes	glucose test strips
10-mL graduated cylinders	5% starch suspension
spot plates	0.1% starch suspension
1% amylase solution	

(Note: Amylase must be fresh. Keep it refrigerated between uses, and order a new supply each year.)
distilled water
dropping bottles of Lugol's iodine solution
    labeled *WARNING: Poison if ingested; irritant*

For the demonstration:

10 18 × 150-mm test tubes	10 mL 1% amylase solution
spot plate	10 mL distilled water
test tube rack	10 glucose test strips
10 mL 5% maltose solution	dropping bottle of Lugol's iodine solution
10 mL 5% starch suspension	

PART B   (whole class)

DVD   DVD player

Outcomes and Indicators of Success

The following indicators allow you to assess the students' level of success with the activity and to assess their process of learning.

By the end of this activity, the learners should

1. understand that enzymes break down complex food molecules to simpler food molecules.

   They will show their understanding by

   a. designing and carrying out an experiment to test the catabolic activity of amylase, and

   b. writing an explanation of the role of enzymes in digestion and the effect of different variables on enzyme reactions and pH in the digestive process.

2. understand how organisms use simple food molecules to build or repair body structures.

   They will demonstrate their understanding by discussing the concept of biosynthesis as it applies to a video segment they will view.

3. recognize how to use techniques and tools to design and conduct an experiment.

   They will show their recognition by

   a. identifying the variables and the controls they need in an experiment,

   b. developing their own procedure,

   c. carrying out an experiment, and

   d. analyzing their results.

Safety

Caution

Remind learners to wash their hands at the end of each period and to observe the safety cautions about the Lugol's iodine solution when conducting the experimental procedures.

Preparations

Purchase Lugol's iodine solution ready-made (4 mL per bottle). Prepare the other solutions as follows:

1% amylase solution

Dissolve 1 g powdered amylase in enough distilled water to make 100 mL of solution. Label the container. **(Note: Amylase must be fresh. Keep it refrigerated between uses, and order a new supply each year.)**

5% maltose solution

Dissolve 0.5 g maltose in enough distilled water to make 10 mL of solution. Label the container.

Starch suspension

0.1%: Dissolve 0.1 g soluble starch in 100 mL of distilled water. Label the container.

5%: Dissolve 5 g soluble starch in enough distilled water to make 100 mL of solution. Label the container.

Laundry starch or cornstarch may be substituted. Heat to dissolve and filter through cloth, and then through filter paper. Treat liquid laundry starch as 100%; for a 5% solution, use 5 mL of starch and 95 mL of distilled water.

If you want an opportunity for individual assessment, have teams design and carry out their experiments through the stage of data collection. Then have students individually write a justification for their procedure and for the interpretation of their results. The scoring rubric for laboratory reports on the *GACD* is a suggestion for assessing the learners' laboratory reports. Share the criteria with the students before they begin their reports. Provide appropriate numerical values or tell students what full credit is worth.

Strategies for Guiding Learners

PROCESS AND PROCEDURES

As a class, read orally or silently all introductory materials for the activity and the Process and Procedures to help students build connections between concepts and activities. Use the time spent reading to bring the students' attention into focus.

PART A   Food for Energy

Part A lends itself easily to cooperative learning. Suggest that learners focus on the working-relationship skills of honoring individual differences and sharing responsibilities. Because they need to agree on a design for an experiment, the idea of honoring individual differences is necessary and challenging. Refer to the strategies for introducing a working-relationship skill in the cooperative learning section of the *TRCD*.

In this part of the activity, your challenge as a teacher is to balance the opportunity to let students exercise some creativity as they design an experiment with the pragmatic concerns of safety, availability of supplies, time limitations, classroom management, and desired educational outcomes.

1. Read the background information in the need to know box to yourself.

    See the need to know box on page 273 in the student text for the background information about the materials available in this activity.

2. With your team, develop an outline of a controlled experiment to investigate the process whereby amylase breaks down starch to sugar.

    Use these resources to help you complete this task: the essay *What Happens to the Food You Eat?* (page 334), Background on Controlled Experiments (page 155), and the background information in the need to know box in this activity.

    As the students begin thinking about experiments to test the breakdown of starch to sugar, they must consider what controls, variables, and tests are required to detect the presence of starch and sugar. The nutrient protocols from the previous activity are an ideal place for students to begin outlining how to handle their samples.

3. Choose a variable that might affect the amylase/starch reaction. Develop a hypothesis about its effect on the reaction. Variables that you might consider include

- ◆ presence of light,
- ◆ concentration of amylase,
- ◆ concentration of starch,
- ◆ temperature, and
- ◆ pH.

4. Have your teacher check that your outline demonstrates the appropriate reaction and that you have designed a controlled experiment.

5. Write a hypothesis for your experiment in your journal. Explain how you think your variable will affect the amylase and starch reaction, and why.

You may want to write your hypothesis as an *if . . . then* statement combined with an explanation.

6. Have your teacher approve your hypothesis. Then write a detailed procedure for your experiment. Again, ask your teacher to approve it.

You may need to guide some of the teams so they come up with practical and informative experiments. If the students are daunted by the challenge, use a set of guiding questions to help them break down the problem into steps. You might ask the team, What outcome would demonstrate that amylase causes the breakdown of starch to sugar? The answer, an increase in sugar and a decrease in starch concentrations after exposure to amylase, would be an expected outcome. You then could ask the teams how they could detect these changes.

As you approve the learners' procedures in step 6, make certain that they have included appropriate controls and that they are aware of what the controls are and why they are necessary.

Possibilities for experiments to investigate the question include incubating a known concentration of starch (5 percent solution) with an amylase solution for varying times or for a set time, possibly with varying concentrations of amylase. (Note: Our own lab tests indicate that overnight incubation produces significantly better results than incubation periods of only 1–2 hours.) Learners could test only for the disappearance of starch or only for the appearance of sugar; doing both is preferable.

7. Carry out your experiment, and record all results in your journal.

SAFETY: Put on your safety goggles and lab apron.

Safety Goggles   **Lab Apron**

Take the students' experimentation activity as an opportunity to assess some of their Science as Inquiry skills such as collecting and analyzing data. You also can tell how well they grasp the significance of their experimental design.

8. Wash your hands thoroughly when you are finished.

9. In your journal, prepare a lab report of your experiment. Each team will present its findings to the rest of the class.

You need to report the following information clearly to your classmates:
◆ A statement of the question or hypothesis
◆ The procedure for conducting the experiment
◆ Your results
◆ An analysis of the data
◆ An explanation of the role of enzymes in digestion and the effect of different variables on enzyme reactions

10. Participate in a class presentation and discussion of each team's results.

Take notes on the effects of variables on enzyme reactions. Your classmates' results will be important for your final analysis.

11. Based on your class's data, add to your lab report a final summary and analysis of the effect of different variables on enzyme reactions.

Emphasize that proper lab technique includes practicing proper safety precautions, such as washing hands thoroughly before leaving the laboratory. Make certain that the learners understand the importance of a complete lab report. You may choose to have them record data directly in their journals, but ask them to write a separate report to hand in.

PART B   Food for the Body's Building Blocks

1. Take notes as you watch the DVD segment "Introduction to Biosynthesis."

Show the DVD segment "Introduction to Biosynthesis." This short segment uses animation to show how prey proteins provide a source of amino acids that are assembled into different, predator proteins. Repeat the segment as needed for students to understand the underlying concept of biosynthesis: food provides building blocks with which each organism synthesizes its own unique molecules. Then lead a discussion of the question in step 2.

2. Participate in a class discussion about this question: What happens when a foreign protein enters an animal?

The idea should surface in the discussion that when foreign protein is ingested, the large macromolecules are first broken down to smaller subunits, then reassembled through biosynthesis into macromolecules that are characteristic of the consumer organism.

break it down & build it back up (You ARE what you eat)

3. The digestive system is a group of organs that breaks down food into small molecules. In this way, the molecules can be absorbed into the blood and transported by the circulatory system to all cells of the body (see Figure 7.6). In your journal, create a flowchart or diagram of the digestive system. Trace the path that the nutrients in a cheeseburger would take from being eaten to being absorbed into the bloodstream.

Students can create this flowchart or diagram on a piece of butcher paper, construction paper, or in their journals. Encourage those who wish to draw a diagram to use a simple outline of a person to contain the digestive system (some students may draw a gingerbread-man style outline). The diagram on page 334 in the essay *What Happens to the Food You Eat?* **will be helpful for students as they draw a basic representation of the digestive system's organs or create a flowchart that represents**

the path that food takes. Expect students to represent the following path: mouth, esophagus, stomach, small intestine, nutrients to bloodstream and waste to large intestine, nutrients transported throughout the body, and waste expelled from the body. The pancreas contributes essential enzymes to the digestive process, and the liver produces bile that is delivered to the small intestine to break down fats. However, students should recognize that food never passes through either the pancreas or liver.

4. Along side your flowchart or diagram, write *break down* or *absorption* at each step according to which process occurs at that stage of digestion.

    Students' flowcharts or diagrams should show that breakdown takes place during the portion of digestion that occurs in the mouth and stomach. Students may mistakenly show that all absorption occurs in the stomach, but little absorption actually takes place there. Most absorption happens in the small intestine. The large intestine absorbs some water from the remains before the waste is expelled from the body.

5. Read the essay *Anorexia Nervosa: Dying to Be Thin* (page 337). In your journal, explain where the building blocks for biosynthesis are obtained for a person suffering from anorexia nervosa.

    Persons suffering from anorexia nervosa deny themselves food that would provide building blocks for biosynthesis. Like individuals suffering from starvation for any reason, their bodies first exhaust all fat reserves and then begin to break down internal tissues to obtain nutrients. The breakdown process eventually makes muscles (including the heart) and organs weak and less able to function properly.

Elaborate · Structures and Functions

Major Concepts Muscle structure and function at the micro and macro levels

Overview

In this activity, students watch a video segment and read an essay to learn how organized matter and food energy explain muscle structure and function. To further elaborate the structural basis of movement, the learners observe the contraction of muscles in their own affairs and use simple materials to construct a model of a human leg. Finally, the learners consider how the major concepts of muscle structure and function apply to human fitness and performance.

Materials (per class of 30, teams of 2)

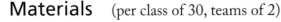

15 brass brads
30 rubber bands
15 pairs of scissors
15 sheets of thin cardboard
   (at least 20 × 20 cm)

15 pieces of string, 25 cm long
15 rolls of tape
DVD
DVD player

Outcomes and Indicators of Success

The following indicators allow you to assess the students' level of success with the activity and to assess their process of learning.

By the end of this activity, the learners should understand that

1. the arrangement of macromolecules dictates the type of movement that muscle fibers can perform.

   They will demonstrate this understanding by

   a. describing the type of movement that muscle structure at the molecular level permits, and

   b. describing the advantages and disadvantages of the structural arrangement of muscle fibers.

2. muscles work in pairs to produce movement.

   They will demonstrate their understanding by

   a. describing the action of their own biceps and triceps as they move their arms, and

   b. building a model of a human leg, including bones and muscles, and explaining the model's strengths and weaknesses.

3. organisms exploit a variety of specialized structures and body plans in order to move.

   They will demonstrate their understanding by describing the advantages and disadvantages of a hydroskeleton, an exoskeleton, and an endoskeleton.

4. muscle structure and function are related to human performance.

   They will demonstrate their understanding by

   a. explaining the biological basis of muscle fatigue, and

   b. describing the effect that increased activity has on promoting fitness.

Preparations

Before class, build a leg model (step 3) so that you are aware of the difficulties that the learners might encounter.

If you plan to use the Extensions activity, order the crickets in advance and arrange appropriate containers for them. Order the earthworms, or purchase them from a local bait shop; review NABT's *The Use of Animals in Biology Education* and *Care and Release of Life-Forms* in *Guidelines for Laboratory Safety* in this guide.

Strategies for Guiding Learners

PROCESS AND PROCEDURES

As a class, read orally or silently all introductory materials for the activity and the Process and Procedures to help students build connections between concepts and activities. Use the time spent reading to bring the students' attention into focus.

1. View the DVD segment "Muscle Movement at the Molecular Level." With your partner, suggest an answer to the following questions:

   The learners will work cooperatively with one partner throughout the activity. Begin with the DVD segment "Muscle Movement at the Molecular Level." This segment illustrates muscle structure from the whole muscle down through all the levels of organization to the protein molecules that make up the filaments. Animation shows how these filaments slide past each other to bring about muscle contraction. To summarize, the filaments are built up through the levels of organization to the whole muscle again. After showing the video segment, have the learners write their team responses to the questions in their journals. You might choose to convene a brief class discussion based on their responses.

a. What type of movement does the structure of muscles permit?

After viewing the video segment, the learners should be able to explain that filaments composed of protein molecules slide past each other when energy is expended. This causes the muscle fiber to shorten.

b. What are the advantages and disadvantages of this structural arrangement of muscle fibers?

Muscle cells shorten (contract) in response to stimulation, then passively return to their resting state. A disadvantage of this arrangement is that muscle fibers cannot be lengthened by the sliding-filament mechanism. Muscles can pull very effectively using this mechanism, but they cannot push. Special functional arrangements are needed to capitalize on this arrangement, as is illustrated later in this activity.

2. Perform the following steps to explore the function of muscle fibers at a *higher* level of organization. This is a level at which matter is organized in a way that allows physical motion.

a. Bend and straighten 1 arm while using your other hand to feel what happens to your biceps and triceps.

Consult Figure E7.11 in the essay *The Structural Basis of Physical Mobility* (page 337) if you are not sure where the biceps and triceps are located.

b. Develop an explanation of how your biceps and triceps generate these movements.

c. Discuss your observations and understandings with your partner.

Have the learners use the essay *The Structural Basis of Physical Mobility* as a resource to gain a better understanding of how structure and function are related to mobility.

3. Working with your partner, use the materials provided and the information in Figure 7.7 to construct a working model of your thigh and lower leg. Be sure to show the attachment sites of the quadriceps muscles on the front of the thigh and the hamstring muscles on the back of the thigh.

You might use the cardboard for bone, the string or rubber bands for muscle, the tape for tendons, and the brad for the knee. You may use a different combination of parts to form your model. Try to make the model as realistic as possible.

You may need to help the learners with the models they build by explaining that arms and legs are very similar and that the muscle attachment sites are analogous.

4. Place your model on the table with the leg straight. Grasp the hamstring just below the upper attachment site. Gently pull the hamstring. What happens? Release the muscle, but do not reposition the lower leg. Record your observations in your journal.

5. Now grasp the quadriceps just below its upper attachment site and pull gently. What happens? How does this movement differ from that in step 4? Record your observations and explanation in your journal.

Because all models are somewhat deficient, we include instructions that tell the learners how to move their completed models. These important steps make it clear that muscles cannot push the limbs and explain why it is important that muscles work together in pairs. As the learners work, walk around the room and check each model. This strategy allows you to assess the learners' current level of understanding about opposing muscle pairs and helps you spot any misconceptions that they still might have. You also may want to explain that the quadriceps muscle actually is a composite of four separate muscles. These four muscles have separate origins but one insertion on the kneecap, and they function as a unit to extend the leg. The hamstrings are three posterior thigh muscles that often function as a unit. The hamstrings are particularly vulnerable to injury during certain types of contact sports such as football.

You may wish to have partners bring their finished model to you for a short oral quiz in which you rate the overall success of the model in representing leg movement; the students' abilities to name the muscles and bones; and their ability to locate the flexor, extensor, and points of origins and insertions. Students also might like to see the other models constructed in class.

6. Discuss the following with your partner. Record your responses in your journal.

Move around the classroom and monitor the teams for appropriate responses as the learners discuss the following questions with their partners and record answers in their journals.

a. Explain the statement, Muscles work in pairs. Why is that important?

Movement of the human body requires that joints bend and straighten. Because muscles shorten when they contract and cannot lengthen past their fully relaxed state, joints can move in both directions only through assistance from the opposing muscles. Contraction of a flexor bends a joint; contraction of an extensor straightens it.

b. What is the role of the joint in producing movement?

Muscles cross joints to attach to two different bones. When a muscle contracts, the joint bends to allow one of the bones to move. Without a joint, there would be no movement. If a muscle contracted along a single bone, the result would be a firm-feeling muscle, but no movement.

c. Recall from the DVD segment that the molecular filaments in muscles can shorten muscles but cannot lengthen them. How do you think it is possible for us to push on anything?

You may wish to test your answer by pushing on a wall. Feel both your biceps and triceps muscles. How are they acting to stabilize your arm? Why is this important to your ability to exert force against the wall?

We can push on things because, by expending energy, we can maintain the contraction of our skeletal muscles. Structurally, this can be explained by the fact that the muscle filaments remain in contact with each other after contracting rather than releasing (as they do when the muscle relaxes).

Analysis

Convene a class discussion for the Analysis. As you lead the class discussion, make connections to the major themes of this unit whenever possible: (a) all organisms require matter and energy; (b) matter is the source of energy for all organisms; and (c) matter must be organized in particular ways to produce specific functions. Use the questions to assess the learners' understanding of the major concepts of the activity and to provide a common foundation from which they should be able to suggest how exercise (or an increased activity level) improves fitness.

Participate in a class discussion of the following. For important background information, read the essays *The Structural Basis of Physical Mobility* (page 337), *The Ant That Terrorized Milwaukee* (page 341), and *Energy's Role in Making Structures Functional* (page 342).

1. Explain the *basic* matter and energy requirements needed for a muscle to contract.

    Muscles are composed of proteins and thus require matter in the form of proteins for their structure. As a source of energy, muscles require food molecules (indirectly), which are converted into usable energy in the form of ATP. This ATP powers contraction.

2. What happens *biologically* when muscle fatigue occurs?

    If your learners have difficulty with this question, ask them whether it is likely that fatigue involves a *disintegration* of muscle fibers or any type of *damage* to the actual mass of the muscle. If they answer negatively, ask them what other critical elements must be present for contraction to occur (energy) and how this may change under repeated contraction without rest.

    Studies on athletes have shown that muscle fatigue is directly related to the depletion of glycogen reserves inside the muscle cell. As these reserves diminish, the muscle becomes less able to continue supplying the same work output—the condition we call fatigue. You might point out to your learners that a similar effect occurs when blood flow to a contracting muscle is interrupted. Almost complete fatigue sets in within a minute or so, in this case, due to the obvious lack of oxygen.

3. We build models to mimic a structure or an event. Good models mimic the actual structure or event so closely that changes in the model predict what would happen in the real world. Describe the strengths and weaknesses of your leg model.

    Use this question to review the major elements of muscle structure and function with your learners: attachment to an endoskeleton, contraction by filaments that slide past each other, and skeletal movement by the contraction of opposing muscles attached to different bones across joints.

    The models that the learners developed likely represented the connectivity of muscle, tendon, and bone fairly well. Muscle attachment sites can be placed in appropriate areas of bone, but the muscle itself cannot be modeled well, primarily because of the unique mechanism by which muscles contract. Tension is not the result of stretching, as in rubber bands, but rather of molecules sliding past each other in the muscle filaments. Likewise, string does not make a good model because it is always limp.

4. Vertebrate muscles contract against the resistance of an internal skeleton made of bone. Create a table in your journal. Compare two advantages and two disadvantages of a hydrostatic skeleton, an exoskeleton, and an endoskeleton (see Figure 7.8).

A hydrostatic skeleton is well suited to aquatic or moist environments but does not withstand drying, as evidenced by an earthworm on a dry sidewalk or an anemone in a tide pool when the water recedes. Exoskeletons provide protection for soft internal organs, a very high strength-to-mass ratio for small organisms such as insects, and protection against drying. Disadvantages include the necessity of molting every time the organism outgrows its old shell, which leaves the organism exposed, and the heavy weight of chitin, which limits the size of the organism. (The larger the muscles, the larger the skeleton must be; and the larger the skeleton, the greater its mass and the larger the muscles must be to support and move it.) Endoskeletons also are limited by considerations of mass versus strength, but allow the organism to grow.

You may wish to challenge your better learners with the following question: The mass of a bone increases in proportion to the cube of its diameter, whereas its strength only increases in proportion to the square of its diameter. What does this difference mean in terms of limitations on the size of humans?

Using arbitrary units, a femur with a diameter of 2 would have a strength of 4 and a mass of 8. If you doubled the strength of the femur to 8 (a diameter of 2.8), the mass would be 22.6. Such an increase in mass soon reaches a limit at which the increase in strength no longer keeps pace.

5. How does increased physical activity promote fitness? Be specific. Include the effect of increased activity on the structure and function of an individual muscle.

Learners may suggest that repeated use stimulates further muscle growth. This is important because the strength of a muscle is determined mainly by its size (the maximum contractile force generated by human muscle is between 3 and 4 kg per cm^2 of cross-sectional area). This explains why testosterone, which increases muscle size, also increases muscle strength.

Learners also may suggest that an increased level of activity increases the energy available to the muscle. You may wish to expand on this aspect of training by pointing out that increased muscle use, particularly aerobic conditioning, promotes an increase in the enzyme levels and in the number of mitochondria (thus increasing the muscle's capacity for aerobic energy release). Training also may increase the amount of glycogen and triglyceride (fat) stored in the muscle (thus increasing the muscle's endurance by increasing its immediate fuel reserve).

6. Recall that your heart is a muscle. During vigorous activity, your heart pumps faster and harder. It delivers blood more rapidly to both the lungs and the exercising muscles. How would vigorous activity promote the increased fitness of the heart itself? How would it help muscles in other parts of your body to function more effectively?

Learners should recognize that because their heart is a muscle, increased activity causes it to become stronger and more efficient as well. The heart's ability to provide adequate levels of oxygen and nutrients to vigorously contracting muscles in other parts of the body is a major factor in all types of fitness.

Marathon

Major Concepts Factors involved in human performance, fitness for life, athletic fitness

Overview

This activity allows learners to evaluate their understanding of several factors involved in human performance. It builds on previous activities by incorporating the complementary ideas of fitness for life and fitness for athletic performance. Learners read a story about a marathon and then, through the in-depth study of each runner, integrate several factors related to human performance, including general fitness, training appropriate for an athletic event, diet (composition and caloric intake), and attitude.

Materials (per class of 30, teams of 4)

DVD
DVD player
30 copies of the rubric *Marathon*

Outcomes and Indicators of Success

The following indicators allow you to assess the students' level of success with the activity and to assess their process of learning.

By the end of this activity, the learners should

1. understand the relationships among training, diet, and physical performance.

   They will demonstrate their understanding by

   a. describing the relationship between caloric intake and exercise,

   b. describing various factors that influence caloric requirements,

   c. developing strategies (especially with respect to diet, training patterns, and race day behaviors) that would improve physical performance, and

   d. describing the effect that these strategies would be expected to have on the body.

2. be able to develop if-then statements.

   They will demonstrate their ability by writing if-then statements to propose ways that runners might improve their performance.

3. be able to analyze and use data.

   They will demonstrate their ability by using various physiologic data to justify different strategies that they suggest for both training for and running in a marathon.

Preparations

Place learners in teams of 4 to ensure a balance between those who may be athletically oriented and those who are not. Arrange a system for assigning particular runners to individual learners.

Review the *Marathon* rubric on the *GACD*, and make changes to suit your needs.

Background Information

In his *Textbook of Medical Physiology* (10th edition, © 1991 by W.B. Saunders Co.), Arthur C. Guyton notes that heavy physical exercise places the human body under more extreme stress than any other normal circumstance. The comparison he offers is between a person who has an extremely high fever approaching a lethal level, and a marathon runner. The first individual's body metabolism increases to about 100 percent above normal; the marathoner's metabolism increases to 2,000 percent above normal.

The changes that take place in a marathon runner's body during a race, as well as the changes that take place as he or she trains for a race, are very complex, and scientists do not understand all of them. Nevertheless, the information in the paragraphs below, as well as the physiologic data in the student pages and the suggested answers to the analysis questions, should be useful to you as the learners begin to think about the runners in this simulated marathon.

One purpose of most athletic training is to increase the strength, power, and endurance of the body's muscles. Endurance—that is, how long a muscle can continue to contract—is particularly important in a marathon. Stated somewhat differently, for a marathon runner, finishing the race depends largely on his or her ability to keep moving and to avoid debilitating fatigue. This observation suggests that one way to understand the importance of various factors involved in training and eating in preparation for a marathon is to understand the underlying causes of muscle fatigue.

Most efforts to explain fatigue have centered on the following areas: changes in the muscle's energy systems, the accumulation of by-products from metabolic processes, and changes in the nervous system. Evidence suggests, however, that none of these factors considered alone explains all aspects of fatigue. Many questions about what happens to muscles under extreme stress remain unanswered.

The muscle's energy systems. Muscle ATP levels are maintained by a combination of energy-releasing processes that are too complex to discuss in detail here. A key source of energy, however, especially during activities of long duration, is the muscle's own glycogen reserve. Studies of athletes have shown that one of the most critical factors involved in muscle fatigue is the level of stored glycogen. As glycogen reserves in the muscle diminish, fatigue increases. As Figure 7.9B (in the student book) shows, however, athletes engaged in endurance activities under experimental conditions do not perceive severe fatigue until muscle glycogen levels are almost exhausted. This and other similar evidence suggests that a major part of the sudden onset of extreme fatigue and muscle heaviness that marathon runners refer to as "hitting the wall" is due to muscle glycogen depletion.

Metabolic by-products. Although many people believe that the accumulation of lactic acid in the muscle is responsible for fatigue in all types of exercise, experimental evidence indicates that this is the case only during very brief, highly intense, muscular efforts, for example, during sprints in running, cycling, and swimming. During such efforts, muscles depend heavily on glycolysis as a source of energy, and as a result, produce large amounts of lactic acid. This lactic acid dissociates to form lactate and hydrogen ions, and the hydrogen ions, until they clear from the muscle or are buffered, lower the muscle's internal pH. This lowered pH inhibits a key enzyme in glycolysis, which slows the rate of ATP production and leads to fatigue. In addition, the hydrogen ions may interfere with the action of the protein filaments within the muscle and decrease the muscle's contractile force. In fact, most available evidence suggests that low muscle pH is the primary cause of low performance and muscle fatigue during maximal short-term exercise.

In contrast, energy production in the muscles of a well-conditioned marathon runner is largely *aerobic*, and measurements show that marathon runners may have near-resting levels of lactic acid in their muscles at the end of the race, despite the runners' obvious exhaustion. As noted above, fatigue in a marathon is due largely to inadequate energy supply, not excess lactic acid.

Neuromuscular effects. Some evidence suggests that certain types of fatigue may be due to an inability to activate the muscle fiber. Theories for how this might occur remain speculative. Nevertheless, early studies that showed that both verbal encouragement and direct electrical stimulation could increase the strength of muscle contraction, even when the muscle is nearly exhausted, suggest that some of the factors involved in severe fatigue may be psychological. It may be, for example, that the pain of exhaustive exercise acts either consciously or unconsciously to inhibit an individual's willingness to tolerate further trauma, and so acts to slow the level of the exercise, thereby protecting the body. Consistent with this, comparisons of the available physiological and psychological data indicate that the perception of severe discomfort precedes the onset of complete metabolic exhaustion. Unless they are highly motivated, most individuals stop exercising before their muscles are fully fatigued. Trained marathon runners learn to pace themselves so that their energy reserves last as long as possible and also learn to tolerate the high levels of physical discomfort that are associated with almost complete muscle fatigue.

Strategies for Guiding Learners

PROCESS AND PROCEDURES

As a class, read orally or silently all introductory materials for the activity and the Process and Procedures to help students build connections between concepts and activities. Use the time spent reading to bring the students' attention into focus.

1. As a class, watch the DVD segment "A Good Day for Running."

    Use the DVD segment "A Good Day for Running" to engage the learners in this activity. The segment shows runners in scenes from different portions of marathons—at the start, at an aid station along the way, and at the finish.

2. With your team of 4, read *The Race*. This story describes a marathon and the training and performance of 4 people who participated in it.

3. Decide which person in your team will study each runner in depth.

   Before the learners begin step 4, distribute copies of the *Marathon* scoring rubric from the *GACD* so that they are aware of how you will assess them. Discuss the rubric and emphasize to students that their responses must reflect the biological basis of fitness addressed in this chapter, not their prior knowledge.

4. Review the information in Figure 7.9, Physiologic Data Related to Physical Performance.

   Think about how each set of information might help you analyze your runner's training and performance. It might also help you suggest general strategies for a marathon runner.

As the learners review the physiologic data presented in Figure 7.9 at the end of the activity, walk around the room and listen to the discussions. This strategy will provide you with an opportunity to assess the learners' ability to interpret and analyze data. If the learners cannot make connections between the data and their runners, ask guiding questions such as, How or why are these data important to a marathon runner?

5. Copy Figure 7.9A, Energy Expended in Training and Racing, into your journal. Use information in Figure 7.9C, Exercise and Energy Expenditure, as well as information in *The Race* to complete the table in your journal.

Do not let teams get bogged down in calculations of caloric requirements. Instead, guide them through a sample calculation and let each team member calculate values for his or her specific runner. See the completed table in Figure T7.2.

Figure T7.2 Energy expended in training and racing

Runner	Weight mass	Kcals used/week normal workout (assume 7 min/mile pace)	Kcals used/week race training (assume 7 min/mile pace)	Kcals used for marathon (see finish time)
Neal	68 kg (150 lb)	N/A	3,990	2,636
Amy	50 kg (110 lb)	N/A	2,926	2,046
Mel	82 kg (181 lb)	2,394	3,830	3,553
John	75 kg (165 lb)	1,649	2,638	3,415

Sample Calculation

Note: The figure *0.95 kcal/10 minutes* (below) is taken from the table Exercise and Energy Expenditure (Figure 7.9C) in the student text.

Neal (training)
0.95 kcal/10 minutes × 150 lb = 142.5 kcal/10 minutes
10 miles × 7 minutes/mile = 70 minutes
70 minutes × 142.5 kcal/10 minutes = 997.5 kcals
997.5 kcal/day × 4 days/week = 3,990 kcal/week

Neal (racing)
raced 26 miles in 3 hours, 5 minutes, or 26 miles in 185 minutes
185 minutes ÷ 26 miles = 7.12 minute/mile
running a 7 minute/mile uses 0.95 kcal/pound every 10 minutes (from Figure 7.9C)
0.95 kcal/lb • 10 minutes × 150 lb = 142.5 kcals/10 minutes
142.5 kcal/10 minutes × 185 minutes = 2,636.25 kcals

6. Use your understanding of biology, the data in Figure 7.9A–G, and the table that you just completed to analyze your runner's training and performance on race day. Consider each of the points listed below. Record brief notes about any important information that may help you in the analysis.

Although each of you should analyze only your own runner, you may wish to remain in your teams as you do so. This strategy will allow you to share ideas and begin comparing the runners as you examine their training and performance.

Again, walk around the room and listen as the learners analyze their runners. This will give you an opportunity to assess how well they can apply the data in a meaningful way.

a. Examine your runner's training schedule. In what ways did this schedule prepare him or her to finish the race? How did your runner's energy expenditure per week of race training compare with the amount of energy he or she expended during the marathon?

Mel, Amy, and Neal each worked out at a moderate pace until several weeks before the marathon. Mel increased his running to 13K, 4 days a week, for about 1 month before the marathon. Amy and Neal stepped up their regimen to 16K, 4 days a week, for about 6 weeks before the marathon. This allowed them time to build up their endurance. John, on the other hand, limited his initial training to about 5K, 5 days a week. Six weeks before the marathon, he increased his training to 10K, 4 days a week. Mel, Amy, and Neal each expended considerably more energy per week in their race training than they did during the marathon. John, however, expended almost as much energy in the marathon as he had expended each week during race training. This is not surprising because Mel, Amy, and Neal had adopted much more rigorous training regimens than John, and consequently, were much better conditioned for the race.

b. Examine the diet of your runner in the weeks preceding the race. Did your runner appear to be increasing or decreasing his or her intake of any particular class of nutrients during training?

Mel and John essentially ate regular meals with their families during training. Mel's meals were well balanced. Amy and Neal ate meals that emphasized carbohydrates, and they "loaded" on carbohydrates for several days before the race. This would give them extra energy reserves for endurance and help to prevent them from "hitting the wall."

c. Summarize the strategy that you think your runner was using during training.

All four runners used strategies that they thought would condition them for the race by first gradually building their endurance with moderate training regimens, then by increasing their regimen several weeks before the marathon. The differences between the training regimens of the runners were in terms of degree. For example, Amy and Neal adhered to the most rigorous program, John's was the least rigorous, and Mel's was intermediate. By emphasizing carbohydrate intake, Amy and Neal also followed diets that were very compatible with their physical conditioning.

d. Examine your runner's behavior on the race day before the race began. What strategies do you think he or she was using to prepare for the race?

Mel probably thought that a breakfast of French toast and juice would provide him with a quick energy source of carbohydrates along with necessary fluids. Amy and Neal used a similar strategy with their breakfast of oatmeal, milk, and juice. We might infer that Mel didn't drink as much juice, however. John's breakfast included fluids and carbohydrates, but in addition, he ate other items such as ham and eggs, which were higher in protein and fat. He probably thought a continued balanced diet would provide him with quick energy and longer-term energy for use later in the race. The ham and eggs, however, added bulk to his body, but did not provide him with the energy needed for the race.

e. Examine your runner's performance during the marathon. (For example, look at his or her pace, fluid intake, and apparent stamina and success.) What strategies did he or she seem to be using?

> All four of the runners seemed to be using a moderate pace that would allow them to complete the race, although the rigorous training regimen and resulting stamina of Amy and Neal ultimately proved superior.

f. Propose reasons why your runner's body behaved as it did.

> All four runners eventually "hit the wall," but because of the differences in training regimens, John, then Mel, experienced the wall effect earlier. Their diets during training and on race day probably contributed to these results as well.

g. Propose ways your runner could have improved his or her performance.

> A student using John as an example might point out that "If John had used a more rigorous training regimen, he might not have hit the wall so soon, and would have finished the marathon earlier." Or, "If John had emphasized carbohydrates in his diet, he might have postponed the wall effect slightly." Learners should be able to use examples from student Figure 7.9A–G, Physiologic Data Related to Physical Performance to help support their responses.

7. Meet with members of other teams who studied the same runner, and compare your findings. Modify your conclusions based on the group input.

> Encourage the interchange of ideas among members of different teams who have studied the same runner. If this strategy is appropriate in your classroom, you will find that it enriches the activity.

Analysis

As the learners complete the Analysis, monitor their responses to help you assess their understanding of the concepts. Remind the learners that you will collect and read their journals. For questions 2 and 3 of the Analysis, learners should understand the factors involved in human performance thoroughly enough to be able to propose reasonable strategies for training, diet, and race day behaviors. Remind the learners to base their strategies on the more objective data given in the tables. If learners have difficulty understanding or using these data, ask them a series of guiding questions such as, What does this table show? and How might that be relevant to the runner? Point out to the learners that many of the data relate to the functions of the circulatory and gas exchange systems, and thus, form an important link back to Chapter 5.

Learners probably are aware that completing a marathon is a rather extraordinary feat of human performance. An important objective here is to get learners beyond the thinking that some people are just fit, strong, and fast, and thus able to do it. Therefore, the activity emphasizes the specific factors that are responsible for anyone's successful effort.

When the learners have completed the Analysis, collect the journals and use the scoring rubric to assess their understanding.

Work individually to answer the following questions. Record your responses in your journal.

Refer to the essay *Factors Influencing Performance* (page 343) to provide greater depth to your understanding of fitness and performance.

Remember, your answers should involve evidence of everything you learned in Chapter 7 about the biological basis of human performance and fitness. Draw from the data in Tables 7.9 A–G to give specific evidence to support your analysis.

1. Which runner expended the most energy during training? Which runner expended the most energy during the marathon? Explain the relationship between the energy expended during training and the energy used on race day.

> **Figure 7.9A indicates that Neal expended the most energy in training, with Mel a close second. In the marathon, Mel expended the most energy. Neal expended the most energy during training because of the length of time he trained. Mel expended large amounts of energy because of his need to move a much greater body mass. Distance across time (rate of travel), time spent practicing and racing, and body mass are the largest factors in caloric use during both training and racing.**

2. Compare the training schedules and diets of the four runners before the race. Complete the following tasks:

    a. List at least two training and dietary strategies that you think would be valuable for a person to consider if he or she were preparing for the same race next year.

    b. Explain the physiologic change(s) that you would expect to occur as a result of each strategy.

    c. Describe why such changes would be important to finishing the marathon. Support your answer with specific data from Tables 7.9A–G.

    > **Expect your learners to mention some of the strategies, physical effects, and evidence listed below. Note that the physiologic data presented in the student pages offer only a sample of the types of data that scientists use to explain the effects of training, diet, and specific race day strategies. Expect learners to make reasonable use of these data (that is, to recognize that there are relevant data available and to use them appropriately), but do not require them to support every suggestion they make rigorously.**

    > ***Strategy***: **Begin to train several months in advance of the race, running between 8 to 10 miles four times each week during the last 6 weeks before race day.**

    > ***Physical effect***: **Prolonged physical exercise of this sort increases the number of mitochondria in the muscles and the levels of mitochondrial enzymes, which increases the production of ATP. Prolonged exercise increases growth in the capillaries serving the muscles, which increases the amount of oxygen and other nutrients that can be delivered to the muscles. This type of training also will bring about important changes in the body's cardiovascular capacity, such as a greater volume of blood delivered with each stroke and a lower resting heart rate.**

    > ***Evidence***: **Data in Table 7.9F, Effect of Exercise on Muscle Structure.**

    > ***Strategy***: **Eat a diet rich in complex carbohydrates, especially during the last few days before the race.**

    > ***Physical effect***: **A person on a high carbohydrate diet stores more glycogen in his or her muscles than a person on either a mixed diet or a high fat diet. Because muscle endurance depends primarily on these stored glycogen reserves, an individual's capacity to finish a marathon is greatly enhanced by such a diet. In other words, because muscle fatigue is linked closely to the depletion of muscle glycogen, an individual who begins the race with more stored glycogen is likely to reach exhaustion much later in the race.**

Evidence: Data in Table 7.9B, Muscle Glycogen Levels.

Strategy: Train by running a variety of distances at different speeds, or by running hills if the course is hilly.

Physical effect: Data indicate that muscle fibers are recruited and used in specific patterns during different levels of exercise intensity. For example, some fibers are more heavily used during high-intensity activities of short duration (as in sprinting), and other fibers are more heavily used during low-intensity activities of long duration (as in a marathon). Because Neal and Amy hoped to win the race, they needed to develop both types of muscle fibers. This allowed them to sustain an appropriate pace during the low-intensity endurance portion of the race and also to make a high-intensity, sprintlike effort at the end to edge out any close competitors.

Evidence: The tables do not provide the complex physiologic data required to demonstrate this to learners. The only evidence learners will have to offer is that both Neal and Amy trained in this manner.

*The learners may or may not notice this aspect of Neal and Amy's training regimen. Because of the complexity of the issues involved, we also have not provided the learners with the data that would be required to recognize and explain this effect. We offer the brief explanation above in case some learners ask you about this issue.

3. Explain how humans obtain energy.

   At this point in the unit, students have not studied the role of chemical bonds in providing energy for human activity. Expect their answers to explain that humans obtain energy through aerobic energy release that takes place in the mitochondria of cells and through anaerobic energy release. Glycogen is the fuel for those processes.

4. Explain how the process of energy release from matter is more efficient in highly trained athletes than in most other people.

   The muscles of highly trained athletes have a greater capacity for glycogen storage, and they receive an increased blood supply because there is a greater number of capillaries serving the muscles. Well-conditioned athletes also have increased numbers of mitochondria. The effect of having increased glycogen reserves, more capillaries, and more mitochondria is a greater ability to convert fuel into useful energy.

5. Write a two- or three-paragraph explanation for how digestion, breakdown, and biosynthesis relate to the repair of a torn muscle in a marathon racer.

   Expect students' answers to include the concepts that digestion involves both breakdown and absorption of nutrients that are necessary for biosynthesis. When a muscle is torn, it must be repaired through biosynthesis. The matter needed to rebuild the muscle is obtained by eating and digesting food. During digestion, the food is broken down into building blocks that are absorbed into the bloodstream, transported to the torn muscle, and used by the body to make the repair.

Chapter 8

The Cellular Basis of Activity

In this chapter, the students shift their view of energy, matter, and activity from a macroscopic (organismal) level to a microscopic level. They will examine the cellular and molecular basis of the activities that humans and all living organisms must perform to maintain life. Understanding how energy is made available to the cells of an organism is an essential part of understanding activity.

We engage students in the concepts of energy and matter by asking them to read a surprising story about energy storage and release. They explore these ideas by examining how changes in the organization of matter result in changes in the energy stored in molecules. They then design a calorimetry experiment to test the energy content of certain foods, and they use their data and essays to develop a brochure in which they explain how matter is made available in the human body. To investigate how energy and matter first enter living systems, the students design an experiment that tests the effects of several variables on photosynthesis. As an elaboration of these concepts, students study human metabolism and revisit their critter to learn how the breakdown and synthesis processes of metabolism affect the organization of matter and the flow of energy in living organisms. Finally, the students have an opportunity to evaluate their understanding of the concepts in this chapter by tracing a carbon atom from atmospheric carbon dioxide to the protein in human muscle.

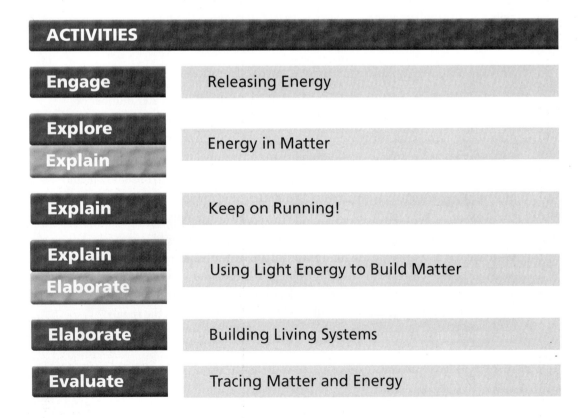

ACTIVITIES

Engage	Releasing Energy
Explore **Explain**	Energy in Matter
Explain	Keep on Running!
Explain **Elaborate**	Using Light Energy to Build Matter
Elaborate	Building Living Systems
Evaluate	Tracing Matter and Energy

Instructional Flow | | | | | **Classroom Support**

Activity/ Student Text pp. Teacher Guide pp.	GACD, TRCD, DVD, and CD-ROM Resources	Essays/ Student Text pp.	Estimated Time	Team Size/ Cooperative Learning Focus	Strategies and Tools	Assessment Opportunities	Special Considerations
ENGAGE *Releasing Energy* pp. 288–289 TG pp. 283–285			20 minutes	*Team size:* individuals and whole class	Reading; class discussion	Prior knowledge of concepts: matter and energy are related	Enlarge print materials and/or read aloud if needed.
EXPLORE/ EXPLAIN *Energy in Matter* pp. 289–293 TG pp. 285–294	DVD: *Molecular Models*	*Matter and Energy Are Related* pp. 348–351; *Energy Is Converted and Conserved* pp. 351–356; *Historical Connections between Matter and Energy* pp. 357–358	100 minutes	*Team size:* 2 *Skill:* Listening to your teammates; contributing ideas	Reading; wet lab; video; class discussion; diagramming (optional)	Journals; team and class discussions; model building	Plan ahead for students who have difficulty with fine motor control or vision. Pair them with partners who can assist in conducting the chemical reactions and building the models.
EXPLAIN *Keep on Running!* pp. 294–298 TG pp. 295–302	Rubric: *Tudor Valley Marathon Snack Brochure*	*Controlling the Release of Energy from Matter: An Overview of Cellular Respiration* pp. 358–359; *Cellular Respiration: A Closer Look at Converting Food Energy into Cell Energy* pp. 359–363; *Regulation and Energy Production* pp. 363–365	100–150 minutes	*Team size:* 3; jigsaw *Skill:* Managing and organizing team tasks; sharing perspectives	Reading; wet lab; project	Experimental strategy (inquiry skills); project with partner	Plan ahead for students who have difficulty with fine motor control or vision. Pair them with partners who can assist in conducting the calorimetry protocol, if needed.
EXPLAIN/ ELABORATE *Using Light Energy to Build Matter* pp. 299–303 TG pp. 303–310		*Whose Discovery Is This?* pp. 365–366; *Getting Energy and Matter into Biological Systems* pp. 367–372	100 minutes	*Team size:* 4; jigsaw *Skill:* Practice active listening; reaching consensus	Reading; wet lab; graphing	Inquiry skills; class presentations; quiz developed by students; current understanding of biosynthesis	Plan ahead for students who have difficulty with fine motor control or vision. Pair them with partners who can assist in the experimental setup, if needed.

continued

Instructional Flow

Classroom Support

Activity/ Student Text pp. Teacher Guide pp.	GACD, TRCD, DVD, and CD-ROM Resources	Essays/ Student Text pp.	Estimated Time	Team Size/ Cooperative Learning Focus	Strategies and Tools	Assessment Opportunities	Special Considerations
ELABORATE *Building Living Systems* pp. 303–305 TG pp. 310–313	Rubric: *Energy and Matter for Your Critter*	*Metabolism Includes Synthesis and Breakdown* pp. 372–374	100 minutes	*Team size:* 2 and individuals *Skill:* Contributing ideas; sharing perspectives	Reading; video; critter project	Current understanding of the relationship between matter and energy; biosynthesis and breakdown reactions	If you have students who have joined your class recently, plan ahead for them to create a critter or select one that you provide as the basis for this activity.
EVALUATE *Tracing Matter and Energy* pp. 306–307 TG pp. 313–317			50 minutes	*Team size:* individuals and whole class	Diagramming	Peer and/or teacher evaluation of diagrams; ability to synthesize and apply major concepts from Chapters 7 and 8	Some students may be better able to communicate their understanding to you orally, by describing the set of events rather than drawing them.

Chapter Goals

By the end of this chapter, students should understand that

◆ matter and energy are related;

◆ energy exists in different forms, such as heat, light, and chemical;

◆ cells have mechanisms that alter matter to store and release energy;

◆ solar energy is the energy source for almost all living systems on earth;

◆ photosynthesis converts light energy into chemical energy;

◆ cellular respiration breaks down food molecules and releases energy; and

◆ biosynthesis depends on energy-releasing reactions.

The learners also will

◆ demonstrate their ability to design certain aspects of an experiment,

◆ continue to collect and analyze data, and

◆ be able to draw conclusions based on available data.

Advance Preparation

If you have not already ordered *Anacharis* (elodea) for *Using Light Energy to Build Matter* in this chapter and *Exploring the Cycling of Matter in Communities* in Chapter 9, do so as soon as possible. Refer to the Preparations sections of those activities for more details. You will need a DVD player for the second activity, *Energy in Matter*. Review Materials and Preparations for *Energy in Matter*, *Keep on Running!*, and *Using Light Energy to Build Matter* so that you can assemble the necessary materials. Have students save and bring in 16-oz tin cans for the calorimeters in *Keep on Running!*, and pay particular attention to the safety information for that activity. *Keep on Running!* and *Using Light Energy to Build Matter* are enhanced by the use of a probe ware system. If computers are available, reserve them for these activities, and preview the activity to customize the probe ware instructions to match your equipment.

Releasing Energy

Engage

Major Concepts   Energy in matter (potential energy); uncontrolled energy conversion

Overview

In this activity, learners begin to extend their understanding of the nutritional and training requirements necessary for fitness and performance (Chapter 7) by learning about the underlying molecular events that convert food energy into cellular energy. To engage their thinking about how food releases energy, the students read an opening story that describes an explosion and then are challenged with several questions.

Outcomes and Indicators of Success

The following indicators allow you to assess the students' level of success with the activity and to assess their process of learning.

By the end of this activity, the learners should become engaged in thinking about the relationship between energy and matter.

They will demonstrate their interest by participating in a discussion about how energy is contained in food.

Preparations

If you set up Part A of the second activity *Energy in Matter* in advance, you can move directly from this activity to that one.

Strategies for Guiding Learners

PROCESS AND PROCEDURES

As a class, read orally or silently all introductory materials for the activity and the Process and Procedures to help students build connections between concepts and activities. Use the time spent reading to bring the students' attention into focus.

This activity engages the students' interest in the organization of matter and its relationship to energy at a molecular level. Begin the lesson by dramatically telling the story of the grain elevator explosion described in the opening story *A Matter of Explosions*, or have the students read this to themselves. This story is based on actual events that have occurred in various grain elevators during this century. If some of your students live on working farms, they may have stories to contribute about similar grain explosions.

1. Read the story *A Matter of Explosions* [page 288], and think about the following questions:

    Allow 1 or 2 minutes for the students to read through and consider the questions.

    ◆ Where did the energy for the grain explosion come from?

    Prompt the students to identify the grain as a tremendous storehouse of energy—enough energy to fuel an explosion. They also may recognize that sparks created by the contact between the shovel and the concrete introduced energy into the system.

    ◆ How can energy be stored in grain?

    Students may have no answer for this question yet; its purpose is to pique their curiosity about stored or potential energy without formally applying that label. Draw students to the idea that energy is stored in grain, which is a source of food. They should know from Chapter 7 that food is the source of their energy.

    ◆ What started the explosion that released the energy?

    A spark ignited the explosion in the grain. This is an example of an uncontrolled release of energy. Ask students for other examples of uncontrolled releases of energy (dynamite, grenades, firecrackers, forest fires). Then ask them to contrast these examples with controlled releases of energy (gasoline or diesel engines, a lawn mower, a furnace or air conditioner). They should recognize that controlled releases of energy provide useful work for humans and uncontrolled releases are destructive in human terms.

◆ How do you explain the fact that you do not explode when you eat grain products such as cereal or bread?

This question should help students speculate about how the energy in food is converted in the body and why there are no explosions. Students will learn about energy release in living systems throughout this chapter.

◆ What would you do to decrease the danger of explosion and better protect a grain storage facility and its employees?

Students may suggest that rules should disallow anyone from entering the facility without proper instruction about the danger. In addition, most grain storage facilities today are equipped with humidifier systems that reduce the risk of static and spark. Also, such a facility would not allow a metal shovel to be kept in with the grain; tools likely would be plastic or rubber.

2. Contribute your thoughts about the questions in step 1 to a class discussion.

Lead a discussion that allows the students to describe the connections they see between the ideas in Chapter 7 regarding energy and matter and the explosion at the grain elevator. Conclude this activity and move on to the next one within 20 minutes. The ideas in this activity are relatively simple and will interest students only if used to lead into something more complex.

Extensions

Arrange a field trip to a grain elevator if you live in an area where they are common.

Energy in Matter

Major Concepts
Energy is stored in matter; difference between potential and kinetic energy; organization of matter; conversion and transfer of energy; conservation of energy

Overview

Students investigate the relationship between matter and energy using simple wet lab experiences that demonstrate exothermic and endothermic reactions. They also explore the organization of matter by watching a solution evaporate to form ordered crystals of urea and by building molecular models of urea.

Materials   (per class of 30, teams of 2)

PART A
30 pairs of safety goggles

30 lab aprons

15 125-mL flasks

15 10 × 75-mm Pyrex test tubes **(Caution: These tubes must be Pyrex to avoid breakage.)**

15 10-mL or 25-mL graduated cylinders

30 microscope slides

15 dropping pipets

15 test tube racks

15 spatulas or spoons

5 hand lenses or microscopes (optional)

15 2-cm-long pieces of magnesium ribbon

5 15-g containers of ammonium nitrate labeled *CAUTION: Irritant*

5 20-mL bottles of 0.7*M* hydrochloric acid solution labeled *WARNING: Strong irritant*

5 10-mL bottles of saturated urea solution

PART B

DVD

DVD player

materials for building molecule models (see Preparations)

Outcomes and Indicators of Success

The following indicators allow you to assess the students' level of success with the activity and to assess their process of learning.

By the end of this activity, the learners should

1. understand that there is a relationship between energy and matter.

   They will show the development of their understanding by

   a. initially defining energy and matter and the relationship between them in their own words;

   b. evaluating their initial definitions after further investigation of energy and matter;

   c. referring to their experiences in Part A as evidence for a relationship between energy, matter, and organization; and

   d. using the terms *exothermic* and *endothermic* appropriately.

2. understand that matter is organized.

   They will demonstrate their understanding by

   a. choosing a preferred style for representing molecular models,

   b. explaining how atoms of simple molecules serve as building blocks for complex molecules,

   c. building a molecular model of urea, and

   d. drawing a diagram of the macromolecule starch (optional).

3. understand that there is energy in matter and that the energy is conserved even when it is transferred.

They will demonstrate their understanding by

   a. applying their understanding of energy to the terms *exothermic* and *endothermic*,

   b. explaining the difference between potential and kinetic energy,

   c. explaining how energy is not destroyed when molecules break down,

   d. defining the role of ATP in linking matter to energy, and

   e. drawing a diagram of the macromolecule starch and explaining how the arrangement of matter determines its potential energy (optional).

4. recognize that current understanding of science affects the interpretation of new data.

They will demonstrate this recognition by using a historical case of interpretation (in the essay *Historical Connections between Matter and Energy*) to illustrate the nature of the changing body of scientific knowledge.

Safety

Pyrex test tubes are essential for Part A. Non-Pyrex tubes may break during the temperature change of the exothermic reaction. Students should not handle these test tubes after they have added acid to them; they should make their observations while the tubes are seated firmly in the rack.

Caution

If you use edible materials for building the molecular models, remind students not to eat anything in the laboratory. Also, remind the students to observe the safety cautions for hydrochloric acid, ammonium nitrate, and urea solution.

Preparations

PART A. Three brief experiences allow students to begin to explore the relationships among energy, matter, and organization. If materials are a problem, increase the team size to 4. You also may find that the work goes more smoothly if you set up stations for each of the experiments.

Prepare enough 0.7*M* hydrochloric acid solution so that each team can work with 5 mL. This concentration of acid is ideal for producing a very warm acid solution. Higher concentrations of acid (1.0*M* and above) will cause the test tube to become hot and potentially dangerous. You may use concentrations as low as 0.5*M*, which will result in test tubes that are less warm; lower concentrations may result in test tube temperatures that do not differ noticeably from the starting temperature.

If you choose not to use magnesium and hydrochloric acid for the demonstration of exothermic reactions, you can substitute chemically activated heat packs. Small heat packs are available from sporting goods stores for $2 or less. Generally, you can reuse them after heating in a microwave or in boiling water; ask when you purchase them. The chemical reactions used in heat packs vary by manufacturer, and you should determine how yours work in preparation for student questions.

Approximately 5 g of ammonium nitrate is needed to make 40 mL of water noticeably colder. So that the students are not distracted from the focus of the activity, determine in advance a convenient way to measure about 5 g of ammonium nitrate without using a balance. For example, in your lab you may have spatulas whose size is such that "2 spatulas of ammonium nitrate" is sufficient to give approximately 5 g. Notify the students about the convenient measure that you identify.

Prepare a saturated urea solution by adding urea to 50 mL of room-temperature water until no more urea will dissolve (final concentration will be somewhat greater than 1 mg/mL). Stir thoroughly while dissolving the urea. Filter out any undissolved urea.

PART B. For the molecular models, you can supply actual kits or use more creative materials, such as flat toothpicks and gumdrops. It will help the students' understanding of molecules if these creative materials are grouped by color; for example, all red gumdrops are oxygen atoms, white gumdrops are hydrogen atoms, blue are nitrogen, black are carbon.

Background Information

The presentation of bioenergetics in this activity and the remaining activities of the chapter is intended to be primarily conceptual rather than detail oriented. The complex and somewhat abstract nature of the subject, however, makes simplification difficult without including certain chemical details. We have chosen to present a somewhat simplified view of energy and matter, although this necessitated a less comprehensive treatment than can be found in texts such as *BSCS Biology: A Molecular Approach*. For further details on bioenergetics, see *BSCS: A Molecular Approach* or any number of college biochemistry texts. For an interesting review of common misconceptions in biology, see the following articles by Dr. Richard Storey in *The American Biology Teacher*: "Textbook Errors and Misconceptions: Cell Metabolism" (1991) *53*, 339–343, and "Textbook Errors and Misconceptions: Cell Energetics" (1992) *54*, 161–166.

Strategies for Guiding Learners

PROCESS AND PROCEDURES

PART A   *Energy in Reactions*

As a class, read orally or silently all introductory materials for the activity and the Process and Procedures to help students build connections between concepts and activities. Use the time spent reading to bring the students' attention into focus.

To make the best use of class time, organize Part A of this activity to follow directly after the previous activity, *Releasing Energy*. Set up the materials in advance, and when you finish the discussion of the grain elevator, alert students to the location of the materials for each of the exercises. After you provide this organizational prelab information, encourage the students to proceed through steps 1–5 on their own. Move through the lab to get a sense of how much students understand or struggle with the ideas in the first part of the activity.

SAFETY: Put on your safety goggles and lab apron.

Safety Goggles   Lab Apron

1. Discuss with your partner how you would define *matter*. In your journal, write your definition and 3 examples of matter.

2. Discuss with your partner how you would define *energy*. In your journal, write your definition and 3 examples of energy.

As the learners discuss their definitions, watch that both partners contribute to the discussion and that they do not spend too much time on this step. Any definitions are acceptable now. This step allows you to hear the range of conceptions students have about these concepts.

3. Explain how matter and energy are related. Record your explanation in your journal. Include 1 or 2 examples to illustrate your ideas.

When students identify their examples, they should recognize that heat and explosions are indications of a relationship between energy and matter. Encourage creativity at this step. For steps 4 through 8, encourage a reasonable amount of independence and self-pacing. Students should be able to go to a lab station (or their bench area), conduct each short exercise, record their observations, and return to their seats.

As the learners conduct these exercises, they should discuss the observed energy changes with their partners. Depending on their prior experience, these descriptions could include anything from energy equated to heat, to correct uses of the terms *potential* and *kinetic energy*, to distinctions between chemical and thermal energy. Review these responses as you walk around the lab to assess what your students already know about matter, energy, and organization.

4. Try this exercise:

   a. Use a graduated cylinder to measure 5 mL of 0.7M hydrochloric acid. Pour this into a test tube that is firmly seated in a test tube rack. Do not remove the test tube from the rack.

WARNING: 0.7M HCl is a *strong irritant*. Avoid skin/eye contact; do not ingest. If contact occurs, flush affected area with water for 15 minutes; rinse mouth with water. Call the teacher.

   b. Feel the outside of the test tube to note the relative temperature (Figure 8.4).

   c. Place 2 cm of magnesium ribbon into the acid in the test tube. Observe what happens as the solid dissolves. In your journal, record your observations.

   d. Feel the test tube, and record your observations.

   e. Discuss the energy changes that you observed. Compare these changes with the events in the opening story.

   Perhaps you or your partner recall the terms that describe the types of chemical reactions that release and absorb energy from their surroundings (see Figure 8.5).
   Watch closely to make certain that all students are conducting safe exothermic reactions. As the magnesium dissolves in the acid, the solution, and hence the test tube, will become warm to the touch. The bubbles produced during the reaction are hydrogen gas. You might challenge the learners to realize that the grain explosion in the opening story is a dangerous example of an exothermic reaction. (For your information: The heat packs that Ward's supplies contain a solution of sodium acetate and a chemical in the trigger that starts a rapid crystallization reaction. Other heat packs may use different chemicals.)

5. Now, try another exercise:

   a. Put approximately 40 mL of room-temperature tap water in a flask.

   b. Feel the flask to note the relative temperature.

   c. Put about 2 spatulas of dry ammonium nitrate into the water in the flask. Swirl it gently to dissolve the powder.

Caution

CAUTION: Ammonium nitrate is an *irritant*. Avoid creating dust; avoid skin/eye contact; do not ingest. If contact occurs, flush affected area with water for 15 minutes; rinse mouth with water. Call the teacher.

    d. Feel the flask. Record your observations in your journal.

    e. Discuss the energy changes that you observed.

> The dissolution of ammonium nitrate lets students experience the cooling associated with an endothermic reaction. As the solute interacts with and reorganizes the solvent, heat is absorbed from the solvent and surroundings. Emphasize the idea that heat is molecular motion (the students will learn the term *kinetic energy* in the essays), and that cold is simply less heat.

6. Finally, try this exercise:

    a. Use a dropping pipet to place 1 drop of saturated urea solution on a microscope slide.

Caution

CAUTION: Urea solution is an *irritant*. Avoid skin/eye contact; do not ingest. If contact occurs, flush affected area with water for 15 minutes; rinse mouth with water. Call the teacher.

    b. Use the edge of the 2nd slide to spread the drop in a thin layer across the surface of the 1st slide.

    c. Watch the layer closely for changes. This may take several minutes to develop. Use hand lenses or microscopes, if available. In your journal, record your observations.

    Include drawings to record the changes that you see.

    d. Read the following information. Then answer the question in your journal.

> In the urea solution that you used, water was the solvent and urea was the solute. The solute molecules in a solution move about freely, according to the forces of diffusion. In other words, these molecules have a great deal of entropy. Explain what appears to happen to the organization of urea molecules as the water in the urea solution evaporates. What do you think happened to the level of entropy?

> For the urea crystallization, demonstrate how to use a second slide to spread a very thin layer of saturated urea solution across the top of a slide so that evaporation proceeds quickly. In dry climates, this should take only about 5 minutes, but in humid climates it will take longer. If your classroom is humid, remind the students to use as thin a layer of urea solution as possible. If the students blow very gently on the solution, the water will evaporate more quickly. You may want to warn students that once crystallization begins, it proceeds rapidly, so they may miss it if they are not monitoring the evaporation. The formation of crystals is easily seen with the naked eye and is a simple but clear demonstration of an increase in the organization of matter. Have microscopes or hand lenses available for a more exciting and detailed examination of the crystal formation process.

> If you have the equipment to project the image from a microscope for all students to see, then this step can be done as a demonstration quite effectively.

7. Wash your hands thoroughly with soap and water.

8. Complete the following tasks in your journal. Be prepared to participate in a class discussion about the relationship between energy and the organization of matter.

If time is short, you may choose to assign these questions and the essay *Matter and Energy Are Related* as homework. After the learners have answered the questions, conduct a class discussion to review the results of the lab experiences, the students' interpretation of their results, and their understanding of the essay. This discussion is essential for tracking the construction of student understanding and for identifying persistent misconceptions. Learners often confuse state changes with chemical reactions. Make certain that they understand that substances can change state (that is, become more or less organized) without undergoing any rearrangement of atoms, such as when solid ice melts to liquid water or when dry ice (CO_2) sublimates to a gas. Chemical reactions alter the structure of molecules through bond-making and bond-breaking. This is what happens when hydrochloric acid combines with magnesium, forming $MgCl_2$.

a. Is the reaction in step 4 exothermic or endothermic? What about the reaction in step 5? State your evidence in each case.

> **The step 4 reaction is exothermic because the reaction releases heat to the surroundings (test tube gets warmer). The step 5 reaction is endothermic because the reaction takes in or removes heat from the surroundings (flask gets colder).**

b. Describe where the energy needed for the endothermic reaction came from. Describe where the energy produced by the exothermic reaction went.

> **The energy needed for the endothermic reaction came from the heat present in the water and flask before the ammonium nitrate was added. In other words, the small amount of room-temperature heat energy present initially was transferred to the reaction that dissolved the solid; hence the water and flask became colder. The energy produced by the exothermic reaction was transferred to the surrounding water and glass, which caused the test tube to become warmer.**

c. What do you think happened to the organization of the solid ammonium nitrate molecules when they dissolved in water? How did that differ from what happened to urea?

> Answer these questions thoroughly, because you will refer to your notes throughout this chapter.

> Read the essay *Matter and Energy Are Related* (page 348) for helpful background information.

> **The molecules in solids, particularly crystalline solids such as ammonium nitrate, are relatively highly organized (the system has relatively low entropy). When solids dissolve, the molecules associate with solvent molecules spread out to occupy more volume, and become less ordered (the system has relatively more entropy). The reverse happens as a urea solution crystallizes. As solvent molecules evaporate from the solution (which decreases the volume), the urea molecules are forced closer together, until finally they crystallize and form a more organized material.**

PART B   Molecular Models

Complete Part B individually.

1. Figure 8.6 shows several ways that molecules can be represented. Which representation would you use to demonstrate molecular structure (atoms bonded together) to a 6th-grade student who did not understand that matter is organized? Explain your choice.

Encourage the students to focus on the strong points of each model. For instance, the structural representation is simple to write and communicates the bonding arrangement quite effectively, and the space-filling model communicates the relative size of atoms. There are no correct answers to this question, but you should monitor the students' answers to see how their preconceptions of atoms and bonding fit with established ways of representing molecules.

2. Watch the DVD segment "Molecular Models." Be prepared to answer the following question:

   How do the atoms of simple molecules serve as building blocks for much larger and more complex molecules?

    Use the DVD segment "Molecular Models," which shows turning, three-dimensional models of a variety of molecules, to direct a discussion about how the same types of atoms can occur in simple molecules as well as in very complex molecules. It is important that the students realize that the constituents of matter (atoms) in living organisms do not vary much, but the arrangement of those constituents does. Emphasize carbon, oxygen, hydrogen, nitrogen, phosphorus, and sulfur as the principal building blocks of all organic matter.

3. Use the materials that your teacher provides to construct a model of a urea molecule. Base your model on information from the DVD, the essays, the rule of molecular bonding, and the typical number of molecular bonds that the atoms in urea form (see the information below).

   The number of bonds that an atom usually forms is based on the number of electrons in its outer shell.

   ◆ Urea is represented by the chemical formula $CO(NH_2)_2$.
   ◆ Carbon usually has 4 bonds.
   ◆ Oxygen usually has 2 bonds.
   ◆ Nitrogen usually has 3 bonds.
   ◆ Hydrogen usually has 1 bond.

   To help students process this information, provide 10–15 minutes for them to build the urea molecule model. It is less important that they build an accurate model than it is for them to recognize that there are patterns of how atoms bond and that atoms are the building blocks of simple molecules, which are in turn the building blocks of more complex molecules. Monitor their progress, and help learners who do not recognize the ordered patterns present when atoms bond to each other.

Analysis

 You may want to assign the Analysis as homework. Based on the conceptual progress the class is making, either conduct a summarizing class discussion that pulls together the concepts or collect their written responses to the Analysis and assess them based on the potential responses indicated below. Remind students to read and use the essay *Energy Is Converted and Conserved* as an important resource for their analysis.

Respond to the following tasks in your journal. Be prepared to share your responses in a class discussion.

Read the essay *Energy Is Converted and Conserved* (page 351) for additional information.

1. If an exothermic reaction releases heat, why is it inaccurate to say that an endothermic reaction releases cold?

   It is inaccurate because cold is simply a relative absence of heat energy. An endothermic reaction takes in energy from its surroundings—it transfers heat away from the surroundings.

2. What is the difference between kinetic energy and potential energy? Provide at least two examples of each to help with your explanation.

   Kinetic energy is the energy of motion (such as heat), and potential energy is energy of position or arrangement of matter, such as water behind a dam, a brick on top of a ladder, or a molecule. Examples will vary; for example, a moving baseball has kinetic energy, while a wound spring has potential energy. If students use the boulder example from the essays, they may realize that the rolling boulder does not exhaust all the potential energy. If the boulder ended up at the edge of a cliff and someone pushed it, the boulder would move again. The boulder always has some potential energy.

3. Explain why the energy that is stored in the chemical bonds of a molecule is not destroyed when that molecule is broken down into smaller molecules.

   Energy is stored in the structure of bonds and atoms that make up all molecules, and any differences in energy are due to transfers with the surroundings. Energy is conserved, it is never destroyed. When one molecule (the reactant) is split into two (the products), the product molecules will contain a certain amount of energy. If they contain more energy than the starting molecule, the excess will have to come from other molecules involved in the reaction, such as ATP, or from surrounding heat. If the product molecules contain less energy than the starting molecule, the difference will have been lost as heat or transferred to other molecules.

4. Define ATP's role as a link between matter and energy.

   ATP is like any other molecule in that it is a carrier of energy. ATP is unlike most molecules, however, in that it happens to be the source of molecular energy that living organisms use in cellular reactions. That is, ATP is a form of chemical energy used in cells when chemical reactions require an input of energy. Answers should include some discussion of the inaccessible energy stored in the matter of macromolecules and the need to convert that energy into a form that is easily available to the cell.

5. Refine your definitions of matter, energy, and their relationship from those that you developed in steps 1–3 of Part A. It may be helpful to use diagrams or other visual aids with captions to explain your definitions.

   Answers will vary, but should reflect a more sophisticated understanding of matter and energy.

6. Read the essay *Historical Connections between Matter and Energy* (page 357). Write one or two paragraphs to Joseph Priestley if you had the chance to correct his explanation that phlogiston killed the mouse in his experiment.

   Be sure to include descriptions of both the energy and matter involved in that experiment.

   The students should write an imaginary letter to Joseph Priestley. In their letters, students should return to the historical vignette given in the reading to examine Priestley's experiment and conclusions. (Priestley determined that phlogiston was the cause of a mouse's inability to live in air that had been tainted by a burning candle.)

Because he believed the then-current doctrine that phlogiston was released through combustion, he interpreted his results as evidence that this substance was toxic. His reasoning was logical, but given the incorrect understanding of phlogiston's importance, the explanation was incorrect. A reverse situation actually existed. A depletion of oxygen from the air was the reason that the mouse died. This shows the influence that a current body of knowledge, albeit a dynamic body, has on the progress of scientific development. Students should realize that everyone views the world through lenses of current understanding, and this influences how we interpret new information. The example also implies the importance of thorough controls in experiments.

Further Challenges

If your students understand the concepts in this activity and would like additional practice applying their knowledge, have them complete these questions.

1. In your journal, draw a diagram to show that starch is a macromolecule made up of many glucose molecules. Then explain how the arrangement of matter determines its energy content.

   Student diagrams will differ, but all should show some repetition of symbols that represent glucose and bonds that connect the glucose monomers. For example, some representations might be as simple as beads on a string; others may be more detailed. Students' understanding of how much energy a molecule contains probably will not be well developed, but they should understand that large molecules contain more energy than small molecules because they have many more bonds and atoms.

2. A saturated solution is a solution in which the concentration of solute is so high that no more solute can dissolve. With that knowledge, explain what happened during the crystallization of urea in step 6, Part A.

   Do you think a dilute solution of urea (one in which the concentration of solute is very low), if left uncovered for a long time, would eventually form crystals as well? Explain your answer.

   During crystallization, the water gradually evaporates and the concentration of solute increases beyond the level at which all solute can stay in solution. At this point, the urea molecules begin to have a greater attraction for one another than for the molecules of the solvent (water). Because urea molecules are small and regular, they can crystallize to form an ordered solid rather than simply a precipitate. (By contrast, rapid evaporation causes most very large molecules, such as proteins, to precipitate out of solution. Special slow crystallization conditions are necessary for macromolecular crystallizations.) Crystals would form eventually from a dilute urea solution, but it would take longer for enough urea molecules to come into contact with each other for crystals to form. (For crystallization to occur, a critical concentration must be reached.) To see how well students understand the physical basis of crystallization, use probing questions to assess the relevant fundamental concepts, such as temperature (molecular motion), solubility, and molecular order.

Keep on Running!

Major Concepts Sources of energy and matter in food; cellular respiration; dynamic body of scientific knowledge

Overview

In this activity, the students are challenged to design a food snack for marathon runners. They rely on a calorimetry protocol to gather most of their data. This experience provides concrete information that enables the students to explain the idea that energy is contained in common food substances and that it can be measured. They also read about cellular respiration and how it provides the link between the matter in food and the controlled release of usable energy in living organisms. They use this information to explain how energy can be extracted from food to perform the work of biological reactions.

Materials (per class of 30, teams of 3)

30 pairs of safety goggles
30 lab aprons
10 100-mL graduated cylinders
10 250-mL Erlenmeyer flasks
10 thermistors and their associated probe ware system
10 15-cm nonroll, nonmercury thermometers (if probe ware systems are not available)
10 balances
10 forceps
10 16-oz tin cans with cutout air and viewing holes
10 #20 corks with sample holders
box of 2-in kitchen matches (or fireplace matches)
10 3-cm^2 pieces of sandpaper
masking tape
10 20 × 30-cm pieces of extra heavy aluminum foil
20 pot holders
10 small containers of water
enough food types and samples for the teams to run their tests (see Preparations)
duct tape, pliers, tin snips (for preparing tin cans)
materials to design food labels
overhead transparencies (optional; see Hints for the Calorimetry Protocol)
30 copies of the *Peer Review* rubric *Tudor Valley Marathon Snack Brochure*

Outcomes and Indicators of Success

The following indicators allow you to assess the students' level of success with the activity and to assess their process of learning.

By the end of this activity, the learners should

1. be able to create a food snack for marathon runners that has a nutritional value they can explain and support scientifically.

They will demonstrate this explanation by

    a. designing a package or label for the snack that answers key questions about it in terms of matter and energy,

    b. calculating the kcal of energy produced per gram of food burned, and

    c. using experimental data to justify this snack as a good choice for runners.

2. understand that cellular respiration releases the energy in food in an efficient and controlled manner.

They will demonstrate this understanding by

    a. describing how energy is released in the human body, and

    b. connecting the ideas from Chapter 7 about fitness and nutrition to how the body can use a particular food source to help a runner keep running.

3. realize that energy production, like other homeostatic processes, is regulated (optional, in Further Challenges).

They will demonstrate this realization by drawing a feedback loop that explains how energy is regulated.

Safety

Caution

Demonstrate how to assemble and disassemble the calorimeter and the best technique for igniting the samples. Tape a small piece of sandpaper to each lab table, and distribute a container with 10 kitchen matches to each team; replenish matches as needed. Remind students to be cautious when using matches and handling hot objects and to place burned matches and charred food samples in the container of water. Be sure students place extra heavy aluminum foil under the calorimeter while samples are burning. Instruct safety monitors to throw water from the container onto any flames that appear out of control. Warn students not to eat any foods in the laboratory.

Because this experiment involves an open flame, extra precautions are called for. Before students begin, check on the following:

◆ No flammable liquids or vapors are present in the lab.

◆ A recently tested ABC-type fire extinguisher is at hand.

◆ Lab tables are clear of all materials except those required.

◆ The piece of aluminum foil is in place under each calorimeter.

◆ Books and journals are at least 30 cm away from the piece of aluminum foil.

◆ All students are wearing goggles and lab aprons and have tied back long hair and rolled up long sleeves.

◆ All students are familiar with correct and relevant safety procedures.

Preparations

Use Figure 8.10 in the student book as a model for preparing the tin-can calorimeters. To support the 250-mL flask, use a 16-oz tin can (vegetable-can size). With a can/bottle opener, punch out 4 triangular openings on the top of the can and 2 on the side near the top. Use tin snips to cut a viewing hole at the bottom large enough to see the burning sample (about 5 cm tall, 2.5 cm wide at the top, and 4 cm wide at the base). Cover the cut edges with duct tape. Mold a piece of aluminum foil around the cork to prevent it from catching fire. (If the cork is more than 2 cm high, cut off the excess so the viewing hole does not need to be too large.) Use a large paper clip to fashion a sample holder such that the sample fits firmly *between* the wires. Insert the holder into the cork. Have some extra heavy aluminum foil available for students who need to fashion a boatlike sample holder for runny foods, such as peanut butter and honey. For ease of igniting the sample, the sample holder should be held 1.5 cm above the cork surface.

Use Figure T8.1 as a guide for the types of foods to assemble. To cut expenses and add interest, have the students review this activity a day or 2 in advance, and volunteer to bring in different food samples that they think might be useful for their marathon snack. Oil-roasted nuts and snack foods such as potato chips, corn chips, and cheese snacks burn the most easily in the calorimeter. Many dried fruits, such as dates and peaches, are fairly moist and will burn better if they have been thoroughly dried.

Figure T8.1 Energy in kcal of common foods burned in a highly efficient calorimenter

Foods	Kcal/100 g	Foods	Kcal/100 g
Almonds	640	Oatmeal	238
Cashews*	609	Potato chips*	536
Cornflakes*	359	Peanut butter*	619
Dried coconut*	570	Pretzels*	362
Corn chips*	571	Raisins*	325
Cheese snacks*	571	Roasted peanuts*	600
Honey	286	Walnuts* (English)	702

* These foods are likely to burn well in this calorimeter.

If you are using thermistors for this investigation, review the procedures necessary for your equipment and prepare accordingly. Determine how best to suspend your thermistors in the flasks. If you are not using a probe ware system, substitute the nonmercury thermometers for the thermistors; the general experimental design remains the same. A cork that fits the flask can be cut to support the thermistor or thermometer provided it does not seal the flask.

Caution

Review the rubric on the *GACD* for the Tudor Valley Marathon Snack brochure, and modify it to suit your class. Plan an appropriate prize for the winner (and a couple of runners-up) of the Tudor Valley Marathon Snack Contest. Some suggestions include a photo of the winner and her or his brochure on your Web page, a bag of healthy trail mix, or a certificate of accomplishment.

Strategies for Guiding Learners

PROCESS AND PROCEDURES

As a class, read orally or silently all introductory materials for the activity and the Process and Procedures to help students build connections between concepts and activities. Use the time spent reading to bring the students' attention into focus.

You can start off this lesson with a dramatic flair by arriving at class in athletic attire, all excited about an advertisement for a contest. When the students are settled, read the advertisement portion of the introduction as though it came from a runner's magazine. A quieter way to introduce this activity would be to have the students read the introduction.

Caution

Before the students look at the Process and Procedures, review the safety cautions for the calorimetry protocol and the location of safety equipment, especially the location of the fire extinguisher. Be sure students have tied back long hair and secured flowing clothing out of the way. Set strict safety rules for this activity and enforce them. Assign teams of two or three, and make certain that the team members understand the importance of monitoring safety throughout the activity.

Then review the assembly of the calorimeter with the whole class in the context of the entire activity. This will allow you to let the students work at their own pace for the rest of the activity as long as they know where to find the materials and what procedures to follow for safety and cleanup.

1. Your challenge is to select 3 different foods from the available choices. You will measure the calories in each according to the calorimetry protocol. You will then use at least 2 of these foods and up to 3 additional ingredients (plus your understanding of energy, matter, and nutrition) in a recipe that has the best chance of winning the Tudor Valley Marathon Snack Contest. Discuss and develop your strategy with your partner. Record it in your journal. A good strategy will include the following:

   ◆ A brief, written explanation about why you would like to test the 3 foods you have chosen

   You might look back at Chapter 7 to remind yourself about the role of the different components of food.

   ◆ The use of the Calorimetry Protocol

   ◆ Predictions for the results

   ◆ Plans to average multiple calorimetry tests for each chosen food sample

   ◆ A data table for recording your results

   Divide the responsibilities of the calorimetry protocol evenly between team partners. Be sure to follow the correct safety procedures.

   When you have finished this whole-class instruction, have the students work with their teammates and begin the procedure. Except for actually carrying out the calorimetry protocol, this activity does not require a lab. To keep up the pace of the chapter, require that students get to a certain point each day. Students should be able to complete steps 1 and 2 the first day so they can walk in the second day and immediately start the calorimetry tests (step 3).

2. Have your teacher approve your strategy.

   As you review the students' strategies, look for the following:

   ◆ The use of multiple food sources that can be burned with some degree of success

   ◆ Explanations that describe the nutritional advantages of the selected foods (This will indicate how well the learners connect the ideas from Chapter 7 to the composition of the snack for marathon runners.)

- ◆ An understanding of the purpose of the calorimetry protocol
- ◆ A preliminary data table
- ◆ A written plan for conducting their work

3. Conduct your tests.

4. Discuss the calorimetry results with your partner. Modify your recipe for the marathon food if your predictions were not supported by the results.

   Students should choose to make their marathon food from high calorie ingredients.

5. Compare the kcals per gram that you measured with the Calories per gram given on labels for the same foods. Explain any discrepancies that you find.

   Some of the foods that you tested may be listed in Figure 7.9D, Chapter 7. Note that these values are given in kcal/100 g.

   Remember to follow the required safety cautions.

SAFETY: Put on your safety goggles and lab apron. Tie back long hair, and roll up long, loose sleeves.

Safety Goggles   Lab Apron

Expect that students' values for kcal/100 g will be significantly lower than those listed in Figure 7.9D, because calories are lost to the environment in these simple calorimeters.

HINTS FOR THE CALORIMETRY PROTOCOL

See the protocol box on page 295 in the student text for the steps.

When the learners begin working on the calorimetry protocol, walk through the class to monitor the calorimeter setups and make certain that they are safe and stable and that the sensing elements of the thermistors do not touch the glass of the flask.

Students may need to modify the sample holder into a platform shape for some foods. Encourage learners to come up with safe, creative ways to maximize the possibility of combustion, such as using smaller amounts of food or spreading food thinly. Small holes in the bottom of the foil platform may help.

Once the students begin burning their samples, they should be attentive and focused on the experiment. They may have to relight their samples if the flame goes out. This should be done quickly so that the water in the calorimeter does not begin to cool. Remind the students that even when their entire sample has burned, the temperature will continue to rise. This happens as heat continues to transfer from the tin can to the flask of water. If time is limited in your class, you can shorten the experiment by conducting only two trials of each food sample rather than three.

Some students may have difficulty calculating the calories for their samples. Use these sample data (Figure T8.2) for three samples of roasted peanuts as an example of how to do the calculations.

	Trial 1	Trial 2	Trial 3	Average
Final water T = 26°C		24°C	30°C	26.67°C
Initial water T = 20°C		20°C	20°C	20°C
Change in T = 6°C		4°C	10°C	6.67°C
Sample mass = 0.2 g		0.1 g	0.2 g	0.17 g
(T change) × (H₂O vol) = calories 6°C × 100 mL H₂O = 600 calories		400 calories	1,000 calories	667 calories
Calories/1,000 = kilocalories				
600 cal ÷ 1,000 = 0.6 kcal		0.4 kcal	1.0 kcal	0.667 kcal
Kcal ÷ sample mass = kcal/mass				
0.6 kcal ÷ 0.2 g = 3.0 kcal/g		4.0 kcal/g	5.0 kcal/g	3.92 kcal/g

Figure T8.2 Sample calorimetry data and calculations

Note that students either need to calculate the kcal/g nine times—three trials for each sample of three foods (or six times if only two foods are used), and then average the kcal/g for the three trials, or calculate the average for the three trials initially. Determine which method to use by the students' prior experience with calculating averages and change.

The student text explains the steps to find the average kcal produced in the three trials and divide that by the average number of grams burned (for example, $[(6.0 + 4.0 + 10.0) /100] \div 3 = .667$ kcal and $.667 \div [.2 + .1 + .2]/3 = 3.92$ kcal/g). This method requires fewer calculations overall (and so tends to introduce fewer chances for error), but some students may find the steps confusing. Alternatively, an average of the three kcal/g values for each food can be determined easily if each was calculated separately and then averaged (for example, $[3.0 + 4.0 + 5.0]/3 = 4.0$ kcal/g).

Ask the students why it is important to test multiple samples and calculate averages rather than trusting only one value. The precision of separate measurements is one important indicator of reliability. If separate trials yield numbers that vary by three or four times (3.0 kcal/g and 12.0 kcal/g), there likely is a problem in the design, setup, or execution of the experiment. If the variations are relatively small, averaging smoothes out minor inconsistencies and inspires confidence that no uncontrolled errors have significantly affected the final results.

The average value for each food provides sufficient information for completing the tasks in the snack contest design criteria and in the Analysis. For example, if students determine the average for three samples of roasted peanuts (for example, 4.0 kcal/g) and scale that up for 30 g (for example, 4.0 kcal/g × 30 g = 120 kcal), they obtain a value that is relatively close to the 200 kcal/30 g goal defined by the contest criteria. Because this food is slightly less calorie dense than 200 kcal/30 g, the students might decide to combine roasted peanuts with another food that they tested that is more calorie dense. (See below to deal with significant variations.)

When the learners have finished their calculations, use an overhead projector or distribute copies of Figure T8.1 (in Preparations), the actual caloric values for a number of common snack foods. The following sample data may help students with the adjustment to 100 g samples used in Figure T8.1.

Continuing with the 4.0 kcal/g average value for roasted peanuts:

$$\frac{4.0 \text{ kcal}}{\text{g}} \times \frac{100}{100} = \frac{400 \text{ kcal}}{100 \text{ g}}$$

The students probably will notice that their experimental values are significantly lower than the actual values. Ask them to speculate why the values differ. In fact, their experimental values will be lower due to the relative inefficiency of their calorimeters. For completely accurate results, the food must be burned completely, and all of the heat must be transferred to the water. In the student calorimeters, much heat is lost through the holes or is radiated into the air rather than transferred to the water, and the burning is incomplete. The calorimeters used by physical chemists are far more sophisticated and efficient, although the principles are the same.

If your students are motivated to determine the efficiency of their calorimeters, have them divide their values for caloric density by those in Figure T8.1. Values in the range of 0.20 to 0.40, or 20–40 percent, will not be uncommon. A value of 20 percent would mean that a calorimeter captured 20 percent of the energy released during burning.

The students may need several days to complete their packages or labels. If their labels or brochures indicate remaining misconceptions, supplement the essay about cellular respiration (*Controlling the Release of Energy from Matter*) with a class discussion focused on the detail and organization of the reading. The figures may be useful as overhead transparencies.

Analysis

Use this Analysis as an opportunity for mid-chapter assessment. The scoring rubric may help you evaluate student understanding of the key concepts of the chapter as reflected on the package or label. If you choose to use the rubric, share it with the students before they begin working on their brochures. The essays *Controlling the Release of Energy from Matter* and *Cellular Respiration: A Closer Look at Converting Food Energy into Cell Energy* will help the students with this task.

Read the essays *Controlling the Release of Energy from Matter: An Overview of Cellular Respiration* (page 358) and *Cellular Respiration: A Closer Look at Converting Food Energy into Cell Energy* (page 359). These readings provide important background information that will be helpful in completing this task.

1. Develop a package label or brochure that is informative and is an effective marketing tool for your Tudor Valley Marathon Snack. Your package label or brochure should answer the following questions:

   ◆ What combination of foods did you decide to use in your snack?

   ◆ How did your calorimetry data and your understandings of nutrition influence your decision to make your snack using these particular foods?

   ◆ What are the qualities that make the matter in your foods particularly good as a snack for marathon runners?

◆ How does the matter in the food become usable energy for the body? In particular, how does it help a marathon runner keep on running?

Your explanations should include information about nutrients, digestion, breakdown, synthesis, absorption, macromolecules, building blocks the runner will need, and how energy is obtained at the cellular level.

The diet of an individual should contribute to his or her performance, but the diet itself depends in part on the individual's activity. In most cases, this requires a balance of foods. Carbohydrates are the body's preferred source of calories for aerobic performance even though they are lower in calories (per gram) than fats. It is possible that some foods may not be metabolized as efficiently as others, even though they may contain more kcal/unit. As students describe cellular respiration, they should mention that energy release in cellular respiration is slow, stepwise, regulated, catalyzed by enzymes, and produces ATP and hydrogen carrier molecules rather than heat (exclusively).

2. Submit your package label or brochure to the snack contest judges, and wait for a decision on the winner.

Use the scoring rubric to help you judge the entries. You might want to involve other teachers or even another class. Don't forget to have an appropriate prize for the winner and perhaps for one or two runners-up.

Further Challenges

Living organisms have evolved complex processes for extracting energy from matter and using it to fuel cellular reactions. As a result, when a cheetah accelerates toward a gazelle, it can produce enough ATP in its muscles to fuel the rapid contractions necessary for an explosive sprint. The same is true for an escaping gazelle. If the cheetah had too little energy, it would not catch its prey. Think back to the work that you did learning about homeostasis. Is it necessary for organisms to maintain a balance of energy to stay alive? Regulating the appropriate energy levels is another aspect of maintaining homeostasis. How do organisms balance their energy needs with their energy supplies? Read the essay *Regulation and Energy Production* (page 363). Draw a feedback loop that demonstrates how energy is regulated.

◆ If you assign Further Challenges, look for feedback loops that show an understanding of the ATP/ADP cycle, the differences between aerobic respiration and fermentation, and the role of aerobic conditioning in providing the potential for greater energy release. Students might find that Figure E8.17 is a useful illustration of how energy regulation occurs.

◆ This activity dabbles in food science or food chemistry. Many communities have resources related to this industry. Contact a major food processor, diet and nutrition center, or county extension agent for a resource person who could visit the classroom and discuss careers in this area. Or, arrange a field trip to a laboratory where food testing takes place.

◆ Animal diets require attention to calories and nutritional content just as human diets do. A zookeeper, veterinarian, or pet supplier may be able to address the matter and energy needs of different animals. This could be set up as a classroom visit or a field trip.

Using Light Energy to Build Matter

Major Concepts
Sources of energy and matter in photosynthesis; energy conversions; variables in experimental design

Overview

In this activity, the students build on their understanding of how energy is contained in matter by studying the role that plants play in trapping solar energy in a biologically accessible form. Learners use a photosynthetic system to conduct an experiment that examines the factors that affect the rate of photosynthesis. An associated essay provides background for their designs and helps round out their understanding of the processes by which energy and matter are brought into living systems. To synthesize this knowledge, the learners develop a number of test questions to contribute to a class quiz.

Materials   (per class of 30, teams of 4)

8 2-L beakers
8 100-mL beakers or small jars
8 250-mL flasks
8 250-mL graduated cylinders
16 25 × 200-mm test tubes
16 1-mL pipets (if a probe ware system is unavailable)
8 petri dish halves (if a probe ware system is unavailable)
8 wrapped drinking straws
8 lamps with 100-watt spotlights or fluorescent bulbs
20 mL 0.04% aqueous bromothymol blue solution (see Preparations)
16 pH probes
8 thermistors
4 pkgs narrow-range pH indicator paper (if a probe ware system is unavailable;
    see Preparations)
8 nonmercury thermometers (if a probe ware system is unavailable)
8 squares each of red, blue, and green cellophane (large enough to wrap a test tube)
roll of tape
8 forceps (if a probe ware system is unavailable; see Preparations)
8 rulers
glass-marking pencils
aluminum foil
2 gal distilled water
supply of tap water (25°C)
supply of ice water (10°C)
8 jars of tap water for storing pH probes
16 15-cm sprigs of young, healthy *Anacharis* (elodea)

Outcomes and Indicators of Success

The following indicators allow you to assess the students' level of success with the activity and to assess their process of learning.

By the end of this activity, the learners should

1. understand that the rate of photosynthesis depends on environmental factors.

   They will indicate their understanding by

   a. developing a list of factors that affect photosynthesis,

   b. writing an if-then statement with an appropriate relationship between a factor and the rate of photosynthesis,

   c. interpreting their experimental results from measuring rates of photosynthesis, and

   d. crafting a meaningful test question that includes a reference to environmental factors.

2. understand that photosynthesis is the process that brings energy and matter into living systems.

   They will indicate their understanding by

   a. writing test questions that address concepts involving how plants use light, carbon dioxide, and water to produce carbohydrates,

   b. explaining how plants carry out cellular respiration in addition to photosynthesis, and

   c. explaining how the trapping of light provides energy for carbon fixation.

3. be able to use some of the methods of science.

   They will demonstrate this ability by

   a. developing a list of variables,

   b. following a protocol,

   c. writing a testable if-then statement,

   d. using a control in an experiment,

   e. recording reliable data that can be used to develop a graph and draw conclusions, and

   f. drawing a graph and analyzing class results.

Preparations

Young, healthy *Anacharis* (elodea) is essential to gathering useful data. Maintain the *Anacharis* under a grow light so that it is actively photosynthesizing when students begin the experiment. Use only sprigs with growing tips. Water temperature should be at least 25°C. A 2°–4°C increase in water temperature during the course of the experiment is not significant, but students should maintain the temperature as closely as possible. The fluorescent bulbs now available for lamps give satisfactory results and do not produce heat. It is helpful to fashion a shield from aluminum foil to direct the light toward the plant.

Results are better with distilled water in the test tubes. If you will be using pH paper, test the pH of your distilled water to determine which narrow-range pH paper to purchase. (Also, test the decrease in pH when you blow into the water for 3 minutes.) Contact your local science supplier for availability of pH papers that are sensitive to different pH ranges. You can buy rolls of pH sensitive paper that are sensitive to specific pH ranges (pH 1.0–2.5, 3.0–5.5, 6.0–8.0, 8.0–9.5, 10.0–12.0, 12.5–14.0). Or you can buy a set of seven rolls, each with a different sensitivity. Students can use 1-mL pipets (with a finger) to transfer a drop from each test tube to the pH paper, or they can fold the pH paper and dip it into the test tube by holding it with forceps.

Caution

A probe ware system with pH probes gives much more accurate data for small changes in pH than pH paper. Use such a system if available. If your probe ware system involves having computers in the laboratory, see the *Guidelines for Laboratory Safety* in this guide for safety requirements. Whether using pH probes or paper, students also can observe color changes in the bromothymol blue as an indication of the carbon dioxide concentration. Bromothymol blue turns yellow in the presence of carbon dioxide—the greater the carbon dioxide concentration, the more yellow it appears. Purchase or prepare a 0.04% aqueous bromothymol blue solution.

If you are using probes, each team will need two pH probes and one thermistor. Preview the activity and determine how best to accommodate that configuration with your probe ware system. Contact your probe ware manufacturer for assistance in configuring software to record the ranges of data that students will collect. In particular, it is best to view a narrow range of pH on the graph produced by probe ware so that small changes are easy to detect.

Check your probe ware manufacturer's instructions ahead of time for correct preparations, handling, and probe care. Most pH probes are sensitive instruments and require specific handling. Some pH probes must be removed from their soaking bottles the day before the activity and be placed in tap water. Most pH probes must not be allowed to dry out because salts will accumulate in the glass pores, requiring a 1-hour soak in tap water to dissolve out. In addition, most pH probes must *not* be stored in distilled water, which will leach the fill solution from the electrodes. For more information about the pH probes, consult the manufacturer.

Strategies for Guiding Learners

PROCESS AND PROCEDURES

Review the introduction of the activity with the students to be sure they understand the transition from cellular respiration to photosynthesis. It is important that they begin to see how the ideas in this chapter build on each other and that they do not consider each activity as an isolated set of ideas.

1. With your teammates, develop a list of at least 3 variables that could affect the rate of photosynthesis.

   To help you generate your list, read the essay *Whose Discovery Is This?* (page 365) and the introduction to the essay *Getting Energy and Matter into Biological Systems* (page 367).

2. Compare your list with another team's list. Add any new ideas to your list.

   If your students need a break from team work, suggest that they develop the list of variables individually or have the whole class generate the list. The concept of *variable* as a factor that can be tested in an experiment should be familiar to the learners by this point in the program. If they are not comfortable with this word, spend some time reviewing the idea and providing examples to clarify. The lists of variables the students generate should include at least three items and may include the following: intensity of light, color of light, amount of rainfall, quality of soil, amount of air pollution, amount of water pollution, number of leaves, size of leaves, temperature, color of leaves, amount of chlorophyll, or plant height.

3. Participate in a class discussion to identify at least 2 variables that you could test easily in your classroom.

   Use the teams' lists of variables to generate a discussion about which variables could be tested easily in your classroom. Some variables can be eliminated quickly, such as size of leaves, because *Anacharis* leaves all are approximately the same size, or amount of chlorophyll, because testing this would involve complex techniques and sophisticated expertise. Use directed questions and a review of the materials available to get the learners to suggest that light intensity and wavelength could be tested in class. Consider inviting a physics teacher into your classroom to give a 10–15-minute talk or demonstration about light energy, absorption and reflection of light by substances such as pigments, and the relationship between wavelength and color. A more thorough understanding of the properties of light may help the students design better experiments.

4. Use the Photosynthesis Protocol and the materials available to you to outline an experiment that tests the influence of 1 of these variables on the rate of photosynthesis. Your experiment should

   ◆ answer some variation of the question, What affects the rate of photosynthesis?, and

   ◆ include an if-then statement that relates your question to your experiment.

5. Write a plan for your experiment, and have your teacher approve it.

   If your class works well independently, students should be able to review the protocol and move on to developing a plan. If your students have difficulty with this type of work, lead this step as a whole-class activity. Review the materials, techniques, and safety precautions appropriate to the protocol. Remind the students that a protocol is only a tool for conducting an experiment and should not be confused with a complete experiment, which involves choosing variables and controls, collecting and analyzing data, and drawing conclusions.

   Focus the students on formulating an if-then statement that is a hypothesis related to the question, What affects the rate of photosynthesis? To be testable, these hypotheses need to be developed in the context of the protocol and materials available. You may want to expand the list of variables that can be tested based on the materials available in your classroom. If any teams are struggling to agree upon a variable to test, encourage them to consider the basic variable, which is plain light at distances between 10 and 50 centimeters.

As learners decide how to use the cellophane, which works by isolating light in a narrow range of visible wavelengths (or colors), warn them not to put cellophane on the light source; it could melt or catch fire. Prompt the learners to see that alternatively they can wrap it around the beaker. Also, remind them that if more than one layer of cellophane is used, it will dramatically alter the light intensity in addition to changing the range of wavelengths. In addition, there likely will not be enough teams to test the outcomes when two variables are altered at once (for example, wavelength *and* intensity). For this reason, encourage teams testing various colors of cellophane to agree to use a common light source distance (intensity). This will make class data comparisons more meaningful when the analysis is complete. (Alternatively, teams could alter two variables if the data from *all class periods* are pooled for analysis.) For this protocol to be used successfully, it is essential to use *healthy Anacharis* and to take readings for at least 30 minutes. An on-task and experienced group of students can complete steps 1–5 in one class period.

6. In your journal, write your prediction for how your chosen variable will affect the rate of photosynthesis. Explain your prediction.

7. Conduct your experiment.

   Record your data in your journal.

   Allow a minimum of a full class period for conducting the experiment. Move from team to team as students set up and conduct their experiments. Help troubleshoot any difficulties they have.

8. Draw a graph for the variable that your team tested. Plot the rate of photosynthesis, as indicated by pH, on the *y*-axis (vertical) against elapsed time on the *x*-axis (horizontal).

   Remember, include a line that represents your control.

   For more efficient use of class time, have students complete their graphs as a homework assignment. In successful experiments, graphs should show a rise in pH as photosynthesis proceeds. This is because actively photosynthesizing *Anacharis* remove carbon dioxide from the water, which lowers the concentration of carbonic acid and increases the pH. Depending on the variables chosen, graphs will show varying levels of photosynthetic activity.

9. Record your team's data in a class data table, and present your team's conclusions to the class.

   Note the variables that the class tested and the range of values recorded.

10. Review the graphs from each team. You and your team can discuss your conclusions about the effects of each variable tested on the rate of photosynthesis.

    A comparison among teams is essential so that students have a basis for understanding how their results compare with those based on different variables. They need to understand their own experiment well enough to present it briefly to the class and listen well enough to others to draw conclusions about others' work. Choose a spokesperson from each team to present the results. Set a time limit for the presentations (2–3 minutes should be sufficient). Then have the teams post their graphs so that others can refer to their data. Experimental results may vary but should show an increase in photosynthetic rate at greater light intensities and the lowest photosynthetic rate in the green wavelengths of light. (This is because chlorophyll reflects green light but absorbs other colors, such as red and blue.) The bromothymol blue should not turn yellow in conditions where photosynthesis was taking place (carbon dioxide was being used), but likely turned yellow under conditions when the plant was unable to perform photosynthesis (producing carbon dioxide through cellular respiration). If all variables are tested, students should be able to draw this conclusion themselves.

Analysis

Complete the following tasks and questions individually:

1. Write three questions (with answers) for a quiz designed to assess your understanding of the experimental results and the concepts in the essay *Getting Energy and Matter into Biological Systems* (page 367). Your teacher will collect these questions from the class and develop a quiz.

    This analysis task differs from others in the program in that it asks students to develop questions as a measure of their own understanding. Some students will be frustrated by this assignment, but if you allow time for them to think about it or work with them individually, they should be able to write at least two questions that could qualify for a quiz. Ask the students to write the answers for their questions as well. Questions that clearly link the experimental results to the concepts elaborated in the essay are best.

    The following are questions you could add to the student-generated questions from task 1:

    a. The 18th-century scientist Joseph Priestley did an experiment on "phlogisticated" air—air in a glass container that had been "injured" by an animal breathing it or by a candle burning it. If Priestley put an illuminated green plant in such a container, the air in it was said to be restored. It was "de-phlogisticated" and would once again support the life of an animal such as a mouse. Explain in what way the plant can restore the air.

        When the plant gives off excess oxygen as a result of photosynthetic splitting of water, the air is restored ("dephlogisticated").

    b. Make a diagram or other visual representation that shows the energy source and carbon source for humans and three other species with at least one plant example and one animal example.

        Students should distinguish that some organisms get energy from organic chemical sources (humans do) while others use light energy. A few use nonorganic chemical sources. With regard to carbon, the key distinction is whether it comes from organic molecules that already have been processed in a living system (as do humans) or whether they used a nonliving source, such as the carbon dioxide fixed during photosynthesis.

c. Why do we say that solar energy is the ultimate source of energy for almost all living systems?

> *Nonphotosynthetic organisms (chemotrophs) get their matter and energy by consuming carbon compounds that were built by other organisms. Ultimately, this chain leads back to organisms that synthesize macromolecules photosynthetically. (Chemosynthetic bacteria are an exception to this generality. They obtain energy by oxidizing reduced forms of inorganic compounds, such as nitrogen and sulfur.)*

d. How does organization play a role in the trapping of light energy?

> *The organization of membranes and other structures in the chloroplast aids photosynthesis by providing for an organized array of pigment molecules, including chlorophyll, which enables the pigments to absorb and transfer light energy. The simple act of fixing carbon organizes matter as well because it generates a more complex molecule from a less complex one.*

e. How does the internal structure of the chloroplast facilitate providing potential energy for making ATP?

> *The thylakoid membrane forms a subcompartment across which a proton gradient is built. The proton gradient, in turn, provides a source of potential energy for the synthesis of ATP.*

2. The earth's early atmosphere had no oxygen. Use your understanding of plant photosynthesis to explain how photosynthetic organisms made the evolution of aerobic organisms possible.

   The first photosynthetic organisms must have been anaerobic because the atmosphere had no oxygen. Thus, they did not use the oxygen that was released when they split water in photosynthesis, and the oxygen began to accumulate in the atmosphere. (In fact, the oxygen would have been toxic to most cells, and organelles such as peroxisomes might have evolved that lowered the oxygen concentration in the cells.) Eventually, mitochondria developed that could use the oxygen to produce ATP, and organisms that incorporated mitochondria led to the evolution of other aerobic organisms.

3. Do plants carry out cellular respiration? Explain your response.

   Plants, like other organisms, must have a way to release and use the energy stored in macromolecules such as carbohydrates. Thus, they do carry out cellular respiration. The oxygen-requiring reactions that go on in mitochondria do use oxygen, but it is less than the amount produced during photosynthesis, so plants give off excess oxygen to the air.

4. How does the trapping of light energy provide energy for carbon fixation?

   Light energy is used to produce NADPH and ATP, and they supply energy to carbon fixation reactions.

Extensions

◆ The essay *Whose Discovery Is This?* offers an interesting historical and nature-of-science perspective that provides good background information for a brief discussion of its central points. Questions such as, Do you think a scientific credit discrepancy like this could arise today? and How do scientists keep track of who discovers what? will help students think about the societal context in which science is conducted. In the 18th century, news of discoveries traveled very slowly, scientists tended to work in isolation, and many discovered new phenomena independently. Thus, it was quite common for different scientists to think they were the first to discover something new. Lectures and debates played an important role in communicating new information. Today, the widespread publication of important findings and the highly collaborative nature of science mean that competing groups often know how close their competitors may be to a breakthrough. Such competition often facilitates rapid progress in popular research areas, but occasionally scientists fall victim to the same mistakes that can hurt the reputations of overly ambitious people in any career field. When unethical behaviors are uncovered, such as claiming credit for another's work, scientific and/or funding agencies may censure the guilty individuals.

◆ The LOGAL computer simulation *Biology Explorer: Photosynthesis* provides a useful resource for this activity. The program allows students to investigate the effects of light intensity, light wavelength, air composition, temperature, and humidity on the rate of photosynthesis, and provides for detailed study of the light reactions and carbon fixation as well as the interaction between plant respiration and photosynthesis.

Elaborate Building Living Systems

Major Concepts
Metabolism is the breakdown and buildup of macromolecules; link between energy-producing and energy-requiring reactions

Overview

Learners elaborate on the fundamental concepts in this chapter by examining metabolism and using the new ideas associated with metabolism, such as biosynthesis and breakdown reactions and the energy links between them, to explain how humans process the matter of other organisms into matter that is useful for their own bodies. Part A employs a short story to focus student attention on how biosynthesis can explain the processing of cow material into human material. In Part B, the students apply the knowledge gained in Chapters 7 and 8 about the organization of energy and matter in living systems to the descriptions of their critters.

Materials   (per class of 30, individuals and teams of 2)

descriptions and diagrams of critters from Chapter 5
30 copies of rubric *Energy and Matter for Your Critter*

Outcomes and Indicators of Success

The following indicators allow you to assess the students' level of success with the activity and to assess their process of learning.

By the end of this activity, the learners should

1. apply their understanding of energy and the organization of matter to explain how the body converts matter from an outside source into building materials for their own bodies.

    They will demonstrate the application of their knowledge by

    a. explaining how the macromolecules from a cow can be made into a part of their bodies,

    b. listing three biosynthetic and/or breakdown processes that they think are necessary for maintaining the human body, and

    c. writing an explanation of how energy and matter are organized in one of the previously identified processes.

2. apply the unifying principle of using matter and energy to maintain organization to the description of their critters.

    They will demonstrate this application by adding to the descriptions of their critters an explanation, diagram, model, or demonstration of how their critters obtain and use energy and matter.

Preparations

Preview the rubric on the *GACD* for the critter activity in Part B. Modify it as needed to suit your class.

Strategies for Guiding Learners

PROCESS AND PROCEDURES

PART A   Metabolism

As a class, read orally or silently all introductory materials for the activity and the Process and Procedures to help students build connections between concepts and activities. Use the time spent reading to bring the students' attention into focus.

1. Read the following short story. Use the story and your understanding of energy, matter, and cellular respiration to answer this question: How can my body take in materials from a cow and make it a part of me?

    See the scenario box on page 304 of the student text.

    As students answer the question, check that they are focusing on the major idea of the story: biosynthesis occurs in animals and makes the macromolecules from another organism usable for themselves. Answers should include some discussion of digestion as a means for beginning the breakdown of food to the molecular level, the role of enzymes in this process, the storage of simple food molecules in more complex forms (such as the storage of glucose as glycogen), the need to release energy from food for the activities of life, and the requirement that all organisms have for matter to build their own structures.

Students' ideas about *how* starch becomes glycogen or *how* amino acids become proteins will be vague at this time, but the fact that these transitions occur, as communicated via the concepts in Chapter 7, should be clear. The links between breakdown and synthesis processes should become clearer to the students in step 3 when the essay is used to develop more detailed explanations. Wander through the room asking students to read you their answers as they develop them and note their responses, particularly any misconceptions. Keep their answers in mind as you facilitate student understanding through the remainder of the activity.

2. With your partner, list 3 biological processes involving biosynthesis and/or breakdown that you think are necessary for maintaining the human body.

3. Choose 1 of the processes your team identified in step 2. Write an explanation in your journal of how energy and matter are organized during this process. Consider the following questions as you write your explanation:

   ◆ Why is this process necessary for survival?

   ◆ What is a source of energy for this process?

   ◆ What is a source of matter for this process?

   The essay *Metabolism Includes Synthesis and Breakdown* (page 372) will help you with your explanation.

These steps provide a structured inquiry into the significance of metabolism, using humans as the example. Make connections between this material and what students have learned about diet, nutrition, and digestion from Chapter 7. Teams should create a list of processes, such as building human proteins (muscles) from cow proteins, building cell structures, building enzymes, using carbohydrates to fuel activities, or burning fat to stay warm. You may need to initiate the identification of ideas in step 2 if students appear to be confused. As they develop their explanations in step 3, help them think back to what they do know: that cells and tissues consist of macromolecules, that living systems require energy to organize matter, and so on. The essay *Metabolism Includes Synthesis and Breakdown* should help them with this step.

PART B Energy and Matter for Your Critter

1. How does your critter use matter and energy to maintain its organization? Respond with an explanation, diagram, model, or demonstration of your choice.

   You will know that you have adequately addressed the preceding question if your response meets the following criteria:

   ◆ It indicates the critter's source of energy and matter and how these are obtained from its surroundings.

   ◆ It demonstrates how energy is stored and made available for the critter's activities.

   ◆ It distinguishes the macromolecules that your critter can synthesize from those that it must obtain from its external environment (through diet or other means).

   ◆ It uses specific examples from your work in Chapters 7 and 8 as evidence of what you have learned.

2. Obtain a rubric for this "critter" assignment from your teacher.

Your teacher will use these criteria to evaluate your project.

Either read the rubric as a class, or give students time to read it individually and ask questions. Encourage student creativity while reminding them that they are demonstrating their understanding of a unifying principle by showing how it applies to their critters. Such creativity might take the form of schematic diagrams that indicate molecular conversions that their critters accomplish when taking in food, breaking it down, storing it, and synthesizing it into new macromolecules.

Thoughtful students will realize that the relatively small set of elements that compose all organisms and the many common metabolic features shared by organisms place limits on their creativity. For example, even though newly discovered organisms often have features that are surprising to scientists, there are many features that scientists expect to observe and always do. (This is the reason we based our curriculum on six unifying principles. For example, scientists expect that all newly discovered species will have some means of obtaining energy for cellular processes from the environment. Recent research indicates a greater range of energy-harvesting strategies than were known decades ago, such as chemosynthesis, but the fundamental requirement for energy never has been violated. Likewise, the same small set of elements present in humans composes all organisms.) Thus, every student's newly discovered critter should use energy to build and maintain the structures of its body. Although there is no correct answer per se, you can assess the learners' understanding through their logic in showing their critters' ability to obtain and use energy and matter.

Tracing Matter and Energy

Evaluate

Major Concepts Organization of matter; conversion of energy; sources of matter and energy for living systems

Overview

Students evaluate their knowledge of energy, matter, and organization by tracing the path of a carbon atom that originates in carbon dioxide and ends up in a muscle protein in the human arm.

Outcomes and Indicators of Success

The following indicators allow you to assess the students' level of success with the activity and to assess their process of learning.

By the end of this activity, the learners should be able to apply their understanding of energy, matter, and organization to a new situation by explaining

- The labeled sugars then are broken down further by the process of cellular respiration, which releases energy in the metabolically useful form of ATP. (breakdown)

- Energy from cellular respiration can be linked to the biosynthesis of protein, during which anabolic reactions incorporate labeled amino acids into protein. This labeled protein may be incorporated into muscle tissue in the cow. (synthesis)

- The cow is slaughtered and processed, then a human eats a hamburger that includes the labeled protein. (breakdown)

- Human digestion breaks down this labeled protein to its component amino acids, one of which contains the labeled carbon atom. (breakdown)

- Some amino acids may become involved in aerobic respiration, releasing energy. (breakdown)

- In biosynthetic reactions in the human, which require energy, the labeled amino acid becomes incorporated into muscle protein as the body rebuilds tissue after exercise; thus, the labeled carbon from carbon dioxide becomes incorporated into protein in a human muscle. (synthesis)

Student answers need not be this complete. It is essential, however, that students understand that the muscle protein of humans is not deposited intact from the muscle protein of the cow.

After students have completed the activity, you may want to collect their written efforts for evaluation, or display the diagrams and have the students evaluate the work of their peers. If you choose the latter option, you will need to provide some evaluation criteria. One possibility for simultaneous class summary and peer evaluation is for the learners to create their own rubric by contributing ideas about what an acceptable scenario should contain. After constructing the rubric, show an example that is complete and properly sequenced, such as the bulleted sequence above, on an overhead projector. (The outcomes and indicators also offer specific ideas to look for in each student example.) This way, the students can follow the flow of ideas and compare them with the displayed diagrams.

Analysis

1. Join the class in answering the discussion questions that your teacher raises.

   Conclude this lesson and chapter by leading a discussion based on the following questions:

   a. Could all the reactions in the scenarios (viewed or discussed) take place within a human body?

   Students need to recognize that humans cannot trap energy from the sun or trap carbon from carbon dioxide. The life-sustaining reactions are possible only in photosynthetic organisms.

   b. What is the ultimate source of energy for the necessary events?

   Excluding the trapping of energy by chemosynthetic bacteria, the ultimate source of energy is solar energy, which is used initially in photosynthesis.

c. Explain the transfer of energy during these events.

Energy is converted from solar into chemical energy. Energy stored in some molecules, such as sugars, starch, or proteins, later will be released, and some newly available energy, such as that stored in ATP, can be used to power other reactions. Some energy is converted into heat.

d. How will biosynthesis play a role in the fate of the carbon atom?

Biosynthetic reactions are closely linked to photosynthesis because carbon becomes fixed into sugars and starch in plants. Biosynthetic reactions are necessary to convert simpler, intermediate compounds into amino acids and finally into a chain of amino acids—a protein.

e. Suggest a way in which the labeled carbon in the last step of your sequence could complete the cycle and find its way back into a labeled carbon dioxide molecule in the air.

If the labeled protein in the human muscle is broken down to its component amino acids, then the amino acids could be metabolized into a carbon skeleton that can enter glycolysis and aerobic respiration. (In the essay Metabolism Includes Synthesis and Breakdown, *the students see a diagram illustrating the metabolism of a variety of macromolecules.) The labeled carbon could be part of the carbon dioxide given off as metabolic waste. The circulatory system would pick it up and carry it to the lungs, where it could be expelled from the body during exhalation.*

2. After participating in the discussion, note in your journal any appropriate changes to steps in your sequence from Process and Procedures, step 2.

Students might discover that important steps, such as the conversion of plant macromolecules into cow macromolecules, were missing or incorrect in their diagrams of events. Allow them time to correct these omissions or mistakes, because the opportunity to reflect on previous thinking is an important part of the learning process.

Chapter 9

The Cycling of Matter and the Flow of Energy in Communities

The major concept in this chapter is the cycling of matter (mostly food) within communities and the flow of energy through communities. The chapter addresses organization and interaction of community organisms, and it shows how matter cycles, but energy does not.

The students explore the cycling of matter and further develop their inquiry skills as they make observations of how earthworms interact with matter in their environment. The students then use this experiment as a model for setting up one of their own involving the cycling of matter between snails and *Anacharis*. The learners develop an explanation for the concepts that they have been exploring by explaining the idea of food webs. By relating the food they eat for one day to the plants and animals from which it came, they begin to develop an explanation of their role, as well as the role of other organisms, in a food web within a community.

Toward the end of the chapter, the students elaborate on their knowledge of matter and energy in biological systems by creating an efficient composting system. The chapter concludes with an evaluate activity in which the learners forecast the consequences of massive changes to communities on the earth that are brought about by a natural catastrophe.

ACTIVITIES

Engage / Explore	A Matter of Trash
Explore	Exploring the Cycling of Matter in Communities
Explain	Spinning the Web of Life
Elaborate	Generating Some Heat
Evaluate	What Have I Learned about Energy and Matter in Communities?

CHAPTER 9 IMPLEMENTATION

	Instructional Flow				Classroom Support		
Activity/ Student Text pp. Teacher Guide pp.	GACD, TRCD, DVD, and, CD-ROM Resources	Essays/ Student Text pp.	Estimated Time	Team Size/ Cooperative Learning Focus	Strategies and Tools	Assessment Opportunities	Special Considerations
ENGAGE/ EXPLORE *A Matter of Trash* pp. 310–311 TG pp. 321–325		*Garbage among Us— From Then until Now!* pp. 374–377	50 minutes	*Team size:* individuals	Demonstration; class discussion	Prior knowledge of concepts: cycling of matter and flow of energy in organisms and communities	Plan ahead for students who have difficulty with vision. Have trash that can be handled directly and safely for identification.
EXPLORE *Exploring the Cycling of Matter in Communities* pp. 311–315 TG pp. 325–333	Rubric: *Laboratory Reports*	*Matter in Nature Is Going Around in Cycles . . . What Next?* pp. 377–381; *Worms, Insects, Bacteria, and Fungi— Who Needs Them?* pp. 381–382; *Cellular Respiration: A Closer Look at Converting Food Energy into Cell Energy* pp. 359–363; *Getting Energy and Matter into Biological Systems* pp. 367–372	150–200 minutes	*Team size:* 4 *Skill:* Checking for accuracy and understanding	Wet lab; lab report; concept map	Designing and conducting a controlled experiment; quantifying and analyzing results	Plan ahead for students who have difficulty with vision. Pair them with partners who can assist in making visual observations.
EXPLAIN *Spinning the Web of Life* pp. 316–319 TG pp. 333–338		*Let's Ask Drs. Ricardo and Rita* pp. 383–388; *Losing Heat* pp. 388–389	50 minutes	*Team size:* individuals	Diagrams and food webs; class discussion	Current understanding of the cycling of matter and flow of energy in organisms and communities; using information to construct explanations	You may wish to provide cutout images of plants, herbivores, omnivores, and detritivores for students with visual or fine motor challenges that would make it difficult to draw. Alternatively, those students could work with a partner who would create the diagram, while they work together to decide how it should be constructed.

continued

CHAPTER 9 IMPLEMENTATION (continued)

Instructional Flow / Classroom Support

Activity/ Student Text pp. Teacher Guide pp.	GACD, TRCD, DVD, and, CD-ROM Resources	Essays/ Student Text pp.	Estimated Time	Team Size/ Cooperative Learning Focus	Strategies and Tools	Assessment Opportunities	Special Considerations
ELABORATE *Generating Some Heat* pp. 320–322 TG pp. 338–342			100 minutes	*Team size:* 4 *Skill:* Reaching consensus	Wet lab	Applying understanding to new situations; making connections between related ideas; current understanding of the cycling of matter and flow of energy in organisms and communities	Plan ahead for accessibility. If needed, pair students so that teams can work together to obtain composting materials.
EVALUATE *What Have I Learned about Energy and Matter in Communities?* pp. 323–325 TG pp. 342–347	Rubric: *What Have I Learned about Energy and Matter in Communities?*		50–75 minutes	*Team size:* individuals, 2 *Skill:* Sharing perspectives	Scenario	Applying understanding to new situations; making connections between related ideas; current understanding of the concepts in Unit 3	Enlarge print materials and/or read aloud if needed. Some students may better express their understanding orally than in written format.

Optional activities:
- Engage/Explore: *Field Observation*

Chapter Goals

By the end of this chapter, students should understand that

◆ the cycling of matter and the flow of energy occurs within communities as well as within individual organisms;

◆ all matter contains energy—including the matter in discarded materials (trash) or biological waste;

◆ matter cycles in biological communities, but energy does not; and

◆ energy flows through biological communities, is neither created nor destroyed, and eventually becomes unavailable for use by biological systems.

The learners also will

◆ make observations and collect data,

◆ set up their own controlled experiment,

◆ analyze data and develop explanations, and

◆ apply concepts to new situations.

Advanced Preparation

Part A of the activity *Exploring the Cycling of Matter in Communities* needs to be set up 2–3 weeks in advance. We suggest that you do this at the beginning of Unit 3, before you begin Chapter 7. Part B of this same activity and the activity *Generating Some Heat* require extra time for collecting materials. Young, healthy *Anacharis* (elodea) and snails are needed for the protocol in Part B of *Exploring the Cycling of Matter in Communities.*

If you have a probe ware system available, it will enable students to collect continuous data for the compost temperatures in *Generating Some Heat* and the snail and *Anacharis* protocol in Part B of *Exploring the Cycling of Matter in Communities.*

Refer to Preparations for each of the activities mentioned above.

A Matter of Trash

Engage

Explore

Major Concepts The cycling of matter

Overview

This activity engages the students in the cycling of matter and the flow of energy through communities by exploring garbage. If the weather permits, you may want to have the students complete the optional activity *Field Observation* instead of, or in addition to, this activity.

Materials   (per class of 30, individuals)

3 or 4 transparent plastic bags (14 gal or larger) of garbage that include the following items:

metal object(s)

wood object(s)

paper products

plastic object(s)

glass

aluminum can(s)

polystyrene foam

garbage (banana peels or similar material)

Outcomes and Indicators of Success

The following indicators allow you to assess the students' level of success with the activity and to assess their process of learning.

By the end of this activity, the learners should

1. become aware that materials that they regard as discarded are made up of matter and are still part of the environment.

   They will show their awareness by

   a. itemizing discarded materials,

   b. speculating on the environmental fate of the discarded materials, and

   c. categorizing the waste materials that are described in the essays.

2. begin to understand that some of the discarded matter can be recycled either for nonbiological use or as part of the natural recycling that occurs in living systems.

   They will show their awareness by

   a. citing examples of nonbiological materials that are recyclable for human use,

   b. citing examples of matter that can be reincorporated into living systems, and

   c. tying in evidence from the essays that relates to recycling and reuse of matter within a community.

Safety

Caution

Caution students not to open the garbage bag or handle individual objects, even if they regard the items as harmless. The reasoning behind this safety caution is that certain food refuse harbors pathogens, for example, egg shells may contain *Salmonella*. If you have students with special challenges who need to inspect the trash by touching it, create a collection of trash that does not include food refuse, and ask the student to imagine one or two food items likely to be found in the trash.

Preparations

Assemble the garbage items in the bag before the class begins, and seal the bag so that the students are not exposed to the contents directly (or see instructions above for trash bag items that can be touched).

The engage part of this activity should be conducted as a fairly fast-moving attention-getter in which the students work individually. In assembling your bag of garbage, do your best to provide an accumulation of items that looks like typical household discards, but include an item or two to intrigue the students.

Strategies for Guiding Learners

PROCESS AND PROCEDURES

As a class, read orally or silently all introductory materials for the activity and the Process and Procedures to help students build connections between concepts and activities. Use the time spent reading to bring the students' attention into focus.

During this activity, help the students begin to build an understanding that energy neither can be created nor destroyed. We want them to understand that energy flows (rather than cycles) through biological systems, and that beyond a certain point, it is no longer present in a form that organisms can use. To build that understanding, the students may need to set aside the popular misconception that the energy in discarded matter is "lost." This activity provides you with an opportunity to assess the students' prior knowledge of these concepts.

1. Examine the discarded items in the trash demonstration that your teacher presents. Create a table or other visual diagram that includes the following information:

    ◆ A list of the trash in the demonstration

    ◆ A list of the trash's origin (for example, newspaper originated from trees, wood, and pulp)

    ◆ An indication of which trash items match your household trash (yes or no)

    ◆ A list of at least 2 possible fates for each trash item (for example, in a landfill, recycling plant, food for another animal, reused, etc.)

    As students itemize what they see, ask them whether this garbage is fairly representative of what they throw out in their trash. Ask for examples of discarded items that they think should be included in a representative sample of trash. For each item, ask what they think would become of it in the environment. Have students estimate the percentage of matter discarded from homes that has its origin as human food. Cite various examples of what humans have done with garbage historically (for example, dumping in rivers or at sea, incineration, land burial, or open landfill).

    The students' data table may look something like the one in Figure T9.1.

Figure T9.1 A sample student data table

Trash	Original material	Matches mine	Possible fates
Soda pop cans	Aluminum	Yes	Recycling plant, landfill
Small branches from Trees in yard	Tree	Yes	Landfill, compost, burned in woodstove, made into mulch
Newspaper	Tree, wood pulp	Yes	Recycling plant, burned in woodstove, landfill
Plastic milk carton	Made by humans	Yes	Recycling plant, landfill, reused
Empty glass jar	Made by humans	Yes	Recycling plant, reused
Apple core	Food item, plant	No	Landfill, compost, hamster food
Orange peeling	Food item, plant	Yes	Landfill, compost
Tea bags	Food item, plant	No	Landfill, compost
Polystyrene foam tray	Made by humans	Yes	Landfill, recycling plant

2. In your journal, write a short description of what you think might happen to the matter and energy in this trash after it is thrown out.

As the students record their ideas about the matter and energy in the trash, use this as an opportunity to assess their prior knowledge of these concepts. Expect that some students will know that some of the matter may recycle—that is, be used by other organisms—some of it may be used again by humans, and some students may know that some energy is converted into heat.

Analysis

Ask the learners to work on the Analysis individually, and remind them to read the essay *Garbage among Us—From Then until Now!* for helpful information. When the students have completed the Analysis, you may want to convene a class discussion of their responses to these questions.

1. In what ways might the waste of one organism be useful to another organism? Give examples to support your answer.

Expect students to indicate that the waste of one organism might become food for another organism. For example, when a person discards an apple core, a squirrel or rabbit might eat it. Students also might indicate that even when it looks as though an apple core may go unclaimed by another animal, bacteria and other microorganisms eventually will recycle it to become part of the soil.

2. How does your answer to question 1 support the idea that organisms in communities depend on one another for matter and energy?

   Expect the students to indicate that many organisms depend on other organisms for their food supply, and that even though plants make their own food through photosynthesis, they still depend on decomposers to make available certain nutrients such as nitrates.

3. As you compare how matter cycles in different communities, what do you notice about the type of matter and the length of the cycle? What problems have these differences caused for modern human societies?

   Expect the students to be aware that naturally occurring matter from plants and animals recycles more easily and faster than humanmade materials such as plastic. This situation has caused problems in finding ways to dispose of trash and has caused overflowing landfills.

Further Challenges

On a separate piece of paper, write 10–15 things you have thrown away in the past week. Exchange lists with your partner. Write four or five things that you might infer about your partner from his or her trash. Support your inferences.

If the students complete the Further Challenges, expect them to realize that they might be able to make inferences about what the people like to eat, what subjects they are studying in school, and perhaps how well they are doing in school.

Exploring the Cycling of Matter in Communities

Explore

Major Concepts Interactions among organisms; the cycling of matter

Overview

In this activity, the students explore the relationship between matter and energy in living systems. The students set up Part A of this activity several weeks ago, and it should be ready for final observations and data collection during this class period. The results of this experiment will provide the students with a foundation for further study. In Part B, the learners use their experiences from Part A to set up and conduct a controlled experiment involving interactions between snails and *Anacharis*.

Materials   (per class of 30)

30 copies of the rubric *Laboratory Reports*

PART A (teams of 2)

30 slides

15 hand lenses

5–7 stereomicroscopes

humus testing kit

materials for making 1 set of 4 habitats:

5–7 spoons

3–4 rolls of paper towels

5–7 small trays

> 4 plastic shoe-box-size containers or other large containers (no more than 10 cm high)
>
> 40–60 earthworms (obtain from a biological supply company, fish and tackle store, or garden center)
>
> large bag of topsoil (obtain from garden center)
>
> 200–300 g of organic waste (grass clippings, leaf litter, coffee grounds, ground-up fruit rinds and most vegetables) (**Note:** Do not use eggshells because they may contain *Salmonella*. Refrain from using broccoli or cauliflower due to their odors.)

2 small plastic cups

water

PART B (teams of 4)

8 25 × 200-mm test tubes

petri dish halves (if pH paper is used)

2 test tube racks

roll of aluminum foil

2 light sources

50 mL .04% aqueous bromothymol blue solution (see Preparations)

8 pH probes

2 rolls wide-range pH paper (if a probe ware system is not available)

4 forceps (if pH paper is used)

1 L dechlorinated water

2 jars of tap water (for storing pH probes)

20 1- to 1½-cm freshwater snails

4 15-cm sprigs of *Anacharis*

Outcomes and Indicators of Success

The following indicators allow you to assess the students' level of success with the activity and to assess their process of learning.

By the end of this activity, the learners should

1. understand the importance of a controlled experiment.

    They will demonstrate their understanding by

    a. describing the purpose of each earthworm habitat,

    b. using the earthworm habitats as a model to design an experiment that controls the variables in a snail/*Anacharis* experiment, and

    c. successfully preparing a lab report that describes the importance of controls.

2. appreciate the cycling of matter in communities.

    They will demonstrate their appreciation by

    a. developing a hypothesis about the cycling of matter between snails and *Anacharis*,

    b. designing and conducting an experiment to look for evidence of the cyclical movement of matter in a community,

c. drawing a conclusion about the cycling of matter, and

d. creating a visual diagram that represents the cycling of matter within a community.

3. have more information with which to begin to develop an understanding of the interaction between plants and animals as it relates to the cycling of matter in a community.

They will demonstrate their understanding by

a. articulating an appropriate question that arises from their experimental results, and

b. creating a concept map or other visual diagram that represents these interactions.

Safety

See *Guidelines for Laboratory Safety* in this guide for safety requirements for using a computer in the laboratory if you are using probe ware with associated computers.

Preparations

The preparations for both parts of this activity require some key planning and preparations as described below.

PART A. If you want all teams to make observations of the same habitats, 1 set of 4 habitats is all you will need. If you prepare 2 sets of these 4 habitats, then half of the teams could observe one set and the other half could observe the other set.

Together with your students, prepare at least 1 set of 4 habitats. About 3 weeks before you plan to do this activity, prepare the habitats as follows:

1. Fill each plastic container 3/4 full with the topsoil.

   a. Leave 1 container as it is. (Habitat 1)

   b. Add 20–30 earthworms to the 2nd container. (Habitat 2, worm control)

   c. Scoop out a hole in the middle of the 3rd container, and add 100 g of organic matter. (Habitat 3, matter control)

   d. Scoop out a hole in the middle of the 4th container, and add 100 g of the same organic matter and 20–30 earthworms. (Habitat 4)

For the organic matter, you could use grass clippings or vegetable and fruit wastes. Also, use the same number of earthworms in the 2 habitats that include them.

2. Sprinkle the top of each container with about 150 mL of water. Use the same amount of water per container.

3. Label each container carefully, describing what each contains.

4. Cover containers with lids that have air holes in them, and keep the containers away from extreme heat or direct sunlight.

5. Have the students check the containers every 3 days. Sprinkle with additional water if the soil becomes dry, but do not keep the soil too wet.

6. Have the students make observations of the habitats every 2 or 3 days during the 2–3 weeks before they do the rest of this activity. Each team of students should observe all 4 habitats.

Ask the students to set up a data table in their journal to keep simple but accurate entries of their observations. The table should include the date and time of observations, the appearance of the soil, the appearance and the amount of the organic matter, the amount of humus, and activity of the worms. See Figure T9.2 for a sample data table.

Figure T9.2 Sample data table

	Date: Time:	Date: Time:	Date: Time:	Continue data table as needed to record observations. →
Habitat 1 • appearance of soil • sprayed with water				
Habitat 2 • appearance of soil • activity of worms • amount of humus • sprayed with water				
Habitat 3 • appearance of soil • appearance of organic matter • sprayed with water				
Habitat 4 • appearance of soil • activity of worms • appearance of organic matter • amount of humus • sprayed with water				

Students can estimate the amount of humus in the 4th habitat by measuring the width of the humus ring that appears between the organic matter and the soil. The humus in the 2nd habitat may be nonexistent or negligible depending on what the earthworms find in the soil to process. The students will have to make a general statement about the relative amount of humus in this habitat.

Because Habitats 3 and 4 each began with 100 g of organic matter, at the end of the observation period, the students can actually weigh the amount of organic matter remaining in each of these habitats.

When the students are collecting data, you may choose to have them use the humus testing kit that is available from Ward's, which shows a color change when humus is present. If you decide to do so, you may want to perform only 2 tests per class—1 on a habitat with earthworms and 1 on a habitat without.

PART B. Young, healthy *Anacharis* is essential to gathering useful data. Maintain the *Anacharis* under a grow light so that it is actively photosynthesizing when students begin the experiment. Use only sprigs with growing tips. Also, relatively large snails give better results than small ones.

For the snail/*Anacharis* protocol, results are more meaningful if there are many data points for each tube throughout the duration of the experiment. If you are not using a probe ware system, and if it is not practical for students to return at intervals during each day to take pH readings, consider having the 1st class of the day set up the tubes and take pH readings at the beginning and end of the period. Either you, students in subsequent classes, or student volunteers could take additional pH readings for all tubes. In any case, it will be essential to have a data table posted beside each set of tubes in which to record the date, time, interval since the beginning of the experiment, and name of the person who records the data. To keep quantities manageable, we suggest 2 setups per class. Pooled data from all classes will provide a good sample size.

The best use of a probe ware system for this protocol is to have 2 teams in each class set up the experiment with 8 pH probes and set them to take readings every 15 minutes. If you have only 4 pH probes, consider having 1 team use the probes and the other team collect their data by using pH paper. Students should observe their tubes according to the directions in the protocol. At the end of the experiment, have the students print a graph of the saved data as well as a listing of the numeric data.

For information about the pH probes, consult the instructions that accompany your probe ware. Check the proper procedure for storing pH probes when not in use. If you are not using pH probes, substitute pH paper. Whether using pH probes or paper, students also will be able to observe color changes in the bromothymol blue as an indication of the carbon dioxide concentration. Bromothymol blue turns yellow in the presence of carbon dioxide—the greater the carbon dioxide concentration, the more yellow it appears. Purchase or prepare a 0.04% aqueous bromothymol blue solution.

Strategies for Guiding Learners

PROCESS AND PROCEDURES

As a class, read orally or silently all introductory materials for the activity and the Process and Procedures to help students build connections between concepts and activities. Use the time spent reading to bring the students' attention into focus.

Encourage the learners to use the scientific attitudes of curiosity and creativity in expressing their ideas and to practice the working-relationship skill of checking for accuracy and understanding. This skill will be especially important as the students record their observations and prepare their reports.

Before the students begin, convene a brief class discussion to review the earthworm setup and the students' work during the past few weeks.

PART A   Reflections on the Earthworm Habitats

1. With your teammates, look at the earthworm habitats that you set up several weeks ago. Study the observations that you have recorded in your journal.

   Remember that the purpose of these habitats was to provide evidence of interactions between living systems and the physical environment, as well as evidence about the nature of these interactions.

As the students review the observations that they have recorded in their data tables, listen to the discussions to see what they understand about their data. Expect that the students will find an obvious margin of humus, probably several millimeters wide, along the edge of the organic matter in the container that included organic matter and earthworms (see Figure T9.3). They probably will see only small amounts of humus in the container with soil and earthworms. They probably will see no humus in the containers without the earthworms.

Figure T9.3 The margin of humus might look something like this:

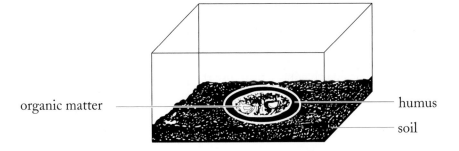

organic matter — humus — soil

The students may note some change in the appearance or moisture content of the soil and will note some decay in the organic matter in Habitat 3. Depending on the activity level of the earthworms, the students may observe no remaining organic matter in Habitat 4. If there was some remaining and they weighed it, expect that there will be a lot less than the 100 g with which they began. Also, expect the students to notice some variation in the activity level of the earthworms during the observation period.

2. Discuss the following with your teammates. Record your ideas in your journal.

As the learners discuss their ideas with their teammates, remind them to think critically and clearly about each design element in this experiment.

a. What evidence did you collect that supports the idea that earthworms modify (interact with) their environment?

The students will note that there is very little or no organic matter left in Habitat 4, that the soil has been modified somewhat (the appearance of tunnels or small modulations), and that a fine, dark substance is now present in at least one of the containers.

b. Describe this interaction. What do you think happened in the earthworm containers?

Expect the students to indicate that the earthworms probably ate the organic matter, processed it, and eliminated the waste products.

c. What was the specific purpose of each container in helping you identify and describe the interaction of earthworms and their environment?

Compare the containers that had earthworms with each other. (One contained soil and organic matter and one only soil.) Why was it important to observe both types of containers? What did your comparisons tell you about the interactions of earthworms with their environment?

Expect the students to indicate that each container told them something different about the interactions of earthworms in their environment and about different aspects of the environment itself.

Habitat 1 provided information about whether soil by itself can change.

Habitat 2 provided information about the results of interactions between the earthworms and the soil.

Habitat 3 provided information about the results of interactions between the soil and additional organic matter.

Habitat 4 provided information about the results of interactions between the soil, the earthworms, and additional organic matter.

3. Read the essays *Matter in Nature Is Going Around in Cycles . . . What Next?* (page 377) and *Worms, Insects, Bacteria, and Fungi—Who Needs Them?* (page 381). The information in these essays will help generate a context for your observations. It will also prepare you to design your own experiment that explores the transformation of matter.

Check to see that your teammates understand the concepts in the readings and how they relate to your findings.

As students read the essays, remind them to think about how the information relates to the experiment they just completed and to check that their teammates understand the concepts presented.

PART B   Snails and Anacharis: What Can I Learn from Them?

1. Devise an experiment to provide evidence of the cyclical movement of matter in a community. See the Materials section for the materials and equipment that are available.

   a. What have you learned about photosynthesis and respiration? Think back to previous chapters. In addition, read this need to know box for important background information.

   Before the teams begin to design an experiment, go over the materials and equipment that are available and discuss how each of the items might be used. Suggest that they review the essays *Cellular Respiration: A Closer Look at Converting Food Energy into Cell Energy* and *Getting Energy and Matter into Biological Systems* (in Chapter 8), and read the background information on carbon dioxide and pH in step 1a.

   b. Develop a hypothesis about the cyclical movement of matter in an aquatic community. Record your hypothesis in your journal.

   You must be able to test the hypothesis using the materials and information listed above.

   Be certain the students formulate a complete hypothesis and record it in their journals so they are thoroughly engaged in the activity before proceeding. As the teams are developing their hypotheses, check to see that they actually can test them with the materials and equipment available. A good hypothesis might be as follows: If snails produce CO_2 (which would tend to lower the pH of the water) and *Anacharis* uses CO_2 (which would tend to raise the pH), then eventually, the pH of the water should stabilize.

c. Design an experiment to test your hypothesis. Outline your experiment in your journal.

Look at the design of the earthworm habitats. Apply your understanding of that design to the one you develop here.

Also, consider the experiment that you designed to investigate factors that influenced the rate of photosynthesis in Chapter 8. You may use a similar experimental procedure.

d. Have your teacher approve your design.

> **As the learners design their experiments, remind them to use the earthworm habitats as a model. Provide hints to the teams that seem to be struggling. For example, mention that the test tubes will be the containers this time; they will use water instead of soil; they will use snails instead of earthworms; and they will use *Anacharis* instead of additional organic matter. With the information provided and perhaps a few hints, the students should be able to design an experiment to test a hypothesis about the interactions of the snail and *Anacharis*. Ask the students questions to determine how well they understand their controls.**

2. Use the Protocol for Monitoring Change in pH to conduct your experiment during the next 2 hours.

> **As the students conduct their experiment, monitor all teams to see that they are able to follow the protocol. If they are using pH paper, instruct them to hold the end of the pH paper with forceps so that they can dip it into the test tube, and to discard used strips in the petri dish half.**

> **The bromothymol blue also will provide valuable qualitative evidence for the processes taking place within the experimental systems. If cellular respiration is the dominant process taking place, it will turn more and more yellow as the concentration of carbon dioxide increases. If photosynthesis is the predominant process taking place, carbon dioxide in the water will be used, and the bromothymol blue will remain blue (or any yellow generated by the initial carbon dioxide content will diminish).**

3. Prepare a lab report of your findings.

You may want to refer to the guidelines in Part A, step 9, of the activity *You Are What You Eat*, in Chapter 7. Be sure to answer the following questions as part of your report:

a. What was the specific purpose of each test tube that you set up? That is, what evidence did each test tube provide? What did you learn from each test tube?

b. How was each test tube important in helping you develop your conclusion?

c. Do your data support your hypothesis? Explain.

d. Based on what you have learned from this experiment, what question would you like to ask and answer next?

> **Use the rubric for lab reports on the *GACD* as a template to develop your own scoring rubric for this activity. Distribute copies to the learners so that they are aware of how you will assess them. Have them complete their work on the reports for homework or in class the next day and then present them.**

Analysis

1. Take turns presenting your team's experimental design and results to the rest of the class. Also, share ideas from your lab report.

2. Participate in a class discussion of the various experiments conducted and the results that emerged.

3. With your teammates, create a visual diagram, such as a concept map, that represents your current understanding of the cycling of matter through a community. Base your diagram on the two populations that you studied in this activity.

Ask the teams to take turns presenting their experimental designs and results to the rest of the class. Then convene a short class discussion of the various experiments and results. Be sure not to focus entirely on the mechanics of the experiment. The concepts of interacting organisms and cycling of matter also should be prominent in the discussion.

As the learners create their own concept map or visual diagram, remind them to include all information that is relevant to the cycling of matter in a community. You may want to collect the journals to assess the diagrams more closely.

Extensions

- ◆ As an extension to this activity, you may want to have the students design and conduct a follow-up investigation to further their understanding of the relationships that exist with the snails/*Anacharis* and earthworms. The students might be interested in pursuing the study of other plant and animal relationships that exist in nature. Longer experiments could generate information for the students to use in Unit 6.

- ◆ In *Generating Some Heat*, the students could use earthworms in their compost designs.

Spinning the Web of Life

Explain

Major Concepts Energy flow; the cycling of matter; organization in communities

Overview

In this activity, students construct an understanding of the cycling of matter and the flow of energy within the structure of a community. They do that by examining their own food web and analyzing the transfer of energy. This activity expands on the ideas introduced during the first two activities by linking the flow of energy and cycling of matter directly to students' lives.

Materials (per class of 30, individuals)

30 sets of colored pens or pencils, 3 colors each
overhead transparency (optional)

Outcomes and Indicators of Success

The following indicators allow you to assess the students' level of success with the activity and to assess their process of learning.

By the end of this activity, the learners should

1. understand the relationships among the producers and consumers in a food web.

   They will demonstrate their understanding by creating a web that links organisms according to those relationships.

2. understand that energy flows through a community in specific ways.

   They will demonstrate their understanding by tracing the flow of energy through trophic levels on a diagram that they create.

3. be able to relate the interrelationships within a food web to their personal eating habits.

   They will demonstrate their ability by analyzing the food web based on foods in their diets.

Preparations

You may need to prepare a list of foods that different animals commonly eat. For example, cattle eat alfalfa, grass, hay, corn, barley, and oats; chickens eat corn, fish products, and millet; and fish eat other fish and aquatic plant life. You may want to make an overhead transparency of this information so that all students can use it at the same time.

Strategies for Guiding Learners

PROCESS AND PROCEDURES

As a class, read orally or silently all introductory materials for the activity and the Process and Procedures to help students build connections between concepts and activities. Use the time spent reading to bring the students' attention into focus.

1. Following the steps outlined below, generate a food web. A **food web** is a visual diagram of the interactions of matter and the consequent flow of energy.

   a. In your journal, create your ideal menu for 1 day. Include snacks as well as meals.

      Choose your favorite foods and snacks.

      The students typically find this step in the activity highly engaging. Encourage them to choose their favorite meals, but limit them to three meals and snacks.

      During the next steps, as students generate the components for the food web, you may wish to keep the atmosphere informal and encourage students to ask and answer questions for each other about their foods' origins. The students will work individually during this activity, but they likely will have many questions about the ingredients in their favorite foods and the sources for those ingredients.

   b. Make a 3-column chart in your journal. List the foods from your ideal menu in the 1st column and the ingredients in each menu item in the 2nd column.

      Remember, many foods are combinations of different plants, animals, fungi, or bacteria. Record the ingredients of each food separately. For example, if you have a piece of cake for dessert, you should list oil, flour, sugar, butter, eggs, and milk.

c. In the 3rd column of your chart, list the sources for the ingredients of each menu item.

For example, write *wheat* next to *flour*, *sugar cane* or *sugar beet* next to *sugar*, and *chicken* next to *egg*.

> After the students have listed their chosen foods' ingredients, they need to go back and list the plant or animal source of each ingredient. For example, if they listed beef, they need to write *cattle* beside it; if they listed eggs, they need to write *chicken*. If the students seem to have difficulty thinking of what a particular animal eats, you may want to use the overhead transparency that you created as a resource.

d. Create another 3-column chart in your journal. In the 2nd (center) column, list all of the animals that appeared in your 1st chart.

e. For every animal that you have listed, do the following:

♦ In the 3rd column, list several foods that it eats.

For example, next to cow you would list the grass and corn that cattle eat.

♦ In the 1st column, next to the animals that you listed in step d, record 2 animals that might eat each animal.

For example, next to cow you might list wolf, bear, mountain lion, or human. Next to fish, you might list raccoon, otter, or sea gull, depending on the type of fish it is.

> The students' first task is to list all the animals from their first chart in a column in the second chart. Then they will add several foods that each of those animals eat and other animals that could eat the animals on their list.

f. Create a food web from the information that you generated in your journal as follows. Use 1 different-colored pen or pencil for each step.

♦ Obtain a large sheet of paper from your teacher. Fold it like an accordion to create 5 equal-sized sections.

♦ List all the names of the plants in the bottom section.

♦ Write the names of all the herbivores (plant eaters) in the next section, above the plants.

♦ Write all the names of the omnivores (animals that eat plants and animals) in the next section, above the herbivores. Write your name at the end of this row.

♦ Write all the names of the carnivores (animals that eat only meat) in the section above the omnivore row.

> For the food web, students should use the organisms that they listed in both charts created in steps 1b and 1d. Circulate among the students while they group their organisms according to the way they obtain matter and energy, and ask probing questions to help guide them to categorize the organisms correctly. For example, if a student is struggling to categorize a bear, first ask him or her what a bear eats, and if he or she is unsure, direct the question to the whole class. As they work on their food webs, check that students are listing plants at the bottom, herbivores in the middle, then a row of omnivores, and carnivores at the top.

g. After you have all the names of the plants and animals organized, draw arrows from the organisms that provide energy to the organisms that receive energy.

Pay particular attention to the direction that you draw your arrows. They should show the direction of energy flow, *not* who will be eaten. Say, for example, your plant row includes grass and your herbivore row includes cattle. You would draw an arrow from grass to cattle with the point of the arrow aimed at the cattle.

Remind the students that the arrowheads should point *to* the organism that obtains energy by eating the organism where the arrow originates.

2. Expand your food web in the following manner:

a. Think of other organisms that might compete with you for your food. In your journal, make a list of organisms that eat some of the same foods that you eat.

b. Using a pen or pencil of a different color, add the organisms that you listed in step 2a to the appropriate level of your food web. Add the appropriate arrows.

As the students add things to their food webs, be certain that they use a different-colored pen or pencil and add the appropriate arrows.

3. Work with a classmate to discuss briefly the following questions:

This strategy provides you with an opportunity to develop the skill of using your classmates as a resource.

As the students work in pairs to answer these questions, remind them to use the essays *Let's Ask Drs. Ricardo and Rita* and *Losing Heat* as resources.

a. What is the key difference between the way that producers and consumers accomplish biosynthesis?

Producers make their own food by using matter and energy from the nonliving world. Consumers feed on other organisms to obtain the matter and energy necessary for biosynthesis.

b. What sorts of matter do you think archaeologists might uncover years from now from the suburban family in Maineville, Ohio? How would this compare to what archaeologists have uncovered from the Ancestral Puebloans?

You read about how matter cycles in other communities in the essay *Garbage Among Us—From Then Until Now!*

The matter left behind by a suburban family likely will contain many of the objects found in the garbage bags in the engage for this chapter. Those remains include items made of plastics, metals, and highly processed materials. In comparison, the matter left by the Ancestral Puebloans was primarily made up of organic materials that decay rapidly. The Ancestral Puebloans' artifacts are items made from bone, rock, and shells.

c. Why is there no predator in Africa that lives by eating only lions and leopards?

Lions and leopards are carnivores. Because they are farthest from the producers on the energy pyramid, an organism eating only lions and leopards would have to consume too much biomass to support their energy needs.

d. What effect are cattle and other domesticated livestock having on certain ecosystems?

To help you with this task, read the letters in *Let's Ask Drs. Ricardo and Rita* (page 383) and the essay *Losing Heat* (page 388).

Cattle are large herbivores that must consume a lot of biomass through grazing. Introducing them to certain ecosystems places a large burden on the producers in the system. If the producers cannot keep up with the demand for food, the other herbivores, omnivores, and carnivores are deprived of the matter and energy they need, and the ecosystem is thrown out of balance. Overgrazing also leads to soil erosion. Cattle grazing contributes to the increasing number of deserts on earth.

4. To demonstrate your more complete understanding of food webs, use a pen or pencil of a 3rd color to add detritivores to the top section of your food web. Detritivores feed off dead organisms and the wastes or cast-off fragments of living organisms. If you had mushrooms in your list of foods, they belong in this section. Use arrows to indicate the relationship of these decomposers to the other organisms present.

Now that the students have read the essays, they should be able to add decomposers to their food webs.

Analysis

When the students have completed the reading, use these questions as a guide for a concluding class discussion.

1. Describe how energy flows through the community, as shown in your food web.

The energy flows from the sun and is converted into food energy by the producers. A portion of the energy is passed to the herbivores as they graze on the producers. This pattern continues throughout the web as indicated by the arrows.

2. Where is the most energy available in your food web? Explain your answer.

By this time, expect that most students will indicate that the greatest available energy is present at the producers' level. In their responses, the students should explain why less energy is available at the higher trophic levels.

3. Compare the food web of a vegetarian in your class with the food web of someone who is not a vegetarian.

◆ What differences are evident?

◆ What do you think is significant about those differences?

◆ How does this relate to the recipe for one pound of beef?

The food web of a vegetarian may not have any animals on it. Or, the food web might include a cow, if, for example, the person drinks milk or eats cheese or yogurt. The food web might include a chicken if the person eats eggs. Such a food web probably includes more producers than consumers, and in general, the person is eating lower on the food chain, that is, eating the producers directly instead of eating the consumers that ate the producers or that ate other consumers. In this way, the person is getting more energy from the area of the food web that has the most energy available.

4. How have we made our task of acquiring food easier than it was for the Ancestral Puebloans?

As human societies evolved, humans discovered ways to domesticate certain plants and animals, so that instead of constantly gathering and hunting for their food, they began to grow their own plants in gardens and to confine and care for animals.

Extensions

- ◆ If you have enough time, ask the students to research the origins of the plants and animals that appear in their food webs. Have them determine the original range of the organisms, whether or not they have been domesticated, and where they are raised now.

- ◆ You also could pursue a discussion about cross-cultural approaches to agriculture and the role of technology in modern agriculture.

Elaborate

Generating Some Heat

Major Concepts
Energy is converted into heat as matter cycles in a biological system

Overview

In this activity, the learners elaborate on their knowledge of the cycling of matter in biological systems. They design their own composting systems to see which team can devise the most effective system. In the most effective system, the decomposers will be the most active (as measured by the amount of heat they produce). As the students compare results, they will see that an efficient composting system is not just a random combination of ingredients, but rather contains a list of components with some important properties. This activity not only will be an illustration of an important phase of the cycling of matter, but also an illustration of how energy, although not destroyed, is not cycled. Rather, it is converted into heat and ultimately is unavailable to biological systems as an energy source.

Materials   (per class of 30, teams of 4)

30 pairs of plastic gloves
8 thermistors or nonmercury
    thermometers
8 1-gal plastic milk containers with
    4 cm of tops cut off
8 230–250 mL measuring cups
4 rolls of masking tape
8 4-gal plastic trash bags
8 rulers
8 felt-tipped markers
8 large sheets of newspaper
8 large sheets of plain newsprint

8 trowels or spatulas for mixing compost
foam insulation material sufficient
    to cover 8 milk containers
compost starter inoculum (available
    from garden supply stores in
    2 lb boxes)
water
40 lb bag of potting soil
5 gal of grass clippings
5 gal of shredded leaf mulch or
    bark mulch
pan balance

Outcomes and Indicators of Success

The following indicators allow you to assess the students' level of success with the activity and to assess their process of learning.

By the end of this activity, the learners should

1. understand that decomposers are an important part of biological systems.

   They will show their understanding by constructing a system that demonstrates the action of decomposers in nutrient cycling.

2. understand that, in biological systems, energy flows and does not cycle.

   They will show their understanding by

   a. describing the form that the energy took before it was expressed as heat, and

   b. describing heat as a form of energy that is no longer usable in biological systems as an energy source.

Preparations

Assemble all of the materials necessary for the compost system competition. If you feel it is appropriate for your students, allow them to bring in their own ingredients for the compost system, too. Depending on the time of year, either obtain fresh grass clippings or plan ahead and freeze them until you need them. You should be able to obtain shredded leaf mulch and shredded bark mulch in any store that sells lawn and garden materials. Compost starter inoculum is available from garden supply stores in 2 lb boxes. The cost generally is under $10. Prepare a set of materials for each team. Provide each team with about ½ cup of compost starter inoculum in a zip bag. Ask the students to collect gallon-sized plastic milk containers.

If you have probe ware systems, you may wish to substitute thermistors for thermometers. To track the fluctuations in temperature more closely (if your probe ware system is capable), allow the thermistors to collect data at regular intervals during the 2 days when the compost is allowed to work.

Strategies for Guiding Learners

PROCESS AND PROCEDURES

As a class, read orally or silently all introductory materials for the activity and the Process and Procedures to help students build connections between concepts and activities. Use the time spent reading to bring the students' attention into focus.

Begin this activity by conducting a short discussion about the general topic of landfills, biodegradation, and the cycling of matter. Ask the students if they have any experience with composting and how they used the composted materials.

1. As a class, make the following decisions about your compost designs:

   ◆ How much compost starter inoculum all teams will use

   ◆ How much water all teams will use

   ◆ How much total organic matter (the mass) all teams will use

   Why is it important that all teams keep certain features constant?

Before the class makes these decisions about the compost designs, make sure that everyone understands the importance of keeping these features constant. Have each team of two join another team of two to create teams of four.

2. With your team, consider some recipes that you might use for your composting system. Discuss the following questions with your team to help you decide on a recipe. Record your answers and your recipe in your journal. Be sure to justify your decisions.

   a. What organic matter should you use?

   b. Should you use 1 source of organic matter or a combination of sources?

   c. If you use a combination, what proportions should you use?

   Composting is not an exact science. Gardeners frequently have their own personal compost recipes. Now it's your turn to create a compost recipe. You have all of the materials necessary for decomposers to work effectively. The grass clippings, shredded leaf mulch, and shredded bark mulch provide excellent carbon sources (organic matter to be consumed as food) for the microorganisms (starter inoculum). Check with your teacher if you wish to bring in and use any other matter in your recipe. Be prepared to explain why. Because these microorganisms thrive in soil, the potting soil should provide a suitable environment for initial growth. Remember, your entire compost needs to fit in the plastic milk container.

   As you develop your recipe, practice the working-relationship skill of reaching consensus.

   As the students are considering some composting recipes and making decisions, listen to the conversations and the justifications for their decisions. This is an opportunity to assess their level of understanding of the chapter concepts. During this activity, have the students practice the working-relationship skill of reaching consensus.

   Note: Have the teams share their recipe with you for approval. Be sure that the students have justifiable reasons for their recipe and are not just guessing.

3. Carefully, create your composting system.

Lab Gloves

SAFETY: Put on your plastic gloves.

   a. Use the recipe that your team agreed on. Measure your soil and your food sources 1 at a time from materials you have available. Pour them into the plastic bag.

   b. Mix the ingredients thoroughly with a trowel.

   c. Add the amount of compost starter inoculum that your class decided to include.

   d. Add the amount of water that your class decided to include.

   e. Again, use the trowel to mix the compost ingredients thoroughly. Then place your mixed compost into the plastic milk container.

   f. Insulate your container of compost.

   Cut enough insulation material to surround the container. Tape the insulation in place. Cut a small piece of insulation for the top. For the composting inoculum to work most efficiently, the system must retain the heat that the microorganisms generate. If they are not insulated, the compost systems will lose this heat to the environment.

As the students put together their systems, make certain that they wear disposable gloves throughout the handling of composting materials. If they work on large sheets of newspaper, cleanup should be much easier. You also may want them to write their recipe on a large piece of newsprint and post it in the room.

4. Keep your system going for 2 more days. Record the temperature in the center of the compost twice a day. If you are using a thermistor, you may be able to set your data-collection device to save and record temperatures at regular intervals over the time of the experiment.

Create a data table in your journal in which to record the temperature of your compost.

As the students are creating data tables, check that the tables are appropriate for recording the temperature for 2 or 3 days. Remind them to record their first temperature. Have them record their second temperature either later that day (for your morning classes) or before school the next day (for your afternoon classes). During the second day of the activity, have the students take their readings once during class and a second time either before or after school. In a well-constructed and well-insulated composting system, heat should continue to build through several days.

5. Graph the temperature changes that you observed in your composting system.

After they have collected data for at least 2 days, have the learners graph the temperature changes that occurred. This step provides you with an opportunity to assess the students' graphing skills.

Analysis

Complete the following tasks as a team:

1. Present your team's compost recipe and results to the class. Be sure to share the graph of your results.

2. Based on all of the teams' reports, determine which compost recipes generated the most change in temperature.

   You and your classmates will judge the effectiveness of each composting recipe by examining each team's data.

   a. Why do you think the most effective recipes worked better than others did?

   b. What do your results tell you about the cycling of matter and the flow of energy?

   c. What role did the microorganisms play?

      You may want to conduct the Analysis as a news program and have each team report its findings in the style and format of a news story. Then have the class examine each team's data and determine which team's composting recipe generated the greatest change in temperature.

      The students probably will discover that composting is an inexact science. However, they will find that systems tend to work well that have a balance of organic matter and soil and are not too wet or too dry. The presence of too much water will result in anaerobic conditions. The presence of too little water will result in very little microbial growth. If the containers are not well insulated, any heat that is produced will be lost to the environment. If that happens, any

a. What might be the effect if, instead, 80–85 percent of the sunlight were blocked from the earth? What might be the effect on the following organisms: an earthworm, a shark, a maple tree, a saguaro cactus, and a teenager?

If enough producers were able to survive and reproduce using only 15–20 percent of the amount of sunlight that they had been used to, then we might not see the continued starvation of all consumers. If species of plants are able to evolve adaptations to these conditions, and if some of the herbivores are able to adjust to this change in diet, then certain carnivores likely would have some food resources. It could take hundreds of years before communities on earth would find a balance again.

The fate of the following organisms if 80–85 percent of the sunlight were blocked might include the following:

◆ Earthworms. No initial effect. With the death of some producers and consumers, the population of earthworms might increase in response to the abundance of food. After the initial impact, the population eventually would stabilize.

◆ Sharks. These are secondary consumers, and they would be faced with fewer food items because the oceanic plant life would be reduced due to less sunlight. If some of the oceanic plants adapted to the reduction in sunlight, then some of the herbivores also might adapt. As a result, the sharks could survive if they adjusted their food preferences.

◆ Maple trees. As producers, maple trees might flower less due to a reduction in available sunlight. As a result, fewer seeds might be produced and fewer maple trees might germinate. If the species is able to adapt, then these side effects would be lessened. Likewise, animals that feed on maple leaves, flowers, and seeds would have fewer food items available. As a result, they would need to adjust their food preferences.

◆ Saguaro cactus. The cactus lives in very sunny, hot, dry areas, so the reduction in sunlight may cause a severe impact to its reproductive and photosynthetic capabilities. Because cacti are specialists in storing food and water resources, they may be better able to survive the initial shift in the amount of sunlight.

◆ Teenager. The teenager would see an increase in food prices, especially for those plants that make up his or her diet. In turn, the price of hamburger and other grain-fed animal products would increase greatly. Products derived from plants, such as paper, medicines, textiles, and other items also would become limited in their availability, hence their prices would rise. The teenager would be more dependent on synthetic materials, assuming the energy were available to produce them.

b. Imagine that all sunlight is blocked from reaching the earth's surface.

◆ What might be the effect on the following organisms: the producers, the consumers, and the decomposers?

◆ Describe how the cycling of matter through a community would be affected.

Expect the students to realize that if the sunlight were completely blocked from reaching the earth, the photosynthetic organisms (the producers) would be affected immediately because their source of energy would be cut off. Students also will state that since the producers are no longer engaging in photosynthesis, then the oxygen supply will decrease. Students probably will realize that herbivores would be affected more gradually, but that they would begin to starve as the supply of edible plant biomass dwindled. Consumers that are large predators would be affected only after starvation had seriously reduced the number of herbivores and smaller predators. Decomposers would continue to do well longer than any other group. Students may mention that some humans may be able to survive longer if they have plenty of stored food.

The students should realize that the cycling of matter will continue for a brief time until all the producers, and ultimately the consumers, die. At this point, the decomposers will continue to break down the remains of the producers and the consumers until all decomposition has occurred. The decomposers will then die, and life on earth would almost cease to exist.

PART B   Strategies for Survival

Have the students work with a partner to discuss the questions in this part of the activity, and have them record their answers in their journal.

1. From the thousands that sprout, why will only 1 or 2 healthy trees grow into the available space between other existing trees?

   Expect the students to realize that the small sprouts will compete with each other for the available resources (water, sunlight, nutrients), and that some will do better than others. Once one or two of the more successful trees have reached a certain height, they will compete more successfully for the resources available, especially the amount of sunlight, and eventually the still small seedlings will die off.

2. Are the fish that live 2 km (1.2 mi) deep in the ocean likely to be herbivores or predators? Explain.

   The students most likely will indicate that the fish that live this deep in the ocean would be predators because very little sunlight would reach this level. As a result, the number of plants available for food would be small or nonexistent.

3. There were many years when DDT (a pesticide) was widely used in the United States. During this period, the populations of birds of prey, such as bald eagles, peregrine falcons, and ospreys, declined more than the populations of small songbirds. Why do you think that was so?

   Expect that some students might know that DDT becomes more concentrated as it moves from one trophic level to the next. This would mean that the herbivores and omnivores (the songbirds) would not be as seriously affected as the carnivores (birds of prey). The students also might suggest that difference in size and the relative amounts of food (hence pesticides) that the larger birds would ingest might contribute to these results.

4. Human societies that live by hunting and gathering usually have much smaller populations than groups in a similar setting that live primarily by growing crops. Why do you think that is so?

The students most likely will indicate that collecting food by hunting and gathering usually sustains smaller populations because the amount of food obtained this way usually is less, and the amount of space required to obtain a suitable amount of food is usually greater than when societies grow crops. Because of these circumstances, hunter/gatherer societies usually have smaller populations than societies that grow crops. The students may indicate different physiological and behavioral factors that might contribute to smaller populations in hunter/gatherer societies, for example: higher infant mortality rate, higher mortality rate in general, the tendency for females to be infertile while they are nursing their young (and the tendency for females in hunter/gatherer societies to nurse their young for several years), sexual taboos following the birth of a child, and the tendency for individuals to leave the society.

5. Suppose you found yourself snowed in for the winter in a remote mountain cabin with no way of contacting the outside world. You must survive for several months with only what is on hand to eat. Aside from a small supply of canned peaches, your only resources are 2 100-lb sacks of wheat and a flock of 8 hens. Discuss the relative merits of the following strategies:

   a. Feed the grain to the hens and eat their eggs until the wheat is gone. Then eat the hens.

   b. Kill the hens at once, and freeze their carcasses in the snow. Live on a diet of wheat porridge and chicken.

   c. Eat a mixture of wheat porridge, eggs, and 1 hen a week. Feed the hens well to keep the eggs coming until all of the hens are killed.

   Expect the students to apply the rule of eating low on the food chain and the logic of not trying to feed the chickens to keep them alive as well as feeding themselves. If they apply those ideas, the students would choose option b.

6. Every breeding pair of bullfrogs produces hundreds of eggs each spring. During the time they are growing up in the pond, the small tadpoles feed entirely on microscopic water plants. Predators living in the pond eat a large fraction of the tadpoles before they transform into frogs. As adults, however, bullfrogs themselves are predators. Discuss why this strategy is more advantageous than one in which the tadpoles would be predators and the adults would be herbivores.

   Expect the students to think back to what they have learned about the amount of energy in the biomass present at each trophic level. It makes sense that the tadpoles are herbivores and the adult frogs are carnivores because the most plentiful food source would be the water plants, and there are many more tadpoles than adults. If the tadpoles were carnivores, because of their relative numbers, they would have a difficult time finding enough food.

Further Challenges

1. There are several hypotheses about how dinosaurs became extinct. One of these hypotheses involves a climatic catastrophe that has some similarities to the one presented in Part A. See what you can find out about this hypothesis. Report your findings to the class.

   If your students have access to the Internet, it is a good resource for learning about dinosaur extinction hypotheses. The Digital Library for Earth System Education (www.dlese.org) is an excellent resource for educational materials and includes searchable resources about dinosaur extinction. The school and local libraries also are excellent resources for students to conduct research.

2. Write and perform a skit that depicts organisms defending their role in a community. In it, describe the advantages, the disadvantages, and the importance to the community of a producer, a predator, and a decomposer.

   Encourage students to be creative in portraying the community they choose. This activity could be a good alternative assessment opportunity for students who have difficulty expressing themselves in writing.

Conducting Your Own Inquiry

This section of *BSCS Biology: A Human Approach* serves as an opportunity for students to evaluate new scientific information using the habits of mind and inquiry skills that they have developed since the beginning of the program. First, the learners identify and analyze a news article that reports on a scientific phenomenon of interest to them. This allows students to practice applying their critical-thinking skills in a typical, real-world interaction with science. It also helps the learners choose a scientific question for the second part of this section. In the second part, the learners explain some of the big ideas learned thus far in the program in the context of a full inquiry of their own choosing. You might use this inquiry in place of a science fair project or as the framework for conducting a science fair.

Section Goals

By the end of this section, the learners should

◆ demonstrate the ability to think about and analyze scientific questions and the process of investigating those questions, and

◆ successfully design and conduct their own research project, including asking a testable question, developing a hypothesis, designing an experiment, gathering information, conducting an experiment, analyzing data, drawing conclusions, and communicating results.

Advance Preparation

For *Science All Around You*, the students will need a selection of newspapers and magazines containing stories that deal with scientific issues. See Preparations for *Science All Around You* for suggestions about how to collect these.

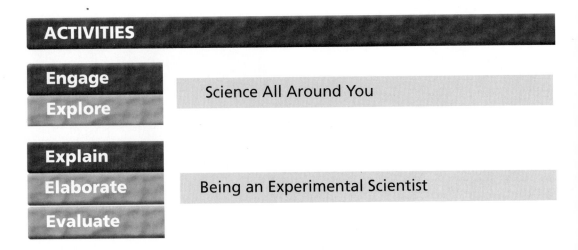

Your students may need access to a wide variety of materials for the experiments that they design and conduct in *Being an Experimental Scientist*. Allow 6–8 weeks for students to complete this activity. See Preparations to develop a better understanding of how to plan for this open-ended and flexible project.

Science All Around You

Major Concepts Science literacy; recognizing scientific methods

Overview

This activity allows students to survey scientific ideas reported in the popular press and to analyze the presentation of those ideas. Through this experience, the learners will come to appreciate how the methods of science and research are reported in newspapers and magazines.

Materials (per class of 30, individuals)

30 newspapers or news magazines
15–30 pairs of scissors
collection of glue, tape, or staplers

Outcomes and Indicators of Success

The following indicators allow you to assess the students' level of success with the activity and to assess their process of learning.

By the end of this activity, the learners should be able to

1. recognize science in the news.

   They will demonstrate this ability by selecting an article for analysis.

2. analyze their article for the methods of science.

   They will demonstrate their ability by identifying the questions asked, background information used, type of experiment conducted, conclusions drawn, and new questions raised.

Preparations

Ask your students to bring in magazines, newspapers, or videotapes that relate news stories reported in the weeks before this activity. Alternatively, you may want to post a note in the teachers' work/prep room to solicit enough news sources so that students will have a selection of interesting choices. If your library subscribes to *Time*, *Newsweek*, *U.S. News and World Report*, or any other periodic news magazine that reports on science issues, you may want to reserve these as well.

Strategies for Guiding Learners

PROCESS AND PROCEDURES

As a class, read orally or silently all introductory materials for the activity and the Process and Procedures to help students build connections between concepts and activities. Use the time spent reading to bring the students' attention into focus.

1. Scan the newspaper or news magazine for articles about science.

2. Cut out the article that most interests you, and attach it to a page in your journal.

   Encourage the students to look for articles that have to do with any discipline of science that interests them. Medical news is likely to be a common choice. If so, encourage a broad cross section of stories related to the science of medicine. After the learners locate an article of interest, they should attach copies of those articles to pages in their journals and note the sources in which they found them.

3. To analyze this news article, answer the following questions in your journal:

   Base your answers on the information in the article itself and what you infer.

   ◆ What question did the scientists ask?
   ◆ What background information informed the scientists?
   ◆ What type of investigation did the scientists conduct?
   ◆ What tools did the scientists use?
   ◆ What results did the scientists get?
   ◆ What conclusions did the scientists draw?
   ◆ What new questions did the scientists ask?

   As the students analyze their articles, walk through the classroom and ask how they are progressing. Many learners are unlikely to find all the information requested. This realization is an important part of the activity. In fact, most articles in the popular press that deal with science issues present significantly less information than is necessary to fully evaluate whether the science was good or poor. Learners can leave these responses blank or speculate on possible responses, given the information available.

   If you include some science journals in the collection of magazines, the students should notice the contrast in the amount and quality of information reported. Students may be able to answer all the questions using a science magazine, whereas a tabloid news article likely will include very little information that is useful for answering these questions. An interesting discussion would be to compare the range of ways science news is reported. Make clear to students that by doing this activity, they should be able to better analyze the scientific research reported in the popular press.

Analysis

1. Discuss your article and analysis with a partner.

   Students should be able to summarize both the article and their analysis. If you do not want to take the class time for this task, students could complete it as a homework assignment.

2. Record in your journal at least two scientific questions that you would like to research.

   These may be related to the article you analyzed or to another area of science.

   Remind students that they do not have to use any ideas from the articles they analyzed. They can use questions related to this program, questions of personal interest, or questions prompted by this activity. The intent of this question really is to get students thinking about science topics that interest them.

Explain
Elaborate
Evaluate

Being an Experimental Scientist

Major Concepts
Asking a biological question; developing a hypothesis; identifying experimental controls; conducting and analyzing an experiment; connecting unifying principles and program subthemes to an experimental inquiry

Overview

This activity parallels the Engage Section in that the students once again assume more direct roles in carrying out open-ended scientific investigations. They do this by completing a full inquiry. In a successful full inquiry, learners will propose, design, carry out, analyze, and communicate the results of a scientific inquiry. The opportunity to conduct a full inquiry provides a comprehensive way for students to apply and evaluate their critical-thinking and scientific-process skills. Students have had a chance through the first three units to develop all of the skills required to complete this process, and a full inquiry authentically assesses the students' performance of the complete process. This activity should have an independent feeling for the students, and we anticipate that the majority of the work will be conducted outside of class hours.

The techniques and processes promoted in this activity are similar to those required by many science fairs. If you usually ask students to complete science fair projects, this activity could serve as a template for meeting that goal, but doing so in the context of a complete curriculum. Students will need 6–8 weeks to execute the inquiry that is the essence of this activity.

Materials (per class of 30, individuals)

These will vary from project to project.

growth and/or development. By contrast, plants do not require music for life, so there is no reason to think that rock music would benefit plant growth more than classical music. Students often have a hard time distinguishing between meaningful questions and trivial questions, and your guidance at this step can help set them in the direction of a rich and rewarding experience.

Identifying the unifying principles that relate to the hypothesis will help the students place their inquiry in a broader biological context. Although most of this step can be completed outside of class, you will want to check their progress in class.

2. Show your question to your teacher for approval before you proceed.

During your review, look for testable ideas, safe ideas, and connections to the unifying principles. This will be your last opportunity to identify insignificant or untestable questions that are not appropriate for this full inquiry. If a learner suggests building a model of a volcano or adding ethanol to a plant, help him or her see that such ideas do not test meaningful scientific questions. Encourage these learners to think of more appropriate alternatives, and provide suggestions as necessary.

II. Gathering Information

1. Use the library, local scientists, the Internet, or other available resources to gather information related to your question.

Scientists use data that others collect as well as data that they gather directly through experimental investigations. You should use a similar process at this time.

Encourage students to be creative and diverse in locating sources of information. Discourage use of encyclopedias as the sole source of information. In addition, there are sites on the World Wide Web for students to talk to other students, scientists, and teachers. Science magazines, journals, and topic-specific books offer different types of information.

2. Design an experiment to test or answer your question by doing the following:

   a. Describe your experimental design in your journal and include these sections:

      ◆ Rationale, that is, how this experiment will test your question (include a description of your controls and the role that they will play)

      ◆ Hypothesis (explain what you think the answer to your question may be and why you think so)

      ◆ Procedure (include the materials you will need)

      ◆ Data analysis (explain how you will analyze the data)

      Your teacher may have specific suggestions about the length of time that you will have or the equipment that is available.

   b. Write in your journal a safety plan for your experiment. In your procedures, record the precautions that you will follow when you

      ◆ use chemicals,

      ◆ handle equipment, and

      ◆ handle biological hazards such as bacteria or yeast.

      Ask your teacher to explain any hazards that you do not understand. Your teacher should also help you identify the precautions necessary to prevent harm from an accident.

Review Appendix A, *Laboratory Safety*, on pages 683–689. Be sure that you understand all the safety considerations involved in your experimental design. Make sure that you have read and understood the hazards and precautions described on the labels and Material Safety Data Sheets for all the chemicals you plan to use in your experiment. Report all accidents, no matter how small, to your teacher.

As learners write descriptions of their experimental designs, they should mimic the type of procedural text they have experienced in this program. Emphasize the need for a controlled experiment and one that consciously attends to safety issues. (The student text does not include any suggestions for team size for this activity, but the assumption is that students will work individually. Depending on materials, space, and the nature of your students, you should clarify whether they should work alone, with a partner, or in a larger team.)

3. Discuss your library research, experimental design, and safety plan with your teacher before you continue. If your plans are reasonable and safe, your teacher will approve further work.

   Arrange a method to review the students' plans, either in writing or verbally. It may help to schedule 5–10 minutes with each student to discuss your impressions and any suggestions that you might have for improvements.

4. When you have your teacher's approval, carry out the experiment you have designed to test your hypothesis.

   Remember, record data carefully in your journal. Use the proper controls to make it a valid test.

   As appropriate, monitor students' work to ensure safety as they conduct their experiments. Remind the students to use their journals to record data. You also may want to review the many methods for recording data: photographing, videotaping, sketching, or recording readings such as temperature, time, and growth.

   Note: If time or materials are in short supply and it truly is impractical to have students conduct their experiment, you may decide to eliminate this step. The processes of developing the question and plan and conducting the background research for an experiment constitute much of the intellectual work of an inquiry. Thus, doing a library inquiry, although not a full inquiry, is nonetheless better than not doing any research project. Except in unusual circumstances, however, we do not recommend omitting the experiment. Learners are more apt to remember their performance in this full inquiry if they actually conduct the proposed experiments.

III. Analyzing Your Data

1. Organize your data in a way that makes it easier to see patterns or understand what the data show you (see Figure Ex.3).

   This step will help you when you present your work in Part V.

2. Decide what your data tell you, and record your preliminary conclusions. Include a description of any limitations of your experimental design and any unexpected results that you may have found.

You may want to provide class time for students to analyze their data. If so, have them work in pairs and review each other's analysis as they look for problems. This process will increase the quality of the presentations later. This intermediate critique of the analysis also provides an opportunity for learners to repeat parts of their experiment that may have been problematic. Encourage learners to revise their procedures to accommodate suggestions for improving the experiments.

IV. Drawing Conclusions

1. In your journal, explain what your conclusions indicate about the question you asked.

   Support your conclusions by making specific references to your data.

2. Describe how your work connects to the unifying principle most related to your inquiry.

   Encourage the students to do more than restate their results. Results summarize data that has been gathered, whereas conclusions tie the results to the hypothesis. The learners should state whether their hypothesis was supported or disproved and suggest how future experiments might reveal an even better understanding of the process or phenomenon being investigated. Look for evidence of thoughtful analysis and an effort to connect the inquiry with the larger conceptual picture of biology represented by one or more unifying principles.

V. Communicating Your Results

1. Assemble a presentation of your full inquiry that makes it possible for someone else to understand what you did, why you did it, and what you found out.

   A poster, a written or verbal report, or a videotape are some examples of how you can communicate your results.

   Make the parameters for this section clear to students. Some possibilities for the presentations include the following:

   - Private presentations such as verbal or written reports that are presented to the teacher
   - Public displays in a hallway, showcase, or the classroom
   - Posters and oral presentations to their peers
   - A science fair after school in the gymnasium or other large area

2. Be sure to identify the connections between your inquiry and the following aspects of biology:

   - The unifying principles of biology
   - Technology
   - Culture
   - History
   - Ethics

   All inquiries will have connections to at least 1 of the unifying principles of biology. However, your inquiry may not have connections to all of the other aspects of biology. If you cannot identify a technological, historical, cultural, or ethical connection relevant to your inquiry, explain this in your presentation.

3. As you listen to other students present their results, look for evidence or examples that illustrate why the approach they took to answering their question was scientific.

The learners should identify ways in which their project depended upon or connected with technology, culture, history, and ethics issues. For example, a project that investigates the dependence of plant growth on particular wavelengths of visible light would rely on technology that enables the isolation of specific wavelengths of light. This phase of the inquiry offers another opportunity for learners to discuss the generation of new hypotheses and predictions about the direction of subsequent related investigations. To close the inquiry in a manner that relates the experiment to the larger context of the program, encourage the students to put a lot of thought into their responses for this step. Making the connections to the unifying principles, technology, culture, ethics, and history relates directly to the program goals for *BSCS Biology: A Human Approach* because it reinforces the relevance of biology and the importance of science in society. In addition, reflecting on the characteristic nature of scientific approaches to knowing the world distinguishes science from other ways of knowing the world.

Continuity: Reproduction and Inheritance in Living Systems

In Unit 4, the students focus on continuity in biological systems. In Chapter 10, they develop a conceptual view of reproduction. They are introduced to both asexual and sexual reproduction, with human reproduction and its cultural influences as a major example. In Chapter 11, the students begin their study of genetics and explore the transmission of information, genetic variation, inheritance patterns, and the role of genetics in evolution and behavior. In Chapter 12, the students explore the dynamics of gene expression and replication at a molecular level. This exploration provides them with a basis for examining some of the fundamental techniques that underlie genetic engineering.

Unit Goals

By the end of this unit, the learners should

- understand that the continuity of a species depends on the transfer of genetic information;
- understand how information is transferred and preserved through reproduction and the behavior of the genetic material;
- understand the processes by which genetic information is expressed;
- understand how sexual reproduction and mutation increase genetic variation and why this is important for the evolution of a species;
- appreciate that human reproduction takes place within a cultural setting and involves ethical issues; and
- become aware of the impact of genetic engineering technology.

Prior Conceptions

Reproduction and inheritance are areas many students find fascinating. Nevertheless, high school students continue to have several misconceptions about both reproduction and the inheritance of characteristics. As with incorrect conceptions in other areas of biology, prior conceptions about reproduction and inheritance may be difficult to dislodge, but the BSCS 5E instructional model offers multiple opportunities to confront these prior conceptions and replace them with biologically correct understandings.

The authors of *Making Sense of Secondary Science* summarize several incorrect ideas about reproduction that are common among middle school and high school students (Driver, Squires, Rushworth, and Wood-Robinson, 1994). Students often equate sexual reproduction with copulation. For example, many students consider *in vitro* fertilization an example of asexual reproduction. They do not understand that sexual reproduction is the fusion of specialized cells from two parents that does not necessarily require physical contact between the parents. Students also often assume that males of all species are larger and stronger than females, and that the offspring produced by asexual reproduction are weaker than those produced by sexual reproduction. Students will confront these and other prior conceptions about reproduction as they complete *Making Sense of Reproductive Strategies*, the explore activity of Chapter 10.

The Project 2061 *Atlas of Science Literacy* identifies several incorrect ideas that middle school students and some high school students often have about inheritance. Some students believe that the characteristics of each parent are "blended" in their offspring. Other common, incorrect prior conceptions about heredity are that offspring inherit characteristics from just one parent, either the mother or the same-sex parent, or that certain characteristics are inherited solely from the mother, and others are inherited solely from the father (AAAS, 2001). The activities in *Patterns of Inheritance*, the explore/explain activity of Chapter 11, address all of these incorrect prior conceptions. They will help students recognize that genes are discrete entities inherited from both parents. The genes from each parent combine to form particular characteristics.

Part D of *Can You Sort It Out?*, the explain/elaborate activity of Chapter 11, helps students work through the challenging case of X-linked traits, which often appear to be inherited only by males from their mothers. Completing this activity will help students see that females also inherit genes associated with X-linked traits, from either their mothers or their fathers (or both). The incorrect idea that some characteristics produced by the environment can be inherited over several generations persists among high school students (AAAS, 2001). *The Genetic Basis of Human Variation*, the elaborate activity of Chapter 11, helps reinforce the correct notion that populations have *preexisting* variations, some of which may be favored by changing environmental conditions. Over many generations, the favored variations become more prevalent in a population.

Research studies have found that upper–middle school and high school students have some understanding that genes carry translatable information (AAAS, 2001). This general understanding is reinforced and made more concrete in two activities in Chapter 12, *Gene Expression*, the explain activity, and *A Closer Look at Protein Synthesis*, the elaborate activity.

Advance Preparation for the Unit

You will need to order materials for the lab activities in Chapters 10 and 11. The Advance Preparation section of each chapter will direct you to the specific activities that require materials and planning in advance.

We recommend that you set up a question box in the classroom in which students can leave questions that they may feel are tangential to the concepts in this unit but that they are embarrassed to ask aloud. Let students know the purpose of the box ahead of time and indicate that you will review and answer questions as time permits.

Reproduction in Humans and Other Organisms

Chapter
10

In this chapter, the learners explore concepts about reproduction in general and about human reproduction specifically. As the students complete a variety of activities and read related essays, they begin to develop an understanding of how reproduction contributes to the continuation of life on earth and to the continuity of the species as well. This chapter prepares the students for a closer look in Chapters 11 and 12 at how information is passed from one generation to the next. In addition to the essays and DVD resources, we also recommend the videos *The Miracle of Life* (NOVA) and *The Nature of Sex* (Nature) as resources.

ACTIVITIES

Engage	A Zillion Ways to Make More
Explore	Making Sense of Reproductive Strategies
Explain	Making Sense of Human Reproduction
Elaborate	Observing Reproductive Behavior in Nonhuman Animals
Elaborate	Cultural Influences on Human Mating Behavior
Evaluate	A Reproductive Strategy for Your Critter

CHAPTER 10 IMPLEMENTATION

Instructional Flow

Classroom Support

Activity/ Student Text pp. Teacher Guide pp.	GACD, TRCD, DVD, and CD-ROM Resources	Essays/ Student Text pp.	Estimated Time	Team Size/ Cooperative Learning Focus	Strategies and Tools	Assessment Opportunities	Special Considerations
ENGAGE A Zillion Ways to Make More pp. 402–403 TG pp. 366–367	DVD: What's Going on Here?		50 minutes	Team size: individuals	Opening story; DVD segment	Prior knowledge and misconceptions about the biological basis for reproduction	Plan time to stop and describe/ discuss the images shown in the video as a whole class for the benefit of students who cannot see the images.
EXPLORE Making Sense of Reproductive Strategies pp. 403–405 TG pp. 368–373	Copymasters Reproduction Cards; DVD: Yeast Reproduction	Continuity through Reproduction pp. 474–476; Cloning pp. 476–477	100–150 minutes	Team size: 2 Skill: Using initiative; questioning techniques; probing for understanding	DVD segment; visual presentation	Prior knowledge of reproduction; current understanding; observation skills	Enlarge the copymasters or plan an alternative to the reproduction card for students who might have difficulty reading the card. For students who might struggle researching their assigned organism's reproductive strategy, plan to assign one of the more familiar strategies (for example, the elephant or chimpanzee).
EXPLAIN Making Sense of Human Reproduction pp. 407–411 TG pp. 373–377	DVD: Human Menstrual Cycle, Parts 1–5; Copymaster Sample Letters for Concerned Parents; Rubric: Birth Control Brochure	Making More People pp. 477–481; Hormones and Sexual Reproduction pp. 481–484; Sexual Activity and Health Hazards pp. 484–486; Infertility p. 486	100–150 minutes	Team size: individuals	DVD segment; developing a brochure	Using information to develop an explanation; current understanding and transformation of prior misconceptions about reproduction	Most students, particularly those who have difficulty grasping written information, benefit from seeing sample birth control items while discussing their impact on reproductive systems and effectiveness. Supplement the video segment with copies of the narration for students with hearing challenges, and for students who cannot see the video. Consider working with these students outside of class to review the menstrual cycle processes.
ELABORATE Observing Reproductive Behavior in Nonhuman Animals pp. 411–412 TG pp. 378–379	DVD: Animal Mating Behaviors	Mating Behaviors of Nonhuman Animals pp. 486–488	50 minutes	Team size: 4 Skill: Dealing with specific problems; summarizing	DVD segment	Applying understanding of reproduction to new situations	Plan time to stop and describe/ discuss as a whole class each organism's mating behavior shown in the video for the benefit of students who cannot see the images.

continued

	Instructional Flow				Classroom Support		
Activity/ Student Text pp. Teacher Guide pp.	GACD, TRCD, DVD, and CD-ROM Resources	Essays/ Student Text pp.	Estimated Time	Team Size/ Cooperative Learning Focus	Strategies and Tools	Assessment Opportunities	Special Considerations
ELABORATE *Cultural Influences on Human Mating Behavior* pp. 412–414 TG pp. 380–382		*Human Mating Behaviors* p. 489; *Cultures and Mating Patterns* pp. 489–491	50 minutes	*Team size:* 4 *Skill:* Providing constructive criticism; using initiative	Creating a display	Synthesizing ideas to develop explanations	You may wish to enlarge some images from magazines for students with visual challenges to use in creating their poster. You also might consider providing oral report options for any students who cannot construct a poster.
EVALUATE *A Reproductive Strategy for Your Critter* pp. 414–415 TG pp. 383–384	Rubric: *Your Critter's Reproductive Strategy*		100 minutes	*Team size:* individuals	Revisiting your critter	Applying understanding to new situations; current level of understanding of biological continuity	If you have students who joined your class recently, plan ahead for them to create a critter or select one that you provide to use as the basis for this activity.

11 days

Chapter Goals

By the end of this chapter, students should

- ◆ understand that reproduction is necessary for continuity;
- ◆ understand that genetic information is transferred to offspring;
- ◆ understand the significance of sexual and asexual reproduction;
- ◆ have a general understanding of the human reproductive process and regulation;
- ◆ appreciate that human cultures influence mating behaviors; and
- ◆ appreciate similarities and differences in reproductive strategies.

The learners also will continue

- ◆ making observations and comparisons,
- ◆ interpreting data,
- ◆ drawing conclusions, and
- ◆ exploring the use of technology.

Advance Preparation

Making Sense of Reproductive Strategies requires that you duplicate copymasters of reproduction cards for the students. *Cultural Influences on Human Mating Behavior* requires that the students collect materials ahead of time. See Preparations for each of these activities for more information. The Public Broadcasting Service series *Nature* produced a six-part video titled *The Nature of Sex*. This video series has some extraordinary footage of an incredible variety of organisms and is organized around conceptual themes. It is an extremely valuable resource for this chapter.

Engage

A Zillion Ways to Make More

Major Concepts   The diversity of reproductive strategies

Overview

This brief engage activity reminds the learners that even though human reproductive strategies are the most familiar to them, there are many ways of making more organisms.

Materials   (per class of 30, individuals)

DVD
DVD player

Outcomes and Indicators of Success

The following indicators allow you to assess the students' level of success with the activity and to assess their process of learning.

By the end of this activity, the learners should

1. begin to appreciate the diversity of reproductive strategies.

   They will demonstrate their appreciation by mentioning some of the strategies in their statement about biological continuity.

2. begin thinking about what the term *biological continuity* means to them.

   They will demonstrate their current understanding by writing a statement about what this term means to them at this point in their study of biology.

Strategies for Guiding Learners

PROCESS AND PROCEDURES

As a class, read orally or silently all introductory materials for the activity and the Process and Procedures to help students build connections between concepts and activities. Use the time spent reading to bring the students' attention into focus.

1. How does a small cluster of trees become a forest? To begin thinking about that question, read *The Aspen Story*.

   After the students read the story, you may want to convene an informal class discussion of the question, How does a small cluster of trees become a forest?

2. What other ways are there to make more? To give you some idea of the range of reproductive strategies and behaviors that exist, watch the DVD segment "What's Going on Here?" Think about what is happening in each of the images.

   In the segment "What's Going on Here?," the students are exposed to a number of brief scenes that demonstrate a range of reproductive and mating behaviors in a variety of organisms. After you have shown the video segment, convene a class discussion of what the students think is going on in each scene. Remember, this stage in the instructional model provides you with an opportunity to assess the students' prior knowledge, but do not expect that their ideas will be well developed at this point.

Analysis

Now that you have begun to think about how organisms reproduce, create a concept map in your journal that shows what the term *biological continuity* means to you at this point in your study of biology. Begin your map as shown in Figure 10.1. Add other factors that represent your current understanding of biological continuity. Leave room to add more concepts and to make changes to your map later in the chapter. Be sure to include descriptors on the links between concepts that explain how the ideas are related.

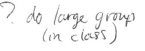
? do large group (in class)

> This concept map is a way for you to record your early ideas on the subject. You will refer back to it and reflect on how your view changes as you work through this chapter and unit.

Again, have the students work individually to complete their concept maps. Remind them that this is an opportunity for them to guide their own learning, and it provides a basis from which to measure their own learning throughout the chapter and the unit.

Making Sense of Reproductive Strategies

2-3 days

Major Concepts
Continuity of a species requires reproduction; reproductive strategies vary

Overview

In this activity, the learners work in teams to explore similarities and differences in reproductive strategies by comparing information about a pair of organisms and then sharing this information with the class. During the activity, the students begin to grapple with the significance of the difference between asexual and sexual reproduction and to describe the biological value of reproduction for species as compared to individuals. This activity reflects the significant contributions of Jim Happel, a biology teacher at Manatee High School in Bradenton, Florida. Jim field tested this program in 1994–1995.

Materials   (per class of 30, teams of 2)

felt-tipped marking pens
large sheets of paper or poster board
2 or 3 sets of reproduction cards
    (Copymasters *Reproductive Cards* 1–16);
    see Preparations

specimens (live or preserved; optional)
resource materials (optional)
DVD
DVD player

Outcomes and Indicators of Success

The following indicators allow you to assess the students' level of success with the activity and to assess their process of learning.

By the end of this activity, learners should

1. understand that there is a diversity of reproductive strategies.

   They will demonstrate their understanding by

   a. distinguishing the differences between two specific reproductive strategies,

   b. describing the advantages and disadvantages of each of these reproductive strategies, and

   c. describing patterns that emerge when considering a variety of reproductive strategies.

2. understand the biological function of reproduction.

   They will indicate their understanding by

   a. describing the interaction between reproduction and natural selection for the continuation of a species,

   b. comparing the necessity of reproduction for an individual and for a species, and

   c. creating a visual representation of their understanding of reproduction.

3. have a better understanding of biological continuity.

They will demonstrate their understanding by revising their statement on biological continuity that they wrote in *A Zillion Ways to Make More.*

Preparations

Duplicate the reproduction cards from Copymasters 1–16. They will be more durable if you copy them onto cardstock and laminate them. Each team needs two different species, but there can be repetition between teams.

We include sufficient examples for the activity, but you may want to substitute or add different species from those we offer. If so, you will need to make up equivalent reproduction cards ahead of time.

The video series *The Nature of Sex* from the Public Broadcasting Service's *Nature* program provides wonderful, detailed examples of a range of reproduction strategies, especially those of insects, birds, and fish. You may want to preview some of the segments and select those you find most educational or intriguing to share with the class.

If you have access to live or preserved samples of certain species, you may want to have them on hand for examination. You also could display additional resource materials such as botany and zoology references that students might consult for more information about their species. Keep the activity manageable by focusing on the big ideas rather than on the details of reproduction for each species.

Strategies for Guiding Learners

PROCESS AND PROCEDURES

As a class, read orally or silently all introductory materials for the activity and the Process and Procedures to help students build connections between concepts and activities. Use the time spent reading to bring the students' attention into focus.

Begin this activity by calling students' attention to the questions raised in the introduction. Consider writing the questions on the board so that students can start thinking about them as soon as they enter the classroom. You might conduct a *brief* survey of the students' ideas related to these questions.

Before you move on to step 1, we recommend that you show the DVD segment "Yeast Reproduction," which shows still images, motion sequences, and animated sequences of the yeast reproductive processes. This provides the learners with concrete introductory images and terminology. Teams that choose yeast as one of their reproductive cards will want to return to this video segment on their own.

1. To begin studying the variety of reproductive strategies, choose 2 reproduction cards with your partner. Read through the material on each one.

Your teacher will provide these cards. The glossary on page 705 will help with unfamiliar terms.

As the teams choose their reproduction cards, make certain that each team has two different species to consider and that the two choices represent a sufficient diversity to show similarities and differences in reproductive strategies.

Venn

2. With your partner, look for similarities and differences in the reproductive strategies described on your cards. Record this information in your journal.

As the teams study their cards and look for similarities and differences, circulate and listen to their discussions to assess their conceptual understanding. You may notice some interpretations that indicate underlying misconceptions. Suggest significant characteristics if the students are having trouble getting started. For example, salmon and frogs both fertilize eggs externally in water, but frog eggs hatch tadpoles in just a few days. Salmon eggs, on the other hand, hatch after several months.

3. Prepare a short (3- to 5-minute) presentation that compares and contrasts the reproductive strategies of the 2 organisms that you and your partner studied. In your presentation, answer the following questions:

   a. What are some characteristics of each organism's reproductive strategies?

      You might include these characteristics:
      ◆ Number of offspring produced during each reproductive cycle
      ◆ Frequency of the reproductive cycle
      ◆ Structures that are involved in reproduction
      ◆ Age of sexual maturity
      ◆ Length of gestation
      ◆ Length of the period of offspring dependency
      ◆ Life span of individuals
      ◆ Mating behaviors

   b. How are the reproductive strategies similar? How are they different?

   c. What are the advantages and disadvantages of the reproductive strategies of your 2 organisms?

      For example, consider the amount of time and energy each strategy requires and the survival rate for the offspring.

   d. How does each strategy ensure survival of the species?

      The essay Continuity through Reproduction on page 474 has important background information to help you with this task. Your teacher may have other resources available for you as well.

   As the teams prepare their presentations, you may need to help teams that are struggling. These questions may be useful as you circulate from team to team:

      ◆ Tell me about your organism. What are the advantages of its reproductive strategies?
      ◆ What is the most interesting characteristic of your organism?
      ◆ How do the animals differ from the plants?
      ◆ What complex organism do you have? What makes it complex?
      ◆ What simple organism do you have? What makes it simple?
      ◆ How do the reproductive strategies of simple and complex organisms differ?

   Also remind them to use the essay *Continuity through Reproduction* as a resource to help them prepare their presentations.

4. Create a visual diagram to use with your presentation.

Make your presentation interesting and informative. Practice pronouncing the names of your organisms and the terms used to describe their reproductive strategies before you present. If either of your organisms is unusual, be prepared to describe it so that your classmates have an idea of what it is like.

5. Make your presentation to the rest of your classmates.

As you listen to the other presentations, take notes in your journal. Record the similarities, differences, and patterns in reproductive strategies.

6. When the presentations are finished, participate in a class discussion of the patterns that are emerging.

As the teams make their presentations, direct the students to take notes so that they can more easily participate in the class discussion. Guide the discussion to help students see similarities and differences in reproductive strategies, recognize significant characteristics, and make correlations between characteristics where they exist. Use questions such as the following to elicit significant characteristics and to assess their current understanding of the concepts:

♦ Why might large numbers of offspring be beneficial to the survival of a species? What is the biological cost?

♦ What is the role of gametes in reproduction?

♦ How might evolution help account for the diversity of reproductive strategies?

Some of the patterns that students may identify include the following:

♦ Asexual reproduction is a predominant mode among smaller, less complex organisms, although it also is carried out by complex organisms such as plants.

♦ Larger body sizes correlate to longer gestation periods (in animals).

♦ Plants in open areas produce more seeds than woodland plants.

♦ Some organisms reproduce sexually and asexually, and they may shift from one mode to another, sometimes in response to stress.

♦ Generally, the greater the likelihood of fertilization, the fewer female gametes are released.

♦ Organisms with long life spans may invest a lower total percentage of their time and energy in reproduction.

♦ Longer generation time (and often larger size) correlates with fewer total offspring produced.

♦ Greater parental care usually correlates with fewer offspring.

♦ Sexual reproduction is characterized by two sexes or mating types.

7. Read the essay *Cloning* on page 476 for background information about laboratory cloning techniques. In your journal, explain the difference between *somatic cell nuclear transfer* and *fertilization*.

The essay on cloning explains artificial cloning, a topic likely to come up in your class when discussing asexual reproduction. After reading the essay (which you may wish to supplement with other current articles of interest on cloning), students should be able to respond to the challenge in step 7. Some students may need help understanding what a somatic cell is. Somatic cell nuclear transfer refers to the

Handwritten margin notes:
Day 2 — prepare presentation — present
Class discussion (left margin, vertical)
Class — discussion (right margin)
Day 3 Cloning video & #7 or ws Show video? video on cloning (right margin)

process of removing the nucleus of an ovum and replacing it with the nucleus of a somatic cell. The genetic information transferred into the ovum may have no relation to the ovum in somatic cell nuclear transfer.

8. In your journal, make a list of 3 concepts related to reproduction and continuity that you think are important to the study of biology.

   Consider general ideas about reproduction rather than reproductive structures. For example, you might list the idea that reproduction can be a sexual or an asexual process.

   As the learners record ideas in their journals, expect them to include ideas such as reproduction can be sexual or asexual; reproduction involves passing on information from one generation to the next; sexual reproductive strategies introduce genetic changes to the next generation; inefficient reproduction might lead to extinction; and successful reproduction helps ensure species survival.

9. Add your 3 concepts from step 8 to the concept map on biological continuity that you started in the previous activity. Include appropriate descriptions for how the concepts are related.

10. Compare your concept map with your partner's. Discuss any differences or similarities that you see. Make any additions to your concept map that reflect your current understanding of biological continuity.

    Circulate among your students as they add to and discuss their concept maps. Listen for misconceptions about the relationships between concepts students choose and the broader concept of biological continuity.

Analysis

Complete the first item as a class. Then complete the two remaining items individually.

1. Participate in a class discussion and construction of a biological continuity concept map.

   Contribute ideas and explanations from your own concept map.

   Gather student input while constructing a large concept map on an overhead or board that the whole class can see. Take this opportunity to clarify any misconceptions that you detected previously in steps 9 and 10. You may wish to post this concept map in your room for later reference.

2. Think about the following questions. Record your responses in your journal.

   a. Is reproduction necessary for the survival of an individual? Explain.
      Students should recognize that individuals can and do live without reproducing, although they may argue that without reproduction, an individual cannot complete a life cycle.

   b. Is reproduction necessary for the survival of a species? Explain.
      Students should recognize that reproduction is essential for the continuation of a species. Without producing new individuals, the species eventually would die out.

c. Explain the relationship between changes in a species' environment and the effectiveness of that species' reproductive strategies.

Consider whether a species' reproductive strategies might change over time. How might fast or slow changes in the environment affect those changes?

Students should understand that this would depend on how the organisms' environments change. If they change quickly and dramatically, then the same strategies probably would not be effective. If they change slowly, many of the strategies remain effective.

3. Explain the connection between natural selection and reproduction in a way that describes their importance to biological continuity.

Biological continuity involves change across time. Evolutionary change depends on the gradual changes that occur in a population as new genetic information is introduced across many generations. Natural selection provides a mechanism that determines which characteristics will persist in a population.

If it would be helpful for students to have additional information about reproduction in plants, refer to *Eukaryotes: Plants* in Section 7 on the *TRCD*. You could copy all or part of the chapter for students.

Making Sense of Human Reproduction

Explain

Major Concepts
Regulation of human reproduction; structure and function of the human reproductive system; birth control as a form of technology

Overview

The learners are motivated to learn about the physiology, anatomy, and regulation of human reproduction as they develop a brochure that explains the biological basis of birth control technology. Their resources are the NOVA video *The Miracle of Life*, the DVD segments *Human Menstrual Cycle* and *Conception*, several essays, and any additional information you provide. In addition to the brochure, the students develop an explanation of how reproductive behavior can be regulated to enhance conception. They also join the class in a discussion that extends the major concepts.

Materials (per class of 30, individuals)

video, *The Miracle of Life* (NOVA), available as videotape
VCR and monitor (if videotape is used)
DVD
DVD player
additional resources (optional)
30 copies of the Copymaster *Sample Letters for Concerned Parents*
30 copies of the rubric *Birth Control Brochure*
miscellaneous art supplies

Outcomes and Indicators of Success

The following indicators allow you to assess the students' level of success with the activity and to assess their process of learning.

By the end of this activity, the learners should

1. know the basic human male and female anatomical structures involved in the reproductive process.

   They will demonstrate their understanding by

   a. explaining how different birth control methods interfere with reproduction, and

   b. explaining how different birth control methods affect the reproductive systems of males and females.

2. understand that human reproduction is based on cycles that are regulated by hormones.

   They will demonstrate their understanding by

   a. correctly addressing hormonal issues in their brochure on birth control, and

   b. explaining how the timing of ovulation is significant for fertility.

3. be able to explain the biological basis for birth control and fertility methods.

   They will demonstrate their ability by

   a. proposing a biological rationale for three types of contraceptive methods,

   b. explaining why specific birth control methods are effective,

   c. stating why fertility drugs do not solve the problem of blocked oviducts, and

   d. describing how reproductive behavior can be regulated to increase chances of conception.

4. be able to relate the idea of the interchange of genetic information during sexual reproduction with the idea of continuity.

   They will demonstrate this ability by stating that gametes contain half of the information and when they join, new combinations of information result.

Preparations

Review the rubric for the birth control brochures on the *GACD*, and modify it to your class.

Obtain and preview a copy of *The Miracle of Life* (NOVA). This film often is available at video rental outlets. You may want to purchase it for use here and in Unit 5. If the NOVA video is not available, you may want to substitute other resources or a short lecture to make certain the information is covered.

The video series *The Nature of Sex* (Nature) includes a segment on the evolution of human sexual behavior. The developers do a nice job of providing a probable context for the evolution of various human reproductive behaviors. You may want to preview this segment and then share it with your class. For information on this video, see Advance Preparation for this chapter.

Handwritten margin notes:
- 13 Days to prepare brochures
- 1 Day to show "Miracle of Life"
- 1 Day to teach Male / Female cycles... (picture pages)
- HW: analysis

Collect additional sources about the anatomy and physiology of the human reproductive system if you choose to extend the students' resources for constructing their explanation. Some suggestions include *Our Bodies, Ourselves for the New Century* (Boston Women's Health Book Collective, Touchstone Books, Simon and Schuster, Inc., New York, 1998), a reference textbook on human physiology, materials for distribution by your local health department or a medical office, and the volume on reproduction from a general or science encyclopedia.

Strategies for Guiding Learners

PROCESS AND PROCEDURES

As a class, read orally or silently all introductory materials for the activity and the Process and Procedures to help students build connections between concepts and activities. Use the time spent reading to bring the students' attention into focus.

Some difficulty may arise with this sensitive topic of reproduction. To encourage the students to learn the related concepts, we assign the task of explaining the biological basis of reproduction technology—both contraception and fertility enhancement.

You may need to make clear to students and concerned parents that you are not promoting the use of birth control. Instead, the students' task in this activity is a powerful technique to help ensure that students are fully informed about the impact of technology on various aspects of reproduction. The technologies provide a concrete way for students to focus their explanation of the underlying biology and regulatory systems of the human reproductive processes. We include two sample letters as copymasters that you might want to use to inform parents about this chapter. Use school stationery and sign the letters if you decide to send them.

If you feel that students will work more productively as a team, set them up to do so. Whatever option you decide on, make it clear to students at the beginning of the activity. We have included a rubric to help you assess the students' explanations; be sure to distribute a copy to the students so they are aware of your expectations.

It may help to begin by having the entire class watch the NOVA video *The Miracle of Life* together. This video displays spectacular fiber optic photography by Lennart Nilsson of the steps in conception and development. We recommend that you watch only the first half of the video at this time and use it again in Unit 5 to explore the steps in development of the embryo. After viewing the video, you can foreshadow what the students will learn about genetics in Chapter 11 by asking them to think about the significance of having male and female gametes and how this situation affects the contribution of information to offspring.

1. Classify the birth control methods from the examples in the need to know box. Place them into the following categories: physical barriers, chemical methods, and behavioral methods.

   In your journal, record the birth control methods and the way that you classified them. Remember that you have a variety of resources to help you decide how to categorize these methods.

As the learners work to divide the birth control methods into different categories, circulate around the room to see that they are on the right track. Expect the students to come up with the following distribution:

Physical barriers: cervical cap, condom, diaphragm, and IUD (may include tubal ligation and vasectomy)

Chemical methods: injectable progesterone, implant devices, oral contraceptives, and spermicides (may include douche)

Behavioral methods: abstinence, douche, natural family planning, tubal ligation, and vasectomy

2. Using the available resources, prepare a brochure about 1 contraceptive method from each category in step 1. Your brochure should give the *biological* explanation for how the contraceptive methods work.

You will know you have developed a good brochure if you do each of the following:

◆ Describe how each birth control method interferes with reproduction.

◆ Explain how each method affects the reproductive systems of males or females. (For example, does the method alter the hormonal levels of the male? the female?)

◆ Explain why each method needs to be used at a particular time.

◆ Explain the differences in the effectiveness of the methods that you chose in each category.

You can develop 1 brochure that describes all of the methods, or 1 brochure for each method. Remember, your goal is to show that you understand the *biology* behind these methods. For example, you will discuss how birth control pills influence the hormone cycles during the menstrual cycle.

Before the students begin working on their brochures, show the DVD segments *Human Menstrual Cycle* and *Conception*. The first is an animated segment that shows the female reproductive system, the events that occur during the menstrual cycle, and the effects of hormones on development of an ovum and on the uterine lining. The second is a combination of animation and live footage that shows the events surrounding conception, including the male reproductive system, fertilization, and early development of the zygote with implantation in the uterus.

As students work on their brochures, remind them of the criteria listed in their books and the rubric. Many students likely will think that the brochure only needs to be something like those found in doctors' offices or on the Internet that compare the relative effectiveness of different methods. Emphasize that this brochure must explain and compare the biological reasons as to why their chosen methods reduce the chance of conception.

Walk around the room and be available for individual questions that may arise from the essays or other resources. Look for opportunities to help students make connections back to the concept of homeostasis in Unit 2 where they learned some basics about regulation and communication between body systems. For example, as students look at the *Human Menstrual Cycle* animation on the DVD, ask them to recall some roles of hormones that they learned in Unit 2.

Encourage the learners to use the essays and additional materials that you supply as resources. Take this opportunity to assess the students' current understanding of the concepts.

Both DVD segments, *Human Menstrual Cycle* and *Conception*, are animations that provide day-by-day or stage-by-stage images of these processes. If students use the video workstation on their own, be available to answer questions about using the video or about the material.

Analysis

Assign the analysis questions as homework if time is short. After the learners complete the questions, convene a brief class discussion and use the following expected responses as a guide:

1. The word *progesterone* means "to promote gestation." *Estrogen* means "to generate estrus." Explain why these are appropriate names. What do you think the prefix *contra-*, as in *contraception*, means?

   Progesterone essentially maintains pregnancy while estrogen sets up the chances for fertilization. The prefix *contra-* means "against."

2. Explain the role that gametes play in sexual reproduction. How do they assure the *continuity of information* that must take place for a species to survive?

   In sexual reproduction, genetic information for producing offspring comes from two individuals. Special reproductive cells (gametes) have half the information of normal cells. The combination of two gametes then provides the appropriate amount of genetic information.

3. Consider the rhythm method of birth control. Explain how a couple that desires children could modify and use it to increase the chances of conception.

   As the students work on their explanations, remind them that they should use any resources that they wish. Take this opportunity to assess their ability to use information to develop an explanation.

4. Imagine that a couple wants to have children. But tests show that the man has a low sperm count and the female has blocked oviducts. Read the short essay *Infertility* on page 486 for background information. In your journal, explain whether the use of pharmaceutical drugs alone will improve their chances for beginning a pregnancy.

   Expect the students to realize that while there may be pharmaceutical methods for improving the male's sperm count, these drugs will not unblock the female's oviducts.

Further Challenges

1. Research and report on current progress in developing oral contraceptives for men.

2. Research and report on current technological methods that are being used to assist couples who are having difficulties conceiving a child.

   The Internet and current medical journals provide resources that you may wish to direct your students to use for their research.

Observing Reproductive Behavior in Nonhuman Animals

Major Concepts Mating behavior in nonhuman species; evolutionary implications of mating behaviors

Overview

In this activity, students use a variety of video observations to compare and contrast the mating behaviors of a variety of animals. The students view DVD segments that present the mating behaviors of sharp-tailed grouse, elephant seals, and Siamese fighting fish. The students use their observations and the essay *Mating Behaviors of Nonhuman Animals* as resources to study the adaptive advantages that specific mating behaviors provide.

Materials   (per class of 30, teams of 4)

DVD
DVD player

Outcomes and Indicators of Success

The following indicators allow you to assess the students' level of success with the activity and to assess their process of learning.

By the end of this activity, the learners should understand the importance of behavior in the reproduction of nonhuman animals.

They will demonstrate their understanding by comparing and contrasting what they have learned about human mating behavior with other animals' behaviors that they observe on the DVD.

Background Information

Sharp-tailed grouse. Male grouse perform a mating dance that attracts the females. Male sharp-tailed grouse perform an elaborate dance that includes very rapid foot stomping, rattling tail feathers, and moving in almost perfect unison with other males. As the males go through their ritual, the females move through the area and appear almost to ignore the males.

Elephant seal. The northern elephant seal breeds on islands from central California to central Baja California. Males grow to a length of 420 cm (14 ft) and weigh about 2,300 kg (5,071 lb). Females grow to 310 cm (10 ft) and weigh about 900 kg (1,984 lb). Males develop pendulous nasal cavities and emit threatening vocalizations as they establish their status and their right to breed. See the DVD guide on the *TRCD* for more information.

Siamese fighting fish. The natural habitat of Siamese fighting fish is slow-moving water with dense plant growth. Before mating, the male drives away other males and builds a bubble nest. During fertilization, the male wraps himself around the female and squeezes her, which forces out her eggs. The male fish captures the fertilized eggs in his mouth and places them in the bubble nest. He watches the eggs and drives away any other male fighting fish. However, he completely ignores other species of fish that feed on the eggs.

Preparations

Again, *The Nature of Sex* video series includes many intriguing segments on insects, birds, and fish. Preview some segments and select a few to share with the class. For information about the video, see the Advance Preparation for this chapter.

Strategies for Guiding Learners

PROCESS AND PROCEDURES

As a class, read orally or silently all introductory materials for the activity and the Process and Procedures to help students build connections between concepts and activities. Use the time spent reading to bring the students' attention into focus.

1. Study the mating behavior of the animals in the DVD segment "Animal Mating Behaviors." In your journal, record your observations.

   Have the students watch the segment "Animal Mating Behaviors" on the DVD. Direct them to take notes in their journals about their observations. This segment includes live footage of mating behavior in three organisms: sharp-tailed grouse, elephant seals, and Siamese fighting fish.

2. Read the essay *Mating Behaviors of Nonhuman Animals* on page 486. Take brief notes about the advantages and disadvantages of showy mating behavior.

   Encourage the students to make note of the particular sexual mating behavior roles that males and females tend to exhibit.

Analysis

Work individually to answer the following questions. Record your responses in your journal.

1. List three showy mating behaviors in nonhuman animals that were not used as examples in the essay *Mating Behaviors of Nonhuman Animals*.

   Expect that students may list behaviors such as those seen in peacocks, elk, turkeys, or other familiar species.

2. For each of the mating behavior examples listed above, explain one benefit and one cost each behavior brings to the individual organisms or populations who exhibit the behavior.

   Refer specifically to the behaviors that you have chosen. Explain whether the costs and benefits affect the individual, the population, or both.

   Students should recognize how showy displays and/or fighting are expensive in terms of expended energy, lost time, susceptibility to predators, and injury. Benefits should include explanations for how such behaviors indicate that the organism displaying the behavior is healthy and strong. Potential mates select these individuals because these matings tend to increase the likelihood of having healthy and able-bodied offspring.

Cultural Influences on Human Mating Behavior

Skip

Major Concepts   Cultural aspects of human mating behavior

Overview

The students use the materials they gathered to prepare a team display that shows how various aspects of popular culture influence human mating behaviors. The students also compare patterns of mate selection in America today with patterns 200 years ago.

Materials   (per class of 30, teams of 4)

scissors
poster board or large sheets of paper
tape
glue
materials the students collected earlier

Outcomes and Indicators of Success

The following indicators allow you to assess the students' level of success with the activity and to assess their process of learning.

By the end of this activity, the learners should be able to relate the concept of mating behaviors to certain rites, rituals, and practices in human culture.

They will demonstrate their ability by

a. creating a display that illustrates examples of mating behaviors in American culture,

b. showing how aspects of the culture influence related behaviors, and

c. comparing present-day mating behaviors in America to those that existed 200 years ago.

Preparations

As mentioned in Advance Preparation for the chapter, have students begin ahead of time to collect materials related to cultural ideas of human attractiveness. The students likely will find material in magazines and in advertisements in a variety of sources. They also might collect lyrics or photographs, for example.

TV (MTV in particular), movies, books, and magazines will provide examples of various clothing, health and cosmetic products, or other items designed to enhance human attractiveness. Remind students to make detailed written observations from media that cannot be brought into class. Students may find examples in advertisements for various health products or home exercise equipment, items enhancing human "mating displays," advertisements for other products that use a youth and vigor or "dating" orientation, and articles about the many aspects of courting behavior. Encourage the students to be observant and resourceful.

Strategies for Guiding Learners

PROCESS AND PROCEDURES

As a class, read orally or silently all introductory materials for the activity and the Process and Procedures to help students build connections between concepts and activities. Use the time spent reading to bring the students' attention into focus.

1. Use the materials that you have collected to create a display that demonstrates various cultural behaviors associated with human reproduction. You may focus on either American (USA) culture or another culture that you know something about. Include characteristics of human behavior that you think are similar to those of other animals and those that you think are distinctive.

   Include at least 5 different types of cultural influences on your poster. Consider both modern influences, like the subtle messages included in television commercials, and long-standing influences that have been in our culture for many generations.

   Read and use the 2 essays *Human Mating Behaviors* (page 489) and *Cultures and Mating Patterns* (page 489), and any other valid resource to support your claims. Reading about cultures other than your own helps you realize the variety of patterns that exist. This often helps you observe your own culture more objectively.

   Before the students begin work on their displays, you may want to review the materials that they have collected to be sure that they are appropriate for the classroom. Encourage the students to use the essay to learn about mating behaviors in other cultures. Depending on your time constraints, you may provide class time for students to complete these displays, or you may ask that they work outside of class to complete them.

2. Set up your display in your classroom.

3. Study the displays of other teams. Look for patterns in the cultural influences that lead to human mating behaviors.

   Remember that you are looking for patterns about behaviors that might lead to mating, not about the mechanisms of mating.

   After the learners have set up their displays, ask them to study the displays of other teams. Encourage them to take notes on the range of items in the displays and to note items or patterns that they did not include in their own. Ask them to summarize their critiques in two or three paragraphs in their journals. You might have them work in their teams or individually as they complete step 3.

Analysis

Work in your team to respond to the following. Record your responses in your journal, and be prepared to discuss your responses with the class.

After the teams have completed their review of the displays, have them discuss the analysis questions and record their responses in their journals.

1. List the various aspects of American culture that you think most influence human mating behaviors today. For example, you may think American music has an important influence.

   In addition to American music, the students also might indicate that television, MTV, the movie and entertainment industry, popular literature, the church, and cultural attitudes about health influence mating behaviors today.

2. Compare and contrast human mate selection in the United States 200 years ago with mate selection today. Explain three specific examples of changes in American culture that contributed to differences in mate selection now and then.

Expect students to respond with ideas similar to the following. Two hundred years ago, the average American woman probably considered how much land a man had, what type of livestock he owned, how strong he was, how healthy he was, and how hard he worked. The average American man probably considered how strong a woman was, how healthy she was, and whether he thought she would provide him with children.

Today, the average American woman might consider how independent a man is, how much money he earns, what he does for a living, what type of car he owns, how big of a house he owns, whether or not he wants children, and whether they have common interests. The average man might consider how self-sufficient a woman is, what she does for a living, what type of car she owns, how big of a house she owns, whether or not she wants children, and whether they have common interests.

Many students will indicate that some qualities probably have not changed much across time. For example, how attracted one person is to another, how smart they are, and how similar their religious and political beliefs are qualities that may have been important 200 years ago and are still important today.

Further Challenges

These two Further Challenges provide an opportunity for the students to explore different aspects of human sexual behavior in more detail.

1. An ongoing debate in the scientific community is whether or not most human sexual behavior is biologically based. Research the scientific literature to learn about this debate. Report the conclusions that your evidence supports.

2. In the United States, families historically use the surname of the father. Perhaps for this reason, Americans may think automatically of the male as the head of the household. That view, however, is changing as most women now work outside the home. Males do not play the same role in all cultures. For instance, among some Native American tribes in the Pacific Northwest, each tribe is composed of clans that are linked through the mothers' lines.

Consider the following observations. Then discuss how societies draw their conclusions about the importance of men and women.

◆ A human embryo automatically develops with female characteristics unless it receives male hormones such as testosterone very soon after conception.

◆ The ancient Greek philosopher Aristotle suggested that the female is a defective male because she does not have a penis.

A Reproductive Strategy for Your Critter

Major Concepts
Relationship between reproduction and continuity; mechanisms for reproduction; regulation of reproduction

Overview

In this activity, learners apply their understanding of reproductive strategies to their critter as they develop a detailed description of their critter's method of reproduction. In the Analysis, the learners have a chance to further evaluate their knowledge and understanding of the major concepts in the chapter by expanding the visual representation that they created earlier in the chapter.

Materials   (per class of 30, individuals)

descriptions and diagrams of your critter from previous chapters
30 felt-tipped marking pens
30 large sheets of paper
30 copies of the rubric *Your Critter's Reproductive Strategy*

Outcomes and Indicators of Success

The following indicators allow you to assess the students' level of success with the activity and to assess their process of learning.

By the end of this activity, the learners should

1. be able to apply their understanding of reproductive mechanisms to a novel organism.

   They will demonstrate their ability by writing a detailed description of their critter's method of reproduction.

2. have a deeper understanding of the relationship between reproduction and continuity of information within a species.

   They will demonstrate this understanding by revising their visual representation of the major chapter concepts that they created earlier in the chapter.

Preparations

In using the scoring rubric, make any changes that you want, duplicate it, and distribute it to the students before they begin their work.

Strategies for Guiding Learners

PROCESS AND PROCEDURES

As a class, read orally or silently all introductory materials for the activity and the Process and Procedures to help students build connections between concepts and activities. Use the time spent reading to bring the students' attention into focus.

CHAPTER 11 IMPLEMENTATION

	Instructional Flow			Classroom Support			
Activity/ Student Text pp. Teacher Guide pp.	GACD, TRCD, DVD, and CD-ROM Resources	Essays/ Student Text pp.	Estimated Time	Team Size/ Cooperative Learning Focus	Strategies and Tools	Assessment Opportunities	Special Considerations
ENGAGE Gifts from Your Parents pp. 418–419 TG pp. 392–394			30 minutes	*Team size:* individuals and class *Skill:* Sharing perspectives	Class discussion	Prior knowledge of molecular basis for heredity concepts	Enlarge print materials and/or read aloud if needed.
EXPLORE Game of Chance pp. 420–426 TG pp. 395–403	DVD: *Yeast Monohybrid Cross, Parts 1–4*		50 minutes	*Team size:* 2 *Skill:* Synthesizing the team's ideas	Team discussions; video; wet lab	Prior knowledge of laboratory techniques; ability to follow lab protocol	Enlarge print materials if needed. Plan partners so that students with visual or fine motor control difficulty can rely on their partner if needed.
EXPLORE/ EXPLAIN Understanding Patterns of Inheritance pp. 427–431 TG pp. 403–409		*Phenotype and Genotype* pp. 492–495; *Case Studies of Two Genetic Disorders* pp. 496–498	100 minutes	*Team size:* 2 *Skill:* Sharing perspectives	Team discussions; class discussion	Prior knowledge of genetics vocabulary and concepts; current understanding of the molecular basis of heredity	Enlarge print materials and/or read aloud if needed.
EXPLAIN Understanding Inherited Patterns pp. 431–433 TG pp. 409–414	DVD: *Meiosis*	*Meiosis: The Mechanism behind Patterns of Inheritance* pp. 498–502	75 minutes	*Team size:* 2 *Skill:* Taking responsibility	Video; paper lab with modeling clay models	Making connections between related ideas; using models to construct explanations	Plan ahead for students who have difficulty with vision or fine motor control to have partners who can assist in constructing the chromosomes for the meiosis model if needed.
EXPLAIN/ ELABORATE Can You Sort It Out? pp. 434–437 TG pp. 414–420	DVD: *Mendel's Peas, Parts 1–5*, and *Crossing Over*; Copymaster: *Mendel's Data*		75 minutes	*Team size:* 2 *Skill:* Sharing perspectives	Video; paper lab; team discussions; class discussion	Applying understanding to new situations	Enlarge print materials and/or read aloud if needed.
ELABORATE The Genetic Basis of Human Variation pp. 437–440 TG pp. 420–426		*The Role of Variation in Evolution* pp. 503–507; *Genetic Complexity* pp. 507–510	75 minutes	*Team size:* Individual and 2 *Skill:* Contributing ideas	Paper lab; class discussion	Using graphs to construct explanations; applying understandings to new situations	Enlarge print materials and/or read aloud if needed.

Instructional Flow   **Classroom Support**

Activity/ Student Text pp. Teacher Guide pp.	GACD, TRCD, DVD, and CD-ROM Resources	Essays/ Student Text pp.	Estimated Time	Team Size/ Cooperative Learning Focus	Strategies and Tools	Assessment Opportunities	Special Considerations
EVALUATE *Continuity and Change* pp. 440–443 TG pp. 426–431	Copymaster *Yeast Reproduction;* Rubric: *Yeast Experiment Analysis;* Rubric: *Continuity and Change*	*Incomplete Dominance* pp. 510–511	100 minutes	*Team size:* 2 and individuals *Skill:* Taking responsibility	Team discussions; experimental analysis; journal entries	Synthesizing ideas; applying understandings to new situations	Enlarge print materials and/or read aloud if needed. Some students may be better able to show their understanding of the chapter's concepts by presenting their yeast experiment results and analyses of Part B orally.

Chapter Goals

By the end of this chapter, students should understand that

- the flow of genetic information from one generation to the next provides continuity for species;
- the genotype of an organism limits the range of potential phenotypes;
- the environment plays an important role in determining phenotype;
- there are biological mechanisms that account for the predictability and variability of genetic patterns; and
- genetics plays a role in determining complex traits such as behavior.

The learners also will

- make observations;
- use models to help develop explanations;
- use probability to make predictions;
- collect, analyze, and summarize data, using the appropriate sampling size; and
- interpret data to develop explanations.

Advance Preparation

Review the flowcharts for this chapter and preview all DVD segments. You need to arrange for a DVD player for the Yeast Genetics Protocol, which you will use at the end of the activity *Game of Chance.* You also need the DVD player for the activities *Understanding Inherited Patterns* and *Can You Sort It Out?*

Embedded in this cycle of activities is a yeast genetics experiment. You need to prepare some starter plates before the students begin their work. Begin the actual experiment around the time the students are finishing the activity *Game of Chance.* You may decide to begin it earlier. Review the list of materials for this experiment to ensure that you will have everything that you need. Also review both the student and teacher versions of the Yeast Genetics Protocol before the students begin this procedure. The estimated times we indicate on the implementation chart for each activity do not take into account the embedded yeast lab. Consult the timeline in Figure T11.1 on page 389 for times that include the embedded yeast lab.

Timeline for Yeast Genetics Protocol

The Yeast Genetics Protocol allows students to experience a hands-on genetics experiment within the framework of activities that develop the concepts in the chapter. The students apply their understanding of genetic principles to the results of their yeast experiments during the evaluate activity. This experiment is presented as a separate protocol. Figure T11.1 suggests a timeline for the protocol that integrates it with the activities. If you do not have an incubator, you will need to start the protocol earlier than indicated here. If the students' plates are incubated at room temperature, allow 2 days for the yeast to grow at each step. This species will grow faster in a 30°C incubator (optimal temperature for this species of yeast), and each growth step will take only 1 day. Day 3 should begin on a Monday, Tuesday, Thursday, or Friday to allow completion of incubation on a school day. Make adjustments as needed, depending on the pacing of the activities in your class. See Preparations for details.

Figure T11.1 Timeline* for yeast genetics protocol

Activity	Yeast protocol	
Patterns of Inheritance (100 min)	Streak Plate I for students, and incubate it overnight.	
Yeast Genetics Protocol	Day 0	Students examine yeast microscopically, prepare Plate II (replate the mating types and make a mating mix), and incubate 3 hours, then refrigerate (or vice versa).
Yeast Genetics Protocol	Day 1	Students examine Plate II, examine mating mixture microscopically, prepare Plate III (subculture on MIN medium, both mating types and the mating mix), and incubate overnight.
Understanding Inherited Patterns (150 min)	Day 2	Students examine Plate III, examine mating mixture microscopically, prepare Plate IV (subculture mating mixture on YED medium), and incubate overnight. (This is the presporulation plate.)
Understanding Inherited Patterns	Day 3	Students prepare Plate V (streak subculture from Plate IV to "unknown" medium) and incubate it at room temperature 3 or more days.
Understanding Inherited Patterns/Can You Sort It Out?	Day 4	Incubate Plate V.
Can You Sort It Out? (75 min)	Day 5	Incubate Plate V.
The Genetic Basis of Human Variation (150 min)	Day 6	Incubate Plate V.
The Genetic Basis of Human Variation	Day 7	Students examine yeast from Plate V microscopically, prepare Plate VI (transfer from Plate V), and incubate it 5 hours, then refrigerate (or vice versa).
The Genetic Basis of Human Variation	Day 8	Students examine colonies on Plate VI and examine cells microscopically.

*Timeline includes the yeast protocol time plus the activity and is based on incubation at 30°C. Times will double if the yeast is incubated at normal room temperature. If you do not have an incubator, allow 2 days for each step except sporulation (Plate V).

If you cannot provide this wet-lab experience for your students, the DVD segment *Yeast Monohybrid Cross* shows the procedures that are included in the protocol and the expected results. Use this segment to support a dry-lab version of the protocol at the beginning of the activity *Continuity and Change*. The concepts developed in the protocol are important to the students' understanding of genetics.

Yeast Genetics Protocol

This *Saccharomyces cerevisiae* (baker's yeast) life-cycle experiment involves the mating of two haploid strains, zygote formation and budding, sporulation, and return to the haploid state. The experiment connects Chapter 11 to Chapters 10 and 12 by serving as a bridge between the discussion of reproduction and the underlying molecular concepts of genetics. It also serves as a simple prelude to development and differentiation (Unit 5). For example, the production of four yeast spores in an ascus is a visible result of meiosis, and the development of a gamete from a haploid cell in response to the mating pheromone is a visible example of differentiation. The procedures introduce simple microbiological techniques and provide experience in preparing samples and observing them under the microscope.

If the students' plates are incubated at room temperature, allow 2 days for the yeast to grow at each step. This species will grow faster in a 30°C incubator (optimal temperature for this species of yeast), and each growth step will take only 1 day. Sporulation requires 3–4 days at either room temperature or at 30°C but is strongly inhibited by higher temperatures. You can hold the experiment in the refrigerator at almost any stage. It is preferable to refrigerate after mating and zygote formation (step 4), not before. Arrange for students in afternoon classes to refrigerate plates from morning classes for steps 5 and 26. After sporulation, you can keep the cultures for more than a week at room temperature; after that, store the cultures in the refrigerator for future use.

Engage

Gifts from Your Parents

Major Concepts Inheritance of genetic information (continuity); acquired versus inherited traits; generation-skipping traits

Overview

From Chapter 10 to this chapter, learners move from thinking about reproduction as a way of perpetuating species to understanding the underlying mechanisms that account for continuity of information. The opening story describes the transmission of hemophilia through the royal families of Europe and Russia in the early 1900s. This interesting story engages the learners in thinking about traits that people possess, how these traits are inherited, and the fact that not all traits appear in all generations. The learners draw on some of their own experiences as well as information presented in the story. They should make the connection that continuity exists because genetic information is passed on through inheritance.

Outcomes and Indicators of Success

The following indicators allow you to assess the students' level of success with the activity and to assess their process of learning.

By the end of this activity, the learners should

1. be interested in the phenomenon of inheritance.

    They will indicate their interest through participating in a discussion of inheritance questions.

2. become aware that some traits are inherited and can be traced in family lineage, that inherited traits are not necessarily expressed at each generation, and that traits can be acquired or genetically determined.

    They will demonstrate their awareness by using these ideas in their responses to questions of inheritance, including examples of acquired and inherited traits.

Strategies for Guiding Learners

PROCESS AND PROCEDURES

As a class, read orally or silently all introductory materials for the activity and the Process and Procedures to help students build connections between concepts and activities. Use the time spent reading to bring the students' attention into focus.

1. Read *A Royal Tragedy*. This story describes a disease that was inherited through several famous families.

   Allow the learners 5–10 minutes to read the story; then guide them through a short (5-minute) discussion to bring out the pertinent points. Make certain that they understand why the czarina suspected her family of passing down the hemophilia trait (examining a lineage offers clues to the inheritance of traits). That parents and children have similar traits is certainly not a new idea for learners; they will have had personal experience with these similarities, so do not belabor the point. Use this opportunity to help learners begin to question how this similarity occurs. By contrast, the learners may not be familiar with traits that skip generations and reappear later in a lineage.

   Link the genetic ideas in the story to the learners' personal experience by spending about 5–10 minutes determining whether they have any of the following classic Mendelian traits:

   - Cleft chin—presence of a dimple in the chin
   - Camptodactyly—"bent pinky syndrome"; the presence of a digit or digits that bend noticeably toward the other fingers
   - Mid-digital hair—the presence of hair on the middle section of a finger

   Emphasize to the learners that these traits are shared by many of us and are not considered abnormalities. Other traits that are not classic Mendelian traits but that may be interesting as well include detached ear lobes and freckles. Distinguish that the quantity of freckles has an environmental component. A somewhat more colorful trait, but one that is potentially more disruptive to classroom decorum, is the genetically controlled ability to produce smelly urine after eating asparagus and the genetically controlled ability to smell the odiferous urine that some people produce after eating asparagus. For an interesting summary of the genetics underlying these two abilities, see Jay Ingrams' book *The Science of Everyday Life* published by Viking.

   Challenge the learners to establish a link between these traits and inheritance from parents. Include learners who may be adopted or otherwise unfamiliar with their biological parents by having them describe acquired traits or speculate what their own offspring may inherit from them.

2. Discuss the following questions as a class:

   Wrap up the story by leading a 10-minute discussion of the questions. Once the learners suggest that inheritance is the reason that Czarevitch Alexis became ill, go on to the question about why his parents were not afflicted. Learners may not have a clear idea why this is so or they may reiterate, without knowing the reason, the czarina's concern that the disease came from her side of the family. Use student answers to help you gauge their current understanding of genetics. At this time, it is only important that the learners realize that some traits can appear in some generations and then be absent for some time. They may be able to offer some examples from their own experience. If learners ask why Alexis's sisters were not affected, ask them to speculate, then tell them that they will learn why later in the chapter.

Finally, you may need to help learners recognize how they can distinguish acquired traits from inherited ones. For example, you might ask, Can scars be inherited? How do you know this? Examples of acquired traits that learners suggest will involve environmental factors, and you should encourage them to recognize this distinction.

a. How did the young czarevitch come to have hemophilia?

> The young czarevitch was afflicted with hemophilia because he inherited it from his mother's side of the family.

b. How is it possible that the mother and father showed no signs of the disease?

> The learners may answer that they don't know why the czarevitch's parents didn't have the disease. Some may suggest that the disease was hidden in the parents but visible in the boy. Or, if they have some prior knowledge, they may realize that the mother carried the gene for hemophilia on one of her X chromosomes, but did not have the disorder because she carried an allele for normal clotting on her other X chromosome.

c. Suggest some traits that people acquire during their lifetime. What is the difference between acquired traits and inherited traits?

> Scars, cosmetic changes in hair or eye color, accident-induced limps, tans and freckles caused by the sun, and so forth are all examples of acquired traits. Genetic factors for inherited traits are present at birth, whereas acquired traits arise as the result of accidents or intentional changes that occur after birth. Classifying these traits is not always easy, however, because some traits that appear long after birth, such as the shuffling gait of someone with osteoarthritis, have an inherited (genetic) component as well.

d. How might cultural practices have influenced the frequency of hemophilia occurring among the czar's family?

> Because members of the royal families of 19th-century Europe often intermarried, the frequent occurrence of hemophilia and the number of carriers was unusually high.

Extensions

As a supplement to the story of the Romanovs, you might suggest that the learners construct their own family trees (genealogies). This task would personalize the technique and further engage their interest as they begin the study of genetics. Computer software to aid in constructing family trees is available.

Game of Chance

Major Concepts Probability and sample size

Overview

In this activity, students use data from coin tosses and rabbit crosses to explore the role of probability in predicting outcomes and the effect of sample size when testing such predictions. To achieve a large sample size for the coin tossing process, students from different teams combine data. Students also begin their wet lab with yeast to help them experience genetic principles in living organisms.

Materials (per class of 30, teams of 2)

15 coins
15 calculators
overhead projector and transparency (optional)

Outcomes and Indicators of Success

The following indicators allow you to assess the students' level of success with the activity and to assess their process of learning.

By the end of this activity, the learners should have a working understanding of the importance of sample size and how it affects conclusions based on statistical relationships.

They will demonstrate their understanding by

    a. explaining why predicted and actual results may differ in the flipping of coins and in genetic crosses,

    b. stating the importance of sample size with regard to how well actual results match predictions that are based on probability, and

    c. evaluating a mock medical study that relies on a small sample size.

Preparations

Have students begin the Yeast Genetics Protocol as soon as they finish this activity. See Timeline for Yeast Genetics Protocol and Figure T11.1 (page 389 of this teacher's guide) in the Preparations at the beginning of this chapter for timing and initial preparations.

Begin each day with the yeast protocol and weave in the parts of the activity as time best allows. More time will be necessary on the 1st day of the experiment because students must watch a video segment, familiarize themselves with the protocol, and use the microscope to observe 5 yeast cells.

The Yeast Genetics Protocol provides the opportunity for students to set up a real genetic experiment, collect their own data, and relate genetic principles to living organisms. This experiment continues through several activities, so you will need to allow time as indicated in Figure T11.1. The protocol format helps students recognize coherent steps in an experiment.

The learners use colored beans for the next activity, *Patterns of Inheritance*. Purchase red and white beans at a supermarket.

Strategies for Guiding Learners

PROCESS AND PROCEDURES

As a class, read orally or silently all introductory materials for the activity and the Process and Procedures to help students build connections between concepts and activities. Use the time spent reading to bring the students' attention into focus.

This activity is an exploration of simple probability and the importance of sample size. Keep the students moving quickly through the early steps.

1. Work with your teammate to solve the following problems. Record your answers in your journal.

   a. A pair of rabbits mated and produced 10 offspring. How many males and how many females would you predict are in those offspring?

   Explain how you made your prediction. Did you need additional information?

   Students probably will suggest that half (five) will be females and half (five) will be males.

   b. Even if you are reasonably confident that your prediction is correct, can you guarantee how many males and females will be born in the litter? Explain your answer.

   One cannot make any guarantees because it is a chance process, and with such a small sample size, it is likely that the ratio of females to males will not be exactly 1:1. Avoid the temptation to tell students this. It is better that they discover it for themselves as this activity progresses. Instead, pay attention to the students' answers because many misconceptions exist about probability. You need to be aware of these misconceptions to help students gain an accurate understanding.

2. Test your prediction by using a coin to simulate the sex of the 10 offspring.

   a. In your journal, prepare a table to record your team's predicted and actual results.

   b. Flip the coin 10 times. Record your results.

   c. Explain the role of chance in determining your results.

   Flipping coins is much like sex determination in rabbits. For each coin flip, there is a 50 percent chance that it will land heads up. Because each flip is a chance event, there is no guarantee that five (and only five) of the flips will produce heads.

   The idea in steps 1 and 2 (that male/female distributions are normally about 1:1) is fairly intuitive, although students likely do not yet have any genetic basis for understanding this.

3. Look at the data under the heading Small Sample Size in the need to know box titled Results of Rabbit Matings. These data show the results of 3 rabbit matings. Discuss the following with your teammate:

   a. Do these results match your predictions from step 1 or your test results from step 2? Explain your answer.

   b. The result of each of these 3 crosses obviously is not the same. Explain why the actual outcomes vary from 50 percent males and 50 percent females.

Learners should come to understand that the results often will vary from those predicted, and individual trials will not necessarily come out the same. These variations are due to chance. This step provides you with an opportunity to assess the students' understanding of these concepts.

4. Next, investigate the relationship between probable outcomes, actual results, and sample size. Examine the data under the heading Large Sample Size in Results of Rabbit Matings. Note that the total number of offspring is 600. Calculate the percentage of male rabbits for each group of 600 offspring. Record these results in your journal.

Percentage males = [(# males) ÷ (total # offspring)] × 100.

    Trial 1: 46.5% males, 53.5% females
    Trial 2: 49.3% males, 50.7% females
    Trial 3: 52.7% males, 47.3% females

Learners may need help or practice in calculating percentages.

5. Answer the following questions with your teammate. Record the answers in your journal.

  a. Are these results generally closer to 50 percent than those in the small sample size (step 3)? Explain your answer.

  b. Based on your observation, what effect does sample size have on the match between probable outcomes and actual results?

      Learners should realize quickly that actual results normally will match predicted results more closely when larger samples are used.

6. You can test the accuracy of large sample sizes by generating your own data with coins and combining the data of the entire class.

  a. This time, instead of flipping the coin 10 times, flip it 20 times. Record the results in your table from step 2.

  b. What is the percentage of heads for this sample size of 20 flips?

  c. Contribute your data to a class data table that your teacher develops on the chalkboard.

  d. What is the percentage of heads for this large sample size?

  e. What do these results suggest about the effect of sample size on the match between probable outcomes and actual results?

      Draw a table on the chalkboard that allows you to organize the results of the entire class when the students flip coins. Calculate the percentages so that learners with weak math skills can follow the logic. Learners should record these numbers in their journals so that they can compare the match between predicted and actual outcomes of small versus large sample sizes in question 6e. Make certain that the students see that as the number of events increases, the match between actual and predicted results improves.

      Listen for statements that indicate any learner misconceptions about how probability operates. A common misconception is that the *probability* of an event is an advance statement of what the actual results will be. This confusion may be particularly evident if the students have used Punnett squares in the past, which they often think demonstrate the actual distribution of traits in a generation rather than the *likelihood* of a particular distribution. For this reason,

we introduce the importance of sample size in narrowing the gap between statistically predicted results and actual results and leave the Punnett squares for the activity *Can You Sort It Out?* Continue to emphasize the important distinction between probable and actual outcomes.

Analysis

1. Use what you have learned about the importance of sample size to evaluate the following medical study reported in a local newspaper.

    > "A study reported in the medical journal *Acta Artifacta* appears to link ownership of fast cars with premature balding. The study, consisting of 17 men who own sports cars, found that nearly 60 percent suffered from premature balding. The authors of the study conclude that because this percentage of balding is much higher than in the general population, there is an increased chance of suffering from premature baldness if one owns a fast car."

    Student answers should include some discussion of the fact that a sample size of 17 is very small. Better answers might take this reasoning further by indicating that it might be a coincidence that 10 out of these 17 men are bald. The report doesn't indicate how these men were chosen, so we don't know if it was a random selection method or some less random method. Ultimately, large sample sizes are more effective at showing precise matches between predicted and actual outcomes, and additional information would help determine whether the correlation in this case is valid or just a random effect due to a small sample size. (Some students also might notice that the authors of the study incorrectly equate correlation with cause and effect.)

2. If you flip a coin five times and get heads every time, what is the probability that you will get tails on the next flip?

    The results of past chance events, such as coin flips, have no effect on future chance events, such as the outcome of subsequent flips. Therefore, the probability of getting tails on the next flip is 50 percent regardless of the outcomes of previous flips.

Yeast Genetics

Timeline for Yeast Genetics Protocol

The Yeast Genetics Protocol is presented as a separate protocol. Figure T11.1 on page 389 of this teacher's guide suggests a timeline for the protocol that integrates it with the activities. **See Preparations at the beginning of Chapter 11 for details on preparing for this activity.** This activity will take most of 2 weeks, depending on the incubation temperature. Plan to devote 15–30 minutes of the class period for each of the 6 days that students actually carry out procedures.

Always incubate the plates upside down so that condensation does not drip onto the agar surface. If there is condensation on the lid after refrigeration, keep the plates upside down while you remove the lid and wipe out the condensation with a clean tissue. Alternatively, keep the plates upside down while you remove the lid and, with a flick of the wrist, whip the water out of the lid.

If the students' plates are incubated at room temperature, allow 2 days for the yeast to grow at each step. This species will grow faster in a 30°C incubator (optimal temperature for this species of yeast), and each growth step will take only 1 day. Sporulation requires 3–4 days at either room temperature or at 30°C but is strongly inhibited by higher temperatures. You can hold the experiment in the refrigerator at almost any stage. It is preferable to refrigerate after mating and zygote formation (step 4), not before. Arrange for students in afternoon classes to refrigerate plates from morning classes for steps 5 and 26. After sporulation, you can keep the cultures for more than a week at room temperature; after that, store the cultures in the refrigerator for future use.

If you would like your students to examine the progressive stages of yeast mating in step 4, direct them to make their mating mixtures, incubate for 1 hour, and then transfer plates to the refrigerator at 1/2-hour intervals during a 2-hour period. Different teams can prepare and seal slides from different times and then take turns observing each other's preparations. Sealing the edges of the coverslip with clear nail polish stops the streaming that often occurs, and preserves the preparation for several days. Store the slides flat because they can leak.

Strategies for Guiding Learners

Yeast Genetics Protocol

The complete Yeast Genetics Protocol is on pages 423–426 of the student text. Some sections of that protocol are included here with accompanying teacher's notes.

Day 0

1. Observe the techniques in the DVD segment "Yeast Monohybrid Cross."

    These techniques will help you perform the steps in this experiment.

    Show the first part (Making a Genetic Cross) of the DVD segment " Yeast Monohybrid Cross," which demonstrates the techniques that students will use to streak the cells on a fresh plate and to make the mating mixture (see the DVD guide on the *TRCD*).

    Stop the segment at this point, and have the students perform this procedure and incubate the plates overnight.

    Give each team an agar plate that you have prestreaked with mating types a (pink strain) and α (cream strain), and proceed as directed in the protocol.

    The remainder of the segment shows experimental results and may be helpful as the students discuss their results for each of the plates. The DVD guide identifies the day and step of the protocol for each of the plates; use the video as necessary to supplement the protocol for steps that do not produce expected results or that students cannot complete due to lack of time. The DVD segment "Yeast Reproduction" (Chapter 10) also may be useful as background information for the students.

Day 1

    Expect responses such as the following to the questions in the Procedures:

7. Examine Plate II. Discuss the following with your partner:

    ◆ What is the phenotype of the mating mixture?
        Cream colored. Cream color is the dominant form of the color trait.

◆ After you have completed *Patterns of Inheritance,* Part A, compare the yeast phenotype results with the results of your bean cross. Which color bean is equivalent to the yeast **a** mating type?

> **The cream color of yeast strain a is equivalent to whichever bean color you designated as dominant (red in the example given).**

8. Use the procedure in step 2 to examine the mating mixture through the microscope.

   a. Sketch what you see. Compare it with your earlier drawings.

   b. Describe any differences in the types of cells you see. Explain why those changes may have taken place.

   > **The mating-type cells have become pear-shaped because of the influence of each other's pheromones. Some cells have fused by sticking together at their smaller ends. After fusion, the cell is shaped like a peanut. This peanut-shaped cell forms its first bud at the middle and resembles a fat cloverleaf. (The buds that are released from the fused cells are more oval in appearance than the buds released from cells that have not fused, although this is somewhat difficult to discern.)**

   > *Caution students not to expect to see a field full of zygotes; mating occurs with less than 50 percent efficiency.*

9. Make a subculture of mating type **a**, some of mating type **α**, and some of the mating mixture. Use sterile toothpicks to transfer the yeast to a MIN medium agar growth plate.

   Use the same pattern that you used on Plate II. Make the 2 different mating type streaks and the circular mating mixture colony in the middle. Discard used toothpicks in the waste bag.

10. Label this subculture *Plate III*, and add your names.

11. Invert the plate and incubate overnight.

12. Wash your hands thoroughly before leaving the laboratory.

Day 2

13. Examine Plate III. Discuss the following with your partner:

    ◆ What do you observe about the colonies on Plate III after incubation?

    > **Only the mating mixture grew on the MIN medium plate; the original mating types did not grow.**

    ◆ Explain how the information present in the fused cells differs from the information in either of the original mating types.

    > **Fusion of the cells has produced a new combined (diploid) genotype that allows the cells to grow on MIN medium. The mating type (haploid) cells individually do not have the genetic information necessary to grow on MIN medium. (In fact, the new diploid genotype makes up for specific genetic defects in the parent strains that make it impossible for them to grow on the MIN medium. Each parent has provided a function that is defective in the other.)**

Specifically, the pink strain HAR carries a genetic defect that renders it unable to make adenine (that is, to grow, it must have adenine in its growth medium) and the cream strain HBT carries a different genetic defect that renders it unable to make tryptophan (that is, to grow, it must have tryptophan in its growth medium). MIN medium does not contain either of these nutrients. The diploid strain that results from mating, however, is capable of making both nutrients because HAR can make tryptophan and HBT can make adenine (so these nutrients are not required in the medium). This process is called genetic complementation.

14. Use the procedure in step 2 to examine the freshly grown mating mixture in Plate III through the microscope.

15. Discuss the following with your partner:

    ◆ What types of cells are present? Sketch each type.

      The cells now visible are almost exclusively budding fused cells (cloverleaves).

    ◆ Have any of the types seen in step 8 disappeared? Explain what happened to them.

      The original round mating types and the pear-shaped cells cannot grow on MIN medium. Only the fused cells grow.

16. Make a subculture by transferring some of the mating mixture with a sterile toothpick to a fresh YED medium agar plate.

    a. Streak the cells in 1 horizontal line across the middle of the plate.

      Discard used toothpicks in the waste bag.

    b. Label this subculture *Plate IV*, and add your names.

    c. Invert the plate and incubate overnight.

17. Wash your hands thoroughly before leaving the laboratory.

Day 3

18. On a plate of "unknown" medium, make several thick streaks of the freshly grown subculture from Plate IV.

    Discard used toothpicks in the waste bag.

19. Label this culture *Plate V*, and add your names.

20. Invert the plate. Incubate at room temperature for 3 or more days.

21. Wash your hands thoroughly before leaving the laboratory.

Day 7

22. Use the procedure from step 2 to examine yeast from Plate V through the microscope.

    You may need to use the fine adjustment on the microscope to distinguish cells at different levels.

23. Discuss the following with your partner:

    ◆ What cell types are present now that were not present before? Sketch these cell types.

      Students should sketch the four products of meiosis enclosed in a sac.

    ◆ Compare these cell types with those you saw at other stages.

3. begin to understand the concepts of heterozygous, homozygous, dominant, and recessive.

   They will begin to demonstrate their understanding by

   a. identifying genetic patterns in their bean combinations as homozygous or heterozygous, and

   b. identifying the effect that different bean combinations had on the resulting trait.

4. understand the relationship between genotype and phenotype.

   They will show their understanding by

   a. explaining genetic patterns related to homozygous and heterozygous combinations of alleles in Huntington's disease and cystic fibrosis,

   b. applying the principle of independent assortment to a dihybrid cross of dogs, and

   c. explaining the role of the environment and genetic information in producing phenotype.

Preparations

You can purchase the red and white beans at a supermarket. The beans should be a uniform size. Place all beans in the container and mix them thoroughly. Designate one color (for example, red) to represent the allele for the dominant trait, straight ears, and designate the other color to represent the allele for the recessive trait, floppy ears. In this case, two white beans would confer floppy ears, but one or two red beans in a combination would confer the dominant phenotype of straight ears. On a sheet of poster board, a transparency, or a part of the chalkboard that you can cover, make a key that correlates the three color combinations with the straight-ear and floppy-ear phenotypes. For example, red/red or red/white leads to straight ears, and white/white leads to floppy ears. Do not use the terms *dominant* or *recessive* on this key or in discussions; students will apply these terms in Part A, step 7.

Strategies for Guiding Learners

PROCESS AND PROCEDURES

As a class, read orally or silently all introductory materials for the activity and the Process and Procedures to help students build connections between concepts and activities. Use the time spent reading to bring the students' attention into focus.

PART A   Inheritance of One Trait

1. Select 2 beans randomly from the container that your teacher provides.

   Walk around the room and allow each learner to select two beans at random from the hat or bucket. Make certain that learners cannot see the colors of the beans while making their selections.

2. In your journal, record the color of your beans. Whether your pair is homozygous or heterozygous.

   Each bean represents the genetic information in 1 of the parents. If the beans are the same color, the pair is **homozygous** (*homo* = same). If the beans are different colors, the pair is **heterozygous** (*hetero* = different).

The terms *heterozygous* and *homozygous* are introduced here because the beans are a concrete way to demonstrate these concepts, and the terms will be familiar to the learners when they encounter them in the readings.

3. Choose 1 bean randomly. Shake both in your hands, and then select 1 without looking.

Each parent contributes only half of his or her own genetic information to each offspring. Parents do not know which half they contribute.

4. Add this bean to the 1 your partner selected.

5. Record the color of the 2 beans in the new combination. Indicate whether the pair is homozygous or heterozygous.

The new bean combination represents the genetic information that will determine the condition of the ears in the rabbit offspring.

6. Use the color key that your teacher displays. List in your journal the ear trait that your beans corresponded to initially and finally.

   a. To which condition did your 1st bean combination correspond?

   b. To which condition did your partner's 1st bean combination correspond?

   c. To which condition did the new combination correspond?

     After the learners record their bean colors and form the new combination, show them the trait key. Many aspects of genetics are modeled in this exercise, but it is most important that the learners recognize that genetic information, which comes in different forms, contributes to physical traits and can be combined in different combinations. The terms *dominant* and *recessive* are not necessary for this connection and therefore are not introduced until the next step.

7. As part of a class discussion, use the key once again and the shared results of the class to consider the following:

   a. Did 1 bean color (which corresponds to 1 piece of inherited genetic information) have a greater influence in determining the ear trait than the other bean color?

   b. Read the essay *Phenotype and Genotype* (page 492). This essay introduces the genetic terminology you will need throughout the rest of this unit. In your journal, correctly label the combinations and conditions that you recorded in steps 2, 5, and 6 as phenotype or genotype.

   c. Using genetic terminology, write 1 paragraph that describes the events in steps 1–6.

     In step 7a, the students must share team results with the class to give all teams the opportunity to see how various color combinations correlate with ear type in rabbits. This sharing can be handled quickly by polling the different teams. The idea that one type of genetic information can be "more powerful" or influential than another type should come across to the students as they compare the color combinations from the class with the key. If it is not already apparent, help the students recognize this by asking them to think about examples from their personal experience. For instance, they may have noticed that the children of a blue-eyed parent and a brown-eyed parent nearly always have brown eyes, a case where the genetic information for brown eyes seems to be more influential. There is no reason to belabor the details. (Even though eye color often is taught as an example of simple Mendelian inheritance, eye color is actually a trait influenced by several genes, and several alleles per gene.)

PART B   Inheritance of Two Traits

1. Examine the tables in the need to know box titled Following the Inheritance of Two Traits. These tables show the results of a cross that follows 2 traits in rabbits: ear type (floppy ears or straight ears) and sex (female or male).

   Male rabbits that had floppy ears were mated with female rabbits that had floppy ears. The results for 100 offspring are shown.

2. Based solely on the results of this cross, what conclusions can you draw about these 2 traits?

   The inheritance of floppy and straight ears certainly does not occur in a 1:1 ratio like the inheritance of sex. All rabbits have floppy ears, regardless of sex, because both parents have floppy ears. There are nearly equal numbers of male and female rabbits.

   You might need to help students recognize that the inheritance of traits such as ear type is different from the inheritance of sex (inheritance of all traits does not occur in a simple 1:1 ratio with each cross).

3. Next, male rabbits that had straight ears were mated with female rabbits that had floppy ears. The results for 100 offspring are shown. Calculate the data for sex (female/male) and ear type (floppy ears/straight ears) as percentages.

   Percentage with trait = [(# with trait) ÷ (total # offspring)] × 100.

   For both males and females, the percentage with straight ears was 100 percent regardless of the number of offspring.

4. Discuss the following questions with your teammate:

   a. What overall conclusions can you draw about the inheritance of straight ears versus floppy ears?

   When one of the parents has straight ears and the other has floppy ears, all of the offspring have straight ears. Thus, the straight-ear trait seems stronger than the floppy-ear trait.

   b. Do you think the type of ear a rabbit is born with is affected by whether a rabbit is female or male? Explain your answer.

   There does not seem to be any connection between ear type and sex because the ratio of males to females is always about 1:1, and all of the rabbits are either floppy-eared or straight-eared.

   These steps provide an opportunity for the students to make additional observations that the genetic information for certain parental phenotypes has greater influence on offspring than the information for other phenotypes. You might remind the learners that these observations connect with the basic pattern that they observed in the previous activity (one bean color exerted greater effect on ear type in rabbits than the other color).

Analysis

Work individually to develop responses to the following questions in your journal.

Base your responses on your experiences so far in this chapter and on the information in the essays *Phenotype and Genotype* (page 492) and *Case Studies of Two Genetic Disorders* (page 496).

As you work on and discuss questions that involve genetic disorders, be sensitive to the possibility that some of your classmates may have, or be close to someone who has, one of the genetic disorders we are studying. *Anyone* can be born with a genetic disorder.

1. Although Huntington's disease is a dominant trait, the symptoms do not appear until late adult years. Imagine that you are a doctor treating a young man who has a parent with Huntington's disease. What concerns might you have for your patient and why?

   Because the disease does not appear early, young adults do not know whether they carry the allele until after they reach childbearing age. If a young adult carries the allele, there is a 50 percent chance of passing it on to each offspring. The decision to marry and have children can later cause the parent feelings of guilt if children are affected.

2. Restate the following accurately: One out of every two offspring that result from a cross between parents with the genotypes *Hh* and *hh* definitely will have Huntington's disease.

   The students' answers should reflect an understanding that there is a 50 percent chance that any one offspring will have Huntington's disease. This chance does not mean that one out of every two offspring definitely will have the disease. When you consider a large number of similar crosses, you would expect the total number with Huntington's disease to approach 50 percent. If students are still confused about connections between probability and actual outcomes, take some time to clarify these ideas.

3. Two healthy individuals marry and produce three children. The first two are healthy. But the third is born with cystic fibrosis, indicating that she is homozygous *cc* for the cystic fibrosis alleles. What can you conclude about the genotypes of the other people in the family?

   The birth of the daughter with the genotype *cc* means that both her mother and father must have contributed gametes containing the *c* allele to the zygote that produced her. However, both parents are free of the disease themselves, so each genotype also must carry a normal *C* allele. This means that both the mother and the father are heterozygotes with the genotype *Cc*. In this family, each of the parents is a carrier because in the heterozygous condition, each carries the allele for the recessive trait that results in cystic fibrosis. There is a 50 percent chance that each parent will pass a cystic fibrosis allele to an offspring. The healthy siblings could be *CC* or *Cc*.

4. What is the probability for the couple in question 3 that their future children will have cystic fibrosis? What does this mean for their healthy children?

   Now that they have learned this fact, the couple will need to think carefully about whether to have more children because there will be a 25 percent (.5 × .5 = .25) chance of each child receiving the cystic fibrosis allele from both parents and developing the disease.

Both of the other two children are healthy, so each of them must have inherited the *C* allele from at least one parent. However, each child had a 50 percent chance to inherit the *c* allele from the other parent. In genetic terms, there is a strong possibility that one or both of them is a carrier of the *c* allele for cystic fibrosis.

5. In cocker spaniels, black (*B*) is dominant over red (*b*). Solid color (*S*) is dominant over white spotting (*s*). A red male was mated to a black-and-white female. They had five puppies, as follows: one black, one red, one black-and-white, and two red-and-white.

   a. What genetic principle explains the phenotypes of these offspring?

      The principle of independent assortment accounts for the phenotypes, although the principle of dominance also plays a role. Because this is the first time the learners encounter a problem in independent assortment, expect that many will be confused. Take the time to carefully guide learners through this puzzle. Use their answers to direct the discussion and work through the genotype assignments. Given the parental phenotypes, we can write their genotypes as follows, leaving blanks to fill in after we check the offspring.

      Parents: *bbS_*   ×   *B_ss*
                  (red ♂)   (b&w ♀)

      Given the phenotypes of the offspring, we can write their genotypes as follows:

      Offspring: *B_S_*   *bbS_*   *B_ss*   *bbss*
                   (black)   (red)   (b&w)   (r&w)

      Because two of the red puppies have white spotting, they must have received an *s* allele from each parent, so the red male parent must be *bbSs*. In similar fashion, the red puppy (*bb*) received a *b* allele from each parent, so the female parent must be *Bbss*. By knowing the complete genotypes for these traits in the parents, it is now possible to complete the genotype designations for their offspring.

      The black puppy had to receive a *b* from its father and an *s* from its mother because each is homozygous for those respective alleles. This makes the puppy's genotype *BbSs*.

      Similarly, the red puppy had to receive an *s* allele from its mother, making it *bbSs*.

      Following the same logic, the black-and-white puppy would have received a *b* allele from its father, making it *Bbss*.

   b. Write one or two paragraphs to describe how that principle worked in this cocker spaniel family. Show the genotypes of the parents and their offspring in your explanation. Include the following terms:

      | gene | phenotype |
      | dominant trait | chromosome |
      | recessive trait | allele |
      | genotype | |

      The students' paragraphs should describe how each puppy was a particular color, and its color is its phenotype for the trait of color. Phenotype is an observable trait. The phenotype is coded for by the puppy's genotype, which is determined by the alleles for the genes that determine the hair color the puppy inherited from its parents. Those hair color genes are located on chromosomes in the puppy's cells.

Some alleles are dominant, meaning that if one copy of that allele is present, it determines the phenotype for the puppy. In the cocker spaniel example, black and solid are dominant traits. Dominant traits are expressed in both the homozygous and heterozygous genotypes. Some alleles are recessive, meaning that two copies of the allele must be present for that trait to be expressed. Recessive traits are expressed only in the homozygous genotype. In the cocker spaniel example, red and spotting are both recessive traits.

6. Consider how tall you are. How tall will you likely be when you are fully grown? How tall might you have been if you were raised in a very different situation? How do your genes and the environment interact to determine how tall you will be?

Modify the diagram (Figure T11.2) below to illustrate your answer.

   The diagram (Figure 11.6) from the student book is included here, with the addition of an "environment" component. You will notice that it is an organizer that students may find useful in thinking about genetics. It shows visually the two aspects of genetic information: the information gets expressed (to produce traits) and it gets inherited (through reproduction). Students might add another arrow to the diagram leading from the "environment" to the "genotype→ phenotype" arrow.

Figure T11.2 Relationship between genotype and phenotype

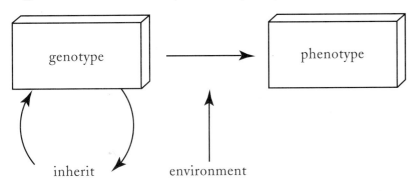

Understanding Inherited Patterns

Explain

Major Concepts Role of meiosis in inheritance; segregation; independent assortment; autosomes versus sex chromosomes; sources of genetic variation

Overview

   Students use the animated DVD segment "Meiosis" and the essay *Meiosis: The Mechanism behind Patterns of Inheritance* to answer the challenge of explaining how gametes come to be haploid. They further expand their explanation of meiosis in inheritance by solving a puzzle about how meiosis results in segregation and independent assortment.

Analysis

1. Explain how your cell diagrams and answers to the questions in Part B illustrate the connection between the segregation of alleles and meiosis.

   By working through the models and sketching meiosis in Part B, students already have demonstrated an understanding of the role of meiosis in segregating alleles. The way students express these points may vary. Some possible responses might include the observation that meiosis leads to gametes that contain only one allele for each trait or that only the paternal or maternal allele is represented in a gamete for a given trait, but never both.

2. If an organism has the genotype *AA*, what can you say about the alleles present in the gametes that gave rise to that organism?

   Both the male and female parental gametes contributed an *A* allele to this organism.

3. Use the principle of segregation to write one or two paragraphs that explain how the alleles of different genes are mixed during mating.

   Use genetic terminology to describe your ideas accurately.

   The alleles for a given gene segregate from each other during meiosis, and each gamete formed after meiosis has an equal chance of receiving one or the other gene, but not both. Depending on which gametes fuse during mating, chance determines which alleles for the various genes in question are passed on to the offspring.

Explain
Elaborate

Can You Sort It Out?

Major Concepts
Simple Mendelian inheritance; prediction of monohybrid and dihybrid ratios from crosses; phenotype and genotype; linkage and recombination; X-linkage

Overview

In this activity, learners further elaborate their understanding of simple Mendelian genetic concepts by using Punnett squares as a tool to predict results from monohybrid and dihybrid crosses of garden peas. They also compare their predictions with data from those crosses and determine the relationships between the phenotypes and genotypes of the parents and offspring. Students elaborate their understanding of the variation present in living organisms by explaining how gene linkage and X-linkage affect phenotype and genotype.

Materials   (per class of 30, teams of 2)

calculator
DVD
DVD player
30 copies of the Copymaster *Mendel's Data*

Outcomes and Indicators of Success

The following indicators allow you to assess the students' level of success with the activity and to assess their process of learning.

By the end of this activity, the learners should

1. understand Mendelian ratios in simple monohybrid and dihybrid crosses.

    They will demonstrate their understanding by predicting the results of monohybrid and dihybrid crosses of garden peas.

2. understand the relationship between genotype and phenotype.

    They will demonstrate their understanding by

    a. predicting the phenotypes that result from simple genetic crosses,

    b. comparing the genotypes and phenotypes of parents and offspring from monohybrid and dihybrid crosses, and

    c. using Punnett squares to make predictions about monohybrid and dihybrid crosses.

3. understand independent assortment of genes.

    They will demonstrate their understanding by predicting the results of a cross with two genes.

4. understand how gene linkage affects phenotype and genotype.

    They will demonstrate their understanding by

    a. describing the effect of recombination on phenotype,

    b. comparing the results of genetic crosses involving linked and unlinked genes,

    c. explaining why males are more likely to express phenotypes associated with X-linked recessive traits, and

    d. explaining the inheritance of hemophilia.

Preparations

Preview the two DVD segments, "Mendel's Peas" and "Crossing-Over."

Strategies for Guiding Learners

PROCESS AND PROCEDURES

As a class, read orally or silently all introductory materials for the activity and the Process and Procedures to help students build connections between concepts and activities. Use the time spent reading to bring the students' attention into focus.

This activity is structured so that learners can work in teams of two. A series of questions is embedded in the procedural steps to help the learners proceed through the activity in a thoughtful manner. Familiarize yourself with these questions so that you can assist the learners when they ask for help. Encourage the students to refer back to the essay *Meiosis: The Mechanism behind Patterns of Inheritance* or other resources for help in answering the questions.

PART A   A Mendelian Trait: Pea Pod Color

Show the DVD segment "Mendel's Peas" to the whole class. It provides a historical context and uses pea pod color to demonstrate how to use a Punnett square to determine predicted outcomes in a monohybrid cross. The students will work through the steps of a monohybrid cross and answer questions on the video. Refer to the DVD guide on the *TRCD* for narration text and specific strategies. Provide each student with a copy of the Copymaster *Mendel's Data*, which supplements the data shown in the segment with data for all of Mendel's crosses.

PART B   Two Mendelian Traits: Pea Pod Color and Shape

Have students continue to work in teams of two and record answers in their journals. Expect responses to the questions similar to those that follow.

1. With regard to pod color and pod shape, record in your journal the genotypes of gametes that can be formed by these parental types. List the genotypes and phenotypes of the F_1 (first generation) offspring.

   The *green, expanded parent* (*GGEE*) can form only *GE* gametes because gametes receive only one allele for each trait. Likewise, the *yellow, constricted* (*ggee*) parent produces only *ge* gametes. *All* of the F_1 offspring will be *green, expanded* (*GgEe*).

2. The F_1 individuals are crossed with each other. Use a Punnett square, as described on the DVD, to show the possible genotypes of the offspring. Record your work in your journal. Include your Punnett square.

   The Punnett square below illustrates the results of the F_1 cross.

Figure T11.4 Punnett square showing results of F_1 cross

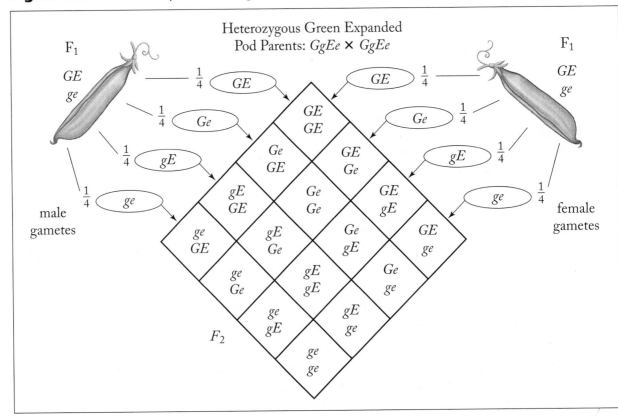

3. Based on the data in your Punnett square, what fraction of the offspring would you predict to have each of the following phenotypes?

   a. The dominant phenotype for pod color and pod shape

   9/16

   b. The dominant phenotype for pod color and the recessive phenotype for pod shape

   3/16

   c. The recessive phenotype for pod color and the dominant phenotype for pod shape

   3/16

   d. The recessive phenotype for pod color and pod shape

   1/16

4. If there were 288 offspring, how many would you predict to have green, expanded pods? green, constricted pods? yellow, expanded pods? yellow, constricted pods?

   In your journal, record how you calculate your predictions.

   You would expect to get 9/16 (288) = 162 with green, expanded pods; 3/16 (288) = 54 with green, constricted pods; 3/16 (288) = 54 with yellow, expanded pods; 1/16 (288) = 18 with yellow, constricted pods.

5. Compare your predictions with the actual results that your teacher provides. Answer the following questions:

   a. Do the results match your predictions?

   Provide the following actual results for the students:

   Green, expanded = 165

   Green, constricted = 51

   Yellow, expanded = 56

   Yellow, constricted = 16

   The students will see that the actual results do not match their predictions exactly.

   b. How can you explain any discrepancies between the result and your predictions?

   The predicted results are not expected to match the actual results perfectly, due to chance, but they should be close. The larger the sample size, the closer to the expected proportion you would expect the actual results to be. If the learners still seem confused by the logic of this discrepancy, take some time to clarify misunderstandings about probability.

PART C   Linked Traits

Begin Part C by showing the DVD segment "Crossing-Over." This short animated segment shows the effects of crossing-over on linked genes when they are far apart and when they are close together on a chromosome. You may want to repeat the segment as the learners work on step 2.

1. Repeat steps 1–3 in Part B. But this time, suppose that the genes for pod color and pod shape are on the same chromosome. (That is, G and E are linked, and g and e are linked.)

   In this case, we would still expect the *green, expanded parents* to produce only *GE* gametes. The *yellow, constricted parent* would produce only *ge* gametes. With these gametes, all F_1 offspring would be *green, expanded* (*GE/ge*). (Note that the slash mark [/] indicates that G and E are linked together, and that g and e are linked together.)

When linked in this fashion, the only gametes we might expect (without crossing-over) would be *GE/* and */ge* from each F₁ parent. When these gametes are combined, we would expect only four F₂ genotypes and two phenotypes in the following fractions: ¼ *GE/GE* (*green, expanded*); ¼ *GE/ge* (*green, expanded*); ¼ *ge/GE* (*green, expanded*); and ¼ *ge/ge* (*yellow, constricted*). When you combine similar phenotypes, you get ¾ *green, expanded* and ¼ *yellow, constricted*.

2. Describe the effect that crossing-over might have on the results.

The DVD segment "Crossing-Over" may help you with your description.

Crossing-over would be expected to produce a small fraction of *gE/* and */Ge* gametes from the F₁ parents, with a larger fraction of the linked combinations (*GE/* and */ge*). This would produce mostly *green, expanded* and *yellow, constricted* individuals, but because of crossing-over, a small number of *green, constricted* and *yellow, expanded* individuals would be produced.

You might use this opportunity to assess if the students understand that linkage is an exception to Mendel's principle of independent assortment, and that crossing-over is an exception to linkage.

PART D   X-Linked Traits

1. In the fruit fly *Drosophila melanogaster*, red eye color is dominant over white eye color (see Figure 11.12). Predict the genotypes and phenotypes you would expect in the F₁ generation when a homozygous red-eyed female fly is mated with a white-eyed male fly.

First, you might want to list the gametes you would expect the parents to produce. Then combine the gametes to show the F₁ offspring. A Punnett square may be useful.

You might expect the following response to question 1:

Let *R* = red and *r* = white. In a simple monohybrid cross (with no X-linkage), one would expect the red-eyed female to produce only *R* gametes and the male to produce only *r* gametes. When combined, they would produce all *Rr* (red-eyed) F₁ individuals.

2. Your teacher will list the actual results of such a cross on the chalkboard. Compare them with your predictions.

Provide the following "actual" results for your students:

Based on 139 offspring, all had red eyes.

3. Say you mated red-eyed *male* flies with white-eyed *female* flies (instead of red-eyed females with white-eyed males). Would you expect similar F₁ results to those obtained in step 2? (When males and females are switched with respect to the traits used in a cross, it is called a *reciprocal* cross.)

The students probably would expect the results to be similar.

4. In the early 1900s, biologist Thomas Hunt Morgan performed a similar cross. But instead of getting all red-eyed flies, he got half red-eyed flies and half white-eyed flies. However, all the red-eyed flies were females, and all the white-eyed flies were males. How might you explain these seemingly unexpected results?

The unexpected results obtained by Morgan can be explained using the diagrams shown for question 5a. The diagram can be simple, using the symbols described in the student pages to represent the genotypes of parents, gametes, and offspring, with phenotypes in parentheses as illustrated on page 419.

5. Use what you know to date to solve the following problems:

a. A superscript letter designates the allele. Often it is used with the chromosome symbol to diagram a cross of a trait that is carried on the X chromosome. For example, the allele for white eyes might be represented by X^r, and the allele for red eyes by X^R. The symbol Y can represent the Y chromosome and does not carry a gene for eye color. Using these symbols, diagram the cross described in step 3. Show the expected genotype and phenotype fractions.

Show your work in your journal.

Parents: $X^R Y \times X^r X^r$

(red ♂ [male symbol]) and (white ♀ [female symbol])

Gametes: ♂ : X^R and Y ♀ : X^r

F_1 offspring: $\frac{1}{2} X^R X^r$ (red-eyed females)

$\frac{1}{2} X^r Y$ (white-eyed males)

b. Diagram the cross that would result if the F_1 offspring were mated. Show the genotype and phenotype fractions you would expect in the F_2 generation.

F_1 gametes: ♀ : X^R and X^r ♂ : X^r and Y

F_2 offspring: $\frac{1}{4} X^R X^r$ (red-eyed females)

$\frac{1}{4} X^R Y$ (red-eyed males)

$\frac{1}{4} X^r X^r$ (white-eyed females)

$\frac{1}{4} X^r Y$ (white-eyed males)

If the students are confused about how to diagram the crosses, you might go through a cross with them, using the chalkboard or an overhead transparency. Demonstrate how the alleles in the gametes are derived and how they combine to produce offspring of particular genotypes.

Analysis

Use these questions as the basis for a class discussion.

1. Predict the possible phenotypes and genotypes of the offspring from a mating of two beagles. A heterozygous female with the dominant phenotype for droopy ears (D) mates with a male with the recessive phenotype for upright ears (d).

If the trait is inherited on an autosome, the male beagle must be *dd* because it expresses the recessive trait. If the female is *Dd*, then the possible outcomes for the offspring are $\frac{1}{2}$ *Dd* with droopy ears and $\frac{1}{2}$ *dd* with upright ears. If the trait is inherited on the X chromosome, the male must be $X^d Y$; the female is $X^D X^d$ or $X^D X^D$. Possible offspring: ♀ : $X^D X^d, X^D X^D$; ♂ : $X^D Y, X^d Y$.

2. Describe the role of a Punnett square in predicting the potential ratio of genotypes that may result from a particular cross.

A Punnett square only reveals the ratio of genotypes that are *possible* given the combination of gametes involved. It is a statistical tool and as such it cannot determine actual outcomes.

3. Recall that crossing-over causes some genes on the same chromosome to assort independently. What relationship might you expect between the spacing of genes on the chromosome and their frequency of independent assortment?

   The further apart the genes on the chromosome, the more likely they are to cross over, and the greater the frequency of independent assortment you would expect.

4. Revisit step 1 of Part D. Remember that the gene for eye color in fruit flies is linked to the X chromosome. Predict the F_2 results of that mating.

Parents:	$X^R X^R$	×	$X^r Y$
Gametes:	X^R		X^r and Y
F_1 results:	$\frac{1}{2} X^R X^r$		$\frac{1}{2} X^R Y$
F_1 gametes:	X^R and X^r		X^R and Y
F_2 results:	$\frac{1}{4} X^R X^R$	$\frac{1}{4} X^R X^r$	$\frac{1}{4} X^R Y$ $\frac{1}{4} X Y$

5. Explain why males are more likely than females to display the phenotypes associated with X-linked recessive traits.

   Males need only one recessive allele to express an X-linked trait because they only have one X chromosome, and the trait is not carried on the Y chromosome.

6. Use your knowledge of X-linked traits to explain the inheritance of hemophilia in the story *A Royal Tragedy*.

   The trait for hemophilia A, an example of X-linked recessive inheritance, was passed on by many female members of the royal families of Europe. Although they were heterozygous carriers, the disease seldom afflicted them because blood-clotting time is usually normal in heterozygous females. On the other hand, males with a recessive allele on the X chromosome always are affected. Because members of the royal families of Europe often intermarried, the incidence of the hemophilia allele was unusually high among them, and the disease afflicted many male members, such as Czarevitch Alexis.

Extensions

If you have the time and the facilities, you may want to conduct similar genetic cross experiments using fruit flies or another suitable organism.

Elaborate

The Genetic Basis of Human Variation

Major Concepts Genetic nature and range of human variation; discrete versus continuous variation; effect of natural selection; relationship between genotype and phenotype; genetics and behavior

Overview

Students have an opportunity to measure a quantitative trait: variation in height. They also consider the effects of natural selection on human traits that exhibit continuous patterns of variation.

Materials   (per class of 30, individuals and teams of 2)

30 white 3 × 5-in cards
30 colored 3 × 5-in cards
30 pencils

1 roll of masking tape
9 small squares of paper

Outcomes and Indicators of Success

The following indicators allow you to assess the students' level of success with the activity and to assess their process of learning.

By the end of this activity, the learners should

1. understand that some traits are discrete (qualitative) and others are continuous (quantitative).

   They will demonstrate this understanding by

   a. making histograms for sex and height,

   b. analyzing the histogram data to explain the differences in the traits, and

   c. listing other human traits that would result in patterns similar to those in the histograms.

2. understand the role of genetics in influencing the degree of variation in continuous human traits.

   They will demonstrate their understanding by

   a. describing changes in height distribution through many generations of living underground,

   b. defining the term *normal* in terms of continuously varying traits, and

   c. explaining the genetic basis for distributions seen in continuous traits.

3. understand the effects of natural selection on continuous human traits.

   They will demonstrate their understanding by

   a. describing how, in a futuristic scenario, drastic environmental changes might affect the range of variation in continuous traits such as height,

   b. speculating how continuously varying traits might arise from the mechanisms of evolution, and

   c. explaining the relationship among human variation, genetic disorders, natural selection, and evolution.

Preparations

Review Part A, *Measuring Variation*, in the student book, and refer to it as you do this activity with your class.

Strategies for Guiding Learners

PROCESS AND PROCEDURES

PART A *Measuring Variation*

As a class, read orally or silently all introductory materials for the activity and the Process and Procedures to help students build connections between concepts and activities. Use the time spent reading to bring the students' attention into focus.

1. Work with your classmates and teacher to construct the axes for the 2 histograms shown in Figure 11.15. Use the masking tape and small pieces of paper. Make and label the axes on a large wall in your classroom, in the hall, or in another large open area.

   Ask for volunteers to help you construct the axes for two graphs as shown in Figure 11.15 in the student book. Masking tape and small squares of paper can be used to make and label the axes on a large wall of your classroom or on another large open area. You might want to keep the same graph and add data from all of your classes to increase the sample size.

2. Next, write XX on a white 3 × 5-inch card if you are a female. Write XY if you are a male. This is your chromosomal sex. On a colored card, write your height in centimeters—round off to the nearest 5 cm.

3. Use masking tape to affix your cards to the proper places on the histograms.

   Students may need help converting their height in inches to centimeters (1 in = 2.54 cm, and 1 ft = 30.48 cm). Alternatively, you might want to make 5 cm marks on a masking-tape height scale mounted on a classroom wall. The patterns are easier to see if male and female students use cards of different colors.

4. When the histograms are complete, work with your partner to answer these questions. Record your answers in your journal.

   Use the data in the histograms and your understanding of genetics to help you.

   Have students work with their partners to answer the questions; expect responses such as the following.

   a. How many different types of individuals are represented on Histogram A?
      Two: females and males. This is a *discrete* distribution; that is, there are a finite number of possible values.

   b. How many different types of individuals are represented on Histogram B?
      Many. This is a *continuous* distribution, indicating a potentially infinite number of values—if height could be measured with great precision. If we include both males and females, there may be a *bimodal* (two-peak) distribution, with one peak for males and the other for females. This should be evident from the clustering of the colored cards. If we included only one sex in the height distribution, and if the sample size were large enough, the shape of the histogram likely would begin to approach a bell-shaped distribution with one peak. The important distinction is that the histogram for height indicates a very different type of trait than does the histogram for males and females.

c. In your journal, draw and label the 2 histograms. Describe how their shapes differ.

Histogram A has only two phenotypes, male and female, and thus there are only two bars on it. Histogram B has many phenotypes, different heights that vary incrementally, and thus there are many bars. There are shorter bars on the two ends of the histogram, and most of the longer bars are clustered in the middle.

d. What is responsible for the shape of Histogram A?

The shape of Histogram A is due to the segregation of one genetic factor: the Y chromosome.

e. What is responsible for the shape of Histogram B?

Height is determined by a number of genes, which in turn interact with a number of environmental variables such as nutrition and childhood illness. We do not, therefore, see the sharp boundaries that result from a trait that is controlled by one genetic factor.

f. What would happen to the shapes of the histograms if you added data from the rest of the students in your school?

The overall shape of Histogram A would not change; it would still be a discrete distribution characteristic of a distinct, qualitative trait. The shape of Histogram B would become more clearly bimodal, with one peak for males and one for females. The distribution, however, would remain continuous and would indicate the presence of a quantitative trait. If your students wish, they can add data from other classes to test these hypotheses.

g. List 3 other human traits that would result in the same type of pattern as Histogram A. Do the same for Histogram B.

Patterns such as that shown in Histogram A would result from single-gene disorders such as cystic fibrosis, sickle-cell disease, or Huntington's disease; one either has the disease or does not. Blood type also would show four discrete, qualitatively different types (A, B, AB, and O). On the other hand, traits such as weight, intelligence (as defined any number of ways), foot size, skin color, wrist circumference, personality, and athletic or artistic ability would show continuous distributions similar to that found in Histogram B. Most human characteristics are, in fact, continuously distributed. Ask the students what such traits have in common. Guide the answers until the learners see that they result from multiple genes interacting with a large number of environmental variables.

PART B   Variation and Evolution

Remind the learners to keep the futuristic scenario in mind (see box on page 439 of the student text) as they use the essays *The Role of Variation in Evolution* (page 503) and *Genetic Complexity* (page 507) as resources. Have them work with their partners to answer the following questions:

1. Describe the change in Histogram B that you might expect to see if the inhabitants of this underground world were to participate in the Part A activity 5,000 years after moving underground.

Be creative. Feel free to illustrate your description. Or expand the story to explain your response.

Most of the learners probably will suggest that the histogram would show much larger numbers at the lower heights and fewer at the taller heights. This shift could result from the selective advantage experienced by the shorter members of the population.

2. How do we define "normal" for traits such as height? What, for example, is "normal" height? Where does "short" end and "tall" begin? How do we define other complex traits such as behavior? Where does "intelligent" end and "really intelligent" begin?

This is a critical discussion. The distribution for height clearly shows that most people aggregate around the mean, and society often has come to associate "average" with "normal." Ask the students to consider as normal the entire range of human variation for height. They should see that the range encompassed by normal extends far beyond average on both sides of the distribution. It is interesting to note that society often is more accepting of "outliers" to the right of the mean than to the left. For example, we hardly consider 210 cm basketball players "abnormal"; in fact, we reward them with large salaries and public commendation. However, we may consider an extremely short person abnormal and may even discriminate against him or her. Our designations are largely arbitrary.

3. What evolutionary interpretation can you give to human traits that exhibit a continuous pattern of variation? Consider the effects of natural selection as you develop your answer.

Throughout human evolution, variations that improved the chances of survival and reproduction in the human species tended to be maintained. Such variations were adaptive in that they enhanced (or at least did not reduce) the ability of humans to deal with their environment. It appears that *extreme* divergence from the usual, average, or normal could decrease the chances of survival and reproduction. Thus, evolution helps us understand both the variations and the commonalities we see in people today.

Analysis

Respond to the following tasks individually. Contribute your answers to a class discussion.

1. One of the most important lessons from Charles Darwin's work is that natural selection acts on naturally occurring variations in populations. How might traits that vary continuously, such as height, arise from the mechanisms of evolution?

Traits characterized by continuous distributions represent the finely graded variation on which natural selection acts. For such a distribution to arise, individuals with heights clustering around the average must, in general, pass their genetic material to the next generation with greater frequency than those individuals whose heights vary significantly from the average. Traits that vary significantly from the average apparently are not adaptive and therefore infrequent.

2. Look again at the shape of Histogram B. What part of the histogram represents inhabitants of the underground world who are likely to fare well in this new environment? Why are so many people represented by the measurements in the middle and so few at the extremes—the "outliers"?

   Individuals at the left end of the histogram (shorter individuals) likely will fare better than the taller individuals due to the unusual environment in which they find themselves. For example, shorter individuals may have fewer head injuries by avoiding collisions with rocks in the tunnel ceiling. They might reproduce more efficiently than tall individuals who spend significant amounts of time recovering from injuries. This and the next question are difficult and subtle; they attempt to make clear the effects of natural selection on the structure of human populations. Most of the genes that influence height in human populations contribute to the "middle-range" heights; those that contribute to the two ends of the distribution are less frequent, and those that contribute to the extremes are rare. It is likely that the environmental factors that contribute to height are distributed in the same way. Those who are very tall or very short, therefore, stand out because of their height and their infrequency. The same is true for all continuously distributed traits.

3. Is the variation observed in Histogram B of the same type as that which causes genetic disorders such as cystic fibrosis? Explain.

   No, the genetic variation of disorders such as cystic fibrosis tends to be discrete (people either have it or they do not).

4. Explain the underlying genetic difference between complex traits and simple traits. Complex traits are those traits that exhibit continuous patterns of distribution. Simple traits are those traits that exhibit discrete patterns of distribution.

   Complex traits are often the result of the interaction of many genes, whereas traits that exhibit discrete patterns of distribution may be governed by one or a few genes. The environment often plays a significant role in the expression of complex traits.

5. What does human variation, including variation in genetic disorders, have to do with natural selection and evolution?

   Some genes are very maladaptive. They result in reduced life expectancy, limited reproduction, and physical and social handicaps. Most of these genes express themselves early in life. They are the first to be removed from the population by natural selection. In fact, more than 90 percent of single-gene disorders such as cystic fibrosis, sickle-cell disease, and muscular dystrophy express themselves by the end of puberty (Childs and Scriver, 1986).

   Although the social and familial consequences of childhood death can be severe, the biological consequences are less serious because only a small number of individuals inherit genetic disorders that are serious enough to cause death prior to reproduction. Natural selection tends to reduce this type of genetic variation somewhat. From a population standpoint, the species does not suffer greatly from this selection because individuals with these disorders are outliers in terms of variation. The evolution of the species usually depends heavily on variation of intermediate forms. Most discrete traits, if extreme, are selected against quickly because there is an absence of graded intermediate forms of which some might be beneficial.

Learners should see many oval cells of the original mating types, budding cells, cells that are pear-shaped because of the influence of mating pheromones, and some zygotes. These stages are visible because the germinated spores released haploid cells ready to begin the entire reproductive life cycle once again.

   c. What evidence is there that a new life cycle has started?

      The peanut-shaped zygotes are evidence that a new life cycle has started.

   d. Use the results of your yeast experiment to explain the statement, *The genetic plan of yeast cells can be transmitted through reproduction.*

      The cells that emerge following meiosis and germination have the same phenotype (pink and cream color) as the original mating cells even though the pink phenotype disappeared after mating. Thus, the genetic information for pink was retained by the (diploid) cells even though it did not result in a visible phenotype after mating.

2. Apply your understanding of genetics to the yeast reproduction diagrams on the Copymaster *Yeast Reproduction*. Complete the following tasks:

      Refer the learners to the Copymaster *Yeast Reproduction*, as a resource for completing these tasks.

   a. At each position where new cells are represented in the sequence, describe whether the cells are haploid or diploid. Justify your responses.

      In the sexual reproduction diagram on the Copymaster *Yeast Reproduction*, the cells are haploid as a and α mating type cells because they just have emerged from meiosis, and they remain haploid until they fuse into a zygote. At this point, the cells become diploid because the genetic information in one cell type combines with the genetic information from the other cell, which doubles the amount of genetic information. Cells remain diploid until they undergo meiosis again. (In the case of asexual reproduction, the situation is somewhat more confusing. Haploid or diploid cells may bud to produce haploid or diploid cells, respectively, and the state of a given budding cell is not particularly obvious—especially from these drawings.)

   b. In the appropriate diagram, label the position where meiosis occurs.

3. Working individually, write 1 or 2 paragraphs in which you compare the mechanisms that yeast and humans use to maintain genetic continuity. In your comparison, include a description or illustration with labels of the following:

   ◆ The haploid and diploid cells in each species

   ◆ The meiotic process each organism uses that leads to gamete formation

   ◆ An obvious phenotype that can be inherited from one generation to the next

   ◆ The life cycle and method of reproduction of each species

      Step 3 is designed to help students make connections between the events in the yeast life cycle and genetics as the mechanism for maintaining continuity. Ask the students to write and illustrate one or two paragraphs describing the similarities between this system and that of humans. This requires that they synthesize the information from this chapter and extrapolate it to the human system (Chapter 10). If students have a difficult time relating yeast to humans, explain that yeast are eukaryotes, like humans, and yeast cells function in many respects like human cells. Scientists have learned much about human meiosis by studying unicellular yeasts because yeasts are simpler and scientists can manipulate them to test their hypotheses. It is not ethically acceptable to perform these types of experiments on humans. Figure T11.5 will help you guide students in making meaningful comparisons.

Figure T11.5 Comparison of the yeast life cycle and sexual reproduction in humans

Yeast	Humans
Mating pheromones	Sex hormones
Mating type **a** and **α** gametes	Gametes (ova and sperm)
Fusion	Fertilization
Zygote	Zygote
Asexually reproducing diploid cells	Diploid body cells
Meiosis and formation of spores	Meiosis and formation of gametes

PART B   Genetic Variation and Human Genetic Disorders

You may assign Part B as a take-home assessment if you choose.

Questions 1–5 require a thorough understanding of the material, and some students may have difficulty with them. We recognize this and hope that the intriguing nature of human genetic disorders will stimulate earnest attempts to answer the questions. Provide students with copies of the rubric *Continuity and Change,* and discuss the criteria before having students respond to the questions. It also may be necessary to review these questions with the students before they attempt them at home. One cautionary note: Genetics chapters invariably focus on the parts of the human system that fail. Be sure that students realize that, for the most part, the genetic systems of the human body function properly to maintain continuity without genetic defects. Disorders often are studied because they provide one of the most informative windows to the processes underlying the normal order. Biologists frequently learn how things work by studying how things fail to work. Also, caution students to be sensitive to the fact that some of their classmates may have firsthand experience with these disorders. Do not allow students to make jokes or hurtful comments about any of the genetic disorders.

Analyze the following questions. Use what you know, the essay *Incomplete Dominance* (page 510), and the material in the need to know box on page 442 titled Human Genetic Disorders.

1. Which disorders show X-linkage? Explain whether you would expect to see them in males or females, or possibly both.

    Hemophilia A and red-green color blindness. Because both are recessive, X-linked traits, you would expect to see these disorders only rarely in females. A mother carrying the allele must mate with an affected male to produce affected females, whereas a male can inherit the trait from a carrier mother and nonrecessive father.

2. Write 1 or 2 paragraphs that describe how young Czarevitch Alexis (from the activity *Gifts from Your Parents* on page 418) could have been affected by hemophilia even though neither parent was affected. Use genetic terminology to accurately describe the biology underlying the situation.

   The alleles for traits can be passed, without change, through many generations in a silent form. Even though Alexis's parents were unaffected, it is clear that his mother possessed an allele for hemophilia, which is a recessive, X-linked disorder. The trait was revealed when the hemophilia allele from Alexis's mother was expressed in Alexis in the absence of a normal clotting allele.

3. Although Huntington's disease is very rare in the total population, it appears at a rate of 50 percent in affected families. Explain this statement in genetic terms.

   Huntington's disease is inherited as an autosomal dominant trait. This means that half of a heterozygous parent's gametes will contain the dominant allele, and there is a 50 percent chance for each of the offspring to develop the disorder.

4. Alleles that cause cystic fibrosis occur at a rate of about 1 in 25 individuals of European descent. Alleles that cause red-green color blindness occur at a rate of about 1 in 20 males in the United States. Picture a school with 500 students (50 percent male and 50 percent female). Would these statistics *guarantee* that 20 students are heterozygous carriers of the cystic fibrosis gene or that at least 12 males are color-blind? Explain your response.

   No. Statistics such as these give estimates of likelihood, not certainty. Within a population of tens or hundreds of thousands, these numbers are relatively accurate in predicting how many individuals will be affected; but in any particular, limited group, they do not guarantee that anyone will be affected.

5. Look at the disorders listed in the table. How does the genetic abnormality of trisomy 21 differ from the others?

   Trisomy 21 is an example of nondisjunction, a process in which the chromosome pairs fail to separate at meiosis. The phenotypic defects arising as a result of carrying an extra copy of chromosome 21 are due not to mutations but rather to the presence of excess genetic material. The other disorders listed are the result of defects in particular genes.

   The questions in steps 6–8 summarize the topic of genetics by considering the role of genetics in quantitative or complex traits such as intelligence and skin color, and considering how genetic variation serves as the raw material of evolution. These issues are covered in the essays *The Role of Variation in Evolution*, *Genetic Complexity*, and *Incomplete Dominance*, which the students will need to use as resources. At this time, the student responses should reflect a considerably improved understanding of the genetic basis for evolution.

6. Use the concept of natural selection to help explain why the frequency of hemophilia A is so different from the frequency of color blindness.

   Hemophilia A is often a life-threatening disorder, whereas color blindness generally is not. The process of natural selection results in the elimination of organisms that carry traits detrimental to survival and reproduction.

7. Charles Darwin did not have an understanding of genetics when he proposed his theory of evolution. Now that you have some understanding of genetic mechanisms, how would you use that knowledge to help explain evolution and the diversity seen in populations of living organisms?

Genetic mutation produces new variation in alleles, which serves as raw material for evolution by natural selection. In addition, recombination leads to new combinations of alleles. These processes provide the variation necessary for natural selection to operate in populations of living organisms and to account for the diversity of phenotypes seen in populations.

8. How might the mechanisms of evolution explain how harmful alleles, such as those that lead to sickle-cell disease, are retained in a population?

Under certain environmental conditions, some harmful alleles may confer an advantage to those individuals possessing them in the heterozygous condition. In such cases, natural selection may help to maintain those alleles in the population. In the case of the sickle-cell allele, heterozygotes are more resistant to malaria, so in those regions where malaria is prevalent, heterozygous individuals have a selective advantage.

Further Challenge

Students may be interested in analyzing karyotypes after completing this chapter. See *Analyzing Karyotypes*, Appendix C of the student text or Appendix 5 in Section 7 on the *TRCD* for an investigation in which the students examine several karyotypes.

Gene Action

During this chapter, the students begin to learn about the molecular mechanisms that govern how genetic information is stored and expressed in living organisms and transferred from one generation to the next. The opening art presents the students with scanning tunneling images of DNA molecules and an unfamiliar linguistic sequence. The meaning hidden within the linguistic sequence symbolizes the power that often accompanies information that is stored and transferred in many forms and situations. In this example, meaning is hidden in a Navajo phrase, which is written using symbols from the International Phonetic Alphabet. This sequence of symbols translates into English as, "What does this sentence really mean when you think about it?" During World War II, the power of transferring information in the Navajo language became apparent when Navajo men in the Marine Corps became involved in a program called the Navajo Code Talkers. They communicated in a Navajo-based code to transfer secret information from base to base.

Just as linguistic codes have rules that govern the storage and transfer of information in languages, there are rules and mechanisms that govern the storage and transfer of genetic information in living systems. Scientists have been working for decades to uncover these rules and understand these mechanisms.

ACTIVITIES

Engage / **Explore**	The Stuff of Life
Explore	Transferring Information
Explore / **Explain**	Modeling DNA
Explain	Gene Expression
Elaborate	A Closer Look at Protein Synthesis
Elaborate	Genetic Technology
Evaluate	Words to Live By

Chapter 12 Implementation

Instructional Flow			Classroom Support				
Activity/ Student Text pp. Teacher Guide pp.	GACD, TRCD, DVD, and CD-ROM Resources	Essays/ Student Text pp.	Estimated Time	Team Size/ Cooperative Learning Focus	Strategies and Tools	Assessment Opportunities	Special Considerations
ENGAGE/ EXPLORE *The Stuff of Life* pp. 446–451 TG pp. 437–442		*Genetic Information Is Stored in Molecular Form* pp. 512–513; *Landmark Discovery: DNA May Be the Stuff of Genes* p. 513	50 minutes	*Team size:* 2 and whole class *Skill:* Contributing ideas	Lab; class discussion	Prior knowledge and current understanding of the molecular basis for heredity; misconceptions	Enlarge print materials if needed. Plan partners so that students with visual or fine motor control difficulty can rely on their partner if needed.
EXPLORE *Transferring Information* pp. 451–452 TG pp. 442–447	Copymaster *Messages for Testing Information Transfer*		70 minutes	*Team size:* 8 and 2 *Skill:* Managing and organizing team tasks	Actively testing information transfer; team and class discussions	Misconceptions about the role that DNA plays in reproduction; applying understanding to new situations	Some students may benefit from going over the instructions that you will give the class in step 3 of Process and Procedures before class time.
EXPLORE/ EXPLAIN *Modeling DNA* pp. 452–458 TG pp. 447–459	DVD: *DNA Structure, Parts 1–2* and *DNA Replication;* Copymaster *Modeling a Double Helix*	*DNA Structure and Replication* pp. 513–518; *Replication Errors and Mutation* pp. 519–520; *Landmark Discovery: Why the Fuss about Watson and Crick?* p. 521	150 minutes	*Team size:* 4 and individuals *Skill:* Providing constructive criticism	Video; pop bead models	Analyzing information; synthesizing ideas; modeling skills; peer assessment	Enlarge print materials if needed. Plan partners so that students with visual or fine motor control difficulty can rely on their partner if needed.
EXPLAIN *Gene Expression* pp. 458–464 TG pp. 459–466	DVD: *Transcription;* Copymaster *DNA Sequences for Hemoglobin Alleles*	*Incomplete Dominance* pp. 510–511; *The Expression of Genetic Information* pp. 521–524; *Translating the Message in mRNA* pp. 524–526; *Landmark Discovery: White-Coated Sleuths Decipher Genetic Code* p. 527	100 minutes	*Team size:* 2 and individuals *Skill:* Setting goals; dealing with specific problems; taking responsibility	Video; poster	Current understanding	Enlarge print materials if needed. Plan partners so that students with visual or fine motor control difficulty can rely on their partner if needed.

continued

CHAPTER 12 IMPLEMENTATION (continued)

| | Instructional Flow | | | Classroom Support | | | |
Activity/ Student Text pp. Teacher Guide pp.	GACD, TRCD, DVD, and CD-ROM Resources	Essays/ Student Text pp.	Estimated Time	Team Size/ Cooperative Learning Focusuals	Strategies and Tools	Assessment Opportunities	Special Considerations
ELABORATE A Closer Look at Protein Synthesis pp. 464–467 TG pp. 466–472	DVD: Translation	Cellular Components in Protein Synthesis pp. 527–530	100 minutes	Team size: 2 Skill: Reaching consensus; synthesizing the team's ideas	Video	Analyzing information; peer assessment; making connections between unifying themes	Provide the written narrative for the video sequence to students with difficulty hearing the narration (see the TRCD DVD guide). Enlarge print materials if needed.
ELABORATE Genetic Technology pp. 467–472 TG pp. 472–479	Copymaster Detecting DNA Sequence Variation	Landmark Discovery: Extraordinary New Technique Changes Biology Forever p. 529; Manipulating Genetic Material pp. 530–535; Landmark Discovery: New Technique Discovered While Driving pp. 536–537; Informatics: Mapping and Sequencing the Human Genome pp. 537–538; Genetic Screening: A Dilemma for All of Us pp. 539–540; Translating the Message in mRNA pp. 524–526; Shaping the Future pp. 540–541	100 minutes	Team size: 2 and individuals Skill: Taking responsibility; sharing perspectives	Pop bead model; restriction analysis; class discussion	Current understanding of heredity; application of new ideas; using critical thinking	Part B and Analysis #1 for this activity are quite rigorous. Consider your students' abilities and current level of understanding when deciding if that part of this activity is appropriate at this time. If you decide to postpone or omit portions of this activity, consider that Part A and Analysis #2 involve pertinent ethical issues that are not addressed elsewhere in the text.
EVALUATE Words to Live By pp. 472–473 TG pp. 480–482	Rubric: Concept Map Criteria		50–75 minutes	Team size: 2 and individuals Skill: Synthesizing the team's ideas	Venn diagram; concept map	Current understanding of biological continuity; ability to synthesize the unit's concepts	Some students may benefit from constructing the concept maps on a large piece of butcher paper or with the assistance of an aide to construct the diagram according to the students' instructions.

Optional activities: • Elaborate: *Jurassic Park* • Elaborate: *Prime Time*

Chapter Goals

By the end of this chapter, students should

◆ understand how the structure of DNA allows for information transfer and expression;

◆ understand the molecular basis of mutations;

◆ appreciate the concept of the genetic code;

◆ have a basic understanding of the process of protein synthesis; and

◆ appreciate the impact of genetic engineering on human societies and on evolution.

The learners also will

◆ develop models,

◆ construct explanations,

◆ use critical-thinking skills, and

◆ apply their ethical analysis skills.

Advance Preparation

The *Stuff of Life* requires 3–5 days of preparation time; refer to the Preparations section of that activity.

Modeling DNA, *Gene Expression*, and *A Closer Look at Protein Synthesis* each make use of a video. Preview the relevant segments before you show them in class and arrange to have a DVD player available on those days.

The Stuff of Life

Major Concepts DNA; genetic engineering technology

Overview

In this activity, the learners have the opportunity to examine real DNA that they extract from a bacterial suspension (or alternatively from onion cells). This activity is based on a procedure for DNA extraction from Lana Hays, Simon Kenton High School, Independence, Kentucky. During the course of their extraction, the students read a true story about the Romanov family. They will read about how genetic evidence enabled scientists to identify the Romanov family remains. Through this engaging example, the students see the importance, for citizens and scientists alike, of understanding DNA and molecular genetics.

Materials (per class of 30, teams of 2)

30 pairs of safety goggles

30 lab aprons

30 pairs of gloves

30 15-mL test tubes

2 or 3 500-mL beakers

15 calibrated pipets or graduated
    cylinders

15 glass stirring rods

15 test tube racks

2 or 3 thermometers

2 or 3 hot plates

7 glass-marking pencils

butcher paper

2 or 3 ice buckets filled with ice

1 small bottle of Woolite or Dawn
            150 mL 95% ethanol

100–150 mL bacterial suspension
    from lima beans

For alternative onion DNA extraction:

30 pairs of safety goggles

30 lab aprons

30 pairs of gloves

15-mL test tubes

30 glass stirring rods

beaker in ice bath

blender

funnel

coffee filter or cheesecloth

150 mL 95% ethanol

50 mL of 6% meat tenderizer solution
    (3 g meat tenderizer, 50 mL distilled
    water)

100 mL buffer mixture
    (1.5 g noniodized salt, 10 mL liquid
    dishwasher detergent [Palmolive],
    90 mL distilled water)

1 yellow onion

Outcomes and Indicators of Success

The following indicators allow you to assess the students' level of success with the activity and to assess their process of learning.

By the end of this activity, the learners should

1. be engaged in thinking about DNA as a real, tangible substance.

    They will demonstrate their engagement through their reactions during a DNA extraction activity.

2. become engaged in the applications of DNA technology.

    They will demonstrate their engagement by describing an application of DNA technology from a news story or personal experience.

Safety

Limit the amount of ethanol in the classroom to 300 mL. Remind students to observe all safety warnings in the procedures.

Preparations

Three to 5 days before you plan to do this activity, prepare a lima bean suspension in which bacteria will grow. You will use the bacterial suspension as the source of bacterial DNA. Empty a 1-lb bag of dried lima beans into a 2-L beaker and add 1.8 L of tap water. Cover the beaker loosely with plastic wrap and let it sit at room temperature for 3–5 days. (If the room temperature is 22.5°C [73°F], the bacteria will grow faster than if the room temperature is 20°C [68°F].) When the solution becomes cloudy, pour it off the beans and save the solution for the extraction.

Decide how many stations for the hot-water baths and the ice buckets you want and set up these stations ahead of time. Depending on your classroom layout and the available equipment, 2 or 3 stations should work well. Prepare the hot-water baths so that the water is between 65°C and 70°C.

Store the ethanol in a freezer the day before you do this activity so that it will be cold when the students place the ethanol in the ice buckets.

The onion DNA extraction produces a greater yield of DNA, but this procedure generally produces "blobs" of nucleic acid rather than fine DNA threads that can be spooled. If you choose to do the onion DNA extraction, which was suggested by field-test teacher Barbara Grosz (Pine Crest School, Florida) and is based on a demonstration given by Peggy O'Neill Skinner (Bush School, Washington), you will need to make the following preparations. Prepare the buffer and meat tenderizer solutions. Prepare an onion slurry by (a) cutting an onion into wedges and placing it in a blender; (b) adding 100 mL of chilled buffer mixture; (c) blending the mixture on a "frappe" setting until well blended (about 1 minute); (d) filtering the mixture using a funnel and coffee filter (or cheesecloth) into the beaker in the ice; (e) distributing approximately 4 mL into each test tube. The students will then do the following to isolate DNA (and RNA):

1. Add approximately 2 mL of meat tenderizer solution to the test tube of onion filtrate.

2. Mix slightly with glass rod.

3. Tilt the test tube and slowly add an equal volume of cold ethanol down the side of the test tube. A distinct and separate layer of clear ethanol should be visible above the colored filtrate. DNA (and RNA) will precipitate almost immediately at the interface.

4. Use a clean glass rod to spool the DNA out of the test tube.

This activity represents a fairly simple and inexpensive procedure for extracting DNA. If you would like to use a more sophisticated extraction process, consider using Ward's DNA Isolation Kit (catalog #88V8106). Such a kit might provide a greater DNA yield. Whichever procedure you decide to use, we recommend that you try the procedure yourself before you ask the students to complete it. This process will make you aware of the steps that might be the most difficult for the students and of the likely results.

Strategies for Guiding Learners

PROCESS AND PROCEDURES

As a class, read orally or silently all introductory materials for the activity and the Process and Procedures to help students build connections between concepts and activities. Use the time spent reading to bring the students' attention into focus.

1. Answer the following questions as part of a class discussion:

   a. When you hear the term *DNA*, what images come to mind?

   b. If you could see DNA, what do you think it would look like?

      Begin the activity with a class discussion of these two questions. Listen carefully to the students' responses, which will serve as an indicator of current understanding and misconceptions. You can use this information in later activities to help the learners construct a firm understanding of molecular genetics.

2. On a half page in your journal, draw what you think or predict that DNA looks like.

The students will work with a partner for most of the rest of this activity. Before they begin, remind them of all necessary safety precautions.

3. Investigate some of your ideas about DNA by using the DNA Isolation Protocol to isolate real DNA from bacteria. This process is called *extraction*.

Throughout the extraction procedure, and especially as the students release DNA from the cells in protocol step 4, it is critical that they are very careful so as not to fragment the DNA. Explain to the students that DNA must be treated gently or the long strands will break into fragments. If the DNA fragments, it will not spool and the visible power of DNA as a long, thin molecule will be lost. After they have placed their suspension in the water bath, remind them to monitor the temperature closely so that it remains between 65°C and 70°C for 15 minutes. Students can move the water bath on and off the hot plate or add small chips of ice to help regulate the temperature. If class time is short, have the students incubate the suspension for only 10–12 minutes, although this short incubation may result in a slightly reduced yield. If you have a longer class period and can let the suspension incubate for 30 minutes, the students likely will have a greater yield.

While the tubes are standing in the hot-water baths (protocol step 5) and the ethanol is in the ice bucket (protocol step 6), ask the students to share some of the questions that came to mind as they read the continued story, *A Royal Tragedy* (step 4). As they raise questions, record them on sheets of butcher paper and post them around the room. (Remember, at this point the students are just generating a list of questions; do not attempt to begin answering them now. For students to construct an understanding of a new topic, they must have time to think about their current impressions and explore new ideas slowly.) Tell the students that during this chapter, they will keep track of the questions that they generate and the answers that they are able to develop.

See pages 447–448 of the student text for the complete DNA Isolation Protocol.

After the suspension has been in the hot-water bath for 15–20 minutes, have the students remove their tubes and allow the tubes to return to room temperature; this will take about 5 minutes (step 8). Explain that now they will have an opportunity to see what DNA looks like.

As the students continue with the extraction, walk around the room to see how successful the extractions are. Explain that the white precipitate in the ethanol layer probably is a complex mixture of several macromolecules, including DNA, RNA, and some proteins and carbohydrates. Remind the students to rotate the rod slowly and to look carefully for the DNA fibers, which will appear as fine, white threads that accumulate around the rod. Because this extraction procedure takes advantage of the tendency of DNA to spool, what is on the rod is mostly DNA.

Make sure that each student has an opportunity to spool the DNA. It is likely that certain teams will have better success than others, and if this is the case, have the rest of the students gather around to see. Explain that even if they do this procedure carefully and follow it exactly, the DNA may not spool. Regardless of how careful they are, some DNA still will fragment and the students' spooling success will vary.

4. During the waiting period in step 7 of the DNA Isolation Protocol, contribute to a team list of questions that come to mind as you read the story *A Royal Tragedy (continued)*.

5. Participate in a class discussion that your teacher guides.

When the spooling is complete, begin an informal discussion by asking some engaging questions, such as the following:

◆ What did you think of the DNA that you saw?

◆ Explain how the DNA was similar to and different from the way you thought it would be.

◆ Can you imagine that DNA really controls the structure and function of the bacteria that you just extracted it from?

◆ If you extracted your own DNA, it would look (externally at least) much like this DNA. Why don't you look like a bacterium?

◆ How can scientists process this stuff so that they might be able to tell from whom it came—and use that information in court to convict or free someone? (Do not expect students to do more than guess at this point. The question is merely intended to get them thinking about technologies that connect DNA to societal issues.)

Keep the discussion short and lively. Record on the sheets of butcher paper any related questions that the students have. (If you run out of time, save this short discussion for the next day.) Explain to the students that the rest of the chapter is designed to help them construct a meaningful understanding of the continuity of information at the molecular level.

Analysis

You might suggest that students do the reading assignment referenced in Task 4 as homework.

Complete the following tasks in your journal:

1. Make a list of your observations on the process of isolating DNA and on what the DNA looked like. Compare these observations with your previous impressions from step 1 of Process and Procedures.

Student answers will vary depending on their success in isolating the bacterial DNA. Answers may include observations about the solution becoming thick or viscous after adding the detergent; the appearance of thick, whitish blobs in the lower layer; and the appearance of DNA before spooling as a cloudy solution and after spooling as an extremely fragile, mucuslike substance. Previous impressions may include visions of DNA as a long thin thread or beads on a string.

2. Is it likely that the cells of living organisms other than bacteria could serve as a source of DNA? Explain your answer.

   Because all living organisms contain DNA—as students may remember from Unit 1 (the evolution unit)—students should suggest that theoretically any organism could be used for such an isolation. They may suspect that it is easier to extract DNA from certain organisms than from others.

3. The story *A Royal Tragedy (continued)* illustrates one example of how the legal system uses DNA technology. What other applications of DNA technology have you heard about? Describe one example from a news story or personal experience.

   The students may suggest the O. J. Simpson trial of 1995, a more recent trial of local interest, or one of the many medical and research applications of DNA technology. Describing applications of DNA will encourage the students to recognize that DNA has achieved a level of prominence in the nonscientific community, a fact that helps justify its importance as a topic of study in high school.

4. Read the essays *Genetic Information Is Stored in Molecular Form* (page 512) and *Landmark Discovery: DNA May Be the Stuff of Genes* (page 513). Then answer the following questions: Do you think you could extract the same material from your skin cells? a leaf? your teeth? a rock? Why or why not?

Explore Transferring Information

Major Concepts Information transfer; the role of templates in facilitating accurate information transfer

Overview

Students work with a partner and in large teams to begin exploring the concepts associated with information transfer. To make the connections between their observations in this classroom exercise and genetic events inside cells, it is essential that students think back to the ideas of continuity of information in genetic inheritance and the variation that arises through mutation. In this exercise, students do two tests that involve the transfer of information. Then they extend their experiences with general information transfer to the transfer of genetic information.

Materials   (per class of 30, teams of 2 and 8)

4 containers
4 Test 1 messages, each the same (Copymaster *Messages for Testing Information Transfer*, see Preparations)
4 sets of mutation instructions for Test 2 (Copymaster *Messages for Testing Information Transfer*, see Preparations)
6 large sheets of paper

Outcomes and Indicators of Success

The following indicators allow you to assess the students' level of success with the activity and to assess their process of learning.

By the end of this activity, the learners should be able to

1. describe several features of genetic information transfer, especially observations about accuracy and the tendency for errors to occur during transfer.

   They will demonstrate their ability by participating in a class discussion about the results of two tests of information transfer.

2. speculate about how observations about genetic information transfer might apply to the genetic mechanisms that are responsible for storing and transferring information.

   They will demonstrate their ability by

   a. trying to connect their test results to genetic information transfer, and

   b. describing the possible effects of inaccurate DNA transfer on an organism or its offspring.

Preparations

Use the Copymaster *Messages for Testing Information Transfer* to make copies of the test messages that you will give to the students in position "number 1" on each team. You will need 4 copies of the message for Test 1. For Test 2, you will need 4 copies of the message and 4 sets of mutation instructions. Place each set (8 slips of mutation instructions) in a separate container, such as a coffee can or a basket.

An interesting mini-engage activity that sets the stage for thinking about nucleic acids as information molecules rather than as complex chemical entities can be found in *The American Biology Teacher*, volume 58 (January 1996). The activity links analog and digital information storage to DNA; you may want to use this as an introduction to *Transferring Information*.

Strategies for Guiding Learners

PROCESS AND PROCEDURES

As a class, read orally or silently all introductory materials for the activity and the Process and Procedures to help students build connections between concepts and activities. Use the time spent reading to bring the students' attention into focus.

Ask the learners to join their partners and discuss the questions related to the essay *Genetic Information Is Stored in Molecular Form*. This step will provide a context for the rest of this activity. As you walk around the classroom listening to team discussions, make a mental note of students' current understanding. In the next two activities, the students will construct a conceptual understanding of how DNA stores information, and you should reassess student understanding to address any misconceptions that remain.

1. To begin thinking about information transfer in living systems, join your teammates to discuss the following questions. Record your answers in your journal.

   At this point in the chapter, your answers may be brief and simple.

a. All molecules store energy. But not all molecules store the information that affects inheritance. Which molecules contain the information that results in an organism's genotype and phenotype? What ideas do you have about how information is stored in molecules?

> **DNA is the nearly universal information molecule in living organisms. Students' ideas about how, precisely, DNA may store information will vary, but the ideas may range from correct, although unsophisticated, to wildly imaginative. Students may not have any idea how information is stored in DNA, which is fine at this time, but any answers that they do offer will reveal their current understanding and/or misconceptions about the function of DNA.**

b. What is the role of genetic information in the life of an individual organism?

> **As the essay notes, the genetic information in an individual organism is expressed in a way that affects the organism's phenotype. DNA contains the instructions for building, maintaining, and regulating the cells of living organisms and thus the organisms themselves.**

c. Why is replication (copying) of DNA important to the continuity of a species?

> **The continuity of organisms depends on the accurate transmission of genetic information from one generation to the next, and because DNA is the molecular form of this information, the replication of DNA affects continuity. Genetic information is passed to offspring during reproduction; this maintains the continuity of the species.**

d. Why is it important that genetic information be passed on, or transmitted, accurately?

> **Inaccuracies in the transfer of genetic information can affect the instructions that living organisms depend on for building, maintaining, and regulating the structures necessary for life. Serious errors in transmission can affect the viability of living organisms.**

2. Join with another team. Briefly discuss your answers to the questions in step 1. Revise your answers if you wish.

> **Ask the learners to join another team and share their answers.**

3. According to your teacher's instructions, create a team of 8. Follow your teacher's directions for carrying out 2 tests of information transfer.

> **Before the learners form their teams of eight, provide an introduction for the information transfer tests by asking the following questions:**
>
> **We already know that DNA stores information, but what is it about its structure that allows it also to transfer this information? How does this transfer happen? First, you will use the information stored in language to explore some general ideas that are related to the process of transferring information. Then you will relate some of these findings to how DNA works.**
>
> **Ask each team of two to join three other teams of two to create teams of eight. Tell the students that they will be conducting tests on the transfer of information in language. One test compares oral versus written transfer; the second investigates the introduction of errors into messages. The tests should be fast-paced and fun, so be sure to keep the pace moving. Ask a team leader to assign a number (from 1–8) to each team member. Explain that this number represents the order in which they will transfer information. For each test, complete the following procedure:**

a. Provide a written copy of the test message to the student assigned to position number 1 on each team. We have listed the suggested test messages on the Copymaster *Messages for Testing Information Transfer*, and the intent of each test is summarized in Figure T12.1.

b. Dictate to the students, one step at a time, the instructions for completing the particular test (see boxes labeled Test 1 and Test 2).

c. Allow each team to complete the test.

d. Ask the teams to report both the message with which they began and the message with which they finished. Record these on the chalkboard or on a piece of butcher paper.

To summarize the results of the test, conduct a class discussion. Ask the students what comments or generalizations they can make about transferring information based on the outcomes of the tests. Record these generalizations in a table on the board or on an overhead transparency so that the students can refer to them during the Analysis. You may need to ask guided questions to get the students to articulate generalizations similar to those in Figure T12.1. For instance, you might ask, Were errors more common in the oral transfer or the written transfer? How might DNA act to preserve information? What effect does a written message (a templated message) have on the transfer of errors?

TEST 1
Half of the teams transfer an oral, coded message; half of the teams transfer the same coded message in writing.

Directions

1. Assign half of the teams to be writing teams and the other half to be speaking teams.

2. Explain that for each speaking team, the person with the message (team member 1) should memorize the message. For each writing team, the person with the message should copy it onto a slip of paper or onto the top of a larger piece of paper.

3. Team member 1 should pass the message to the other teammates (in numerical order) according to the directions below.

   a. Speaking team: These team members should whisper the message to the next person in line (numerically).

      The person passing the message should whisper softly and should not repeat the message or provide clarification about what it might mean.

   b. Writing team: These team members should make a written copy of the message and pass it to the next person in line (numerically). If using a sheet of paper, the student receiving the message can write the new copy of it just below the original and then fold the paper over so that only the new copy is visible.

4. The last person in the sequence should record his or her version of the message in his or her journal.

TEST 2

Directions

1. **Give one container with mutation instructions to each team.**

2. **Ask each of the eight members of a team to draw a slip of paper from the container. This slip describes a task that each team member should perform on a written message.**

   The team members should not reveal the nature of their instructions.

3. **Give team member number 1 a sheet of paper and a copy of the Test 2 written message. Ask that person to copy the message and carry out the task described by his or her mutation instruction.**

4. **Team member 1 should pass the sheet of paper to the next person in line (numerically). The recipient should copy the message and carry out his or her task. The student receiving the message can write the new copy of it just below the original and then fold the paper over so that only the new copy is visible.**

5. **The last person in the sequence should record his or her version of the message in his or her journal.**

Figure T12.1 Summary of tests

Test	Generalization of tests
1. Oral coded vs. written coded	Errors may be introduced, and if they are, they will be transferred; use of templates reduces errors. The messages transmitted orally generally have errors, and the written messages generally are error free.
2. Written coded with change introduced at one position	Use of a template means that any change will be transferred. Regardless of where in a transmission sequence the mutation (the word "in") is introduced, the copying process helps ensure that it remains as part of the permanent message.

Analysis

Ask the learners to complete the *Analysis* in their teams of two. Explain that they should speculate on how their general observations about information transfer could mirror the transfer of information at the molecular level (via genetics). Encourage students to use ideas from Chapter 11 to support their speculations, and remind them to record their responses in their journals. If students have trouble with the questions, prompt them with simpler questions that help them recall the roles of reproduction (continuity) and mutation (variation). For example, you might ask, Do errors (mutations) increase or decrease variation? or After a mutation (the word "in") was introduced into your written message, was the mutation preserved through copying or did the original message return? How was this like mutations in DNA? You may want to tell the students that you will collect their journals to assess their understanding of the ideas in this activity.

1. Examine the results of each test you conducted in step 3. In your journal, explain how each set of observations might apply to the genetic mechanisms that are responsible for storing and transferring information.

    Test 1: In genetics, a molecule might act as a written message or guide to help build another molecule. The exercise underscores the idea that the use of a template reduces the incidence of errors. This concept foreshadows the ideas in *Modeling DNA* and *Gene Expression* (that is, DNA provides a molecular template for replication and transmission of genetic information as well as for expression).

    Test 2: A mutation can be preserved when new copies of mutated genetic material are produced. Students might suggest that the mutated material becomes the new template for the passage of the altered information.

2. In your own words, or in a concept map, briefly describe the relationships among DNA, genes, chromosomes, accurate information transmission, cells, an organism, and offspring.

    Organisms are made up of cells, which contain the organism's chromosomes. Chromosomes are made up of DNA, which codes for the organism's structure and function. The segments of DNA on chromosomes that work together to code for a particular trait or function are called genes. Through reproduction, the organism passes its genetic information to its offspring. Accurate transmission of that genetic information is central to the continuity of the species. Mutations in that transmission are usually fatal, but in some cases, it introduces variation that is retained and may even be beneficial.

Modeling DNA

Major Concepts DNA structure; DNA replication; base pairing as a mechanism for information storage and transmission; modeling a scientific process

Overview

The previous activity provided the learners with insights into some important, but general, aspects of information transfer. In this activity, the students connect those ideas with the molecular storage and transfer of information as it occurs in biological systems. They do so primarily by using plastic pop beads to model DNA structure and replication. Students move through the modeling process one step at a time, gradually building and modifying their models while at the same time building strong explanations of how the structure of DNA allows both the storage of genetic information and its accurate replication. Important sources of information for the students include data provided in the activity itself, two supporting essays, and a video animation.

Materials   (per class of 30, teams of 4)

pop beads (approximately 300 each of colors red, green, black, and white)
an assortment of fastening materials, such as twist ties, wire, rubber bands, and
    double-sided tape
DVD
DVD player
500 m or yards of thread (optional)
overhead projector (optional)
30 copies of the Copymaster *Modeling a Double Helix* (or 1 transparency)

Outcomes and Indicators of Success

The following indicators allow you to assess the students' level of success with the activity and to assess their process of learning.

By the end of this activity, the learners should

1. be able to explain how the structure of DNA is related to its capacity to store information.

    They will demonstrate their ability by

    a. modifying their model of DNA to reflect its structure more and more accurately, and

    b. explaining both orally and in writing how the sequence of bases is related to information storage.

2. be able to explain how the structure of DNA is related to a cell's capacity to copy that information to maintain continuity through reproduction.

    They will demonstrate their ability by

    a. using their pop bead models to demonstrate the process of replication, and

    b. developing a written explanation of how complementary base pairing is related to information transfer.

3. be able to describe a mutation in molecular terms and to explain how a mutation is passed on to subsequent generations through replication.

They will demonstrate their ability by

a. using their pop bead models to illustrate the perpetuation of a mutation during replication, and

b. explaining the molecular basis of mutation and a mutation's possible effects on the organisms possessing it as well as subsequent generations.

Preparations

Make certain that you have adequate quantities of at least 4 colors of beads (or paper clips) in containers with lids to help prevent spills. Each team will need 40–45 beads of each color and access to twist ties, rubber bands, wire, double-sided tape, or other materials for attaching one strand of beads to another. Note: If you are concerned that your students will not respond well to using pop beads to model DNA, you may substitute paper clips of 4 different colors. Because the purpose of this activity is to give students the opportunity to build models of increasing detail and accuracy, we recommend that at this point you do not introduce paper cutouts of actual nucleotides. Students will work with more detailed representations of DNA in the next activity, *Gene Expression*.

If you choose to have your students work with pop beads or with paper clips, you might want to have them work over trays with rims.

You will need a DVD player for Part B of the activity. Make an overhead transparency of the Copymaster *Modeling a Double Helix*, or alternatively, copies for each student.

To help students evaluate their 2nd model (Model 2), you may wish to bring 1 or more large zippers to class.

For an optional mini-engage, unspool 500 m of thread and place it next to the cut-off connector of 1 pop bead; this shows the length of unwound DNA as compared with the nucleus in which it is stored (see Figure T12.2).

Background Information

For a detailed explanation of current thinking about the evolution of the structure and function of nucleic acids, see *The RNA World* by Ray Gesteland and John Atkins (1993), Plainview, NY: Cold Spring Harbor Laboratory Press.

Strategies for Guiding Learners

PROCESS AND PROCEDURES

As a class, read orally or silently all introductory materials for the activity and the Process and Procedures to help students build connections between concepts and activities. Use the time spent reading to bring the students' attention into focus.

One option for quickly engaging student interest in this activity is to unwind a 500-meter spool of thread and pile it next to a small connector from a pop bead. Explain to the students that your demonstration provides a rough comparison of the amount of DNA in a typical human cell nucleus (the thread) with the size of that nucleus (the connector). Figure T12.2 gives you a sense of the power of this visual comparison. If you use this demonstration, refer students during Part B of the activity to Figure E12.2 in the essay *DNA Structure and Replication*. This figure provides a visual explanation of the packing mechanisms that allow such a huge amount of DNA to be packaged efficiently. Challenge students to imagine having to pack an amount of DNA that is analogous to the mass of thread back inside a space the size of the pop bead tip. Note: The diameter of the thread is not scaled appropriately with its length; it is much thicker.

Figure T12.2 Efficiency of DNA packing This figure demonstrates the packing dilemma faced by cells each time they replicate and repackage DNA in a eukaryotic nucleus. The thread, about 500 meters or two to three spools of thread, represents the length of haploid DNA present in one human cell scaled up 500×. The small bead (1.4 mm in diameter) represents a nucleus where the diameter has been scaled up 1,500×. Another way to present the enormity of information and the elegance of packing in chromosomes is to give the following analogy. If the DNA from every human cell in one person were removed and stretched end-to-end, it would extend from the earth to the sun and back more than six times (1,270,000,000 miles). There are about 2 meters of DNA (fully extended) in every human cell except gametes and red blood cells).

PART A   Modeling DNA Structure

Models 1, 2, and *3* in Part A of this activity are exploratory. Students use limited information about the structure of DNA (presented in "bulleted" notes in the boxes labeled *Model 1, Model 2,* and *Model 3*) as one way of exploring the physical aspects of nucleic acid structure and the role of structure in the function of DNA molecules. As students begin to construct their models, watch for patterns in the way they set up the pop beads. These patterns will be clues to their understanding.

Throughout the activity, emphasize the role of structure in carrying out the functions of genetic material.

Model 1

1. Build your 1st model. Use both the pop beads and the following observations about the structure of DNA:

    ◆ DNA is a polymer. A polymer is a very long, chainlike molecule composed of small subunit molecules. Subunit molecules are like the links in a chain. They are attached to each other by covalent bonds.

    ◆ Four different types of subunit molecules exist.

2. Compare your model with those built by the other members of your team. Discuss any differences that you notice.

Keep this activity moving at a brisk pace as students explore with their bead models. If any students appear stuck, facilitate their efforts by prompting or by asking leading questions such as, If DNA has four different types of subunits, how many different colors of beads do you think you should use in making your long chain of subunits? Do not let your class get stuck in the details of its early models (1 and 2), which intentionally have insufficient data to support the making of a detailed model. The most important issue is for students to do the best job they can with *available* information and then to modify their models as they acquire more data about the structure of DNA. (Part B will provide an opportunity to develop more complete explanations of how DNA's structure influences its function.)

3. Analyze your model by responding to the following in your journal:

a. What features of your model represent the properties of DNA described above?

b. Look closely at your model. How do you think that the structure of DNA might allow it to store information? How might DNA store different information along different parts of its length?

Students may first consider the possibility that information storage in a DNA molecule is linear because some will note that different team members have constructed their DNA chains by connecting subunits in various sequences. If this does not occur to anyone, ask the question, How are you deciding on the order of your colored beads? This may prompt some students to come up with the idea that the order of subunits could be different in different genes, offering a basis for information storage.

Model 2

4. Modify your DNA model. It should reflect the following additional information:

♦ DNA consists of 2 long chains of subunits twisted around each other to form a double helix. (A helix is the shape a pipe cleaner takes when you wrap it around a pencil.)

♦ The 2 helical chains are weakly bonded together. Subunits on 1 chain or strand bond to subunits on the other strand.

♦ The diameter of the DNA molecule is uniform along its length.

5. Compare your new model with those built by the other members of your team. Discuss any differences that you notice.

In Model 2, students explore the interactions between different strands of nucleic acids. If the learners do not quickly begin using tape or twist ties or some other fastener to bind their strands together (thus modeling the weak bonding between strands), ask, What tools do you have access to that might provide a way of modeling the weak bonding that is mentioned as a characteristic of the two helical chains of DNA? Students probably will try many combinations of bonding, and there is no reason they should assume base complementarity. Support all reasonable models and prompt the learners to justify their design. As with Model 1, the learners will gain insights into other possibilities by comparing their models with those of other students.

6. Analyze your 2nd model by responding to the following in your journal:

   a. How well does your pop bead model represent each of the 5 structural characteristics of DNA listed so far? Briefly list these 5 characteristics. Then explain how your model represents each.

   b. Examine the figures that your teacher presents. Compare the superficial resemblances with a spiral staircase and with a zipper. List the strengths and weaknesses of using a spiral staircase or a zipper to illustrate DNA structure. How do these models compare with your pop bead model?

   Help students critique their models' usefulness in representing the various aspects of DNA structure; this not only will help them understand DNA's structure and function, it will give them experience in recognizing the limits of models. For example, the pop bead model offers a way of representing the sequence of bases covalently bonded to form two chains, but it does not model the hydrogen bonding that holds the two chains together. By tying together two bead strands, as in Figure T12.3, the students will at least be able to keep the strands in close association.

Figure T12.3 Example of a pop bead model of double-stranded DNA. Here, strands are tied together with string.

Note how students respond to the questions in step 6, and use their current level of understanding to guide the discussion of comparisons between DNA, spiral staircases, and zippers. To begin reviewing the double helical nature of DNA, place an overhead transparency of the Copymaster *Modeling a Double Helix,* which shows a spiral staircase, a ladder, a zipper, and a simplified double helix, on an overhead projector. If you bring one or more zippers to class, students can see that the zipper models strand-strand interactions nicely but lacks differences in subunits, which makes it an ineffective model of DNA sequence and informational properties. Some students might suggest that a twisted ladder would make a good model of DNA, but the rungs of a ladder are too strong to model well the weak hydrogen bonds that hold DNA strands together, and the plane of the base pairs would not mimic DNA. A ladder wrapped around a telephone pole more accurately represents a double helix, although it too has deficiencies (as do all models).

Model 3

7. Now add another layer of detail to your model of DNA. Consider the following observation. Modify your design accordingly:

◆ The order of subunits in 1 strand of DNA determines the order of subunits in the other strand.

As you try to solve this portion of the model, consider that the aspect of DNA's structure that you now are modeling is the key to how DNA is replicated (copied).

8. Compare your new model with those built by the other members of your team. Discuss any differences that you notice.

9. Analyze your 3rd model by responding to the following in your journal:

a. Use your modeling results to describe the relationship between subunits bonded to each other on opposite strands of the DNA double helix.

b. Think about this last characteristic of DNA. Consider how the relationship between the subunits on each strand might suggest a means of replicating the molecule. Describe your ideas.

> Model 3 provides the next layer of information: that of complementary base pairing. This most likely will be difficult for many students, so be prepared to offer help as needed. To simplify the bulleted criterion even further, restate it as the question, How can the identity of one subunit determine the identity of its pairing partner on the opposite strand? (Answer: If the same two subunits always are paired.) By extension, this principle can define the complete order of subunits on an entire strand if one strand is known. This characteristic of complementary base pairing is what underlies replication.

PART B Analyzing a DVD Model

Show the DVD segment "DNA Structure," which shows the four nucleotides of which DNA is composed and reveals the nature of their complementary pairing. This information should allow the learners to add to their understanding of complementarity, information storage, and the transfer of genetic material.

1. With your class, view the DVD segment "DNA Structure." This segment will give you more information about DNA structure (the 4 subunits and the interactions between subunits on each strand). It will also help you understand the importance of this structure to the replication of DNA molecules.

As you watch the DVD segment, look for information that will help you answer the following questions. Take notes in your journal. The new information that you gather will help you better understand the structure of DNA.

a. What characteristic of the subunits allows for a uniform diameter of the double helix? What type of interaction takes place between the subunits of each strand that encourages a double helix to form?

> Specific base pairing between one large and one small base (adenine [A] with thymine [T], and guanine [G] with cytosine [C]) allows for a uniform diameter of the helix. Hydrogen bonds between complementary bases encourages the formation of a double helix.

b. How does the sequence of subunits on 1 strand provide a template (a pattern or guide) for the sequence of subunits on the other strand? Is that important to replication? Explain your answer.

>The fact that a particular base can pair with only one other base (A with T or G with C) means that pairing partners on the adjacent strand always are defined by the sequence on the first strand. This is important to replication because the complete sequence of a double helical DNA is actually preserved in just one strand, and replication depends on the separation and copying of the two strands of the double helix.

2. Use the new information that you gathered from the DVD segment and the tasks below to reevaluate your 3rd model.

◆ Write a short paragraph in your journal that describes how you would have to modify your 3rd model to reflect this new information.

◆ List 3 ways in which pop beads limit your ability to create a more detailed or more accurate model of a DNA molecule.

◆ State what materials (other than pop beads) you would use. How would you assemble them to model DNA more accurately? (Alternatively, you may use these materials to construct another model on your own.)

>In reevaluating the video model, learners should note that pop beads limit the accuracy of their DNA models in a number of significant ways. For instance, the beads do not allow adequate representation of the size or shape of the subunit bases, the connectivity of the polynucleotide backbone, the hydrogen bonding between bases, or the helical shape. Wire models of accurate chemical nucleotides would be the best materials for a full model of DNA, but even paper cutouts of nucleotides, if available, would provide some advantages. Students may suggest many reasonable alternatives.

PART C Modeling DNA Replication

In Part C of this activity, students use pop bead models, two essays, and the DVD segment "DNA Replication" as resources to answer two questions that help to illustrate the processes of replication and mutation. The video segment shows animation of DNA replicating. At the appropriate times during students' work with this resource (for instance, step 3c), you may need to point out the hydrogen bonds because they are very light. You may wish to use the questions provided in the student pages as an informal checklist to assess the students' understanding of the structure and function of DNA.

As you move from group to group, listen closely to the ideas expressed and observe how the learners manipulate their models. If they do not use some of the available resources, their attempts to model replication largely will be guesses. Encourage them to explain and defend their manipulations. As necessary, offer leading comments or questions to help the students expand or rethink their explanations.

Research Question 1

What are the critical characteristics of DNA that allow both the lasting storage of information and the transfer of information through copying (replication)?

1. Use the pop beads and the key in Figure 12.4 to build a model of a molecule of DNA.

   Although you will work as a team to share information, each of you should build and manipulate your own model. You will need to demonstrate to your teacher your *own* understanding of replication.

2. Manipulate your pop bead model to illustrate the process of replication.

3. Read the essay *Landmark Discovery: Why the Fuss about Watson and Crick?* (page 521). Consider the work that Watson and Crick did now that you have gone through the process of constructing a DNA model. Discuss the following statements and questions with your team and with your teacher when he or she visits your group. Record your conclusions in your journal. It is important that you understand these points before you attempt to complete step 4.

   a. Scientists use the phrase *complementary base pairing* to refer to the pairing of G with C and A with T in the DNA molecule. How does complementary base pairing make accurate replication possible?

      Complementary base pairing makes accurate replication possible because the sequence of bases on one strand defines the sequence of bases on the complementary strand.

   b. The bonds that attach adjacent nucleotide subunits in a strand of DNA are covalent bonds, which are strong. How would strong bonds improve the DNA molecule's ability to store information accurately for a long time?

      Strong covalent bonds between adjacent subunits in a DNA strand favor the storage of linear information because the strands are less likely to break, and thus lose information stored in the sequence, than if the bonds were weak. (Of course, this is not by design. Evolution favored the selection of simple primordial organisms, or perhaps even self-replicating molecules, that could store and transmit information in a stable form.)

   c. The bonds that attach the 2 DNA strands to each other in a double helix are hydrogen bonds. Hydrogen bonds are much weaker than covalent bonds. How would weaker bonds favor the capacity of the DNA molecule to replicate?

      Relatively weak hydrogen bonds between base-paired subunits on opposite DNA strands favor the replication of DNA because the strands can separate and rejoin more easily than if the strands were joined by strong bonds. (Again, this is not by design. Molecules that could be copied and propagated must have held a selective advantage during the earliest phases of DNA's evolution.)

   d. How does your model reflect the difference between the bond strength between nucleotide subunits and the bond strength between the 2 strands of a DNA molecule? Illustrate your answer with specific references to your pop bead model.

      Depending on how students have chosen to model hydrogen bonding, their answers will vary. For example, one learner's model might reflect relatively strong bonding along the pop bead strand because the connectors fit fairly tightly, whereas double-stick tape between strands would not offer much resistance to strand separation.

4. Analyze your work in steps 1–3 above. Then develop an answer to research question 1. Record your answer in your journal.

When the learners have finished with the questions in step 3, direct them to develop a formal answer to research question 1. These answers should summarize the discoveries made in steps 1–3: a combination of strong bonds within strands and weak bonds between them, and complementary base pairing.

Research Question 2

What are the advantages and disadvantages of an information transfer system that uses a physical pattern, or template?

5. Use your pop bead model to demonstrate a mutation in your DNA molecule.

6. Use your pop bead model to demonstrate what would happen to this mutation as your DNA molecule replicates.

7. Discuss the following questions with your team and with your teacher when he or she visits your group. It is important that you understand the answers to these questions before you attempt to complete step 8.

Students will repeat the earlier manipulations except that now they will model the replication of a DNA molecule that contains a mutation. The principles are the same, but this exercise allows students to practice using their understanding of DNA structure and function in a new, but related, situation.

a. Think back to the tests of information transfer that you conducted in the previous activity, *Transferring Information*. How did the accuracy of the orally transferred information compare with the accuracy of the written transfer?

Learners most likely will recall that the oral transfer of information was less accurate than that in the form of a written message. Physical templates preserve information because they are themselves a record of the stored information. Thus, during replication, each strand preserves the information until two new strands can be synthesized.

b. Under what conditions might the extremely high accuracy of replication be advantageous to a species?

The extremely high accuracy of replication can be advantageous to a species because it preserves from one generation to the next the information for building and maintaining the structures necessary for life. Thus, adaptive characteristics will be inherited by the next generation. If the environment in which the species lives does not change much from one generation to the next, then the adaptive characteristics possessed by the parents are likely to be adaptive for the offspring as well.

c. Under what conditions might such accuracy be disadvantageous?

If an organism has mutations that are harmful, highly accurate replication would tend to preserve those mutations and allow them to be passed through inheritance to offspring, which would then suffer the consequences of the same harmful mutations. Alternatively, too few mutations also could be disadvantageous.

In a rapidly changing environment, a species might be at a disadvantage if its DNA replication system was too accurate because the accuracy would limit the number of mutations that occur, which consequently would limit the variation that is so important to adaptation.

8. Review your work in steps 5–7. Then develop an answer to research question 2. Record your answer in your journal.

When the learners have finished with the questions in step 7, direct them to develop a formal answer to research question 2. These answers should summarize the discoveries made in steps 5–7: physical templates are a structural record of stored information, and the replication of DNA templates can preserve the accuracy or the inaccuracy of the information contained within them.

Analysis

During this activity, you used scientific modeling to explore two important characteristics of DNA: (1) its ability to *store* information, and (2) its ability to *transmit* that information to future generations. Fit these characteristics into the big picture of genetic continuity and reproduction by completing the following tasks:

1. Copy Figure E12.1 (page 512) into your journal. Label the portion of the figure that specifically illustrates the *storage* of genetic information. Label the portion of the figure that specifically illustrates the *transmission* of information to subsequent generations. Label the portion of the figure that specifically illustrates the use of genetic information to maintain life.

Students should recognize that the box labeled *genotype* illustrates the storage of genetic information and that the arrow that points from *genotype* to *replicate* and back to *genotype* illustrates the transmission of genetic information from one generation to the next. The box labeled *expression* illustrates the use of genetic information. (Stored information is not sufficient for maintaining the life of an organism; an organism must be able to interpret and use the instructions coded in the genetic information.)

2. In your journal, explain the relationship between DNA structure and

Expect your students to offer explanations similar to those following, and to illustrate their answers with diagrams that show labeled bases (a) and labeled base pairs (b):

a. information storage, and

Genetic information is encoded in the sequence of bases on one strand of the DNA molecule.

b. accurate information transfer during the reproduction of organisms (meiosis).

Include a diagram to illustrate your explanation.

DNA acts as its own template for making new DNA copies during replication. Because subunits are added in a way that matches complementary pairs of bases, the sequence of bases in one strand of DNA determines the sequence in a new strand.

3. Imagine that a mutation takes place in an organism's genotype.

Expect your students to offer explanations similar to those following:

a. Explain *in molecular terms* how this change might have happened. How can it be passed along to offspring and to the next generation of offspring after that.

A mutation is a physical alteration in DNA structure, such as the loss of a subunit, addition of a subunit, or substitution of one subunit for the correct one. Mutations can happen as a consequence of errors introduced during replication or because of exposure to natural and humanmade hazards (mutagens), such as radiation and toxic chemicals. These changes can be passed from one generation to the next because replication can preserve mutations in DNA (because DNA acts as a template), and the altered DNA is transmitted through inheritance. If a mutation is lethal, then the organism possessing it will die and may not pass that mutation to subsequent generations.

b. What effect might this mutation have on an organism carrying it? Why? Refer to Figure E12.7 (page 520) in your answer.

Students might speculate that a mutation would have an effect on the organism's phenotype. This is illustrated in Figure E12.1 by the arrow that leads from the box labeled *genotype* through the box labeled *expression* to the box labeled *phenotype*.

Further Challenges

Review with the learners the tests of information transfer that they completed in *Transferring Information*. Although those tests used written and spoken language instead of the language of DNA, point out that each test actually was a rough model of the *process* by which information is transmitted from one cell to another (or one organism to another) following DNA replication. Review the strengths and weaknesses of each model using the questions in the student book as a guide.

Briefly review the tests of information transfer that you completed in the activity *Transferring Information*. Those tests used written and spoken language instead of the language of DNA. However, each test was a rough model of the process by which information transmits from one cell to another (or one organism to another) following DNA replication. As a model, each test had strengths and weaknesses. Each test portrayed the processes of information transfer with varying degrees of accuracy.

Ask yourself how accurately each test represented the replication of DNA, as you understand the process now. Then answer the two questions below.

1. How does the copying of coded, written words compare with DNA replication? How is it similar? How is it different?

Remember, DNA replication is the biological process by which one molocule of DNA produces a second, identical molecule.

Copying coded language messages obviously is a conscious, intentional process for any humans doing it, whereas DNA replication is carried out biochemically and without purpose. The letters of language have no chemical identity, and although we use letters to represent the DNA code, the actual template is a molecule. DNA templates are double-stranded, and replication of both strands happens simultaneously. This produces two double-stranded molecules, each of which contains one new DNA strand and one old DNA strand. Copying a language message yields one completely new message and one old message.

2. How does the transfer of coded, written words compare with reproduction? How is it similar? How is it different?

Reproduction is the biological mechanism by which genetic information maintains the continuity of a species.

The transfer of a coded language message does not provide the recipient with instructions that build and maintain its body, which is what reproduction provides offspring. Coded languages also are not subject to the same regulation as gametes, the carriers of genetic information.

Explain

Gene Expression

Major Concepts Expression of genetic information; transcription; protein synthesis; genetic code; mutations

Overview

This activity is designed to help students develop a conceptual understanding of the complex phenomenon of gene expression. To help students see the connection between genotype (as it is conventionally described with symbols) and phenotype (as, for example, in visible physical characteristics), the activity requires students to develop a detailed explanation of the molecular basis of sickle-cell disease. Sources of information include essays, information provided in the body of the activity, and a DVD segment. Using these resources, students create a poster with illustrations and descriptions that use the hemoglobin gene to trace the flow of genetic information from DNA to RNA to protein.

Materials (per class of 30, teams of 2)

15 pieces of poster board	tape or glue
assorted construction paper	DVD
a selection of colored, felt-tipped	DVD player
markers	30 copies of the Copymaster *DNA*
several boxes of crayons	*Sequences for Hemoglobin Alleles*
30 pairs of scissors	

Outcomes and Indicators of Success

The following indicators allow you to assess the students' level of success with the activity and to assess their process of learning.

By the end of this activity, the learners should

1. develop an understanding of how the molecular structure of DNA allows for precise and efficient transcription of information.

   They will demonstrate their understanding by building a model of mRNA that corresponds to the coding strand of specific DNA sequences.

2. develop an understanding of the process that translates the language of nucleic acids into the language of proteins.

   They will demonstrate their understanding by translating an mRNA sequence into the proper sequence of amino acids.

3. develop an understanding of the overall scheme of gene expression.

   They will demonstrate their understanding by

   a. creating a poster that compares the results of the expression of the normal and sickle-cell alleles of the hemoglobin gene,

   b. listing the steps involved in the expression of genotype, and

   c. applying their understanding of gene expression to develop an explanation for how the cystic fibrosis gene may exert its effects.

Preparations

Students may need to watch the sequence of events in the DVD segment several times, so it might be helpful for one or two students to learn how to operate the DVD player. These students then may be responsible for replaying the "Transcription" segment.

Background Information

Regulation. The mechanisms of transcription and translation provide many opportunities for the regulation of gene expression. The frequency of transcription and the stability of the mRNAs that are produced determine the number of messages available for translation. Proteins that are needed in large amounts, or very quickly, can be produced by translating the same message many times or by translating many identical messages or both. Likewise, proteins that are needed in only very small amounts can be produced from rare or unstable messages, that is, from mRNAs that are produced at very low levels or that are degraded immediately following translation.

Mutations. Genetic diseases often are caused by mutations in DNA. These mutations lead to defective, inefficient, or unstable (absent) proteins. Quite often, disease can arise as a consequence of a single amino acid change or deletion (as in the cases of sickle-cell disease and cystic fibrosis). The reason for this is that even one incorrect amino acid—if it is located in a critical place—can disrupt the folding of the protein and lead to a nonfunctional product. If, however, a mutation causes a structural change (for example, a different amino acid or one missing amino acid) in an area of the protein that is not critical to folding or function, then there is no harmful effect. In these cases, the mutation is said to be silent.

Single- or double-base deletions in the DNA nearly always lead to a nonfunctional product because the reading frame—the sets of triplet nucleotides that the ribosome reads—is shifted. This leads to the synthesis of a different sequence of amino acids and quite often to a translational stop. The same type of effects can result when extra nucleotides (one or two base insertions) are present in the DNA. Three base insertions or deletions (and multiples of three) are less likely to inactivate the protein because they add or delete amino acids rather than shift the entire reading frame.

Strategies for Guiding Learners

PROCESS AND PROCEDURES

As a class, read orally or silently all introductory materials for the activity and the Process and Procedures to help students build connections between concepts and activities. Use the time spent reading to bring the students' attention into focus.

The central goal of this activity is to help students understand conceptually the processes by which the cell expresses its genetic information. The purpose of the poster is to provide a vehicle through which students can see at a glance the entire scheme of events (from genotype to phenotype) in the expression of the sickle-cell allele. This will help students avoid thinking about molecular biological processes as distinct events that are unrelated to reproduction, inheritance, or development.

Because this scheme of events is long and complex, learners may have some initial difficulty tracking their progress through the various processes and results. This makes it important for students to develop the outline for their posters at the beginning of the activity, and then fill in the details as they move through the activity's parts. Although many of the details will be missing from their posters at the start, the existence of the empty, numbered spots on the poster will remind the students that they are working to describe a complex series of events and consequences. As the students encounter new events and consequences in that series, the poster also will help them see where each fits into the overall scheme.

You may be able to help your students track their progress in understanding gene expression by reminding them often of their overall goal (to explain how the information in a gene is expressed in a phenotype) and by asking them to explain to you and to others how each part of the activity moves them toward that goal. It may help to introduce each part of the activity with a series of leading questions that helps students articulate what they already know about the expression of the sickle-cell gene and what they do not know yet. Suggestions for how to do this are included at the appropriate points in the strategies below.

Notice that the main body of the activity does not require the students to examine either transcription or translation in detail. Rather, the activity focuses on the major results of the events of gene expression: on the production of mRNA by transcription of the DNA, on the linear translation of the information encoded in the mRNA to build a sequence of amino acids, and on the subsequent folding of the resulting polypeptide chain to form a functional protein. You want to develop further the details of transcription and translation. To avoid confusing the emerging conceptual picture with a great deal of technical detail, we recommend further study only after the learners have completed the main tasks in *Gene Expression*.

PART A Looking at Sickle-Cell Disease

1. Begin your study of the molecular basis of sickle-cell disease by reading the information in the need to know about this inherited disorder and its associated gene.

2. Review the essay *Incomplete Dominance* on page 510. Consider what the phenotype might be for a person with the genotype $Hb^A Hb^S$.

   To develop some background, the students read and discuss a brief description of sickle-cell disease and begin their posters. Introduce step 1 by reminding the students that they read about sickle-cell disease in Chapter 11, and by pointing out that completing this activity will help them develop an explanation of how the genotype *Hb^S^Hb^S^* causes the biological and clinical effects associated with the condition. Keep the discussion in step 2 brief but specific, and use the questions to assess the students' current understanding of sickle-cell disease.

3. Discuss the following questions with your partner. Contribute to a class discussion as your teacher directs.

    a. What medical symptoms might a person with sickle-cell disease experience?
        Sickle-cell disease causes pain and organ damage to people with the disease.

    b. What problem in the red blood cells causes these symptoms to happen?
        The red blood cells are sickle-shaped.

    c. What problem in the behavior of the hemoglobin molecules is associated with these changes in an individual's red blood cells?
        When the concentration of oxygen in the blood is low, abnormal hemoglobin molecules clump together, causing red blood cells to form a sickle shape. The sickle shape then causes the cells to block small blood vessels, and this causes the pain and damage associated with the disease.

    d. Think back to your knowledge of DNA structure. What might be the *molecular basis* for the phenotype of sickle-cell disease?
        Students should connect the phenotypic effects of sickle-cell disease with the underlying genotype of the individual. Affected individuals have a mutation in the hemoglobin gene.

4. Work in teams of 2 to create a poster that illustrates the molecular basis of sickle-cell disease. Use the materials that your teacher provides and the information in Figure 12.7. Your poster should have a place for a title (you will add this later). It should have each of the numbered sections that you see in Figure 12.7.

5. Use the information that you gathered in steps 1 and 2 to complete areas 1, 6, 7, and 8 of your poster. Refer to Figure 12.7 to determine the information required in each of these sections.

On your poster, include pictures and words that you think would be appropriate and helpful. Add a descriptive label to each area so that a viewer will understand what each section is displaying.

    Encourage your students to be creative in their use of color and materials as they set up their posters. They may find it strange that they are expected to create and to number eight areas on their poster before they know what their poster will show. For instance, in step 4, students are asked to fill in details about later points in their poster explanation of sickle-cell disease before they can fill in details of some earlier points. If this is problematic for some students, point out that they will be completing various areas on their posters as they gather more and more relevant information, and that sometimes scientists do not understand the first step in a process until long after they understand subsequent steps. Reassure your students that a coherent picture of the full process of gene expression will emerge as they slowly complete their posters.

PART B Looking at the Structure of the Gene Involved in Sickle-Cell Disease

In Parts B and C, the students look closely at the molecular structures of both the normal and the sickle-cell alleles of the hemoglobin gene and at how the structures of these different alleles cause the cell to build proteins of slightly different structure and function. Introduce Part B by referring back to the students' answers in Part A, step 2, question c, and by pointing out that Part B will allow them to examine the genetic and molecular basis of this condition more closely than they did in Chapter 11.

1. To understand in more detail how the information present in the hemoglobin gene is related to sickle-cell disease, refer to the DNA sequences on the copymaster that your teacher provides. Use these sequences as paper models of the same portion of 2 different alleles of the hemoglobin gene.

   To assess your students' prior knowledge of DNA structure, which the previous activity should have strengthened, ask the students to use the DNA sequences on the Copymaster *DNA Sequences for Hemoglobin Alleles* to build models that reflect the double-stranded nature of DNA (models that contain both the coding strand and the complementary, noncoding strand). (The copymaster gives your students only the sequences of the coding strands of the DNA for each allele.) If your students seem to have difficulty with this step, you may wish to use some class time for a brief review of the major features of DNA structure, paying particular attention to the relationship between the nucleotide sequences of the two complementary strands.

2. Compare the 2 nucleotide sequences.

   a. Draw an arrow or a circle on your poster to indicate the nucleotides in the sickle-cell sequence that differ from those in the normal sequence.

   b. What type of mutations exist in the sickle-cell allele?

3. Cut out and attach your DNA sequences to the appropriate places on your team's poster.

   A brief comparison of the normal and sickle-cell alleles should reveal the location of the mutation (nucleotide 21 is a T to A substitution). Once the students have identified the location of the mutation and its type, direct them to post their sequences.

PART C Looking at the Expression of the Gene Involved in Sickle-Cell Disease

As noted above, Part C does not include any *formal* requirement that students examine or discuss the actual mechanical details of transcription or translation. Instead, the activity asks the students to focus almost entirely on the *results* of these processes: on the structures of the mRNAs formed by transcription and on the structures of the polypeptide chains that eventually are produced by translation of this mRNA. This emphasis on results rather than on mechanical details is consistent with the goal of the activity to help your students understand gene expression *conceptually*. (That is, it helps them focus on how these processes lead to the physical results that we collectively call *phenotype* rather than on the detailed steps by which the cell accomplishes either process.) Your learners can examine the detailed steps of translation in the next activity, *A Closer Look at Protein Synthesis*, after they have completed their posters and have a strong understanding of the overall sequence of events involved in gene expression.

1. Determine how the difference in sequence between the normal and sickle-cell alleles of the hemoglobin gene results in the symptoms associated with the disease. Determine the messenger RNA (mRNA) sequence that corresponds to the DNA sequence that you examined in Part B. This will help you understand how protein synthesis, using the 2 DNA sequences, results in the production of different proteins.

   One member of your team should generate an mRNA based on the DNA sequence that represents the allele for normal hemoglobin. The other member of your team should generate an mRNA based on the DNA sequence that represents the sickle-cell allele.

   To complete this step, you will need more information about messenger RNA and the process by which mRNA is synthesized. Read the essay *The Expression of Genetic Information* (page 521), and watch the DVD segment "Transcription."

2. Attach your mRNA models to the appropriate places on your team's poster.

   Each pair of learners on a team should take responsibility for transcribing one of the hemoglobin alleles (they should transcribe the single strand shown on the copymaster). As resources, they can use the essay *The Expression of Genetic Information* and the DVD segment "Transcription," which uses animation to present a simplified overview of the three steps of transcription. Students may need to watch the video several times. Walk around the room and assess how well the students understand the transfer of genetic information that occurs during transcription. Help students with any problems they may experience. Students should attach their mRNA sequences to their poster.

3. Compare (a) the mRNA that results from the transcription of the normal allele of the hemoglobin gene to the (b) mRNA that results from transcription of the sickle-cell allele. On your poster, use an arrow or a circle to indicate the nucleotides in the sickle-cell mRNA that differ from those in the normal sequence.

   The learners should note that the mRNA sequences differ at the same position that the DNA sequences differed. This is because DNA and mRNA sequences are colinear—that is, they contain the same information in the same linear order.

4. Refer to the genetic code table (Figure E12.13, page 526). Use the table to determine the sequence of amino acids that would result from translating the mRNA that you built from your original DNA sequence.

   Each member of the team should translate 1 of the mRNA molecules.

   To complete this step, you will need more information about the genetic code and how mRNA is translated into protein. Read the essays *Translating the Message in mRNA* (page 524) and *Landmark Discovery: White-Coated Sleuths Decipher Genetic Code* (page 527).

5. Post your amino acid sequences in the appropriate places on your team's poster.

   You may find that some of your students need help in step 4 with translating the mRNA sequence into a sequence of amino acids. If this is the case, we suggest that you first help them translate a short sample sequence of your own creation (for example, six or nine nucleotides) and then direct them to return to the task of translating the two hemoglobin sequences. When they finish, the learners should attach their amino acid sequences to their poster.

6. Compare (a) the amino acid sequence that results from transcription and translation of the normal allele for the hemoglobin gene with (b) the amino acid sequence that results from transcription and translation of the sickle-cell allele. On your poster, use an arrow or a circle to indicate the amino acids in the sickle-cell protein sequence that differ from those in the normal sequence.

> **The learners should note on their poster that the normal and abnormal hemoglobin amino acid sequences differ at one position in the sequence. Glutamate (glutamic acid) in the normal hemoglobin is replaced by valine in the sickle hemoglobin.**

7. Read the information in the need to know box. You will learn about the relationship between the sequence of amino acids in a hemoglobin molecule and the molecule's shape.

> **See the need to know box The Sequence of Amino Acids Determines the Hemoglobin Molecule's Shape on page 462 of the student text.**

8. Add what you learned in step 7 to the appropriate places on your team's poster.

9. Complete your team's poster by adding a descriptive title. Include any other details that you think would help someone else understand the information that it presents.

Take this opportunity to check your poster. The information on your poster should reflect what you understand about how human cells use the information stored in the nucleotide sequence of their DNA to build and maintain the human being that those cells compose.

> **As your students finish their posters, circulate among the teams to see that the posters are complete and to monitor the discussions. Verify that each team understands how the physical structure of sickle-cell hemoglobin is related to the physical shape of sickle cells and to the medical symptoms associated with sickle-cell disease. If some of your students cannot connect what they have learned about the molecular structure of sickle-cell hemoglobin to what they learned in Part A about the shape and behavior of sickled red blood cells, ask them to look more closely at Figure 12.8 in the student book. Suggest that they try to explain what they see, first, in light of what they just learned about the amino acid sequence of normal and sickle-cell hemoglobins, and second, in light of what they already knew about the behavior of the two forms of hemoglobin at low oxygen levels.**

Analysis

Use the information on your poster and in the essays to respond to the following. Record your responses in your journal. Your teacher will use your journal to evaluate your understanding of gene expression.

1. Draw Figure 12.9 in your journal. Leave room on your drawing to add components (when necessary) and labels for the following:

amino acid	nucleotide
cytoplasm	protein
mRNA	tRNA
nucleus	

> **The students should draw the diagram shown in Figure 12.9 and enlarge the cell to give room for the components listed above.**

2. In Chapter 11, you read about cystic fibrosis, a common recessive condition. The gene involved in cystic fibrosis normally codes for a transport protein that affects the flow of ions across membranes. When mutated, the now faulty version of that protein limits the body's normal ability to secrete fluids into the respiratory and digestive systems. Think about what you now know about gene expression. Create a flowchart that illustrates how the genotype *cc* might lead to the medical problems associated with the phenotype of cystic fibrosis.

The poster that you made on sickle-cell disease may suggest a general scheme for your outline.

Students should create a flowchart that indicates the following information: the *C* and *c* alleles of the cystic fibrosis gene likely have different nucleotide sequences that result in different mRNA sequences and then ultimately different amino acid sequences in the proteins that cells build from this mRNA. Judging by the phenotypes associated with each genotype, these different proteins apparently behave quite differently in the cell. That is, the protein built as a result of the expression of the normal allele apparently functions in a way that leads to normal fluid secretion, and the protein built as a result of the expression of the cystic fibrosis allele either does not function at all or functions in a manner that leads to abnormal fluid secretion. (The students will revisit this example in the Evaluate Section at the end of the program.)

3. Refer back to the copy of Figure E12.1 in your journal. Redraw that figure. Add the processes of transcription and translation. Explain the locations that you chose.

Transcription and translation fit into the box labeled *gene expression*. These processes allow a cell to access and use the information stored in the DNA (genotype). Many (though not all) of the physical characteristics that we see as phenotype result from using genetic information.

Elaborate

A Closer Look at Protein Synthesis

Major Concepts Protein synthesis; mutations

Overview

This activity elaborates on the ideas of information transfer from nucleic acid to protein by focusing on the steps of translation (protein synthesis). The ideas here go beyond merely a conceptual understanding of the molecular basis of continuity and focus instead on the connection between genotype and proteins, the raw materials of phenotype. The learners discover the structures and processes involved in translation through an inquiry-driven video simulation of protein synthesis.

Materials   (per class of 30, teams of 2)

DVD
DVD player

Outcomes and Indicators of Success

The following indicators allow you to assess the students' level of success with the activity and to assess their process of learning.

By the end of this activity, the learners should

1. understand the process that translates the language of nucleic acids into the language of proteins.

    They will demonstrate their understanding by

    a. using a video animation to write an explanation of the translation process, and

    b. describing why protein synthesis is important to living systems.

2. appreciate the significance and potential consequences of mutations.

    They will demonstrate their appreciation by

    a. modeling the translation of several mutation-containing DNA sequences and identifying the effects of the mutations,

    b. explaining the functional difference between three types of mutations, and

    c. explaining the reason that many mutations do not result in observable changes in phenotype.

Strategies for Guiding Learners

PROCESS AND PROCEDURES

As a class, read orally or silently all introductory materials for the activity and the Process and Procedures to help students build connections between concepts and activities. Use the time spent reading to bring the students' attention into focus.

PART A   Understanding Translation

1. Copy the symbols from Figure 12.10 into your journal. Label them.

    You will need to know these symbols to explain the events in the DVD segment.

    Make certain that the students draw in their journals the symbols that represent the components of the cellular protein synthesis machinery. They will not be able to follow the events depicted on the video segment without first understanding these symbols.

2. Watch the animated DVD segment "A Closer Look at Protein Synthesis: Translation" according to your teacher's instructions.

    Record notes in your journal that describe the steps involved. Watch the segment as many times as necessary.

3. Read the essay *Cellular Components in Protein Synthesis* (page 527). Take brief notes to use as you complete the rest of this activity.

4. With your partner, write an explanation of the translation process. Your teacher will collect your explanation. A thorough explanation will include answers to the following questions:

a. What structures are necessary for protein synthesis?

b. How is the ribosome involved in protein synthesis?

c. How does the nucleotide sequence of each mRNA codon help position each tRNA? How many nucleotides are involved in this positioning?

d. Think about the mechanism of positioning tRNA on mRNA. How is this similar to the mechanism that holds DNA together as a double strand?

e. What happens to adjacent amino acids once they are positioned on the ribosome?

f. How is the sequence of mRNA nucleotides related to the sequence of amino acids in the protein?

g. What events cause protein synthesis to stop? Is there a special mRNA nucleotide sequence or another factor that contributes to stopping translation?

h. What happens to the protein after translation?

    If some of your students know how to operate the DVD player, place them in charge of replaying the segment "Translation" as often as necessary. This video segment shows animation of the formation of a polypeptide chain. Show the video one time to familiarize the students with its general contents. Then encourage teammates to divide responsibilities so each person pays attention to different aspects of the process during replays (for example, one student may watch the tRNAs, another may watch the amino acids, codons, etc.). Most teams will need to watch the segment at least a half dozen times to answer all of the questions listed in step 4. Another efficient strategy is to have each member of a team look for the answer to a different question each time the segment is replayed. After all of the questions have been answered once, the teammates can repeat the process but switch questions. This will allow them to assess the other's work and develop a consensus explanation.

    A thorough explanation that addresses and synthesizes the answers to the questions in step 4 might resemble the following:

> The basic structures needed for protein synthesis are an mRNA template, ribosomes, tRNA molecules with attached amino acids, and release factors that end translation at the appropriate codon. (Also needed, but not depicted on the video segment, are energy molecules and many protein factors that participate in the initiation and elongation processes.)
>
> A ribosome assembles on the mRNA template from two smaller subunits and then proceeds to move along the template. As the ribosome moves, protein is made. The ribosome begins its journey at a triplet of AUG. While the ribosome sits at the AUG, a tRNA molecule, which is linked to an amino acid and contains a three nucleotide sequence (the anticodon), floats into position in such a way that it aligns (or complements) with the AUG. The amino acid linked to this tRNA is the first amino acid in the new protein. The alignment and base pairing between the tRNA and the mRNA is similar to the bonding that holds complementary strands of DNA together because it relies on hydrogen bonding, and the pairing is specific (G always pairs with C, and U always pairs with A).

A second tRNA bearing an amino acid lines up adjacent to the first, and when the ribosome moves, a bond forms between the two amino acids. As the ribosome continues to move down the mRNA in three nucleotide steps, new tRNAs with amino acids line up at complementary mRNA nucleotides, and the growing chain is transferred to the most recent amino acid/tRNA during bond formation. In this way, the linear sequence of amino acids is the same as the linear sequence of nucleotide triplets on the mRNA.

When the ribosome reaches the triplet UAG (a termination codon), a release factor binds to the mRNA triplet, the amino acid chain is released, and the ribosome disassembles. (The triplets UGA and UAA also are termination codons.) At this point, the protein chain folds up and moves or is transported away.

Some students may notice that tRNAs and the release factor sometimes float across the screen without assembling on the ribosome. If they ask about it, you may want to explain that inside the cell, many processes occur in the cytoplasm. The time it takes for an appropriate tRNA-linked amino acid to reach the proper site on the ribosome is, at least in part, determined by the concentration of that component in the cytoplasm. Make sure that your students realize that the inside of a cell is an extremely complex and busy place, and the movement and behavior of cellular molecules probably does not always appear neat and orderly.

5. Watch the 2nd part of the DVD segment "A Closer Look at Protein Synthesis: Translation." Discuss with your partner how that translation sequence differs from the 1st.

After the students finish their explanations, show the second part of the video segment "Translation," which shows three ribosomes translating one mRNA strand. This results in the simultaneous production of three proteins. You may omit this if time is short. The main point is that a single mRNA can give rise to many proteins, which is one example of cellular efficiency and regulation of protein production. Discuss the video to make sure that the students understand the broader aspects of protein synthesis. Students should be able to articulate the following ideas: (1) Proteins have a linear relationship (via mRNA) to the DNA sequences that code for them. This is a consequence of the fact that protein synthesis, like replication and transcription, is directed by a molecular template. (2) Proteins are the primary functional units of cellular activity, that is, they carry out the structural and catalytic processes that DNA cannot.

6. Participate in a class discussion of the explanations that you developed in step 4. What is the significance of what you observed in step 5?

The essay *Cellular Components in Protein Synthesis* should help to clarify the process of protein translation.

During the class discussion, guide the students to the realization that protein synthesis is a regulated process, just as many other processes in cells and organisms are regulated. You might do this by asking leading questions such as, What might be the advantage of translating the same mRNA with such high frequency? (Answer: Cells may need a lot of one particular protein very quickly, for instance, a hormone.) Or, How might cells use protein synthesis to maintain homeostasis? (Answer: When cells detect high levels of a protein that no longer is needed in high amounts, they may respond by slowing the rate of protein synthesis.) This is an example of negative feedback at the molecular level, and molecular processes such as this underlie the tissue- and organ-level feedback mechanisms that the learners examined in Unit 2. With this example as a model, you might ask students to apply this same reasoning to postulating a protein synthesis explanation for positive feedback. Their responses will allow you to assess how well they can integrate broad conceptual themes.

Summarize the essential elements of protein synthesis by leading the class through a review of their step 4 explanations. If the students appear not to have developed accurate or thorough explanations, suggest that they revise them as homework. The essay *Cellular Components in Protein Synthesis* (pages 527–530) provides figures and a description of translation and also specifies the connection between proteins and phenotype.

You might want to collect each team's explanation and use it as an informal assessment to determine how well the students have grasped the concepts. If you decide to score the explanations, make it clear to the students that their teamwork is critical and will be reflected in a single grade.

PART B *Predicting the Effects of Mutations*

In this part of the activity, the learners extend their understanding of mutations by following them from the genetic material of DNA to proteins, the ultimate product of most genes. In transcribing and translating several different DNA sequences, the learners discover that mutations can have several different effects when expressed at the level of proteins. Some of the effects are harmful and result in nonfunctional proteins, whereas others may have no effect at all on protein function.

1. Write the mRNA sequence that would be produced by transcription from the following DNA strand:

   TACTTCGATCAGTAAGCTATGGACGACCAGAGCACGATCGACT

   The single strand of DNA nucleotides shown above is the strand that is transcribed into mRNA. This ultimately gives rise to a protein.

   mRNA:

   AUGAAGCUAGUCAUUCGAUACCUGCUGGUCUCGUGCUAGCUGA

2. Refer to the genetic code table (Figure E12.13, page 526). Determine the sequence of amino acids that would result from translation of the mRNA from step 1.

   The protein sequence begins at the start codon, AUG. The amino acid sequence would be methionine-lysine-leucine-valine-isoleucine-arginine-tyrosine-leucine-leucine-valine-serine-cysteine-(Stop).

3. Use the same process you used in steps 1 and 2 to determine the effect of the following mutation:

   TACTTC<u>T</u>ATCAGTAAGCTATGGACGACCAGAGCACG
   ATCGACT

The mutation changes the third amino acid in the protein from leucine to isoleucine, but does not alter the rest of the sequence. This is a single-base substitution mutation that results in a single amino acid substitution. Depending on the particular amino acid that is changed, the mutation may or may not affect the protein's function. If the altered amino acid is critical to folding or catalysis, one amino acid substitution might render the protein nonfunctional.

4. Identify the mutation in the following strand of DNA. Specify its effect.

    TACTTCGATCGTAAGCTATGGACGACCAGAGCACGA TCGACT

Use the DNA strand from step 1 as your reference.

The mutation in this sequence is a single-base deletion (a deletion of A in the fourth codon). This causes a reading frame shift (in other words, the triplet mRNA nucleotides read by the ribosome have shifted), which alters the sequence of all amino acids downstream from the mutation. The last three nucleotides in this sequence are read in frame as a stop codon. The amino acid sequence would be methionine-lysine-leucine-alanine-phenylalanine-aspartate threonine-cysteine-tryptophan-serine-arginine-alanine-serine-(Stop). Frame shifts, which can be caused by insertions as well as deletions, almost always render proteins nonfunctional.

5. Identify the effect of the following DNA mutation:

    TACTTCGATCAGTAAGCTATGGACGA<u>G</u>CAGAGCACG ATCGACT

The mutation in the DNA is a single-base substitution in the third position of the ninth codon. Because the third position mutation in this particular codon (C to G) does not affect coding, this substitution does not alter any amino acids (both codons code for leucine). Such a mutation is referred to as silent, and the protein will be normal.

6. Which of the 3 mutations in Part B most likely would give rise to a functional protein?

The silent mutation in the last example most likely would give rise to a functional protein because it does not alter the protein sequence, and it is the sequence of a protein that determines its conformation and function. The other mutations might disrupt protein function because they alter the original amino acids. A nonfunctional protein almost certainly would result from the mutation that shifts the translation reading frame because many or most of the amino acids would be different. (If the reading frame shift occurred near the end of the protein, the protein still might retain function.) The effect on protein function might not be so drastic in the case of the single amino acid substitution. However, if the altered amino acid is located in a critical position, then this too would give rise to a nonfunctional protein.

Analysis

Use the learners' answers to these questions to evaluate how well they understand protein synthesis and the functional effects of mutations. If the students do not seem clear on the conceptual link between DNA as an information carrier molecule and proteins as the expression of that information, take the opportunity to clarify these ideas.

Review the essay *Replication Errors and Mutation* (page 519). Discuss the following with your partner. Record your responses in your journal.

1. Describe how mutations takes place.

   Mutations can occur during DNA replication when the replication enzyme mistakenly skips a base or adds a base to the wrong position.

2. When would you expect mutations to be passed from parent to offspring? When would you not expect this to happen?

   Mutations that occur in the DNA of cells that give rise to gametes can potentially be passed from parent to offspring. Mutations that occur in the DNA of somatic cells would not be passed down to offspring.

3. What kinds of effects might mutations have? Explain two different examples.

   Mutations may lead to genetic disease, cancer, and antibiotic resistance, all negative consequences of mutations unless you are a bacterium. Mutations also lead to variability. Variability within a population might allow some organisms to live and reproduce. This is the underlying mechanism through which evolution occurs. Some mutations have no detected effect whatsoever.

4. How might mutations influence evolution? Provide a specific example.

   Mutations in cells that give rise to gametes provide genetic variability. This variability in turn allows certain organisms of a population to survive when an environmental factor acts on the population. Those organisms will reproduce that trait. Populations adapt to their environment by way of random mutations. If an inherited trait (such as the type brought about by mutation) is favored by the environment, those individuals who possess that trait will be more likely to survive and reproduce, passing it on to the next generation.

5. Describe why protein synthesis is important to living systems.

   Proteins are one of the major macromolecules from which living systems are built. Not only are proteins important in biological structures, but functional molecules, such as enzymes and some hormones, also are proteins. Enzymes and hormones are critical to the regulatory functions that organisms depend on for homeostasis. Without proteins, and the ability of living systems to synthesize them generation after generation, life as we know it would cease to exist.

Elaborate

Genetic Technology

Major Concepts Molecular variation; applications of genetic engineering; ethical and social issues associated with genetic engineering

Overview

To elaborate on their understanding of molecular genetics, the students study the technologies that scientists have developed to manipulate DNA. With these technologies, scientists can alter agricultural products, engineer the production of new or rare medicines, and screen humans for genetic disorders. Students experience these concepts by using several essays to explain the molecular basis for these technologies and to consider how these technologies raise important ethical, social, and public policy questions. Then they investigate molecular variability by simulating a DNA-based genetic screening test.

Materials (per class of 30, teams of 2)

pop beads or colored paper clips
30 copies of the Copymaster *Detecting DNA Sequence Variation*

Outcomes and Indicators of Success

The following indicators allow you to assess the students' level of success with the activity and to assess their process of learning.

By the end of this activity, the learners should

1. understand the principles and applications of genetic engineering.

   They will demonstrate their understanding by

   a. describing a recombinant DNA molecule and explaining how scientists make these molecules,

   b. listing some practical applications of recombinant technologies,

   c. explaining how recombinant DNA technology differs from selective breeding as a tool for genetic engineering, and

   d. using pop beads and principles of genetic engineering to model the molecular changes that occur when DNA is cut by restriction enzymes.

2. appreciate the impact of recombinant DNA technology on human populations and societies.

   They will demonstrate their appreciation by

   a. describing circumstances under which it might be permissible to use recombinant DNA technology to alter the genes of future generations,

   b. listing reasons why governments might choose to regulate recombinant DNA research, and

   c. using recombinant DNA principles to solve a genetic test.

Preparations

Suggest assigning the readings for Part A for homework. This will save class time, and you can use the questions in Part A as the basis for a review of the concepts that are essential for Part B.

Background Information

Part B of this activity simulates the cutting of DNA strands by size, but the procedure to separate the resulting different-length fragments is not simulated. At the appropriate time, you may want to explain to students how this procedure works, or alternatively, perform a class demonstration of this technique using electrophoresis tanks and real DNA. The principle is quite simple.

DNA strands are negatively charged because of the many negative charges on the phosphodiester backbone that holds nucleotides together. If DNA is placed in a gelatin-like matrix and that matrix is placed in a buffer-filled chamber in the presence of an electric field, the DNA molecules will move away from the cathode (the negatively charged pole) and toward the anode (the positive pole). The gelatin matrix acts as a sieve that retards large molecules more than small molecules, with the net effect that the small molecules migrate faster (and thus farther) in the electric field than do the large molecules. DNA-specific dyes are used to visualize the separated DNA molecules.

Strategies for Guiding Learners

PROCESS AND PROCEDURES

As a class, read orally or silently all introductory materials for the activity and the Process and Procedures to help students build connections between concepts and activities. Use the time spent reading to bring the students' attention into focus.

PART A   Gene Manipulation: Science and Society

If your students did not read the essays for Part A as homework, allow them to work alone to read them during class.

1. Decide with your teammate who will study genetic engineering and who will study the Human Genome Project.

2. Working individually, read the appropriate essays for your topic. Read carefully so that you will be well prepared to analyze the subject and teach your partner about it.

If you are studying genetic engineering, read the essays *Landmark Discovery: Extraordinary New Technique Changes Biology Forever* (page 529) and *Manipulating Genetic Material* (page 530).

If you are studying the Human Genome Project, read the essays *Landmark Discovery: New Technique Discovered While Driving* (page 536), *Informatics: Mapping and Sequencing the Human Genome* (page 537), and *Genetic Screening: A Dilemma for All of Us* (page 539).

3. Use the information from your assigned essays and any other reliable resources to complete the following tasks. Record your responses in your journal. Be prepared to explain your topic and answers to your teammate.

   a. Identify and summarize at least 2 major ethical issues related to the technology associated with your topic.

   Genetic engineering: There are issues related to introducing genetically engineered food crops to our food chain and introducing genetically engineered human cells into a human body.

   Human Genome Project: The technology to sequence genomes makes it possible to screen individuals for a variety of genetic disorders. It also makes it possible to screen gametes for genetic disorders. Both of these possibilities raise issues about the appropriate use of information available.

b. Explain at least 1 benefit and 1 concern related to each of the major ideas that you summarized in step 3a. Be sure to include discussion of the issue from different views.

Genetic engineering:

1. Genetically engineered food
   a. benefit—crops can be grown using fewer pesticides; better-tasting food
   b. concern—potential for genetically altered genes to enter wild populations and change them forever; nontarget species may be harmed

2. Introducing genetically engineered human cells into a human body
   a. benefit—can provide treatments for diseases that were once untreatable or difficult to treat
   b. concern—unforeseen responses to the introduction of foreign genes or the processes used to introduce them

Human Genome Project:

1. Led to technology that makes it possible to sequence species' genomes
   a. benefit—it is now possible to screen individuals for a variety of genetic disorders, which may make early treatment possible
   b. concern—has the potential to cause individuals to become labeled for disorders before they have any symptoms; has the potential to be the basis for society to limit individual choice; may reveal unforeseen disorders, leading to an ethical dilemma about whether to tell the affected individual

2. Technology can be used to screen gametes genetically
   a. benefit—possible to help parents at risk of having a child with an inherited disorder screen gametes to select for a healthy child before pregnancy occurs
   b. concern—potential for future parents to determine their child's traits for reasons other than the health of the child

c. Describe how the issues that you explained have already affected or might affect you and others in the future.

Expect the students to discuss the likelihood that they will eat (or have already eaten) genetically engineered foods and live among genetically engineered organisms. In addition, they likely may describe how they might have to choose whether or not to undergo genetic screening for themselves or their children.

d. Explain your own opinions with regard to the balance between benefits and concerns that you identified in step 3b.

The students should summarize their own opinions.

e. Recommend what you think should be done about the issues that you have summarized.

The students should summarize their own opinions.

4. With your teammate, take turns teaching each other about your topics.

Discuss the responses that you wrote in step 3a–e. Be sure that you respect your teammate's right to have a different opinion than you.

5. In your journal, write 2 or 3 paragraphs that summarize your teammate's topic. Include the benefits and concerns that are tied to the related technologies.

6. Write 1 paragraph that explains how recombinant DNA technology influenced genetic engineering. Write a 2nd paragraph that explains how polymerase chain reaction techniques influenced the Human Genome Project.

Recombinant DNA technology made genetic engineering possible by providing scientists with the tools to insert new genes into organisms' chromosomes. Polymerase chain reaction techniques accelerated the Human Genome Project by making it possible to obtain large quantities of specific DNA sequences.

When the students have finished, we suggest that you review the major ideas by using the learners' answers to questions 3a–e as a guide. If the students are unclear about the processes, some potential applications, and the social implications of the Human Genome Project and recombinant DNA technology, spend a class period reviewing this critical information.

PART B   Getting a Handle on Molecular Variability

The students will begin the hands-on portion of this activity by reading a short introduction to molecular variability. This passage concludes with several questions that set the stage for working with DNA sequences to examine underlying molecular variation that does not have phenotypic effects.

See the need to know box Hypothetical DNA Sequences on page 469.

2. Use pop beads and the key in Figure 12.12 to make a model of each sequence in Figure 12.11.

   One team member will make a model of Sequence A. The other team member will model Sequence B.

3. Examine the sequences. Identify any differences.

   As the learners work in pairs to build their pop bead sequences of DNA, walk around the room to make certain that each team has built two strands that differ at two nucleotides. Two correct sequences are a prerequisite for the remaining steps.

4. What is the term for an individual carrying both sequences in their DNA?

   Heterozygote.

5. Discuss the following questions with your partner. Record your answers in your journal.

   Move around the room and quiz students on their answers to the questions in step 5. Their answers to (b) and (c) in particular serve as a check on how well they can apply the concepts of transcription and translation. The following is a guide for the types of answers to expect:

   a. What is the molecular difference between Sequence A and Sequence B? Answer specifically.

      The 18th nucleotide in Sequence B is T rather than A, and the 21st nucleotide in Sequence B is T rather than C.

   b. Would you expect that the polypeptide produced by transcription and translation of Sequence A would differ from that produced from B? Why or why not? Support your answer with specific evidence.

      Review the essay *Translating the Message in mRNA* (page 524) before you answer this question. Be sure to support your answer with specific evidence.

The learners should recognize that the two polypeptides would *not* vary in amino acid sequence, despite the difference in the DNA sequences. This is because the last two codons in Sequence B specify the same amino acids as the last two codons in Sequence A. In the case of these two third-position substitutions, the coding sequence does not change.

c. Think about your answer to question 5b. Do you think that you could detect a difference in phenotype between a person with Sequence A and a person with Sequence B? Why or why not?

No. The molecular variability evident in the DNA does not result in a phenotypic difference in individuals carrying these sequences because the amino acid sequences are identical. Thus, these two individuals would have the same phenotype for whatever trait is specified by this DNA.

6. A **restriction enzyme** is a particular kind of protein that cuts DNA at a specific location between nucleotide base sequences. The restriction enzyme *Eco* R1 recognizes the DNA sequence GAATTC. It cuts the DNA between the G and the A each time it encounters that sequence. Locate the places on your model of Sequence A that *Eco* R1 would recognize. Break the strand at the appropriate points. Do the same for Sequence B.

The simulated cutting of the DNA strands (restriction) is simplified in that the students are using only one strand. Remind the learners that real DNA is double stranded, and restriction enzymes actually cleave double-stranded DNA (see Figure E12.15). We use only single strands in this activity to keep students focused on the difference in strand length after cutting.

7. Discuss the following questions with your partner. Record your answers in your journal.

The questions in this step should help the learners appreciate that even though there is variation in Sequences A and B, that does not change the amino acid sequence; this variation still can be detected by the techniques of molecular biology. As they will see, the technique modeled in this activity models the DNA fingerprinting technique that they read about in *A Royal Tragedy (continued)*.

a. When *Eco* R1 cuts Sequence A, how many bases long is each fragment?

You can determine this by counting the beads in each fragment.

Three fragments are produced: one that is seven nucleotides long, one that is nine nucleotides long, and another that is five nucleotides long.

b. When *Eco* R1 cuts Sequence B, how long is each fragment?

Only two fragments are produced: one that is seven nucleotides long and another that is 14 nucleotides long.

c. Special laboratory tests exist that can distinguish DNA pieces of one length from DNA pieces of another length. How could you use *Eco* R1 and these lab tests to distinguish a person carrying Sequence A from another person carrying Sequence B?

The laboratory tests alluded to allow fragments of different sizes to be distinguished from one another, and thus these tests provide a way to distinguish the different results you would obtain if you restricted each DNA sample with the same restriction enzyme. Although the two individuals do not vary *phenotypically*, their DNA does vary in nucleotide sequence. Separating the fragments produced and comparing the fragment lengths could distinguish a person with Sequence A from a person with Sequence B. (Because the activity does not include a simulation of separating the strands produced by cutting with the restriction enzymes, you may want to describe the process of gel electrophoresis briefly to individual groups [see Background Information]. This will help the students to extend their understanding of DNA fingerprint analysis in the Analysis.)

d. How does this procedure give you a way to identify molecular variability?

The procedure allows scientists to recognize sequence variability in the DNA even if it does not lead to phenotypic variability. This technique represents a significant advance in our ability to trace genotypic differences through families and through populations.

Analysis

Distribute a copy of the Copymaster *Detecting DNA Sequence Variation* to each student in your class. To assess the learners' understanding of molecular variation and the restriction fragment techniques that scientists use to detect it, collect their journals at the end of this activity. Questions 1a and 1b provide a review of the molecular differences between a normal hemoglobin allele and a sickle-cell allele. Students may find it helpful to return to the sequences that they worked with in their posters in *Gene Expression* to recognize the similarities. Questions 1c and 1d use these molecular differences to illustrate how prenatal genetic tests can exploit the variation in DNA.

You have just used RFLPs (pronounced "riflips") to test for the presence of a particular genotype difference that occurs among members of the human population. RFLP stands for Restriction Fragment Length Polymorphism. In the laboratory, scientists use **electrophoresis** to determine the lengths of DNA fragments. These fragments are produced when a piece of DNA is treated with a restriction enzyme. During electrophoresis, an electric field is used to draw DNA fragments through a gel medium. Fragments of different lengths will travel different distances through the gel medium. Small fragments will move through the gel more rapidly than do large fragments.

As you have seen, differences in the fragment lengths reveal differences in the nucleotide sequence of the DNA sample. Those sequence differences are examples of variability at the molecular level. Some of those differences appear to be associated with detectable phenotypic differences among humans. Others do not appear to be associated with any differences.

1. Read the information in the need to know box. It describes how a similar test can help scientists distinguish chromosomes that carry the sickle-cell allele from those that carry the normal allele for human hemoglobin. Discuss with your partner the questions that follow. Record your answers in your journal.

See page 471 of the student text for the need to know box A Genetic Test for Sickle-Cell Anemia.

a. Look at Sequences A and B on the copymaster that your teacher provides. These sequences represent the same nucleotide sequence sections of the normal and the sickle-cell alleles of the human hemoglobin gene. What is the difference between Sequence A and Sequence B?

Sequence B has an adenine in the same position in which Sequence A has a thymine.

b. Think about this difference and your knowledge of the genetics that underlie sickle-cell disease. What can you predict about an individual who has only Sequence A in his or her genetic makeup? What if the individual has only Sequence B?

An individual carrying only Sequence A would have normal hemoglobin (a glutamate at amino acid position 7); an individual carrying only Sequence B would have sickle-cell hemoglobin (a valine at amino acid position 7). The students should know this by transcribing and translating both sequences.

c. The restriction enzyme MstII recognizes the DNA sequence GGTCTCC. It cuts the DNA between the first T and the first C each time it encounters that sequence. How could you use MstII to distinguish the gene for sickle hemoglobin from the gene for normal hemoglobin? Answer specifically in terms of the fragment lengths you would expect to see in each case.

MstII can be used to distinguish DNA coding for normal hemoglobin from DNA coding for sickle hemoglobin because different numbers of fragments and different fragment lengths result when the DNA is tested. When Sequence A is cut with MstII, fragment sizes of 4, 5, 10, and 14 are obtained. When Sequence B is cut with MstII, fragment sizes of 4, 5, and 24 are obtained.

d. Assume that a woman undergoes prenatal diagnosis to determine whether her fetus has sickle-cell disease. Below are two possible test results for the developing fetus. What is the diagnosis for each result?

  test result 1: fragment sizes = 4, 14, 10, 5

  test result 2: fragment sizes = 4, 24, 5

Three fragments of 4, 5, and 24 bases reveal the presence of the sickle hemoglobin gene in the fetus. Four fragments of 4, 5, 10, and 14 reveal the presence of the normal hemoglobin gene.

2. Read the essay *Shaping the Future* (page 540). In your journal, choose one issue that you discussed in this activity. Explain how it relates to Loren Eiseley's idea that the power humans have carries with it a responsibility.

The students should construct a well-reasoned answer based on an issue from the activity that interests them. Emphasize that the answer should give examples to explain how it relates to Eiseley's ideas about human responsibility.

Extensions

◆ If your school has the budget and the equipment, supplement this activity with a wet-lab experiment dealing with DNA restriction analysis. This will allow the learners to follow the manipulation of real DNA molecules using the actual techniques that researchers use.

◆ You may want to augment the chapter activities with an engaging discussion based on the novel *Jurassic Park*, by Michael Crichton. The fictitious story in this novel involves the use of genetic information from the fossils of prehistoric organisms (plants and dinosaurs) to reconstruct living examples of the species, with dramatic and dangerous consequences. See the optional activities for Chapter 12 for ideas about using the story as the basis for a genetics lesson.

Evaluate # Words to Live By

Major Concepts DNA replication; protein synthesis

Overview

Many new concepts were introduced in this chapter, and this activity provides an opportunity for the students to evaluate their understanding of the connections between those concepts. In this activity, the students will develop a Venn diagram showing commonalities and differences between DNA replication and protein synthesis. They then will create a concept map that links those characteristics or concepts. This activity was adapted from *BSCS Science: An Inquiry Approach.*

Materials   (per class of 30, teams of 2)

copy of the Venn diagram in Figure 12.13 (page 473) on a large chart or board
30 copies of the rubric *Concept Map Criteria*

Outcomes and Indicators of Success

The following indicators allow you to assess the students' level of success with the activity and to assess their process of learning.

By the end of this activity, the learners should be able to

1. understand the relationship between DNA replication and protein synthesis.

    They will demonstrate their understanding by

    a. placing terms associated with these concepts correctly in a Venn diagram,

    b. justifying placement of terms in a Venn diagram, and

    c. developing a concept map showing the relationships among the terms and concepts.

2. understand the major concepts and processes associated with DNA.

    They will demonstrate their understanding by

    a. using their own words to describe the meaning of concepts and processes: replication and protein synthesis,

    b. relating concepts to each other, and

    c. generating a concept map using concepts associated with DNA that the class has generated.

Background Information

In this activity, students will construct Venn diagrams. Developed by John Venn, these diagrams help describe and compare elements or characteristics of two or more topics. The topics can be concepts, ideas, situations, people, events, and so forth. Venn diagrams are drawn as overlapping circles, where the overlap describes what the two topics have in common. Where there is no overlap, the information in the circle describes characteristics of a topic that are specific to that topic.

Concept maps also are used in this activity. A concept map is a diagram showing relationships between ideas. Each concept is connected by lines that reflect the relationships between them. Linking words are written on the connecting lines to describe how the concepts are related. Each concept map is unique, depending on the thought processes of the person making it. The key to creating a sound concept map is that the person constructing it must understand the relatedness between the ideas or concepts involved. Therefore, concept maps can be assessed for the student's understanding that they represent.

Preparations

Preview the rubric for the concept portion of the activity, and modify it to suit your class.

On a large piece of paper or board in your classroom, start a Venn diagram as shown in Figure 12.13 (page 473).

Strategies for Guiding Learners

PROCESS AND PROCEDURES

As a class, read orally or silently all introductory materials for the activity and the Process and Procedures to help students build connections between concepts and activities. Use the time spent reading to bring the students' attention into focus.

1. Copy the Venn diagram in Figure 12.13 into your journal. Your teacher also will have the Venn diagram drawn on the board.

2. Think about characteristics of DNA replication and protein synthesis. Contribute your ideas to a class list on the board. Copy these class's ideas into your journal.

   Prompt the students to recall all the work they have completed in Unit 4 and to use the Venn diagram opportunity to "put it together." Guide students to include the following concepts if their brainstorming session does not generate them:

DNA Replication	Shared in Common	Protein Synthesis
DNA	mRNA	tRNA
chromosome	RNA	amino acid
nucleus	complementary base pairing	cytoplasm
mutation	genetic disorder	codon
double stranded	transcription	translation
genotype and alleles	genetic code	phenotype
T	A, C, G	U
reproduction	growth	metabolism
evolution	genes	traits
meiosis	reproduction	synthesis

3. Participate in a class discussion about the characteristics listed. In the Venn diagram, list those characteristics that are distinctive to 1 concept or the other (replication or protein synthesis). Then list those characteristics that are common to both concepts. Put characteristics that are common to both concepts in the area where the 2 circles overlap. Put characteristics specific to each concept in the portions of the circles that do not overlap.

Guide the students through the construction of the Venn diagram. This should be both a brainstorming session and an opportunity for students to organize their thoughts and begin thinking about the relationships between the concepts from Chapter 12.

Analysis

You have generated a list of characteristics that describe DNA replication and protein synthesis. How do they relate? In Chapter 10, you used another type of diagram, a concept map, to describe visually how some genetic concepts are related. In this part of the chapter evaluate, you will create a new concept map. This map will reflect your understanding of continuity and gene action.

1. Obtain a rubric from your teacher. Study the guidelines that will be used to evaluate your concept map.

2. Create a concept map about continuity and gene action that follows these guidelines:

   a. Identify the key concepts. In this activity, use the concepts and characteristics your class generated in the Venn diagram.

   b. Start with a main idea. Subdivide it into categories that go from general concepts to more specific ones.

   c. Look for cross-links between concepts on different parts of the map.

      Concept maps can be done in different ways. But it is important that you know how the terms are related to each other. Your concept map is evidence of the understanding that you have developed in Unit 4. Think carefully. Use your journal as a resource for genetic terminology and concepts to include in your map. Remember, your teacher will use your concept map to evaluate your understanding.

   Review the concept map rubric with students to clarify the criteria before they begin creating their maps. Evaluate the maps based on those criteria, focusing primarily on the relationships between the concepts and the descriptions of the relationships.

Development: Growth and Differentiation in Living Systems

13 Processes and Patterns of Development

14 The Human Life Span

In this unit, the learners have the opportunity to explore growth and differentiation in living systems. In Chapter 13, students examine general principles of growth and differentiation across a diversity of organisms as they consider developmental processes and patterns. In Chapter 14, the learners explore the life stages of humans from birth through old age. They also make observations of humans at specific life stages and learn about the social expression of life stages in other cultures.

For this unit, the learners will receive the Unit Assessment before they begin Chapter 13. This procedure provides the students with the opportunity to direct and monitor their own learning.

Unit Goals

By the end of this unit, the learners should understand

- the importance of development in living systems;
- that physical development involves processes of growth and differentiation;
- the role of development in evolution;
- that humans pass through a series of life stages and grow and develop in various ways, including physical, cognitive, emotional, and social development;
- how culture influences the expression of life stages;
- how to make observations of organisms developing in various ways and organize and analyze these data;
- how to interpret and synthesize development data; and
- how to apply their knowledge of development to a new setting.

Prior Conceptions

Unit 5 focuses on growth and differentiation in living systems, which will challenge students to consider development as more than simply a process of getting larger. The BSCS 5E instructional model used throughout this program offers opportunities for teachers and students to develop biologically correct understandings about development in humans and other organisms.

The benchmarks for students in grades 9–12 include understanding that embryonic development unfolds as a succession of mitotic cycles that result in increasing numbers of cells. In addition, students in grades 9–12 should come to understand that small differences in the environment where these embryonic cells develop cause them to develop slightly differently by activating or inactivating different parts of the genetic code (AAAS, 2001). Having just studied inheritance in Unit 4, the students are likely to understand where DNA can be found and how it is passed from parent to offspring. However, most high school students have little understanding of what determines differences between cells, particularly in light of the idea that nearly all cells contain a full complement of the organism's genetic code.

In the engage activity, *One Hundred Years of Questions,* the students will begin to consider the processes that lead to differentiation by examining two experiments conducted 100 years ago. The DVD segments that are incorporated into the explore/explain *A Start in Development* help students visualize the processes in early development. These remarkable images and associated activities will help to dispel the common misconception that growth occurs as a result of cells getting larger rather than by an increase in the number of cells. In addition, the students will investigate the consequences that can result when development goes awry. In that context, they will consider common risk-taking behaviors and their possible long-term effects. The benchmarks for grades 9–12 include understanding that the decisions of one generation may come to bear on another generation. This concept is brought to the forefront in the Chapter 13 essays that describe choices that can lead to birth defects or cancer.

In Unit 5, learners also investigate human stages of growth and development over a lifetime. How culture influences the expression of developmental stages is a significant thread throughout the unit. The Project 2061 *Atlas of Science Literacy* identifies several incorrect prior conceptions related to how culture affects behavior. Research suggests that students tend to overgeneralize information about racial and cultural differences. In this program, students first study the stages of human development in the two explore activities, *Growing Up—What Does That Mean?* and *A View of Life.* During those activities, the students learn about the expression of development in their own culture. The students then compare what they have learned to life in a different culture by researching and presenting their findings in a multicultural fair. This progression provides an opportunity for the learners to abandon the belief that some human cultures are biologically subordinate, a step necessary for them to reason about different world views (AAAS, 2001).

Advance Preparation for the Unit

Before you begin this unit, see the Unit 5 Assessment, which outlines the preparations you will need to make in the classroom.

The Unit 5 Assessment is designed to be used in a formative manner to guide students' learning throughout the unit. Distribute the assessment before students begin Chapter 13 and allow them to use it as a learning tool. Part A of the assessment contains instructions, in activity form, for setting up live organism observations, which will provide living examples of developmental principles. See the Unit 5 Assessment package on the *GACD* for detailed instructions.

For the Chapter 14 activity *Growing Up—What Does That Mean?,* you will need to see whether your school district has specific guidelines and regulations for conducting observations of people. The activities *A View of Life* and *Cultural Diversity in the Human Life Span* also require special arrangements; see the Preparations section for each of these activities.

Processes and Patterns of Development

Chapter

13

Chapter 13 focuses on the specific processes and patterns by which multicellular organisms develop. This chapter presents the learner with two key questions:

◆ How are the body's tissues and organs formed?

◆ What clues does development reveal about the process of evolution?

Learners become engaged in these questions by viewing DVD images of egg and adult pairs, and then of a variety of eggs followed by the adults that develop from those eggs. These images initiate student thinking about the types of change that development involves. A brief history of early experimentation in developmental biology and a report on a 1994 survey of developmental biologists invite students to consider how broad scientific questions are asked and answered. To explore the mechanisms of development, the learners view images that show the intervening developmental events from egg to adult. Guiding questions help the students articulate the major events of development (growth and differentiation). Then learners begin to examine the basic processes of development by viewing a time-lapse sequence on mitosis and working through a set of inquiry questions as they model the steps of mitosis. These steps enable the learners to construct an explanation of how growth takes place.

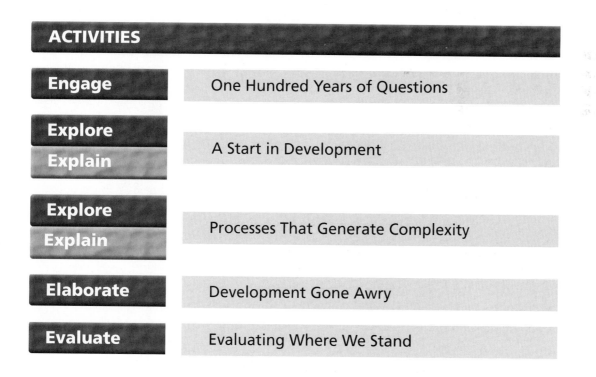

ACTIVITIES

Engage	One Hundred Years of Questions
Explore / Explain	A Start in Development
Explore / Explain	Processes That Generate Complexity
Elaborate	Development Gone Awry
Evaluate	Evaluating Where We Stand

Instructional Flow — Classroom Support

Activity/ Student Text pp. Teacher Guide pp.	GACD, DVD, and CD-ROM Resources	Essays/ Student Text pp.	Estimated Time	Team Size/ Cooperative Learning Focus	Strategies and Tools	Assessment Opportunities	Special Considerations
Unit 5 Assessment *Development: Growth and Differentiation in Living Systems* (on GACD, in assessments)	Unit 5 Assessment on GACD; Rubric: Developmental Observations Report		ongoing— throughout Unit 5	Part A: teams of 4; Parts B & C: individuals (see Part D below— the evaluate)	Wet lab; observations; report; short answer; presentation	Formative and summative assessment opportunities throughout Unit 5	Enlarge print materials if needed. Plan partners so that students with visual or fine motor control difficulty can rely on their partner if needed.
ENGAGE *One Hundred Years of Questions* pp. 546–548 TG pp. 487–491	DVD: *From Egg to Adult* and *A Collection of Eggs: An Assortment of Adults*		50 minutes	*Team size:* individuals and class	DVD segment; class discussion	Prior knowledge of growth and development; applying understanding to new situations	Plan time to stop and describe/ discuss the images shown in the DVD as a class for the benefit of students who cannot see the images.
EXPLORE/ EXPLAIN *A Start in Development* pp. 549–552 TG pp. 491–497	DVD: *A Closer Look and Cell Division*	*The Long and Short of Development* pp. 576–577; *The Cell Cycle and Growth Control* pp. 578–580	100 minutes	*Team size:* 2 *Skill:* Providing constructive criticism	DVD segment; class discussion; modeling	Using evidence; misconceptions; current understanding; using models to construct explanations	Plan time to stop and describe/ discuss the images shown in the DVD as a class for the benefit of students who cannot see the images.
EXPLORE/ EXPLAIN *Processes That Generate Complexity* pp. 552–555 TG pp. 497–502	DVD: *Cells, Cells, and More Cells*	*Coordinating Growth* pp. 581–582; *Differentiation and the Expression of Genetic Information* pp. 582–585	100 minutes	*Team size:* 2 *Skill:* Sharing perspectives	DVD segment; class discussion	Current understanding; using information to construct explanations; applying understanding to new situations	Plan time to stop and describe/ discuss the images shown in the DVD as a class for the benefit of students who cannot see the images.
ELABORATE *Development Gone Awry* pp. 555–558 TG pp. 502–508	DVD: *Cancer in Humans*	*Development and Birth Defects* pp. 586–589; *Cancer: Unregulated Growth* pp. 589–593	100 minutes	*Team size:* individuals	Individual projects (scripts); DVD segment; risk assessment	Synthesizing ideas; applying understandings to new situations	Plan time to stop and describe/ discuss the images shown in the DVD as a class for the benefit of students who cannot see the images.

	Instructional Flow				Classroom Support		
Activity/ Student Text pp. Teacher Guide pp.	GACD, DVD, and CD-ROM Resources	Essays/ Student Text pp.	Estimated Time	Team Size/ Cooperative Learning Focus	Strategies and Tools	Assessment Opportunities	Special Considerations
EVALUATE *Evaluating Where We Stand* pp. 558–561 TG pp. 508–511	Rubric: *Growth and Development in Your Critter*	*Patterns of Development* pp. 593–597	50 minutes	*Team size:* individuals	Critter folders	Applying understanding to new situations; self-assessment	Provide the basic outline of a critter in a particular habitat for any students who are new to your class and have no critter. Some students may be better able to show their understanding by reporting orally about their critter's development in addition to drawing diagrams and/or writing descriptions.

Optional activities:
• Explain: *Looking inside Black Boxes*

Next, the learners discuss a set of images of differentiated plant and animal tissues and examine related experimental data to identify selective gene expression as a key mechanism in differentiation. In an optional activity, learners consider experimental evidence for several specific developmental phenomena (regulation of cell division, cytoplasmic specification, induction, and hormonal interactions), which helps build their explanation of the mechanisms of development through analyzing and interpreting associated data. This activity emphasizes Science as Inquiry by illustrating how a variety of experimental techniques have been used to identify and examine the basic processes of development. In the Analysis, the students use their understanding of the mechanisms of development and of science as a process to examine the key events of reproductive system development.

Then the learners elaborate on their views of regulated growth and differentiation by looking at the consequences of errors in development. They demonstrate their understanding of these issues by scripting a dialogue between physician and patient that describes the biological basis for a developmental disorder (including the connection to normal development), mentions possible causes, and suggests treatments (if any). At last, the students use a set of suggested outcomes and indicators for the chapter to evaluate their own progress in understanding development. They accomplish this by first formalizing their learning about developmental processes and key points in development and then by applying their knowledge to create a developmental scheme for their critter. Students also comment on the scientists' questions from the 1994 *Science* magazine survey introduced in the first activity.

Chapter Goals

By the end of this chapter, students should

◆ understand that the term *development* refers to a progression of long-term changes that occurs in an organism from the beginning of life until death;

◆ understand that biological development occurs as a result of the coordinated events of growth and differentiation;

◆ understand that developmental processes are the expression of a genetic plan;

◆ recognize the relationship between changes in development and evolution; and

◆ understand that complex processes often can be explained by asking and answering questions about simpler systems and by synthesizing these smaller answers into larger pictures.

The learners also will

◆ make observations;

◆ collect, organize, and analyze data;

◆ interpret and synthesize data; and

◆ apply their knowledge to a new setting.

Advance Preparation

Reserve a DVD player for the activities *One Hundred Years of Questions*, *A Start in Development*, *Processes That Generate Complexity*, and *Development Gone Awry*; preview the segments in each activity. The activity *Development Gone Awry* requires a resource search ahead of time. See Preparations for that activity.

Students should already have begun the Unit 5 Assessment (see Advance Preparation for the Unit).

One Hundred Years of Questions

Engage

Major Concepts
Science begins with asking questions; complexity of broad biological questions; accessibility of focused experimental questions

Overview

The goals of this activity are to stimulate students to ask questions about development and to help them see that the fundamental questions that scientists would like to answer about development cannot be answered as phrased. Instead, scientists must approach these broad, fundamental questions by asking smaller, more specific questions about particular developing systems and then by piecing together the specific answers to form coherent explanations of the larger issues.

DVD images of egg and adult pairs, then a variety of eggs together, followed by the adults that develop from those eggs serve to raise in students' minds the basic questions of development. The Analysis expands their thinking to include a historical view of the origin of developmental biology as an area of systematic, experimental investigation. In addition to introducing some fundamental questions of concern to biologists, the Analysis encourages learners to reconsider some aspects of science processes.

Materials   (per class of 30, individuals and whole class)
DVD
DVD player

Outcomes and Indicators of Success

The following indicators allow you to assess the students' level of success with the activity and to assess their process of learning.

By the end of this activity, the learners should

1. remember that the processes of science begin with asking questions.

   They will show their recognition by identifying the questions that the DVD images raise in their minds.

2. be more aware of how developmental biologists pose and answer questions in their study of development.

They will show their perception by

    a. stating how new information (from Driesch's experiment) influenced the interpretation of the results of earlier work (by Roux);

    b. stating how the question that Roux asked is different from the question of how organisms develop, and explaining why the difference between these two questions is important; and

    c. identifying Roux's contributions to science as (1) the introduction of experimental investigation to developmental biology, and (2) the publication of a scientific journal to support communication and dialogue among scientists.

  3. better recognize the difficulty of answering broad, fundamental questions in science.

They will show their recognition by explaining that scientists are still asking and answering questions about the processes of development because these processes are complex and because answering the fundamental questions of biology often requires first asking and answering many smaller questions and assembling those answers into larger explanations.

Preparations

Post the two top questions from the 1994 *Science* magazine survey (see the story *Changes All Around*) somewhere in the room. These should be large enough for students to read from their seats. These two questions are referred to throughout the chapter and should always be foremost in students' minds.

Background Information

The story of the Roux/Driesch controversy (see the story *Changes All Around* in the student book) is included in this opening activity to highlight the importance of experimentation in the practice of science, as well as to draw the learners' attention to the details of early embryogenesis experiments. Your students may wonder how such apparently contradictory results can be reconciled within one view of early development.

We can address this question at two levels. At the simplest level, it is clear that the two experiments were not equivalent: not only did the scientists use different species, they also used different techniques. A crucial difference is that Roux left the dead cell in place. When the experiment with frog embryos is repeated, but the dead cell is removed, complete tadpoles sometimes develop (that is, the remaining cell is capable of supporting development of the full organism). This result suggests that physical contact with the dead cell has some effect on the subsequent development of the embryo and thus partially reconciles the two experiments.

At a more sophisticated level of analysis, we know that embryos of different species show different abilities to adjust to the loss of cellular material. Developmental biologists use the term *regulation* to refer to an embryo's ability to adjust to such a loss and to develop a normal, if smaller, set of structures. The available evidence suggests that embryos vary widely in their ability to regulate. As it happens, a sea urchin embryo is a highly regulative embryo (that is, it adjusts readily to abuse of this type). In contrast, if Driesch's sea urchin experiment is performed in tunicate or molluscan embryos, the result typically is similar to Roux's results: the embryo develops incompletely and often shows specific missing parts.

This difference in regulative ability does not seem to reflect a fundamental difference in the underlying mechanisms or processes of development among species, but rather, to reflect differences in timing. In different species, individual cells become committed to specific fates at different developmental times. In general, the later this commitment occurs, the greater the embryo's ability to regulate. In fact, human embryologists and reproductive specialists have developed a way to select the sex of a human baby by taking advantage of the human embryo's ability to regulate fully even up to the eight-cell stage. In this technique, a clinician removes one cell of an eight-cell embryo (generally, an embryo that has been produced through *in vitro* fertilization) and uses molecular techniques to determine whether the Y chromosome is present. This embryo is then either used or not, depending on whether its sex matches the parents' preference. The testing procedure kills one cell, of course, but the remaining seven-celled embryo usually will regulate and develop normally if it is implanted into the woman's uterus.

Strategies for Guiding Learners

PROCESS AND PROCEDURES

As a class, read orally or silently all introductory materials for the activity and the Process and Procedures to help students build connections between concepts and activities. Use the time spent reading to bring the students' attention into focus.

Your main task in this activity is to help learners direct their thinking toward concepts in development rather than just a description of facts. The major concepts are touched on in an introductory, intriguing manner, not in depth. The power of an engage activity lies in activating interest on the part of the learner, and rapid pacing is critical for this approach to work well.

1. View the DVD segment "From Egg to Adult." What questions do those pairs of images raise in your mind? In your journal, record 2 questions about development that arouse your curiosity.

    As the learners watch the DVD segment "From Egg to Adult," which shows images of eggs and adults of several different organisms, expect learners to ask questions such as, How does an egg turn into an adult? or What processes take place as an adult grows from an egg? You may want to approach this step as a class discussion rather than as solely a journal writing assignment. Doing this orally is likely to stimulate a wider range of questions than each student would come up with individually. However, if you begin by having students write at least one question of their own, they are more likely to actively participate in the discussion.

2. View the DVD segment "A Collection of Eggs: An Assortment of Adults." What questions do those images raise in your mind? In your journal, record 2 more questions that you find interesting.

    This second DVD segment, "A Collection of Eggs: An Assortment of Adults," shows two images that should raise questions about how things that look as similar as the eggs (for instance, all are round) can turn into organisms as diverse as the adults. Use this as an opportunity to remind students of their knowledge of genetics from Unit 4 by asking them to identify the underlying reason that these organisms develop in such different ways.

Analysis

The focus on the history of science and developmental questions offers a nice opportunity to expand the learners' understanding of scientific process. Look for thoughtful responses rather than "correct answers," and use student responses to give you insight into their current thinking regarding development and scientific process.

1. To see how some scientists have approached the study of development, read the story *Changes All Around*. Then join the class in a discussion of the following:

   a. Compare Roux's hot-needle experiment on a frog embryo to Driesch's experiment on sea urchin embryos. Indicate similarities and differences in each of the following aspects of their experiments:

      ◆ Experimental design

         Roux used a frog embryo; Driesch used a sea urchin. Roux killed one cell and left it in place; Driesch removed one cell completely.

      ◆ Results

         Roux found that the remaining live cell produced half an embryo; Driesch found that the remaining live cell produced a whole embryo.

      ◆ Conclusions

         Roux concluded that the remaining cell had only half the information required to make an embryo and interpreted this as evidence for preformation; Driesch concluded that the remaining cell had all the information required and interpreted this as evidence for the opposite view of development—that the structure of the organism is formed during development.

   b. What was the specific question that Roux tried to answer? How was his question different from the question, How do organisms develop? Why was this difference important?

      Roux tried to answer the question, Does each of the first two cells in a frog embryo contain all of the structures and information needed to grow into an organism, or does each cell contain just half of the structures and information? Roux's question was more testable than the question, How do organisms develop?, largely because it was more focused. It was more focused because it asked about a specific relationship—between a cell and information—rather than about a large, complex process, and it asked about this relationship in a specific organism, not for all organisms.

      This difference was important because, although the broad conceptual questions are the questions that really matter (for example, How do organisms develop?), we can answer them only by asking and answering smaller, more focused, testable questions and piecing the answers together to begin to build a picture of the larger answer. Roux asked a question that he could test and answer—an infinitely more valuable contribution than sitting around philosophizing about the "nature" of development.

c. What was Roux's contribution to the science of developmental biology?

> For part of the answer, see question 1b. In asking a question he could answer with an experiment, Roux (and his counterparts) launched the field of experimental embryology, the study of development through experimental manipulation of embryos. He also established the first scientific journal to disseminate scientific results in the field of development.

2. Work individually. Compare the questions that you recorded in Process and Procedures steps 1 and 2 with the questions that scientists in the *Science* survey named as most interesting to them. How are your questions similar to those the scientists asked? How are they different? Record your answers in your journal.

> Expect the students' questions to be some variation on the first of the questions, How are the body's tissues and organs formed?

3. Scientists still are asking and answering questions about development. What does that suggest about the processes of development? What does that suggest about the processes of science? Record your answers in your journal.

> Students may offer a wide variety of explanations. It is important that they understand that although the processes of development are complex and have required many years of study to begin to understand, these processes have not been impossible to investigate. Students should not finish this activity with the sense that more than 100 years of study have resulted in no increase in our understanding of this phenomenon. You might point out, for example, that just as the experiments of Roux and Driesch moved our understanding forward, so too does persistent, creative effort continue to move us steadily toward a better understanding of developmental processes. Students will have a better understanding of how much our knowledge of development has increased when they finish the chapter.

A Start in Development

Explore

Explain

Major Concepts How cells grow; how cells differentiate; how growth and differentiation interact during development

Overview

In this activity, the learners begin to formalize their understanding of development by articulating that development involves both an increase in size (growth) and the appearance of specialized parts (differentiation). The DVD segment *A Closer Look* provides a visual reference to the processes of development. The learners then investigate mitosis as a process by which growth occurs during development

They view the DVD segment *Cell Division* and use clay models to explore the basic steps by which chromosomes duplicate and separate during the cell cycle. Information in the essays and guiding questions help the learners explain the importance of mitosis in development.

Materials   (per class of 30, teams of 2)

DVD
DVD player
modeling clay
15 large sheets of paper

Outcomes and Indicators of Success

The following indicators allow you to assess the students' level of success with the activity and to assess their process of learning.

By the end of this activity, the learners should

1. describe the significant changes that take place between the stages of fertilization, birth or hatching, and adulthood.

   They will demonstrate their ability by describing some of the changes that they see in the DVD segment *A Closer Look*.

2. infer that different types of cells are found as development progresses.

   They will demonstrate their ability by indicating that different types of structures require different types of cells.

3. recognize that technology makes research in development possible.

   They will show their recognition by comparing and contrasting the images that Roux and Driesch might have seen with the images now available.

4. understand that mitosis is an important mechanism by which organisms grow during development.

   They will demonstrate their understanding by

   a. identifying mitosis as the source of new cells produced during development, and

   b. describing the new cells produced during development as genetically equivalent to the parent cell.

5. understand that cell division by mitosis involves (a) the replication of the genetic material, and (b) the equal distribution of this genetic material into two offspring cells.

   They will demonstrate their understanding by modeling both the replication and the distribution of chromosomes that occur during the cell cycle of a hypothetical cell.

Strategies for Guiding Learners

PROCESS AND PROCEDURES

PART A   How Does Development Take Place?

As a class, read orally or silently all introductory materials for the activity and the Process and Procedures to help students build connections between concepts and activities. Use the time spent reading to bring the students' attention into focus.

1. As you view the DVD segment "A Closer Look," think about the questions below. Record your observations and your answers to the questions in your journal.

The DVD segment "A Closer Look" allows students to look in detail at the developmental stages that take place between fertilization and adulthood. Dissolves, motion, and time-lapse photography show development in sea stars, frogs, chickens, fish, mice, and humans. Do not expect the learners to understand the details of what is occurring, but help them gain an appreciation for the increase in size and complexity that these stages reveal. Although the students will not have the names of the various stages, help them recognize that all of the organisms go through similar processes. In discussing their observations, ask them how diversity might result as a product of development. Their responses to the questions should be similar to the following:

a. What types of changes do you observe in these images?

   The types of changes that students can observe include the progressive growth and change in external features. These changes imply that internal changes also take place.

b. How has technology expanded our ability to observe development? Compare the images in "A Closer Look" with the images in the DVD segment "From Egg to Adult" in the previous activity.

   Technology allows us to collapse observation of the development time into a few minutes. We also can see greater details of development through the use of high-powered microscopes connected to fiber-optic cameras. The students might not know the details, but they should recognize that special equipment is needed to produce enlarged images of very small samples.

2. Developmental biologists use the terms *growth* and *differentiation*. These terms describe the fundamental processes that take place during development. Complete the following tasks in your journal:

   Students should be able to answer the questions posed in this step from their reading of the essay *The Long and Short of Development*. Look for responses such as the following:

a. Explain the difference between *growth* and *differentiation*.

   Growth generally means that the organism has increased the number of cells that it contains. Differentiation refers to the cellular changes that occur inside an organism that result in specialization.

b. List 4 specific examples from the DVD segment "A Closer Look" that show evidence of each of those processes taking place.

   Read the essay *The Long and Short of Development* on page 576. This important background information will help you formulate your answers.

   The students should describe examples from the DVD when they can see growth because the organisms get larger, and when they can see differentiation because the organisms develop tails, arms, legs, hearts, and so forth, whereas before there was only a single cell.

5. Look at the *anaphase stage* of mitosis. What is important about the number and types of chromosomes that move to opposite ends of the cell? How does the genetic information in the 2 groups of chromosomes at each end of the cell compare with each other?

Answer each question in your journal.

The groups are identical in terms of the number and types of chromosomes. They also are identical in terms of genetic information.

6. Think carefully about the specific manipulations you just completed with your clay models. In your journal, explain why is it important that

◆ chromosomes *duplicate* during mitosis,

◆ chromosomes *line up in single file* during metaphase of mitosis, and

◆ the duplicated chromosomes *separate* during anaphase of mitosis?

Discuss the movement and distribution of the genetic material that take place during the stage identified in each question.

If the chromosomes did not double, there would not be sufficient genetic information for each offspring cell to receive the full complement of chromosomes that was present in the parent cell. Lining up in single file during metaphase of mitosis assures the equal distribution of chromosomes when the duplicated chromosomes separate during anaphase. (For example, lining up ensures that each daughter cell receives one pair of each chromosome.)

Encourage the learners to review the essay *The Cell Cycle and Growth Control* to learn about the DNA replication that occurs during the cell cycle.

Analysis

See the introductory discussion of observations and conclusions in the student text, Analysis section, page 551.

Read the following statements. Pay attention to any contradictions you find between them. Work individually to answer the questions after the statements in your journal. Then exchange journals with your partner. Let him or her write comments about your answers. After you have read and commented on each other's answers, retrieve your journal. Then rewrite your answers as necessary. Your teacher will collect your journal to assess your current understanding of development.

Examine these statements:

Statement 1: Growth takes place during development because of the mitotic division of cells.

Statement 2: Mitosis results in daughter cells that are genetically identical to each other and to the parent cell that divided.

Statement 3: During development, cells become both structurally and functionally different from one another.

 This Analysis provides the learners with an opportunity to practice the skill of recognizing contradictions among statements that are all correct. As they then critique each other's answers, remind them that constructive criticism of a peer's work is most helpful. Collect their journals so that you can assess their current understanding of development. The students' responses should reflect the following ideas:

1. To the best of your knowledge, is each of the above statements correct as written? Write a brief explanation for each statement to support your answers.

   Students likely will answer yes and will explain their answer by repeating some of what they learned about mitosis in this activity and in the essay *The Cell Cycle and Growth Control*.

2. What contradiction do you see between statements 2 and 3? In other words, what is it about statement 2 that does not appear to be consistent with statement 3? Explain your answer.

   Students may have to think about this, but should see that the statements appear contradictory. If mitosis produces genetically identical cells (statement 2), then how is it possible that cells also become structurally and functionally different from one another (statement 3)?

3. Say you were a scientist who recognized that contradiction. Describe an experiment that you might attempt that explains the inconsistency. Answer specifically.

   This question will be difficult for students, and you may have to help them answer it. The introduction to the Analysis provides a hint. Students should answer that first, they would check to be sure that each statement is accurate as written. If each statement is accurate as written, then the apparent contradiction must mean that there are other aspects of development that we are not yet taking into consideration, and that if we were to add these elements into our analysis, we would see that the contradictions disappear. In this case, although mitosis produces genetically identical offspring cells, the cells may be different in other ways (for example, distribution of cytoplasmic substances, position in the embryo) that ultimately affect the expression of the genetic material and thus help bring about differentiation.

Processes That Generate Complexity

Explore

Explain

Major Concepts The role of differentiation in development; selective gene expression as a mechanism of differentiation

Overview

In this activity, the learners consider selective gene expression as a mechanism by which genetically equivalent cells become structurally and functionally different. The learners view a series of DVD images of plant and animal tissues and organs as a way to explore the results of cellular differentiation in multicellular organisms. Supporting essays and a table of information about the structural, functional, and molecular characteristics of a group of differentiated cells provide a foundation upon which the learners build their own explanation of how genetically equivalent cells can become different from one another during development.

Materials (per class of 30, teams of 2)

DVD
DVD player

Outcomes and Indicators of Success

The following indicators allow you to assess the students' level of success with the activity and to assess their process of learning.

By the end of this activity, the learners should

1. understand that selective gene expression is a mechanism by which differentiation can occur among genetically equivalent cells.

    They will demonstrate their understanding by

    a. raising the question of how to explain the appearance of differentiated structures and functions among the cells produced by mitosis,

    b. correlating differences in mRNA and major proteins present in cells with differences in structure and function,

    c. identifying differences in the use of genetic information as the reason for these differences in mRNA and protein content, and

    d. explaining how a human develops from a fertilized egg into an adult.

2. understand that although growth and differentiation are the central processes of development, more detailed knowledge of both processes is required if we are to understand fully how the body's tissues and organs are formed.

    They will demonstrate their understanding by

    a. identifying the limits of their own understanding of these processes, and

    b. listing some of the difficulties that remain to be answered if they are to understand fully how the body's tissues and organs are formed.

Strategies for Guiding Learners

PROCESS AND PROCEDURES

As a class, read orally or silently all introductory materials for the activity and the Process and Procedures to help students build connections between concepts and activities. Use the time spent reading to bring the students' attention into focus.

Move slowly through the images provided in the DVD segment "Cells, Cells, and More Cells." It contains sets of images that show sections taken through various animal and plant tissues and organs. You may wish to select a limited number of tissues for the class to view and allow interested students to view all of the images at another time. Because you may find that the learners have some difficulty interpreting the images, we recommend that you take the time to explain each image and allow the learners to comment on the appearances of the organs, tissues, and cells that are visible. The teaching notes in the DVD guide on the *TRCD* will help you give the learners a context for interpreting each image; it is not material intended for them to study or to learn. By the end of the segment, the learners should understand that multicellular organisms are composed of a variety of different cell types and that these cell types have specific structures, occupy specific positions, and perform specific roles within the organism. If they miss these points, use some leading questions to bring them to the forefront.

Students should be able to offer the following information in response to the following questions:

1. Observe the DVD segment "Cells, Cells, and More Cells." How do these images relate to the changes that take place as humans develop from a single-celled zygote to a mature person?

   As you watch the segment, compare the physical appearance of the cells within specific organisms. Think about what this tells you about development.

   The images demonstrate the variety in form and appearance of cells within multicellular organisms. Although the images do not provide direct evidence that these cells also have different functions, one might infer this from their quite different appearance, structures, and positions.

2. Examine closely the series of frames that shows the low- and high-magnification views of the cross section through the trachea. The **trachea** is the tube that connects your nose and mouth to your lungs (see Figure 13.7). Discuss the following questions with your class:

   The diversity of cell types produced during development is genetically equivalent. The learners may have some difficulty articulating this problem. You may suggest that they look at one of the DVD images again. Guide their thinking by asking, "What is the relationship between a cell's physical appearance and its genetic information?" You might also point to one cell and ask, "How does this cell's genetic information compare with this one" (point to another very different-looking cell in the same image)?

   Possible responses to the questions include the following:

   a. Describe some of the specialized cells that you see. How are they structurally different from each other?

      The learners can see a variety of cells, such as epithelial cells (including goblet cells), cartilage cells (chondrocytes), muscle cells, and red blood cells. The learners should mention differences in the size, shape, thickness of the cell border, and staining properties.

   b. How do these cells compare with each other genetically?

      In the absence of mutation (mutational change does occur occasionally during mitosis), and with the exception of the red blood cells (which have no nuclei), the cells in view are identical genetically.

   c. How do your answers in steps 2a and 2b relate to the process of differentiation?

      If these cells all are identical genetically, then how is it that they have such different physical appearances? This is, in fact, one of the central questions that scientists ask about the process of differentiation.

3. Work with your partner. Examine the table in the need to know box Cell Types That Make Up the Human Trachea. Identify similarities and differences among the cell types listed. How does gene expression explain how genetically identical cells become structurally different? Be prepared to support your answer with specific examples from the table and to share your answer in a class discussion.

As you examine the information in the table, ask yourself whether the structural differences that you saw among these cells correlate with any molecular differences among them. Read the two essays *Coordinating Growth* (page 581) and *Differentiation and the Expression of Genetic Information* (page 582). These essays will help you learn more about the processes that lead to differentiation. Use your experiences with genetics from Chapter 12 and the information in the essays to complete the Analysis section.

The learners should see that although the DNA does not vary from one type of cell to another, the types of mRNA and protein molecules do vary. This suggests that cells become structurally and functionally different, not because of changes to the DNA itself, but because of differences in the mode of expression of that DNA.

To avoid confusing the learners with unnecessary details, we have provided the information in the need to know box Cell Types That Make Up the Human Trachea (page 554 in the student edition), in a conceptual form rather than as actual experimental data. If your learners ask how scientists know that the mRNA of different cell types differs, explain that it is possible to extract the mRNA molecules that occur in one type of cell and compare their diversity and basic characteristics with the mRNA molecules that occur in other types of cells. Point out that investigations of this sort generally reveal that some types of mRNA molecules appear in most or all cell types within an organism. (These mRNA molecules encode the so-called *housekeeping* proteins found in most cells of that organism.) Some mRNA molecules, however, differ from one cell type to another. (These encode the *specialized* proteins that occur within cells that carry out specific functions.) To make these ideas concrete for your learners, you may wish to explain that examples of some housekeeping proteins include the enzymes involved in cellular respiration and in protein synthesis, and examples of some specialized proteins include actin and myosin (which occur in muscle cells), keratin (which occurs in skin cells), and various digestive enzymes (which occur in cells of the digestive system).

The learners should be able to see that although the DNA of each cell type listed in the aforementioned need to know box is the same, the mRNA transcribed from that DNA and the protein molecules translated from the mRNA are different. You may have to remind students of the connection between mRNA and protein and then help them understand that specific mRNAs will be present within a cell only if the related gene is active. (All genes are not "on" all the time.) Differences in the pattern of mRNA among cell types provide evidence that different genes may be active in the cells involved.

Note: Again, to avoid confusing the learners, we have not extended the discussion of differentiation mechanisms to include protein synthesis regulation by control of mRNA processing after it is transcribed, or by control mechanisms that may operate during or after the exit of the mRNA from the nucleus. We recommend that you do not discuss these matters with your students. For accuracy, however, avoid implying that transcriptional control is the only means by which differences in mRNA or protein populations can be realized.

Analysis

Your students may find the Analysis more challenging than it appears at first glance. At the most fundamental level, these questions are designed to help the students measure the progress that they have made in understanding development. At a deeper level, the learners should see that one of the results of starting to understand a complex issue is that you begin to see just how complex it is and just how much you would have to understand to explain it completely. Encourage your learners to think carefully about the questions and to review the related essay *Differentiation and the Expression of Genetic Information* as a source of clues that will help them identify some of the questions that remain to be answered about both growth and differentiation. We recommend that you assign the analysis questions as homework and that you collect your learners' journals as a way to assess the level of their understanding.

Do not be concerned if your students do not easily see the complexity of these issues or the underlying lesson about the nature and processes of science. Because it may take your learners some time to understand these issues, we have designed an optional activity, *Looking inside Black Boxes*, to address growth and differentiation at a deeper and more detailed level. To establish the connection between the two activities, we suggest that you begin the optional activity with a brief review of the learners' responses to the analysis questions in this activity. Strategies for conducting this discussion are included in the optional activity.

Review your work in this and the previous activity. Participate in a class discussion of the following:

Expect responses such as the following:

1. Explain at a molecular level how genetically identical cells can differentiate into structurally and functionally diverse cells.

    Use specific examples from the table in the need to know box to support your answer.

    Differentiation among genetically identical cells can occur through the mechanism of selective gene expression. Environmental influences both inside and outside the cell cause certain genes to turn on and other genes to turn off.

2. How does a human develop from a fertilized egg into an adult?

    Answers to this question will vary. At the most basic level, expect the learners to say that growth during development occurs by mitosis and that differentiation occurs by selective expression of the genetic information that is transmitted and received through mitosis. More thoughtful learners may add details to this answer by referring to what they have learned about the cell cycle and about the stages of mitosis and/or by explaining the concept of selective gene expression in terms of similarities and differences in the DNA, mRNA, and protein content of differentiated cells.

3. To what extent do you feel that you understand the answer to question 2? List at least two areas of understanding that you would have to know more about to answer this question completely. Explain why that information would be important to explaining the puzzle of how growth and development takes place.

    The learners likely will feel that they have a good grasp of the basic mechanisms of development. Such an answer is expected and fully acceptable. However, push the learners to see beyond the terms *mitosis* and *selective gene expression* to the complexity and the detail that underlie them. The essay *Differentiation and the Expression of Genetic Information* contains a number of hints to this complexity that careful readers should have identified. Learners should see that to give a phenomenon a name (*mitosis*, for example) is not to explain it fully. An important part of understanding the nature of science is to see that answers to questions generally raise more questions, and that the experience of investigating a scientific question is rather like peeling successive layers off an onion: however satisfying it is to reach the next level, one always knows that there are more levels below that still remain to be recognized and addressed.

The types of questions that learners may identify as remaining to be elucidated will vary. Some examples include the following:

◆ What are the internal signals that control the events of the cell cycle?

◆ How is the rate of cell division controlled and coordinated generally throughout the embryo and specifically from one part to another?

◆ What happens at the molecular level to turn genes on and off?

◆ Do errors in growth or differentiation ever occur?

Elaborate # Development Gone Awry

Major Concepts Regulation of development; genetic and environmental influences; cancer; birth defects

Overview

This activity allows learners to consider the medical consequences of developmental problems. Students elaborate on their understanding of the basic processes of development by examining cases in which errors occur. Two essays and a DVD segment provide resources that help the learners understand the disruption of development that results in birth defects and in cancer. Students then use their new understanding to script a conversation between a doctor and a patient (or parent of a patient) suffering from a developmental problem. The script offers a creative chance for the learners to construct and present their understanding of developmental errors. The Analysis examines the role of choice in such situations. Students can look beyond the basic biology of developmental disorders to think about choice, risk, and human behavior.

Materials   (per class of 30, individuals)

resource materials (such as newspapers; magazines such as *Science News*, *Scientific American*, and *Discover;* or medical publications such as *Harvard Health Letter* or University of California at Berkeley *Wellness Letter*)

DVD
DVD player
DVD or video equipment for recording and playing (optional)

Outcomes and Indicators of Success

The following indicators allow you to assess the students' level of success with the activity and to assess their process of learning.

By the end of this activity, the learners should

1. understand the role of developmental errors in human birth defects.

   They will show their understanding by

   a. describing an example of how the developmental scheme can go awry between fertilization and birth (this description may be in the script and/or the response to the Analysis), and

   b. using specific examples to explain how genetic and environmental factors play a role in birth defects.

2. understand the role of developmental errors in cancer.

   They will demonstrate their understanding by

   a. referring to the lack of cell growth regulation among cancerous cells (this reference may be in the script as well as in the Analysis response),

   b. using specific examples to explain how genetic and environmental factors play a role in cancer, and

   c. describing how treatments for cancer work.

3. explain the role of choice in the risks for developmental problems.

   They will indicate their understanding by explaining the choices humans make that influence the risk of birth defects and cancer, including cigarette smoking, alcohol consumption, or exposure to mutagens and carcinogens.

Preparations

We suggest that you assign the search for news articles related to birth defects and/or cancer ahead of time to make it possible for students to locate them. In addition, you may want to establish files in the classroom and select links on a Web page to provide access to resource material for this activity.

In addition to publications you make available to students, you may want to look at more sophisticated journals (such as the *New England Journal of Medicine*) for reports on newsworthy medical advances that you could call to the attention of learners. Local clinics and organizations, such as the March of Dimes or the American Cancer Society, also may provide helpful sources of information.

If you decide to have students record their scripts, arrange for audio or video recording and playing equipment.

Background Information

Researchers are making rapid progress in elucidating the biological factors that give rise to developmental birth defects and cancer. In particular, our understanding of how specific genetic factors influence development is greatly improved. Technological advances such as improved techniques for obtaining and analyzing nucleic acid sequences are particularly helpful. Among the new resources for research is the growing bank of information on

DNA sequences identified during the Human Genome Project. When this sequence information is coupled with corresponding genetic, biochemical, and clinical studies that show the effects of specific genes and the functions of the corresponding gene products, a clear picture of the underlying biology of a genetic disorder emerges. Among the new discoveries are genes that play a role in the occurrence of some cancers. The specific mutations underlying many other inherited disorders, including some prenatal developmental defects, also are being determined.

Disorders often arise through a combination of environmental and genetic influences. Researchers and physicians use medical histories as well as laboratory studies to make the needed connections in understanding a disorder. It frequently is difficult to assemble sufficient evidence to confidently make the connection between a particular behavior or toxic factor and a developmental disorder, so many of the studies are ongoing.

As work progresses and technology offers new tools for research, the bank of knowledge about specific disorders grows. Basic research expands our view of the underlying causes of developmental disorders and opportunities for prevention. Research directed toward clinical studies and new technologies for treatment increase our power to combat the effects of these disorders.

As the essays indicate, the cultural view of developmental disorders (particularly of cancer) changes through time as new information and new treatments emerge. For example, the word *cancer* used to be synonymous with death in the minds of many individuals. Now people recognize that many cancers are treatable, particularly if detected early.

Given the nature of new therapies and tests, a number of ethical questions arise during diagnosis and treatment of developmental disorders. Technologies to diagnose prenatal problems as well as some new gene-screening procedures for adults present questions about ethical choices. For example, to what extent should health care professionals screen for breast cancer genes? How might individuals carrying high risk genes be affected by the knowledge? What choices can parents make if they discover that a defect in a developing fetus will lead to a serious birth defect? Doctors, lawmakers, and private citizens will continue to struggle with the best approaches to obtaining knowledge about genetic risks, the implications of various experimental treatments, and various other ethical issues that arise in our broadening view of developmental process and error.

Strategies for Guiding Learners

PROCESS AND PROCEDURES

As a class, read orally or silently all introductory materials for the activity and the Process and Procedures to help students build connections between concepts and activities. Use the time spent reading to bring the students' attention into focus.

1. Work individually. Choose a disorder to be the topic of your script. Good ways to identify possible topics include the following:

    ◆ Find a news event that relates to either birth defects or cancer. Use this news coverage as the basis for your script. You may find interesting news bulletins on the Internet (be sure to select reputable sites), in newspapers, and in publications such as *Science News*, *Discover*, and *Harvard Health Letter*.

◆ Interview a person who has experienced a birth defect or cancer or someone who has had a family member with a birth defect or cancer.

◆ Use an idea that occurs to you as you review the resources listed in step 2.

2. Discuss your idea with your teacher. Ask her or him to approve your topic. Then collect information about the biology involved in the disorder from the available resources.

It may help you to read through the criteria for a good script. These are listed in step 3. The criteria will help you decide what information you will need.

Read and use the essays *Development and Birth Defects* (page 586) and *Cancer: Unregulated Growth* (page 589) as resources for this project. The DVD segment "Cancer in Humans" also contains important background information. The DVD images show cancerous growths in a variety of human tissues. They also show microscopic images of cancerous blood cells (leukemia), X-ray images of lung cancer before and after treatment, and MRI (magnetic resonance imaging) of brain tumors. For your project, use any other available resources as well.

To use class time most efficiently, direct the learners to search for a news idea and do their background reading outside class. We suggest that you assign the search for an article at an earlier date for this reason.

The essays *Development and Birth Defects* and *Cancer: Unregulated Growth* and the DVD segment "Cancer in Humans" are resources both for background material and to find a topic for the script. Learners will gain a better understanding if they read the material in the essays before beginning their script. It may be helpful to ask a few guiding questions about the essays to help motivate students to focus on what they read. Such questions might include:

◆ How does the timing of exposure to an external hazard influence the effect on development? (Refer to Figure E13.10.)

◆ How may the growth of cells change when they become cancerous?

◆ Are birth defects inherited or caused by an event during pregnancy or both?

The DVD segment "Cancer in Humans" includes a motion clip of cell division in noncancerous and cancerous cells and still images of cancerous tumors and tissues that provide a visual context for students to think about how cancerous cells grow and invade healthy tissue. Although this segment is provided as a resource, we recommend that you show the entire class the motion clip of noncancerous and cancerous cells dividing. If the stills of cancerous tumors and tissues remain as a resource that learners use by their own choice, you will be encouraging their sense of independence and responsibility for their own learning.

Throughout the activity, look for opportunities to point out the interplay between basic research and applications of scientific knowledge, and help students see the importance of technology in both areas. New research tools, including the equipment for discovering DNA sequences and the computer programs used to store and analyze the information, depend on technological advances. Similarly, help learners see that treatments depend not only on new technologies but also on the basic biological knowledge that makes these technologies possible in the first place.

Remind the learners to look ahead to the criteria for step 3. Provide guidance for approval of their topics.

3. Develop your script of a conversation between a doctor (you) and a patient suffering from the disorder you chose in step 1. (The conversation may take place between the doctor and family members as well.)

You will know you have a good script when it does the following:

◆ Describes in detail the disorder you chose

◆ Explains the probable role (if any) of external (environmental) factors in producing the disorder

◆ Explains the probable role (if any) of genetic factors in producing the disorder

◆ Describes how and when (that is, in what way, and if known, through what specific events or mechanisms) growth and/or differentiation have been affected

◆ Describes the long-term effects of the disorder

◆ Mentions any treatments and their likelihood of working

Assume that the patient or family members of the patient are just learning of the diagnosis and are struggling to deal with it. Your goal is to explain (a) what the disorder is, (b) how it came about, and (c) what can be done about it, if anything. Present the information in a way that meets the criteria listed above. Imagine what questions the patient or family members might ask and how the doctor would respond.

Your teacher will tell you if you are to submit your script in writing. You might enlist the help of other students and perform it for your class. Another option may be to record your script on video or audio.

Depending on the time available for this activity, you may have students present their scripts orally or on video; this may increase the personal investment and interest level of the students.

This activity is designed to encourage individual effort. It can be modified to support team work for all or part of the activity if you prefer that approach. For example, a team of students could work together to present a script or to form a discussion group to deal with the issues in the Analysis.

Encourage learners to take an active role in their effort to elaborate their knowledge of developmental processes and errors. Use questions to guide their thinking and to help them make connections to what they have learned without telling them how a script should sound. Remind students that they need to present the basic developmental biology related to the disorder being discussed in a manner that a layperson would understand. The criteria listed in the student pages should help learners take responsibility for creatively combining a view of how the doctor and patient interact with a description of the basic biology of the disorder. You may need to get some learners started by suggesting an example of a disorder or by asking them questions about the nature of the expected conversation. For example, you could challenge a student by asking, What would be the patient's first question after hearing the diagnosis?

As learners design their scripts, check that they are following the criteria sufficiently to construct and demonstrate their understanding of the underlying biology. If they have difficulty, you may wish to refer them to the explanations they constructed in the previous two activities of the basic processes of development: growth and differentiation.

Analysis

The focus of the Analysis shifts from the biology of the disorder and its treatment to the role of choice, risk, and human behavior. When you read the Analysis introduction, point out to your students that the steps in the activity up to this point have prepared them to respond to the questions from an informed viewpoint. During the discussion of the Analysis, be alert to whether your learners' responses indicate that they have read and understood the two general topics covered in the essays. You may find the discussion brings in issues of ethics and risk analysis. If so, some reminder of how these topics were handled in Chapter 6, especially the essay *Ethical Analysis*, will be valuable.

1. Do personal choices have a greater influence in determining an individual's risk of developing cancer or in causing a risk of birth defects? Explain your response.

   Relationships between choices and birth defects include the following: choices about having children if a family history of a particular inherited disorder is known, choices about having children if the mother is not healthy or is of advanced age, and choices about maintaining a woman's health during pregnancy to reduce risk to the infant. Lifestyle choices to avoid infection and toxic substances, such as cigarette smoke, alcohol, or certain drugs, also can affect risk.

   Behavior affects the risk of cancer in a variety of ways. A healthy lifestyle improves immune function and that, in turn, reduces risk. The choice to avoid toxic factors such as cigarette smoke and other known carcinogens also reduces the chances of getting several cancers. Deciding to see a physician for testing as soon as one suspects a cancer can improve chances of survival. Individuals with a family history of certain cancers may opt for screening to detect the presence of a cancer gene or for prophylactic testing for early detection of a tumor. Accept any well-reasoned statement that supports the student's opinion about the likely consequences of risks that result from personal choices.

2. Give three examples of developmental problems that scientists believe are largely or entirely genetic in origin.

   Examples of developmental problems that are largely genetic in origin include disorders such as trisomy 21 (Down's syndrome), cleft palate, achondroplasia, and cri-du-chat syndrome.

3. Give three examples of developmental problems that scientists believe are largely or entirely environmental in origin.

   Examples that are largely environmental in origin include fetal alcohol syndrome as well as defects caused by other toxic substances such as thalidomide or nicotine.

4. Give three examples of developmental problems that scientists believe result from both genetic and environmental causes.

   Learners should use specific examples to support their claims. Responses should indicate that the learner realizes that both genetic and environmental factors can influence cancer and developmental birth defects. Some cases of mental retardation or reduced birth weight might have both genetic and environmental causes. In certain types of cancer, a genetic predisposition may exist, but environmental factors such as exposure to ultraviolet rays of sunlight or dietary habits might increase the individual's risk of developing the disorder.

5. Is it possible for a person to make choices that could result in environmentally induced developmental errors? Explain and support your answer with an example.

> If a person engages in a high-risk behavior, he or she could experience a mutation in the cells that will become gametes. If a mutation occurs, children who inherit that mutation could have environmentally induced developmental errors. For example, if a man allowed himself to be exposed to harmful levels of radiation that caused his sperm to form with a mutation, he could father a child with a birth defect.

Evaluating Where We Stand

Evaluate

Major Concepts
Processes of development; role of development for multicellular organisms; developmental patterns; connection between development and habitat; processes of science

Overview

This evaluate activity involves the learners in evaluating their own progress in understanding development. The first part of the activity challenges students to review goals (outcomes). The students demonstrate their progress toward attaining these goals by answering some structured questions that formalize their knowledge about basic development concepts. Next, they exercise their creativity by applying this learning to the organism that they discovered in Chapter 3. The need to know box Project Goals: Growth and Development in Your Critter on page 560 in the student book provides learners with a way to evaluate their success. In Further Challenges, learners bring closure to their experience in this chapter with the process of scientific inquiry and the history of science by revisiting the questions posed in the engage activity, *One Hundred Years of Questions.*

Materials (per class of 30, individuals)

descriptions and diagrams of your critter from Chapter 10
30 copies of the rubric *Growth and Development in Your Critter*

Outcomes and Indicators of Success

A version of these outcomes and indicators is offered in the need to know box Project Goals: Growth and Development in Your Critter in the student pages. This gives learners a chance for self-evaluation; you also can use the activity for embedded assessment. These outcomes and indicators also are incorporated into the scoring rubric *Growth and Development in Your Critter.* The following indicators allow you to assess the students' level of success with the activity and to assess their process of learning.

By the end of this activity, the learners should

1. demonstrate their understanding of the basic processes of development.

They will demonstrate their understanding by

a. identifying growth and differentiation as key processes of development,

   b. using specific examples to describe what these processes do and how they work, and

   c. applying these concepts to a description of the development of their critter.

2. demonstrate their understanding of patterns in developmental biology.

   They will demonstrate their understanding by

   a. identifying key developmental steps in the life span of a variety of species, and

   b. identifying some of these steps in developing their critter.

3. creatively apply their knowledge of development to a new situation.

   They will show their creativity in this area by

   a. thinking of an interesting and logical way that their critter undergoes development, and

   b. presenting their ideas in a clear and interesting manner.

4. demonstrate their understanding of how scientific study is done.

   They will demonstrate their understanding by

   a. explaining why large questions may be of interest to scientists for many years, and

   b. describing the process scientists use to find answers to complex questions (Further Challenges).

Preparations

Preview the rubric *Growth and Development in Your Critter* on the *TRCD*, and modify it as needed to suit your class.

Strategies for Guiding Learners

PROCESS AND PROCEDURES

As a class, read orally or silently all introductory materials for the activity and the Process and Procedures to help students build connections between concepts and activities. Use the time spent reading to bring the students' attention into focus.

This activity offers a rich opportunity to assess learners' progress in several different areas. You will see evidence of success in learning developmental biology, in understanding scientific processes, and in their creativity and ability for expression. Spend a few minutes explaining how learners can use the project goals in the need to know box in the student pages and the rubric you provide to set goals and evaluate progress. You also may want to indicate how you will consider their self-evaluation along with your own assessment. For example, you might count their self-evaluation as a percentage of their overall score (perhaps 10–25 percent). You might wish to consider both their actual rating of their own progress and how well they expressed their evaluation. The experience of self-evaluation should help reinforce a sense of responsibility for their own learning and help them see you as a partner in that process. As you talk about this part of the activity, use language that helps students see it as a way to display their learning so that they (and you) have a basis on which to evaluate their progress.

Chapter 14

The Human Life Span

In any human society that you might explore, you would find similarities in how members of that culture respond to each other at certain stages of life. In this chapter, learners study physical, cognitive, emotional, and social aspects of human growth and development. They have an opportunity to do this for humans in general and then explore life stages in another culture as well.

We engage the students by showing them a DVD segment of an individual whose photographs from infancy through each year of life have been combined to flow from one image to the next. The students explore life stages by forming teams to observe people in a specific life stage. They then pool this information to begin developing an understanding of the human life span. The learners continue to explore the human life span as they become active listeners in an oral history activity with an elderly guest. Next, the class participates in a debate about how much of human growth and development is influenced by a genetic plan and how much of it is influenced by the greater environment. Finally, learners prepare for a multicultural fair as a way of applying their understanding of the concepts in this chapter. The multicultural fair will be held as part of the Unit 5 Assessment.

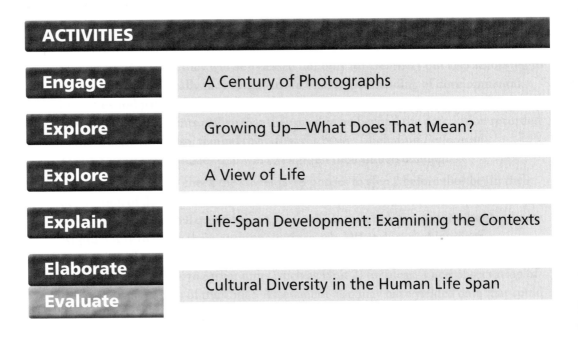

ACTIVITIES

Engage	A Century of Photographs
Explore	Growing Up—What Does That Mean?
Explore	A View of Life
Explain	Life-Span Development: Examining the Contexts
Elaborate / Evaluate	Cultural Diversity in the Human Life Span

	Instructional Flow			Classroom Support			
Activity/ Student Text pp. Teacher Guide pp.	GACD, TRCD, DVD, and CD-ROM Resources	Essays/ Student Text pp.	Estimated Time	Team Size/ Cooperative Learning Focus	Strategies and Tools	Assessment Opportunities	Special Considerations
ENGAGE *A Century of Photographs* p. 564 TG pp. 516–518	DVD: *Age Progression*		30–50 minutes	*Team size:* individuals	DVD segment; morph technology	Prior knowledge	Plan time to stop and describe/discuss the images shown in the video as a class for the benefit of students who cannot see the images.
EXPLORE *Growing Up—What Does That Mean?* pp. 564–568 TG pp. 518–525		*Human Development 101* pp. 597–599; *Growing Up through Life's Phases* pp. 600–604	150 minutes	*Team size:* 4 *Skill:* Contributing ideas; questioning techniques	Observing human subjects	Carrying out an observation plan; current level of understanding	Plan to provide accessible opportunities for students with special needs to make observations. Plan team configurations to facilitate students' participation as well.
EXPLORE *A View of Life* pp. 569–571 TG pp. 525–530			100 minutes	*Team size:* 4 *Skill:* Sharing perspectives	Classroom guest; oral history	Interpreting information; constructing an explanation	Plan to provide accessible opportunities for students with special needs to make observations. Plan team configurations to facilitate students' participation as well.
EXPLAIN *Life-Span Development: Examining the Contexts* pp. 571–572 TG pp. 530–534		*Physical Growth Influences Mental Growth* pp. 604–607; *Physical Growth Influences Social and Emotional Growth* pp. 607–608; *All Phases of Life Require Self-Maintenance* pp. 608–610	150 minutes	*Team size:* 4 *Skill:* Advocating ideas; challenging ideas, not people; disagreeing in a positive way	Debate	Evaluating, interpreting, and synthesizing information; constructing an understanding of the concepts; current level of understanding	Some students may benefit from previewing the debate procedure ahead of class in preparation for participating in this activity.
ELABORATE/ EVALUATE *Cultural Diversity in the Human Life Span* pp. 572–575 TG pp. 534–539	Rubric: *Multicultural Fair Presentation*	*Culture: The Great Shaper of Life* pp. 610–617	150 minutes	*Team size:* 4 *Skill:* Taking responsibility; setting goals; dealing with specific problems; managing and organizing team tasks	Multicultural fair	Applying concepts to a new situation; current level of understanding	Plan to make the multicultural fair setting accessible in terms of time, day, and location for all students and members of their families and community. Enlarge print resources if needed.

Chapter Goals

By the end of this chapter, students should

- understand that human life stages involve physical, emotional, cognitive, and social aspects;
- understand that various aspects of physical development allow for other types of development;
- understand that there is diversity in the expression of human life stages;
- appreciate that making observations of people requires ethical considerations; and
- appreciate that maintaining scientific detachment is difficult.

The learners also will

- make observations,
- interpret results and synthesize information,
- develop explanations, and
- apply concepts to a new situation.

Advance Preparation

You will need to help the students obtain permission from schools, parents, and individuals that they observe. You will find suggested permission forms in the activity *Growing Up—What Does That Mean?* Also, you will need to make arrangements for your special guest in the activity *A View of Life*.

The students also will need to begin working on their study of another culture for the activity *Cultural Diversity in the Human Life Span* before they begin *A View of Life*. See the Preparations section of these activities for specific guidance.

You will need to arrange for a DVD player for the first activity, *A Century of Photographs*.

A Century of Photographs

Major Concepts The progression of a human life

Overview

Technology continues to provide us with tools that allow us to ask questions that begin with, What if...? In this activity, the learners have the chance to see the result of the question, What if you could watch a lifetime? The images should spur their imagination to think of the processes and life stages people progress through across 90 years.

Materials (per class of 30, individuals)

DVD
DVD player

Outcomes and Indicators of Success

The following indicators allow you to assess the students' level of success with the activity and to assess their process of learning.

By the end of this activity, the learners should begin to appreciate that although life proceeds along a continuum from birth to death, we discuss it in terms of life stages. They will show their appreciation by discussing progression through life stages.

Strategies for Guiding Learners

PROCESS AND PROCEDURES

As a class, read orally or silently all introductory materials for the activity and the Process and Procedures to help students build connections between concepts and activities. Use the time spent reading to bring the students' attention into focus.

1. Read through the Analysis questions. Keep them in mind as you view the DVD segment "Age Progression."

   Ask the students to briefly review the questions in the Analysis so that they have them in mind as they watch the DVD segment.

   Show the DVD segment "Age Progression" without interruption. You then may wish to show it again, freezing the DVD on images the learners wish to see.

   The segment shows the age progression of an individual from approximately 1 year old to 94 years old. (The woman is the mother of a past BSCS employee.) The segment was produced by a computer program (Gryphon Software: *Morph*) that uses still photographs and makes the images flow from one to another.

2. In your journal, note 2 or 3 thoughts or additional questions that you had as you viewed the images.

   The questions that the students come up with in this step are intended to be the first questions that come to mind, not in-depth or particularly sophisticated questions, although some of those may come to mind as well. These questions should be helpful in generating a sense of curiosity about this individual's specific life, perhaps about the first 15 or 16 years of the learners' own lives, as well as about the progression of the human life span in general.

3. Discuss your thoughts and questions with your classmates.

   During the discussion, draw out from the learners the idea that although life occurs along a continuum, we divide it into discrete stages.

Analysis

You have now discussed some of the changes associated with aging. Answer the following questions in your journal:

Have the students work individually to answer the following questions, and have them record their answers in their journal:

1. What are the stages in a human life?

   Learners may respond that the stages include infant, toddler, child, adolescent, young adult, adult, middle age, and old age, or any reasonable combination.

2. What do you think identifies particular life stages?

> Learners may respond that age or physical events determine different life stages. They may use negatives such as, "When you can't do . . ." as a way of explaining different stages. They also may respond in terms of cultural attributes, such as getting a driver's license, celebrating one's bar mitzvah, getting married, or leaving home.

3. Is each stage clearly distinctive from the next? Explain your answer.

> Specific events may suggest the ending of one defined life stage and the beginning of the next. Do not expect the learners to know what those events might be. They also should indicate that, other than birth and death, a given stage is not clearly separate from the previous stage or succeeding one.

Extensions

If the equipment and software are available, have interested learners prepare a video segment of themselves or a family member. They will need a sequence of photos of the subject and equipment that digitizes images and converts them into video.

Explore

Growing Up—What Does That Mean?

Major Concepts
Exploring human growth and development: physical, cognitive, social, emotional

Overview

This activity provides the learners with an opportunity to explore aspects of human growth and development in a particular life stage and then to develop a general chronological picture of how humans develop and change. These observations will remain at the descriptive level, and at this stage of the instructional model, your students may not have a clear understanding of the significance of everything that they observe. Also, do not expect the students to make complete and sophisticated observations. Part of the learning in this activity will include the idea that in some ways, it is harder to observe ourselves than it is to observe other species. In the activity *A View of Life*, the students will have the opportunity to begin developing an explanation for what they observed and to create a picture of the salient aspects of human development.

Materials   (per class of 30, teams of 4)

permission forms
sheets of poster board
felt-tipped markers
miscellaneous art supplies
copies of the observation forms that each team develops

Outcomes and Indicators of Success

The following indicators allow you to assess the students' level of success with the activity and to assess their process of learning.

By the end of this activity, the learners should

1. enhance their awareness of the various stages of human development.

    They will demonstrate their awareness by

    a. articulating their current view of a specific life stage, and

    b. planning and making observations of humans in a particular life stage.

2. be cognizant of some of the salient aspects of physical, cognitive, social, and emotional development in humans.

    They will demonstrate this cognizance by observing individuals in a certain life stage and recording specific information in each of these areas of human growth and development.

3. have begun to build on their current understanding of human growth and development.

    They will demonstrate this outcome by participating as they and their classmates create a visual representation of various hallmarks of human development.

Preparations

As we noted in the Advance Preparation for the Unit, check with your school district to determine whether it has certain policies or regulations that you must abide by as you complete this activity. Your district may have special procedures to follow and specific permission forms that you must use, or you may be able to use the sample permission forms that we provide (see Figures T14.1 and T14.2). You will need to duplicate these forms so that each team has enough for the participants they will observe.

For your learners to have a successful experience with this activity, arrange for observations and interviews ahead of time with day-care centers, preschools, elementary schools, middle schools, colleges and universities, places of business, and senior centers. This will provide your students with a pool of people to observe in each age-group. For efficiency, try to arrange these visits so that the students can observe three people during one visit.

If you have a local college or university with a child development or human development program, the institution might be willing to permit students to observe subjects in its professional setting. Many of these labs are equipped with one-way mirrors and sound systems that would allow the students to make observations without disrupting the ongoing work.

Also ask that someone be available to oversee the students as they make their observations. You will need to ask for this person's assistance in acquiring signed permission slips from each of the subjects. Some institutions or agencies will have their own permission or release forms, either in addition to yours or in lieu of yours.

If you feel that you do not have the resources in your community to do this extensive activity, a less desirable alternative would be to ask the students to watch a commercially available video (or DVD) and to make observations as they view segments of it. Some possibilities include the PBS special *Seasons of Life* (see the activity *Life-Span Development: Examining the Contexts* for information on ordering this video). If you choose this alternative, carefully preview the video first. Because this is an explore activity, you will need to keep the audio portion off when the narrators present explanations so that the students can proceed to make their own observations. Later, during *Life-Span Development: Examining the Contexts*, you might want to show the video again—this time with the audio portion that provides one explanation of life stages.

Figure T14.1 Sample permission form for adults

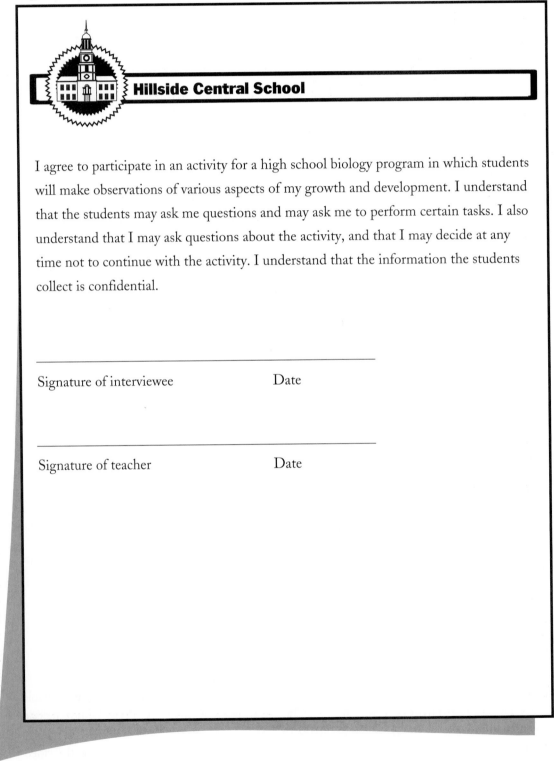

Hillside Central School

I agree to participate in an activity for a high school biology program in which students will make observations of various aspects of my growth and development. I understand that the students may ask me questions and may ask me to perform certain tasks. I also understand that I may ask questions about the activity, and that I may decide at any time not to continue with the activity. I understand that the information the students collect is confidential.

_____

Signature of interviewee   Date

_____

Signature of teacher   Date

Another possible alternative is to combine both of these approaches—the actual observations and the video observations—to give the students a fairly complete picture of human development.

Figure T14.2 Sample permission form for minors

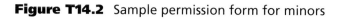
Hillside Central School

I agree to allow my child, _____ , to participate in an activity for a high school biology program in which students will make observations of various aspects of my child's growth and development. I understand that the students may ask my child questions or may ask him or her to perform certain tasks. I also understand that either I or my child may ask questions about the activity. My child or I may decide at any time not to continue with the activity. I understand that the information that the students collect is confidential.

_____

Signature   Date

Strategies for Guiding Learners

PROCESS AND PROCEDURES

As a class, read orally or silently all introductory materials for the activity and the Process and Procedures to help students build connections between concepts and activities. Use the time spent reading to bring the students' attention into focus.

1. Join your team of 4. Decide which one of the following life stages your team will observe:

   ◆ Infancy (birth through 1 year)
   ◆ Early childhood (2 years through 6 years)
   ◆ Middle childhood (7 years through 11 years)
   ◆ Adolescence (12 years through 18 years)
   ◆ Young adult (19 years through 30 years)
   ◆ Prime adult (31 years through 55 years)
   ◆ Middle age (56 years through 70 years)
   ◆ Old age (more than 71 years)

   To assign each team to a certain life stage, you might ask teams to volunteer for each stage, or you might record each stage on a slip of paper and ask that each team draw a slip.

2. Based on your current knowledge, record in your journal your ideas about the following for the age-group you choose:

   a. 3 physical characteristics
   b. 2 cognitive (processes of knowing) characteristics
   c. 2 emotional characteristics
   d. 2 social characteristics

   Do this task individually.

3. Share with the rest of your team your journal entries for each category listed in step 2. Note the similarities and differences in your ideas.

   As the learners record their current understanding of their assigned life stage in their journals, remind them that this can be anything that is part of their current understanding. Encourage learners to record ideas from their own experiences with people in the different life stages. As they share these ideas with their teammates, listen to their conversations to get an idea of what your students understand about human growth and development.

4. With your team of 4, develop a plan for making observations that all team members will follow.

   Your teacher will provide you with information about whom you will observe and how you will accomplish this task. Read *Human Development 101* (page 597). Take notes that will help you to plan and prepare for your observations. That essay is a series of journal entries from a fictitious college student who, at the time of the entries, was just beginning her studies in human development. The information in her journal will provide you with some background about aspects of physical, cognitive, emotional, and social development. You will form pairs within your team and make your observations in these pairs.

a. With your team, hold a brainstorming session. Create a list of ways to observe and obtain information about people in the age-group that you chose to study.

b. Refine your list. Develop an outline with specific strategies, potential questions, and potential tasks that you will use during your observations.

Agree on roles for you and your partner. You both should share the responsibilities of recording observations and interacting as necessary with the participants.

Follow the Guidelines for Observations in the following need to know box.

As the teams develop a plan for the observations that they will conduct, remind them to use the essay *Human Development 101* as a resource. This will provide them with the background information that they need.

As the learners work on their plans, circulate from team to team to keep track of and guide their progress. Remind the students of the guidelines for observations, which follow step 4 (page 566). Also, remind them to have you approve their plans when they are complete. As you review their plans, consider them both from a conceptual and a practical standpoint. That is, ask yourself the following questions: Will this plan help the students obtain the information they need to complete this activity, and is this plan practical and feasible?

Remember that the main focus of this activity is the experience of making observations. Sometimes it is difficult to get enough concrete information from observations alone. At some point, the learners may need to ask specific questions or ask the participants to perform specific tasks in order to be able to observe certain behaviors. Consequently, as the students develop their plans, explain to them why they should include ideas for both questions they might need to ask or tasks they might need the participants to perform. It would be difficult for the students to formulate questions on the spot during the observations.

After the students' plans are complete, but before they begin their observations, make certain that they understand their responsibility to the people they observe. Go over the ethical issues involved as well as the appropriate behavior that you expect. Check with the agencies with which you have made arrangements to ensure that a staff person will be present while the students make their observations and conduct interviews. Ask the students who are observing young children to collect samples of the children's artwork. Remind them to ask for permission to take the samples and explain that they will use them later on in their studies.

c. When you think your plan is complete, ask your teacher to approve it. Make revisions, if necessary, and have your teacher look at it again.

d. Based on your plan, create observation forms that will help you keep track of the information you collect.

Review the Sample Observation Form, Figure 14.4, for some ideas.

5. Conduct your observations in pairs.

You likely will conduct these observations after school or on the weekends. Your teacher will set up the structure and arrangements. When the observations are complete, each pair should have observed 3 people.

By having the students complete the observations in pairs, they should feel more comfortable and should better manage the tasks of interacting with the participants and recording information at the same time. When the students have completed their observations, give them time to go over their notes and make sure that their observation forms are complete. Because this will be the first time that most of the students will have done formal observations of human subjects, do not expect sophisticated, thorough, or even complete observations. Part of what the students will be learning is that it is exceedingly difficult to observe ourselves.

6. Meet with the rest of your team to share and summarize your observations. Include information about each type of development (physical, cognitive, emotional, and social). Discuss the following questions:

   a. How do your actual observations compare with your journal entries from step 2?

   b. Between the 2 pairs of teammates, what were the similarities in your observations? What were the differences?

   c. How might you explain the differences in what you observed?

   Ask each team of four to create a team summary of the life stage on which it focused. Remind the students to encourage the contributions of each team member and create a synthesis of all findings.

7. With your class, share each team's summary. Begin with the earliest life stage.

   Ask the teams to share their summaries with the class in chronological order, that is, begin with the team that observed infants, then move on to young children, and so on. Remind students to ask questions of each other to clarify their own understanding of the observations.

Analysis

Have the students complete step 1 of the Analysis as a class and step 2 individually.

 As a class, the students are to create a chronology of human life stages with both a written and a visual component. Encourage them to be creative, and provide them with a variety of art supplies. By this time in the year, expect the students to be able to work well as a class on this collaborative project, but be prepared to guide the process, if necessary.

Explain to the students that in the next activity, an elderly individual will be visiting the class to share his or her view of life's stages. He or she will have an opportunity to review the class project before coming.

For step 2 of the Analysis, ask the students to write a reflective entry in their journals that describes their current understanding of human life stages. Remind the students that the essay *Growing Up through Life's Phases* should help them as they work on this entry. Collect the journals so that you can assess their current thinking and understanding of human life stages. The questions that they pose may be particularly revealing.

Read the essay *Growing Up through Life's Phases* (page 600). Then complete step 1 as a class. Next, complete step 2 individually. Your teacher will collect your journal after you complete step 2.

1. Create a visual representation of human growth and development based on the aspects of development that you and your classmates observed. Your representation should

   ◆ be chronological;

   ◆ include aspects of physical, cognitive, emotional, and social development; and

   ◆ include a written component.

Use any supplies that your teacher provides. Be creative!

As a class, the students should end up with an overall picture of human growth and development. Because of the likely unevenness of their observations and the range of prior knowledge that students will bring to this activity, expect that there may be gaps in this picture. Encourage the students to reflect on these gaps in step 2.

2. In your journal, write a short, reflective entry that describes your current understanding of development during the human life span. Address the following questions in your entry:

   ◆ Which characteristics of development do you think are specific to the cultural setting?

   ◆ Which characteristics of development do you think are found in most cultures? In other words, which do you consider "universal"?

   ◆ What other questions come to mind that you hope to answer as you continue with this chapter?

   Because this is the explore stage of the instructional model, again do not expect a thorough understanding of human growth and development. Rather, place more emphasis on the reflective nature of the entry and look for questions that will guide the students' learning throughout the rest of the chapter.

A View of Life

Explore

Major Concepts   Exploring an oral history

Overview

In this activity, the learners interview a special guest invited to class and obtain an oral history of his or her life. The guest should be someone more than 70 years old. Before the visit, the students will develop interview questions and you will approve them. This activity complements *Growing Up—What Does That Mean?* by providing an in-depth, retrospective view from someone who has experienced firsthand most of life's stages.

Materials   (per class of 30, teams of 4)

audiocassette recorder/player or video recorder
interview questions (to be developed by the class)

Outcomes and Indicators of Success

The following indicators allow you to assess the students' level of success with the activity and to assess their process of learning.

By the end of this activity, the learners should be able to use the tool of interviewing to expand their understanding of human life stages.

They will demonstrate their ability by

a. constructing interview questions in collaboration with their team members,

b. participating in a class interview,

c. using information from the interview to expand their project from *Growing Up— What Does That Mean?* and to answer questions about human life stages, and

d. discussing the implications of this activity with the class.

Preparations

Make the necessary arrangements to bring in a guest for your class to interview. Select a person who is outgoing and likes to talk about his or her life. You will need to select a person who is at least 70 years old and who is willing and able to respond to interview questions from your students. Provide the potential guest with the rationale for the activity as well as a synopsis. It is important that you provide the guest with a copy of the questions several days before the interview.

To select an interviewee, you might consider relatives or friends of yours, or of your colleagues or students. Other sources you might use are the local historical society, senior citizen centers, retirement communities, or organizations such as a local chapter of American Association of Retired Persons (AARP) or Service Corps of Retired Executives (SCORE).

Decide whether you will have the class videotape the interview or just record it on audiotape, and make arrangements for this equipment.

It is important that you set up and test the taping equipment in advance. Position the microphone so that it records both the questions and answers effectively. The students may need to move close to the microphone when delivering questions.

Develop a simple release form to be signed by you and the guest. This document grants permission to tape (audio or video) the interview and provides written evidence that the interviewee understands the purpose and applications of the interview. It also clarifies the ownership of the tape and the conditions of its use. The document can include any limitations for use designated by the interviewee. A suggested model is shown in Figure T14.3.

Figure T14.3 Sample release and permission form

Hillside Central School

I hereby give permission to Mr./Ms. _____ 's class at
_____ school to tape an interview with me. The tape
may be used by the class for educational purposes, subject to the following restrictions:

_____

_____

_____

_____

Cassette number   Date of interview   Subject of tape

_____

Signature of interviewee   Date

_____

Signature of teacher   Date

3. In your journal, record the major ideas from your guest's responses.

You will have access to a tape recording of the interview. This will allow you to review the responses and add detail to your notes. Make sure that you collect word-for-word quotes as *data* to support your inferences.

Even though you are taping this interview, encourage the students to take some notes in their journal. These notes will help them be more efficient if they review the tapes later.

Analysis

Have the students complete step 1 as a team and step 2 individually.

Revisit the project that your class developed for the activity *Growing Up—What Does That Mean?* Then complete step 1 as a team and step 2 individually.

1. Determine what new information emerged from the interview. Add it to your class project.

As the learners add new information to their project, ask them to be aware of the types of information that they are adding. For example, is it information that changes their understanding of some life stage, or is it information that enriches what they already knew?

2. Use the information from the interview to respond to the following in your journal:

   a. How did the guest's culture influence his or her growth and development?

   Explain how a different cultural setting might have had a different impact on this person.

   Expect a variety of responses. You might expect the learners to include such influences as childhood beliefs, the nature of the communities the guest grew up in, family resources, schools attended, the kind of education received, family expectations, and his or her range of opportunities. A different cultural setting with its different societal expectations and opportunities usually leads to different life experiences.

   b. Provide examples of how technological change during the individual's lifetime influenced her or his development at each life stage.

   The guest may cite the impacts that technological innovations such as automobiles, household appliances, automation in the workplace, television, and finally, computers have had on his or her life. Perhaps these innovations had an impact on his or her education, job opportunities, lifestyle, or where he or she lived.

Life-Span Development: Examining the Contexts

Major Concepts Human growth and development: physical, cognitive, social, emotional

Overview

This activity helps the learners construct an explanation for the types of observations that they made in the explore activities. The learners participate in a debate about how much of the variation we see in individual life stages can be attributed to a specific genetic plan and how much can be attributed to the greater environment.

Materials   (per class of 30, teams of 4)

resources that you provide (refer to Preparations)

Outcomes and Indicators of Success

The following indicators allow you to assess the students' level of success with the activity and to assess their process of learning.

By the end of this activity, the learners should

1. understand that human life stages are characterized by different levels of physical, cognitive, social, and emotional growth and development that are influenced by a genetic plan and by the greater environment.

   They will demonstrate their understanding by

   a. outlining relevant information about human development that addresses aspects of physical, cognitive, social, and emotional growth and development, and

   b. participating in a debate and providing information about human growth and development that justifies how a specific genetic plan or the greater environment contributes to an individual's development.

2. understand that human growth and development is influenced by a specific genetic plan and by the greater environment.

   They will demonstrate their understanding by

   a. providing information in a debate setting that demonstrates how a genetic plan or the greater environment contributes to an individual's growth and development, and

   b. writing a short essay that synthesizes both sides of the debate in a convincing way that they can justify.

Preparations

In addition to the essays that we provide, you may want to assemble resources for the students to use as they prepare for their debate. These resources might include books, articles, or videos that provide information on physical, cognitive, social, and emotional development for different life stages. Consider the following:

> Kotre, J. & Hall, E. (1990). *Seasons of life: Our dramatic journey from birth to death*. Boston: Little, Brown and Company. This book was developed to accompany the *Seasons of Life* television series, produced by the University of Michigan and WQED, Pittsburgh, Pennsylvania. For information on telecourse licensing, purchase of prerecorded video, audiocassettes, and print materials, contact The Annenberg/CPB Project, 1-800-LEARNER (1-800-532-7637).

> Sigelman, C. K. & Shaffer, D. (1995). *Life-span of human development* (2nd ed.). Pacific Grove, CA: Brooks/Cole Publishing.

You may want to ask the forensics coach at your school to help you plan for and carry out the debate for this activity. Once you have a format for the debate outlined, share it with the students before you begin this activity so that everyone has the same idea as they prepare for the debate. A sample format is provided in Figure T14.5.

Figure T14.5 Sample format for debate

1. Each side chooses a spokesperson, and each spokesperson delivers a 5-minute opening argument that briefly states the team's position.

2. Each side also chooses three main speakers, each of whom presents a well-reasoned idea and the information to support that idea (3–5 minutes each). The teams take turns presenting their speakers.

3. After each speaker, any member from the other side can take 3 minutes to respond to what that speaker said.

4. After all presentations have been made, each side meets to formulate closing arguments.

5. The spokesperson for each side delivers a 3- to 5-minute closing argument that summarizes the team's position.

Strategies for Guiding Learners

PROCESS AND PROCEDURES

As a class, read orally or silently all introductory materials for the activity and the Process and Procedures to help students build connections between concepts and activities. Use the time spent reading to bring the students' attention into focus.

1. With your teammates, discuss the following 2 questions. Decide which question your team would like to explore.

   a. How much of the variation that we see in individuals can be attributed to their specific genetic plans?

   b. How much of the variation that we see in individuals can be attributed to their environment?

   Allow time for the teams to discuss each question briefly so that they have some general idea about each position and how strongly teammates feel one way or the other. This step gives you an opportunity to assess their current understanding of these concepts. After 10 minutes or so, poll the teams to see which question they would like to pursue. If the teams are rather evenly divided in their interest to pursue the questions, then let these preferences become their assignments and have them proceed to the next step. If they are not evenly divided, see if some teams are willing to consider the other question. If not, you may need to use a random method such as drawing numbers to assign teams to questions so that the teams are evenly divided.

2. In your journal, begin to develop an answer to your question by outlining significant information. Also, record related questions that come to mind.

   Use the following essays as resources to help you complete this step. They will add to what you already know and what you have learned in this program.

   Physical Growth Influences Mental Growth (page 604)
   Physical Growth Influences Social and Emotional Growth (page 607)
   All Phases of Life Require Self-Maintenance (page 608)

   As the students begin to develop responses to their question, remind them to use the essays as resources along with some of the other books and articles that you may have for them. If you have the time, you may want the students to continue this step for a few days so that they can use libraries and acquire more information and develop more sophisticated answers.

3. Join with the other teams that selected the same question as your team. Prepare for a class discussion of the 2 questions from step 1.

   a. Choose a recorder for your new team.

   b. Summarize what you already know.

   Take turns adding new information to the team's collection of information. Make sure that you can support each statement. You may want to record your ideas on a flip chart.

   c. Make a list of other information that you would like to have. Explore the resources that your teacher has available to determine whether you can answer your questions.

d. Think about what the other group might say and how you might respond.

As the teams join to share ideas and information, remind them to choose a recorder to record the ideas that are expressed. Monitor the discussions so that you can assess the current level of understanding of these concepts. You may need to offer some guidance or additional resources to teams or students as they think through and develop their arguments.

In addition to developing their own arguments, encourage the teams to consider ideas that the opposing team might present and ways that they could respond to those ideas.

If students do not have a good grasp of the concepts or how the information supports their positions, take the extra time now to help students develop this understanding. Do not proceed with the debate until you are certain it will represent a sound understanding of these concepts.

4. Participate in a class debate.

As the debate progresses, record notes and questions in your journal.

Conduct the debate according to the plans and format that you outlined to the students before they began their work. Encourage students to take notes as the debate progresses; these notes will be important as they write their essays in the Analysis.

Analysis

With your classmates, discuss the findings from the debate. Then, individually, write a short essay in your journal that compares and combines the two sets of responses. Briefly summarize the responses to each question. Relate how heredity and environment interact to make us who we are.

To help the students prepare to write their essays, convene a brief discussion of the debate. In addition to a review of the information presented, you may want to discuss why certain arguments were more convincing than others, the quality of the supporting information, and the importance of being able to articulate a well-reasoned response.

In the essays, expect the students to summarize each position and then to relate how both heredity and the environment together interact to make us who we are.

Cultural Diversity in the Human Life Span

Major Concepts Life stages in different cultural settings

Overview

In this activity, the learners have the opportunity to elaborate on what they have been learning in this chapter by applying the concepts of human development to the process of growing up in a different cultural setting. Each team of four will explore a different culture and create a display and a presentation for a multicultural fair. After the students have learned about a different cultural setting, they will be able to evaluate their understanding of this chapter by reflecting on the diversity in the cultural expression of human life stages, the similarities that emerge, and the biological aspects of development that allow for these similarities and differences. The multicultural fair will be held as part of the Unit 5 Assessment.

Materials (per class of 30, teams of 4)

miscellaneous art supplies
30 copies of the rubric *Multicultural Fair Presentation*

Outcomes and Indicators of Success

The following indicators allow you to assess the students' level of success with the activity and to assess their process of learning.

By the end of this activity, the learners should

1. have an appreciation for the diversity in the expression of human life stages.

    They will show their appreciation by

    a. learning about life stages in a culture different from their own, and

    b. preparing a display and a presentation of these life stages for a multicultural fair.

2. understand that there are some common features of human life stages across cultures.

    They will show their understanding by reflecting on these common features in their journal.

3. understand that there are certain aspects of biological development that allow for both differences and similarities.

    They will demonstrate their understanding by describing these aspects of biological development in their journals.

Preparations

Introduce this activity before you begin the activity *A View of Life*, and let the learners work up through step 2b.

Before you introduce this activity, you will need to accumulate resources on at least eight different cultures so the students have a place to begin. The resource list at the end of this activity will help you. You may want to ask both your school library and certain public libraries to develop resource lists of the material that they have available for each of the cultures that your classes are studying.

Also, remind the students to use the scoring rubric to guide them as they work on this activity. Preview the rubric and modify it to suit your class.

Background Information

When we attempt to learn about another culture, the problem arises of trying to observe that culture without judging it in terms of our own cultural values. Do not expect your students to be able to study another culture in a completely objective manner, but encourage, guide, and even challenge them as appropriate.

2. What have you learned about biological development in humans that may help explain both these similarities and differences?

> The students should be able to articulate that the similarities are related to the fact that no matter what cultural setting humans are in, for the most part, they physically develop in the same way. People also have the same biological processes going on, the same basic needs, and the same basic abilities at various stages of life. The students may refer to the work of Piaget. Students may be able to link the differences to the range of cognitive abilities that humans are capable of and to the plasticity of the brain. The students also may link these differences to the ability of humans to learn. Because learning takes place in specific environments, we would expect different results in different environments.

Resource List for *Cultural Diversity in the Human Life Span*

Asian/Middle East

Benedict, R. (1946). *The chrysanthemum and the sword.* Boston: Houghton Mifflin.

Bhattacharyya, N. (1975). *Ancient Indian rituals and their social contents.* London: Curzon Press.

Fried, M. (1980). *Transitions: Four rituals in eight cultures.* New York: Penguin.

Friedl, E. (1992, August). Moonrose watched through a sunny day. *Natural History,* pp. 34–35. (Iran and Turkey)

Lagerwey, J. (1987). *Taoist ritual in Chinese society and history.* New York: Macmillan.

Schuyler, P. D. (1996, May). Jamaa el-fna. *Natural History,* pp. 38–45. (Morocco)

Vesilind, P. (1996, March). Caught in the middle. *National Geographic,* pp. 118–139. (Macedonia)

African

Beattie, J. (1960). *Bunyoro: An African kingdom.* New York: Holt, Rinehart and Winston, Inc. (Japan)

Blier, S. P. (1995, November). The place where vodun was born. *Natural History,* pp. 40–49. (West Africa)

Evans-Pritchard, E. E. (1940). *The Nuer.* London: Oxford University Press.

Kuper, H. (1963). *The Swazi: A South African kingdom.* New York: Holt, Rinehart and Winston, Inc.

Ottenberg, S. (1989). *Boyhood rituals in an African society: An interpretation.* Seattle, WA: University of Washington Press.

Stiles, C. (1996, January). A Swahili port of call. *Natural History,* pp. 52–56. (Kenya)

Thomas, E. M. (1959). *The harmless people.* New York: Vintage Books.

Turnbull, C. (1962). *The forest people.* New York: Anchor Books (Doubleday).

Oceania

Cosgrove, R. (1995, August). The fall and rise of the Tasmainian aborigine. *Natural History,* pp. 32–33.

Hart, C. & Pilling, A. (1964). *The Tiwi of North Australia.* New York: Holt, Rinehart and Winston, Inc.

Mead, M. (1949). *Coming of age in Samoa.* New York: Mentor Books.

O'Neill, T. (1996, February). Irian jaya: Indonesia's wild side. *National Geographic,* pp. 4–43.

Inte
amc
in tl

Ar

In this cha
organisms in v
and interactio
among organi:

use
wh
of t
and

Learners l
Next, the stud
and their resul
understanding
limiting factor
The Commons

The learne
and studying t
Island. The ch
their critter wi

ACTIVIT

Engage

Explore

Explore

Explain

Elabora

Evaluat

Tl

Ma

carr

Stanner, W. (1964). The dreaming, an Australian world view. In P. Hammond (Ed.), *Cultural and Social Anthropology Selected Readings.* New York: MacMillan.

South American

Chagnon, N. (1965). *Yanomamo: The fierce people.* New York: Holt, Rinehart and Winston, Inc.

Good, K. (1995, April). The Yanomami keep on trekking. *Natural History*, pp. 57–65.

McCarry, J. (1996, May). Peru begins again. *National Geographic*, pp. 2–35.

Native American

Chance, N. (1966). *The Eskimo of North Alaska.* New York: Holt, Rinehart and Winston, Inc.

Downs, J. F. (1966). *Two worlds of the Washo: An Indian tribe of California and Nevada.* New York: Holt, Rinehart and Winston, Inc.

Drucker, P. (1965). *Cultures of the North Pacific Coast.* New York: Chandler Publishing Company.

Hoebel, E. A. (1960). *The Cheyennes.* New York: Holt, Rinehart and Winston, Inc.

Kluckhohn, C. & Leighton, D. (1946). *The Navajo.* Cambridge, MA: Harvard University Press.

Lowie, R. (1956). *The Crow Indians.* New York: Holt, Rinehart and Winston, Inc.

Radin, P. (1963). *The autobiography of a Winnebago Indian.* New York: Dover.

Trigger, B. (1969). *The Huron: Farmers of the north.* New York: Holt, Rinehart and Winston, Inc.

Overview

In this activity, the students explore the concepts of resources, interactions that involve shared resources, and carrying capacity by studying the changes that take place in a fictional shared pasture depicted in *The Commons* CD. The students begin to use ecological terminology to describe these concepts. They also analyze and interpret results from their own strategies to manage resources in a computer simulation involving a shared pasture (also on *The Commons* CD).

Materials (per teams of 2–4)

The Commons CD
computer with CD-ROM drive
Copymaster *Pasture Profits* (2 per team for each simulation run)

Outcomes and Indicators of Success

The following indicators allow you to assess the students' level of success with the activity and to assess their process of learning.

By the end of this activity, the learners should have

1. begun to understand the concept of resources.

   They will demonstrate their understanding by

   a. explaining the difference between biotic and abiotic resources, and

   b. identifying renewable and nonrenewable resources.

2. developed a more complete understanding of the role that resources play in determining the size of populations that any ecosystem can support.

   They will demonstrate their understanding by

   a. describing how overuse of limited resources such as food supply can lead to the degradation of a natural resource such as a common pastureland, and

   b. explaining the results of their resource management strategies and evaluating what determined the success or failure of those strategies.

3. begun to understand the concept of carrying capacity.

   They will demonstrate their understanding by

   a. analyzing data and using graphs to explain the changes that occurred in the pasture across time, and

   b. describing the relationship between resources and carrying capacity.

Preparations

This activity (and the next) involves using computers and *The Commons* CD. You will need to arrange that access and decide on team sizes (depending on the number of computers available).

Background Information

In his 1968 essay *The Tragedy of the Commons*, Garrett Hardin uses the scenario of a "pasture open to all" as a metaphor for many of the environmental challenges that humans face in a world of exponentially growing populations and finite resources. The story of the pasture is simple: cowherders who graze their cattle on a pasture "shared by all" discover that there are limits to the number of cows the pasture can sustain. Unfortunately, the cowherders discover these limits by exceeding them and destroying the pasture. The cowherders are not malicious or deliberately destructive but merely act in what they perceive to be their own best interests. Adding yet another cow to the pasture always profits each cowherder more than it costs him . . . until, of course, the cowherders pay the final, cumulative price of the loss of the pasture that sustained them. In Hardin's words, the "tragedy" lies not so much in the loss of the pasture but in the inexorable chain of events that leads to its destruction.

This activity introduces the concept of carrying capacity and resources. Carrying capacity is defined as the number of individuals of a species that the environment can support without diminishing the quality of the environment. On a farm, the carrying capacity of a pasture determines the number of animals that can graze on the land year after year without affecting the overall health of the pasture. A resource is any substance, service, or information that we get from the living or nonliving environment that is useful to us. Material resources such as coal, fresh water, fertile soil, and aluminum are those whose quantities theoretically can be measured. Nonmaterial, or intangible resources, such as beauty, joy, solitude, and stimulation, theoretically are unlimited, although they may not exist in a crowded or degraded setting.

The Commons CD activities engage students in the pasture story and stimulate them to develop their own understanding of natural resources. The students encounter several important terms that scientists use to describe resources. Understanding those terms provides a foundation on which students can build a more detailed understanding of issues related to natural resource commons as well as to population growth and resource consumption in the remainder of Chapter 15 and throughout Chapter 16.

Navigating through *The Commons* CD

The key navigation features of *The Commons* CD are easily understood, and you and your students likely will remember them after you use the program once. For your convenience, the following paragraphs describe some of these features.

The tool bar. The **Tool Bar** is located at the bottom of almost every screen and displays six different puzzle pieces. Each of these puzzle pieces performs a different function:

- Clicking on the **Exit** puzzle piece brings up the program's exit screen.
- Clicking on the **Help** puzzle piece brings up the program's help file.
- Clicking on the **Print** puzzle piece prints all of the screens for a particular sidebar or enrichment resource.
- Clicking on a **Q** (Question) puzzle piece brings up a discussion question for students to answer.
- Clicking on an **I** (Information) puzzle piece brings up information that may be useful to the student.

- Clicking on the **Navigation/Preferences** puzzle piece results in four different functions, depending on the part of the puzzle piece that is clicked. The functions of this puzzle piece are described in the next section.

Using the navigation/preferences puzzle piece.
The Navigation/Preferences puzzle piece appears on the right side of the Tool Bar and looks like a puzzle piece made of four arrows. Three of these arrows allow users to move through the CD. The fourth arrow (the down arrow) changes the program's settings, or preferences.

- Clicking on the **up arrow** opens the program's content map. From the content map, you can jump to any of the program's major resources. Click again on the up arrow to close the content map.

- Clicking on the **forward (right-pointing) arrow** moves you forward from screen to screen through any level of the program. The forward arrow flashes until you reach the end of the resource you are examining.

- Clicking on the **back (left-pointing) arrow** moves you backward from screen to screen through any level of the program.

- Clicking on the **down arrow** opens the program's preferences screen. Information about the program's settings, or preferences, is provided on page 554.

Using the autonavigation feature.
The Commons CD automatically advances video segments from one screen to the next until an I (Information) or Q (Question) puzzle piece appears. Disabling the program's autonavigation feature (see *Setting Preferences*, page 554) allows the user to pause between video segments to take notes or to discuss concepts with a partner.

Accessing resources at the linear level.
The resources in *The Commons* CD are organized into three levels or types of resources. Users see resources at the **linear level** as they move forward through the CD from the introduction through to the program's conclusion. Users also can access linear-level resources by clicking on the appropriate boxes in the program's content map.

Accessing resources
at the sidebar and enrichment levels. Users can access resources at the sidebar and enrichment levels of *The Commons* CD in two ways. One way is to click on the blue or purple puzzle pieces when they appear on the screen at the linear or sidebar levels. Blue puzzle pieces appear at the linear level; clicking on them takes you to simulations, animations, and other features at the **sidebar level**. Purple puzzle pieces appear at the sidebar level; clicking on them takes you to the CD's **enrichment level**, which offers activities that help students explore important concepts in more detail.

A second way to access resources at the sidebar and enrichment levels is to click on the appropriate box in the program's content map.

Using the content map.
As described earlier, the content map illustrates how linear-, sidebar-, and enrichment-level resources are related to one another and allows you to access all of the major resources at each of these levels. Use the content map to gain an overview of the program's contents and organization, locate where you are (a red arrow marks your current position), and move quickly among the program's core sections ("The Pasture as a Commons," "The Gulf of Maine as a Commons," "The World as a Commons," and "A Personal Challenge").

The content map displays the resources available in each of the program's core sections, one at a time. For example, when you access the content map from a position within "The Pasture as a Commons," you will see only the features of this section of the CD displayed. In contrast, when you access the content map from a position within "The Gulf of Maine as a Commons," you will see only the resources of this section displayed.

The upper right corner of the content map shows the title of the core section of the CD that you are viewing. To view another section, click on one of the four photographs below the section title:

◆ To move to "The Pasture as a Commons," click on the photograph of the pasture.

◆ To move to "The Gulf of Maine as a Commons," click on the photograph of the dock.

◆ To move to "The World as a Commons," click on the photograph of the city street.

◆ To move to "A Personal Challenge," click on the photograph of the stoop.

As you roll the mouse over the boxes on the content map, the full title of each resource appears beside the puzzle piece in the upper left corner of the map. To move directly to a new resource at any level, click on the box for that resource. To move to the video segment at the linear level that introduces a sidebar resource, click on the small, unlabeled box that is connected to that resource.

To return to the introduction to *The Commons* CD, click on the box labeled *Intro to the Commons*. To access the program's conclusion, click on the photograph of the stoop to display the content map for "A Personal Challenge," then click on the last box on the right in the linear level.

To open and close the content map, click on the up arrow of the navigation puzzle piece.

Using Q and I puzzle pieces. As you use the resources in the linear level of *The Commons* CD, you will occasionally see Q (Question) puzzle pieces or I (Information) puzzle pieces appear on the Tool Bar.

Q (Question) puzzle pieces pose questions that help students think further about a concept. Click on a Q puzzle piece to open and close it. Note that the program's autonavigation system stops until you click on a Q puzzle piece or until you bypass the puzzle piece by clicking on the forward arrow.

I (Information) puzzle pieces define and supplement new concepts when they are first introduced. Click on an I puzzle piece to open and close it. Note that the program's autonavigation system stops until you click on an I puzzle piece or until you bypass the puzzle piece by clicking on the forward arrow.

Using interactive graphics. You will encounter a variety of interactive graphics on *The Commons* CD. The following list describes some of these graphics and explains their use.

◆ Click on **blue, underlined text,** called **hyperlinks,** to move from screen to screen or to related resources. Such links allow you to move through particular sections of the program in a nonlinear fashion.

◆ **Photographs with blue borders** are interactive. Click on these photographs to watch video segments or hear audio segments.

◆ Some **illustrations** have areas that are activated when you roll over them with the mouse. Information on the screen alerts you to illustrations that are active in this manner. Roll over the illustration or click on parts of it to uncover related resources.

Printing. Some of the resources on *The Commons* CD can be printed. Typically, a Print puzzle piece appears on the Tool Bar with every resource that can be printed. Click on this puzzle piece to print the entire resource.

Files included in the three simulated Internet browsers on *The Commons* CD also can be printed. To print these files, click on the Print button located on the top of the browser screen.

Finally, you can print the full text of the help file by clicking on the Print button located on the bottom right of the help screen.

Accessing the help file. Click on the green Help puzzle piece on the Tool Bar to access the help file. The help file includes information about navigation and troubleshooting.

Setting preferences. The preferences screen on *The Commons* CD allows users to customize the program in a variety of ways. To access the preferences screen, click on the **down arrow** of the Navigation puzzle piece. Once the preferences screen is displayed, click on the appropriate boxes to highlight the settings you wish to save. The preferences screen allows you to

◆ adjust the program's volume without exiting the software,

◆ save your location when you exit the program and automatically return to it when you restart the program,

◆ bypass the introduction to the program and display the content map when you start the program,

◆ disable or enable the program's autonavigation feature, and

◆ turn off or on the display of Q and/or I puzzle pieces.

Because the preference settings are saved on your computer's hard drive, they are not automatically transferred when you use *The Commons* CD on a new computer.

Exiting the program. Click on the green Exit puzzle piece on the Tool Bar to access the exit screen for *The Commons* CD. Confirm your desire to exit by clicking on the Quit button. You also can exit the program by pressing Control-Q on Intel-compatible computers or Command-Q on Macintosh computers.

Note that the exit screen asks you to confirm where you would like *The Commons* CD to begin the next time you use the program.

Accessing credits and references. You can view credits, acknowledgments, and references for *The Commons* CD by clicking on the flashing black and turquoise arrow that appears beside the Quit button on the exit screen.

Strategies for Guiding Learners

PROCESS AND PROCEDURES

As a class, read orally or silently all introductory materials for the activity and the Process and Procedures to help students build connections between concepts and activities. Use the time spent reading to bring the students' attention into focus.

Team sizes for activities involving *The Commons* CD will depend on computer availability. Ideally, students should work in pairs.

1. Work in teams as your teacher directs. View the video "The Pasture Story" on *The Commons* CD.

> The key navigation features of *The Commons* CD are easily understood, and you and the students likely will remember them after using the program once. Refer to the instructions given in the Background Information for details about navigation features.

2. With your teammates, discuss what happened in the video and why.

> Avoid offering any explanation of the title of the CD or the subject or purpose of the video. If the students ask, respond by noting that the video will help them construct their own understanding. Steer their discussion to focus on both what they actually saw take place and explanations for why it occurred, including the role of resources.

3. Go to the "Pasture Profits" simulation on *The Commons* CD. Work with your teammates to assume the role of a dairy farmer who along with another dairy farmer grazes cows on a commonly owned pasture.

Divide your team into 2 groups. Have each group make the decisions for 1 of the dairy farmers. Read the opening screens of the simulation carefully. Follow the instructions provided.

> It is important that the students understand that they earn their living by selling milk, because the goal in the simulation is to maximize milk production, and in so doing, to maximize earnings.

> During the simulation, the computer displays the amount of money the farmers earn, not the amount of milk a farmer's cows produce. The amount of milk produced per cow, however, is an important variable that the computer tracks and then displays at the end of the simulation.

4. Print individual and summary reports at the end of each simulation round. Graph the 4 sets of data on the summary report onto the Copymaster *Pasture Profits*.

Follow your teacher's instructions to try 1 or more management options for the pasture. Work with your group to graph the results from each simulation run.

> Distribute two *Pasture Profits* copymasters to each team for each time the students run the simulation. If time permits, allow teams opportunities to try two or more management options for the pasture. The simulation includes two roles, Sondra and Jason, which can be divided between the team members. Challenge the students to maximize their individual profits. This activity provides an opportunity to create an atmosphere of good-humored competition.

> When teams have finished running the simulation, they will receive individual reports that show how well they and the other farmer did. They will also receive a combined summary report that shows the total number of cows present, the percentage of pasture area covered by grass, the number of units of milk produced per cow at the end of each 6-month period, and the total amount of milk produced by the cows during the simulation. Students are to graph those four sets of data from the combined summary on the *Pasture Profits* copymaster. Review the graphing requirements with the students before they begin to construct their graphs. Be sure they understand what data they are graphing and that all four lines should appear on the same graph.

5. Analyze your graphs with your teammates. Discuss the following questions:

  a. Which management option scenario(s) protected the pasture?
    In the time available, students may or may not have succeeded in protecting the pasture. A strategy that limited the number of cows to a level less than or equal to the carrying capacity of the pasture would protect the pasture.

  b. What is the relationship between the amount of food available per cow and the number of cows?
    The more food that is available per cow, the greater the number of cows that can be sustained.

  c. What is the relationship between the amount of food available and production of milk per cow?
    The production of milk per cow decreases as the pasture's condition and the amount of food available declines.

  d. The maximum number of cows that the pasture can support without destroying its ability to renew itself is called its **carrying capacity**. Using your graphs, determine the carrying capacity for cows on the simulated pasture.

    You may want to look at other teams' graphs for additional information.
    The pasture in the simulation can support 20 cows without declining in quality.

  e. For each different management option available in the simulation, explain what, if any, change takes place in the carrying capacity.

    A larger pasture. **The students may or may not realize that enlarging the pasture will increase the carrying capacity, but there still will be a limit to the number of cows. Whether the pasture is small or large, it has a carrying capacity for cows that cannot be exceeded without the pasture degrading. (The enlarged pasture can support 40 cows without declining in quality.)**

    A different breed. **Using a different breed of cows will not solve the problem because, although these cows consume less grass per unit of milk they produce, there still will be a limit to the number of cows the pasture can sustain. (The pasture's carrying capacity for this breed of cow is approximately 22 cows.)**

    Private pastures. **Dividing the pasture into two private pastures (one for each farmer) reduces the carrying capacity of the pasture available to each farmer by one-half (or 10 cows). Although privatization allows individuals to manage their pastures wisely, it does not *guarantee* that each pasture will be protected. Furthermore, this approach solves the pasture dilemma by eliminating the commons, not by finding a management strategy that protects it.**

    Pay to graze. **Imposing an escalating tax on the total number of cows on the pasture solves the problem because once such a tax is enacted, the farmers simply cannot afford to buy the number of cows that would be dangerous to the pasture.**

6. Read the background information provided in "The Abundant Earth" on the enrichment level of *The Commons* CD (see Figure 15.3). In your own words, explain what a natural resource is. Record your explanation in your journal.

    Answers should show understanding that a resource is any substance, service, or information that we get from the living or nonliving environment that is useful to us.

7. Participate in a class discussion of steps 5 and 6 as your teacher directs.

Analysis

If there is time, the students will benefit from discussing the analysis questions before answering them individually. These may be assigned as homework.

With your team, consider the following questions. Record your answers in your journal.

1. List three examples of resources in the modern world that humans use like the commonly owned pasture in the video. Explain how people manage each example.

   Students may list the world's oceans, our country's national forests, a community's water supply, and clean air as examples of commons. Expect students to give examples of regulations that are used to govern shared resources on a variety of levels.

2. Write a paragraph that summarizes the challenges you and your teammates faced in maximizing personal profits on a pasture owned in common. In your summary, include a response to this question: Is it easier to make decisions about how to best manage the pasture if you know what the rate of resource consumption and carrying capacity are for the pasture?

   The students should develop the idea that once its carrying capacity is exceeded, the pasture will decline in quality. The only way to maintain the high quality of the pasture is to limit the number of cows at or below the carrying capacity. Partners could accomplish this either by cooperating with one another as part of a voluntary agreement or by using the *Pay to Graze* option to force compliance with the community's attempt to conserve the commons. Knowing what the carrying capacity for cows is on the pasture can make it easier to make a voluntary management agreement.

3. Explain the difference between biotic and abiotic resources.

   Biotic resources come from the living environment, while abiotic resources are derived from the nonliving environment.

4. Are renewable resources more likely to be biotic or abiotic? Explain your answer.

   Students may explain that renewable resources are more likely to be biotic or be intangible resources that come from the abiotic environment because the living environment can renew itself through reproduction. However, the cycling of matter results in the renewal of many abiotic resources. Students with a thorough understanding should recognize that the timescale for replenishing resources that we consider renewable is shorter than some of the biogeochemical cycles.

5. What is the relationship between resources and carrying capacity in a particular ecosystem?

   The carrying capacity for a population of organisms in a given ecosystem is determined by the availability of resources that are required by that population.

6. In what ways is the simulation "Pasture Profits" a realistic model of a pasture owned and used in common? In what ways is it unrealistic?

   Record and explain at least two realistic and two unrealistic aspects of the model.

   The simulation realistically models several important features of a common pasture, such as the following:

Farmers:

◆ The farmers have fee access to the pasture.

◆ Neither farmer can control the number of cows put on the pasture by the other farmer.

◆ The farmers can agree among themselves to limit the number of cows they put on the pasture.

Cows:

◆ Farmers must withdraw money from their bank accounts to purchase cows.

◆ Cows cannot obtain their monthly requirements of grass if their numbers on the pasture exceed its carrying capacity.

◆ Milk production per cow declines if it does not obtain its monthly requirement of grass.

◆ Cows begin to die when their monthly intake of grass falls below a minimum.

Grass:

◆ The quality of the pasture begins to decline when the number of cows exceeds the carrying capacity.

◆ The greater the number of cows above carrying capacity, the faster the quality of the pasture declines.

◆ If the pasture has not been ruined, its quality increases across time if the number of cows falls below the carrying capacity after a die-off.

◆ A ruined pasture cannot support any cows, and the vegetation never recovers.

Several unrealistic features of the simulation include the following:

Farmers:

◆ Only two farmers have access to the pasture rather than many farmers.

◆ Farmers cannot remove cows from the pasture.

◆ Farmers cannot sell cows to earn money.

Cows:

◆ The cost of cows remains constant and does not fluctuate with market conditions.

◆ All cows require the same amount of grass.

◆ Maximum milk production per cow is the same for all cows.

◆ If the number of cows on the pasture exceeds carrying capacity, the decline in milk production per cow is the same for all.

Grass:

◆ The growth rate of the grass is the same in all parts of the pasture.

◆ The quality of the pasture is the same in all parts.

Mystery on Easter Island

Major Concepts Limiting factors; resource dependency; resource depletion consequences

Overview

In this activity, the students read a photo essay about the mystery of Easter Island on *The Commons* CD, then propose explanations for the data scientists have collected about that civilization and its demise. Students gain an appreciation for the consequences of human resource depletion and continue analyzing and interpreting graphically represented data.

Materials   (per teams of 2–4)

The Commons CD
computer with CD-ROM drive

Outcomes and Indicators of Success

The following indicators allow you to assess the students' level of success with the activity and to assess their process of learning.

By the end of this activity, the learners should have

1. developed a more complete understanding of the impact of population growth on interactions and interdependence within a community.

   They will demonstrate their understanding by describing what their study of the Easter Island population tells them about some of the principles of population growth.

2. developed a deeper understanding of the concept of limiting factors.

   They will demonstrate their understanding by

   a. describing what factors finally limited the islanders' population growth, and

   b. describing how a small island has limited resources.

3. built more understanding of the concept of carrying capacity.

   They will demonstrate their understanding by analyzing data from the Easter Island population and describing the impact of population growth and limiting factors.

4. gained an understanding that the carrying capacity of an environment will change as the environment changes.

   They will demonstrate their understanding by interpreting data from the Easter Island population and inferring the effect of a change in the environment on the carrying capacity.

Preparations

This activity involves using computers and *The Commons* CD. You will need to arrange that access and decide on team sizes (depending on the number of computers available).

Background Information

Although the concept of carrying capacity was not defined until the 1800s, even Plato commented on the loss of the carrying capacity in Attica. According to Garrett Hardin, Plato said:

> [In earlier days, Attica] yielded far more abundant produce. In comparison of what then was, there are remaining only the bones of the wasted body, all the richer and softer parts of the soil having fallen away, and the mere skeleton of the land being left. But in the primitive state of the country, its mountains were high hills covered with soil, and the plains were full of rich earth, and there was abundance of wood in the mountains . . . (from Hardin, 1993, p. 208)

Plato noticed that as the demand from humans increased, the land was less productive. Hardin states that the devastation of Greece was due to the deforestation that occurred for the sake of fuel and lumber. Greece also suffered from overgrazing by an uncontrolled population of goats that thrived on seedling trees. A similar situation has occurred or is occurring in many other areas on earth. Many of the deserts of the world were created by populations of organisms that exceeded the carrying capacity.

There are individuals in our society who do not believe that carrying capacity is an issue:

> Because of increases in knowledge, the earth's "carrying capacity" has been increasing throughout the decades and centuries and millennia to such an extent that the term carrying capacity has by now no useful meaning.
>
> —Julian Simon and Herman Kahn, 1984 (in Hardin, 1993, p. 205)

Individuals who doubt the importance of carrying capacity believe that technology, money, and ingenuity always will be able to increase the number of organisms that an environment can support.

Students will explore these differing views on the importance of carrying capacity in Chapter 16, *Are There Limits?*

Strategies for Guiding Learners

PROCESS AND PROCEDURES

As a class, read orally or silently all introductory materials for the activity and the Process and Procedures to help students build connections between concepts and activities. Use the time spent reading to bring the students' attention into focus. Then, open up the activity by asking students whether any of them have heard of Easter Island and (if they have) what have they heard?

1. With your teammates, study the graph in Figure 15.7. Answer questions a–j.

   a. What was the approximate size of the colonizing population in the year 450?
   The graph begins when the population was approximately 600. (Scientists believe approximately 100 people made up the first colonizers.)

   b. What was the size of the population in the year 850?
   About 2,500.

c. What was the difference in the number of people between 450 and 850?

> **About 1,900.**

d. What was the average annual increase in the number of people between 450 and 850?

> **4.75**

e. What was the difference in population size between the years 850 and 1250?

> **About 3,500.**

f. What was the average annual increase in the number of people between 850 and 1250?

> **8.75**

g. What was the average annual increase in the number of people between 1250 and 1600?

> **(9,800 − 6,000 = 3,800) 3,800 ÷ 350 = 10.86**

h. During which 1 of the following 3 periods was the increase in the human population greatest: 450–850, 850–1250, or 1250–1600?

> **1250−1600**

i. What was the greatest number of people found on Easter Island between 450 and 2000? In approximately what year did this happen?

> **Just under 10,000 people were on the island in the years near 1600.**

j. By the mid 1700s, only 2,000 Easter Islanders were still alive. The population continued to decline to approximately 100 people during the next century. This was due in part to the slave trade and epidemics brought by Europeans. What is the average annual decrease in the number of people between 1600 and 1950?

> **(9,800 − 400 = 9,400) 9,400 ÷ 350 = 26.86**

2. Refer to the vegetation charts and information in Figure 15.8. Write a brief description of the Easter Island ecosystem. Include at least 3 examples of biotic and 3 examples of abiotic resources that likely influenced the colonizing population.

> **Biotic resources may include the palm trees, grass, shrubs, other small trees, crops, fish, and birds. Abiotic resources may include soil nutrients, soil quality, physical space, drinking water, climate, and stones.**

3. At one time in history, hundreds of giant stone statues overlooked the Easter Island landscape. Hundreds more were being carved in quarries, moved along roads, or waiting to be erected. Ruins of these monoliths remain on the island today.

Study the "Easter Island" segment on *The Commons* CD. You will learn more about the islanders, the mysterious statues, the land, and the vegetation.

4. Discuss with your partner the changes that took place on Easter Island after colonization. In your journal, write 1 or 2 paragraphs that summarize the changes in vegetation on Easter Island between 950 and 1980. Explain what you think caused those changes.

Consider the interactions and interdependence that took place between the people as well as between humans and the shared biotic and abiotic resources.

> **Students' answers should explain some of the interactions included in the following description:**

The changes in island vegetation coincided with an increase in human population size from probably fewer than 100 people at the time of settlement to approximately 10,000 between the 1500s and 1600s. As the population grew, its activities changed the character of the island's vegetation.

Initially, clearing the forest increased food supplies and provided timber for building canoes and houses, for firewood, and for moving and erecting the giant stone statues. The availability of crops, fish, birds, and palm fruits promoted human population growth. Although deforestation continued to meet the demands of a growing population, it was accompanied by increased soil erosion, leaching of soil nutrients, wind damage, diminishing supplies of fresh water, and dwindling numbers of palm trees. By the 1500s, the character of the island's vegetation was very different from that encountered by the first settlers.

Deforestation and the environmental degradation that accompanied it also had profound effects on the culture of the islanders. Scientists believe that the collapse of the Easter Island civilization was connected to the elimination of the forest and its dominant species, the giant palm tree.

5. Participate in a class discussion of steps 1–4.

    In addition to discussing the Process and Procedures questions, you may find opportunities to guide the discussion to include the following points:

    ◆ Resources are limited.

    ◆ A civilization that uses up its resources is at risk.

    ◆ Humans do not necessarily behave in ways that promote long-term survival.

Analysis

Reading the essay and answering the analysis questions should be done individually and can be assigned as homework. When the students have completed their responses, collect their journals to assess their understanding of the concepts.

Read the essay *Interdependence Involves Limiting Factors and Carrying Capacity* (page 650). Use it as a resource for the following questions:

1. Think about the growth in human population between 1000 and 1600. Compare that with the rate of growth during the first years that the colonizers were on the island. What might account for this large increase?

    Remember that students are just exploring the concept of population growth here and have no formal understanding of exponential growth yet. Some students, however, may be able to articulate the basic idea that in the beginning, when a population is small, growth happens slowly, but even with a fixed rate of growth, eventually growth occurs rapidly.

2. What factor or factors finally limited the growth of the human population? What other factors might limit the growth of a population? Give at least three specific examples.

    Expect that the students will indicate that the growth of the island's population was limited by the food supply and by space. Other factors that might limit the size of a population include the amount of water, the amount of protection available, the amount of shelter, or the number of mates. For example, the students might say that the limited amount of water in the desert limits the population of plants and animals that can survive there. The number of suitable nesting sites in a meadow might limit the population of meadowlarks.

3. Work with a partner to redraw the population growth graph in Figure 15.7. Color-code your graph so that each significant trend in the rate of growth is a different color.

Create a legend that shows what type of growth rate happened during each different-colored period.

Student graphs should be colored to show that after periods of slow and then rapid continuous growth, the population fell significantly.

4. The maximum number of people that the island can support without destroying its ability to renew itself is called its carrying capacity. Add a line to your graph that shows where you think the island's carrying capacity for people was when the colonizers first landed on Easter Island. Label this line *initial carrying capacity*. Why did you draw your line there?

Students should justify the number chosen as the island's carrying capacity for humans in terms of some evidence of a time when the island's resources were plentiful in relation to the population size at that time. For example, some students may choose the year 950 as a time when vegetation, according to the vegetation chart, was not degraded, yet. The population at that time was approximately 3,000, so that could be represented by a horizontal line to indicate initial carrying capacity.

5. What evidence is there that the number of people on the island exceeded its carrying capacity?

After a period of continuous growth, the population fell significantly.

6. Add another line to your graph. Show where you think the island's carrying capacity for people was after 1690. Label this line *later carrying capacity*. Why did you draw your line there?

Write your explanation in your journal.

Easter Island's carrying capacity for humans after the environmental degradation had occurred was significantly lower than the initial carrying capacity. The students may place the second carrying capacity around 400, the level after which the population began to grow again.

7. What does this study tell you about unchecked population growth?

This study demonstrates that limiting factors come into play and define the carrying capacity of a given environment for a certain population. Unchecked population growth cannot continue indefinitely.

8. Think about the relationship between the island's population size and resources-available-per-individual. How is that similar to the relationship between the number of cows and the common pasture from the previous activity? What do each of these relationships demonstrate?

Both the situation on Easter Island and the common pasture scenario involved limited resources that became exhausted by a rapidly growing population. Both the number of people on Easter Island and the number of cows on the common pasture demonstrated that if a population continues to grow beyond an ecosystem's carrying capacity, environmental degradation and resource depletion will occur, reducing the carrying capacity for that population.

Extensions

Ask the students to explore the concept of a cultural carrying capacity, and in an essay, try to describe and define it in their own terms.

Some Background on Cultural Carrying Capacity

Thomas Malthus's theories about population implicitly center on the concept of carrying capacity. Garrett Hardin (1993) discusses carrying capacity in cultural terms as well as in biological terms. He claims that not only must we take into account the amount of land needed to support human life, but that we also must consider cultural carrying capacity. He states:

> . . . some goods—the amenities—impose costs that cannot easily be stated in terms of energy: the solitude of lonely beaches, access to wilderness and areas rich in flowers, birds, and butterflies, together with time to enjoy these amenities as well as music and the visual arts. The ability to furnish these goods is also part of the human carrying capacity of the environment; more important to some people, less so to others. "What is the carrying capacity?" and "What is the optimum human population?" are complicated and subtle questions. (p. 213)

According to Hardin, the cultural carrying capacity also must account for the quality of life for humans. One physicist estimated that the globe could support 50 billion people. However, what would be the resulting quality of life?

At the current time, no one knows the earth's carrying capacity for humans. It is clear, however, that with our population size doubling every 25 years, we have reached the point where we must ask ourselves, Are we able to provide a life of quality for our children?

Evaluate | Critters and Interdependence

Major Concepts
Global interdependence; carrying capacity; resources; limiting factors; population dynamics; interactions

Overview

This activity provides you and the students with an opportunity to evaluate their understanding of the key concepts in this chapter. The students use their habitat card from Chapter 3 and imagine that they live in such an ecosystem along with their critter, other students' critters, humans, and other native organisms. They work together to create a story that describes interactions among these various organisms.

Materials   (per class of 30, individuals and small teams)

pencils and paper
colored pencils and markers
DVD
DVD player

descriptions and diagrams of the
    students' critters
30 copies of the rubric *Critters and
    Interdependence*

Outcomes and Indicators of Success

The following indicators allow you to assess the students' level of success with the activity and to assess their process of learning.

By the end of this activity, the learners should

1. demonstrate their understanding of the types of interactions and interdependence present in a specific ecosystem.

   They will demonstrate their understanding by describing the types of interactions and interdependence present when they place their organism and themselves in a particular ecosystem.

2. demonstrate their understanding of the following concepts: resources, carrying capacity, growth rate, and limiting factors.

   They will demonstrate their understanding by making these concepts an integral part of their story.

3. be able to reflect on their own thinking.

   They will demonstrate their ability by answering questions about the process that they used to think about and write their story.

Preparations

Provide additional references about the various ecosystems for students to use as resources. *BSCS Biology: An Ecological Approach* would be a good reference.

You might want to collaborate with a language arts teacher for this activity. If your school has any software programs that are designed to assist students as they write, encourage the students to use them.

Develop a scoring rubric using the *Critters and Interdependence* rubric on the *GACD* as a guide.

Arrange to have a DVD player and monitor available to show the DVD segment "Ecosystems of the Earth" on the DVD.

Strategies for Guiding Learners

PROCESS AND PROCEDURES

As a class, read orally or silently all introductory materials for the activity and the Process and Procedures to help students build connections between concepts and activities. Use the time spent reading to bring the students' attention into focus.

PART A   Resources and Ecosystems

1. Watch the DVD segment "Ecosystems of the Earth." In your journal, record the name of each ecosystem. List at least 4 significant factors found there.

   Remember, include both biotic and abiotic factors.

   As they view images of their habitat on the video segment "Ecosystems of the Earth," remind students to begin thinking of interactions that might take place; encourage them to take notes on what they observe. Students may list biotic factors such as other populations of organisms, and abiotic factors such as water, climate, soil, or sunlight availability.

Instructional Flow

Classroom Support

Activity/ Student Text pp. Teacher Guide pp.	GACD, TRCD, DVD, and CD-ROM Resources	Essays/ Student Text pp.	Estimated Time	Team Size/ Cooperative Learning Focus	Strategies and Tools	Assessment Opportunities	Special Considerations
EVALUATE *Tri-Lakes: Public Policy* pp. 648–649 TG pp. 592–594	Rubric: *Tri-Lakes Letter*		50 minutes	*Team size: 2 Skill:* Providing constructive criticism	Letter writing; critiquing	Critique of peers; ability to advocate a position in writing, using supporting evidence for justification	Students who have difficulty writing may have better success if they word process their letters. If assigned as homework, students can use other writing support if available. Letters can also be presented orally from notes if students cannot write or would better show their understanding if writing was not involved.

Optional activities:

* *Calling the Question*
* *The Sun and Life (or Death?)*
* *Where Do We Go from Here?*

Chapter Goals

By the end of this chapter, the learners should understand that

◆ complex issues are difficult to analyze thoroughly and to resolve fully,

◆ ecological interactions are complex,

◆ humans interact with the ecosystem and these interactions have consequences,

◆ the earth has a finite carrying capacity that depends on many variables,

◆ there are difficult social and ethical implications of humankind's intervention in ecosystems, and

◆ systems analysis is a tool that we can use to study complex interactions.

The learners also will

◆ identify testable questions and appropriate controls,

◆ design and conduct an experiment,

◆ collect and interpret data,

◆ conduct a systems analysis,

◆ conduct an ethical analysis, and

◆ use data to support a policy proposal.

Advance Preparation

Check Materials and Preparations for the activity *Tri-Lakes: The Investigation* so that you can obtain and prepare the materials and organisms ahead of time. You will need computers for students to use with *The Commons* CD for "The Gulf of Maine" and "Are There Limits?" If you have not done so already, make preparations for students to present the results of the full inquiry that they began in the Explain Section. Presenting their projects to other classmates models a critical step in scientific investigations: communicating results so that others may build upon them.

Tri-Lakes: Asking Questions

Engage

Major Concepts Complex scientific and social issues due to the interrelatedness and interactions in ecosystems

Overview

A letter from Chris Tackle, president of the Tri-Lakes Association (a fictitious civic group), will engage the learners in a biological problem. The Tri-Lakes activity spans Chapter 16. In the explore activity, the students investigate the interactions in the lake by identifying their questions about the Tri-Lakes situation, by gathering and analyzing related information, and by conducting lab activities to learn more about the microorganisms in the lake. Later, in the evaluate, students will write responses to the Tri-Lakes Association, advocating a public policy proposal to restore balance to the ecosystem.

Materials

Outcomes and Indicators of Success

The following indicators allow you to assess the students' level of success with the activity and to assess their process of learning.

By the end of this activity, the learners should be interested in investigating the issues surrounding the Tri-Lakes situation.

They will indicate their interest by

a. expressing an interest in continuing the activity, and

b. asking additional questions about the Tri-Lakes issues.

Preparations

In anticipation for the explore activity, make sets of the Tri-Lakes copymasters, and be sure that you have the *Daphnia* and *Gammarus* cultures scheduled to arrive on time.

Strategies for Guiding Learners

PROCESS AND PROCEDURES

As a class, read orally or silently all introductory materials for the activity and the Process and Procedures to help students build connections between concepts and activities. Use the time spent reading to bring the students' attention into focus.

1. Listen to or read to yourself the letter from the Tri-Lakes Association on page 637.

    We recommend that you read the Tri-Lakes Association letter aloud to your class. Your students do not need to open their books at this time. Use the following description of the setting to prepare your students for your dramatic reading of the letter:

    ◆ The letter has been sent to the Tri-Lakes Regional High School, where you teach and the students attend.

    ◆ There are approximately 800 students in the school, grades 9–12.

    ◆ This school serves 14 small townships in rural _____. (Fill in the state of your choice.)

    ◆ This school is the only facility within 50 miles that has scientific equipment such as microscopes.

    ◆ Students in the biology and chemistry classes at the high school have been monitoring the quality of the lakes for about 20 years.

    If you do not think your students will respond well to listening to the letter, have them read the letter to themselves. After the reading, allow students to discuss the letter briefly before moving to step 2.

2. Read the essay *Systems Analysis* on page 653. Consider your own approach to investigating the Tri-Lakes system.

You will be trying to answer the questions asked by the Tri-Lakes Association regarding the Tri-Lakes system. As you read the essay, think about the steps you will take to answer those questions.

The essay *Systems Analysis* can be read aloud by students to help readers who may find the essay too challenging or to encourage and precede class discussion of the systems analysis process.

3. In your journal, create a list of at least 10 biotic and abiotic components in the Tri-Lakes ecological system.

As you create your list, think about which components are most likely to affect the bass population positively or negatively.

This step helps the learners to analyze the letter and identify what they know. Encourage the students to focus on information that is actually in the letter, instead of focusing on conjecture. However, remind the students that this is their initial list and to consider all possibilities.

Circulate among the students and elaborate on step 3 if particular students have difficulty starting their lists. You may ask them to consider the components that affected the cow and human populations in the previous chapter and encourage them to think of similar factors that might affect the bass population.

4. Work with your partner to compare your lists and your ideas about which components might be important in determining the bass population size.

Focus on particular topics or components that you think may be key to understanding the Tri-Lakes situation.

Keep discussion brief at this point; 5–10 minutes should provide sufficient time for the students to share ideas.

Analysis

1. In your journal, record the Tri-Lakes questions that you can identify at this point based on your discussion of the components.

Use information from Chris Tackle's letter and your own knowledge to come up with logical questions about the Tri-Lakes issue. Record each question as precisely as possible. After you have written at least two questions on your own, discuss them with your partner. Add any additional questions that come to mind.

At this stage in the learning process, students should record all questions that come to mind.

2. Write a brief paragraph in your journal that describes your prediction or tentative explanation for what you think may be causing the Tri-Lakes problems.

Remember, these are early ideas that are based on minimal evidence. You likely will revise your ideas as you gather more information.

Remind students that their predictions at this point are based on minimal information, and there are many possibilities for correct solutions.

25 internal comparison pH strips, pH 6.0–8.1 in a petri dish half (for pH protocol stations only)

25 internal comparison pH strips, pH 5.2–6.8 in a petri dish half (for pH protocol stations only)

(Note: You can substitute pH probes for the pH paper.)

50-mL beaker of *Daphnia magna* culture or *Gammarus* culture

Strategies for Guiding Learners

PROCESS AND PROCEDURES

As a class, read orally or silently all introductory materials for the activity and the Process and Procedures to help students build connections between concepts and activities. Use the time spent reading to bring the students' attention into focus.

1. Pick up a data packet from your teacher.

   Each data packet contains information sheets.

   Distribute one data packet for each team of two students. Reserve some packets as needed for absent students to read on their own.

2. Review the titles listed in the need to know box. Choose the information sheets most likely to be helpful to you.

3. Divide the work in half. Study your half of the packet; your partner will study the other half. As you read, take notes and record questions you have about the information.

   Let the students explore the information sheets at their own pace. Encourage them to review the list of titles as one way of narrowing which pieces of information they will read. This step is a critical-thinking skill. If they do not have some criteria for looking at the stacks of information, the students can be overwhelmed.

   Once the students have selected the information to study, let them develop their own system to divide the work among their partners. In some situations, it may be appropriate to assist teams in choosing how to divide their work so that students with special needs can review appropriate information sheets and contribute effectively.

4. When you are finished studying the packet, meet with your partner and share what you have learned. Exchange information and learn things that might help answer a question you have raised. Add that information to your journal.

   At the end of this activity, you will rate yourself and your partner on how well you taught each other about your information sheets.

   After the students are familiar with the contents of the information sheets, be sure that they record notes in their journals. Students should record which data sheets were the source for the information as they take notes so they can find that information again.

5. In your journal, review your initial ideas about the Tri-Lakes problem from the Analysis in the engage activity. Revise or add to your explanation to reflect your current understanding.

You must gather as much information as possible if you are going to apply a limited system analysis to Tri-Lakes. A limited system analysis involves your interpretation of how the system will react when any of its components are altered. For the Tri-Lakes system, it is important to understand the microorganisms that Chris Tackle mentioned. The next steps in this activity will help you learn more about them.

6. Identify a question about the microorganisms that you hope to answer by experimentation. Record this question in your journal if it is different from the questions you already recorded.

> **Identifying questions is often very difficult for students, and even at this point in the program, some students may struggle. Encourage them to keep their questions simple and direct. With the materials listed in this activity, students can answer questions such as, What is the effect of pH changes on *Daphnia/Gammarus*? How are *Daphnia/Gammarus* affected by temperature changes? What is the pH of the lake water? Is that near the "normal" pH for *Daphnia/Gammarus*? The protocols in the student pages also will help the students determine the types of experiments that are possible.**

7. Write in your journal a procedure to use to gather data about your question. After you have written the procedure, ask your teacher to approve it.

The following protocols provide 2 examples of methods for studying the microorganisms *Daphnia* and *Gammarus*. Don't forget, a protocol is not a replacement for your own experiment. However, it may provide a valuable technique for you to incorporate into your work.

> **You may need to demonstrate the use of microscopes, pH strips or probes, and thermometers (recording the correct accuracy) or thermisters before the students write their procedures. Alternatively, you could let them write the procedures in a generic format, and after you know what the students are focusing on, you could demonstrate the relevant pieces of equipment.**

> **Before any students begin their experiments, review safety procedures for your classroom.**

Caution

8. In your journal, create a data table to organize and record your experimental data and observations.

> **At this stage in the program, students should be able to construct effective data tables. Remind the students to look for and record evidence of interactions between the organisms and both biotic and abiotic factors in the environment where the observations are being made. From those observations and the information in the packets (along with prior knowledge), students will be asked to make inferences about interactions in the Tri-Lakes ecosystem.**

9. Conduct your experiment. Record your observations, data, and results in your journal. Consider which, if any, of the questions you wrote may be answered by your results. Record how the evidence you obtained through experimentation supported or contradicted your explanation from step 5.

> **It may take several days for the students to conduct their experiments. Encourage them to repeat their procedures and to refine their techniques as time allows. Be sure they are recording their observations and results in their tables.**

Strategies for Guiding Learners

PROCESS AND PROCEDURES

As a class, read orally or silently all introductory materials for the activity and the Process and Procedures to help students build connections between concepts and activities. Use the time spent reading to bring the students' attention into focus.

1. Follow your teacher's directions for determining which role your team will assume in the upcoming role play.

   Your team will assume one of the following roles: large-fishing-boat owners, small-fishing-boat owners, resource economists, marine biologists, fisheries scientists, or policymakers.

   Distribute one copy of the Copymaster *Thinking about the Gulf* to each student. Explain that these are the general instructions for a role play in which the teams assume the roles of various stakeholders in the Gulf of Maine crisis, conduct research into the management of this resource, and debate the three basic management options available.

   Assign teams to the roles of large-boat owners, small-boat owners, resource economists, marine biologists, fisheries scientists, and policymakers so that each is represented by at least one team.

2. With your team, view the videos on *The Commons*. Begin with "The Fisheries" and continue through to the "Surfing the Gulf" activity.

   View the sidebar *Historical Timeline* to see how the Gulf of Maine has changed over time.

3. Discuss the following questions with the members of your team:

   a. What is the controversy surrounding the Gulf of Maine fisheries?

   b. Who has a stake in the health of the fisheries?

    Circulate among the teams and listen for the discussions to reveal understanding of the variety of interactions within the Gulf of Maine fisheries.

   a. **In addition to the dramatically declining fish population, encourage teams to discuss other interdependence issues that they recognize in the Gulf of Maine ecosystem.**

   b. **In addition to the stakeholders involved in the role play, students should recognize that the American public also has a stake in the health of the fisheries.**

4. Search *BioSeeker* (found in "Surfing the Gulf"). Look for information about 3 of the options that exist for managing the fisheries in the Gulf of Maine. Use the keyword searches and the organizations' Web sites that are listed to gather information about management options.

   Your challenge is to decide which of the 3 options is best *from the perspective of your assigned role*. Identify the files that will be most useful, and take notes about key information. Remember, in *BioSeeker* the Web sites are fictitious. But you can search real Web sites about those issues on the Internet, as well.

Remind students to gather both data that support and do not support each option. Student data should include information similar to the following:

Comparison of Management Options

Management option	Benefits	Management of the option	Data/assumption underlying option	Likely effects on fish, economy, people's lives
Close the fisheries	Users who can afford to wait for the fisheries to reopen will benefit from increased stocks. Users whose livelihoods depend on fishing now will not benefit.	State and federal agencies charged with enforcement; relatively easy to enforce	Data that show depleted stocks; assumption that data and predictions made from those data are correct; assumption that management cannot or will not preserve resources for future generations	Fish—population likely will increase Economy—significant negative impact on fishing industry and on economy of entire area People's lives—significant disruption of lives of people directly involved in fishing industry
Open the fisheries	People currently employed in fishing industry may realize immediate benefits, but if stocks are depleted, these benefits will be short-lived. Future generations of users may suffer the consequences of depleted stocks.	No one	Data that show fishermen can still find fish; assumption that free-market use of resource will not deplete it	Fish—populations likely will decrease Economy—positive immediate effect People's lives—positive immediate effect
Manage the fisheries	If management is successful, some benefits should accrue to both current and future users.	State and federal agencies charged with enforcement; relatively complex to establish and enforce appropriate guidelines	Data that show depleted stocks; assumption that resource can be used in ways that preserve it for future generations	Fish—effect depends on management approach and success Economy—effect depends on management approach and success People's lives—effect depends on management approach and success

5. Discuss the management options with the members of your team. Create a table to help you organize your discussion. Include a brief description of each option. Then identify the advantages and disadvantages of each. During your discussion, consider the following questions:

   a. Who benefits from the option? Who doesn't?

   b. Who manages the option? How difficult is it to manage?

c. What data support the option? What assumptions is the option based on? Are the assumptions correct?

d. What short- and long-term effects is the option likely to have on the fish population? on the economy? on people's lives?

6. Read the information provided on the Copymaster *Gulf of Maine Occupational Sketches*. Begin to think about which management option is best from the perspective of your assumed role.

7. Work as a team to conduct a new search in *BioSeeker*. Prepare for a class discussion on the best management option for the Gulf of Maine fisheries.

Concentrate on locating information and building arguments that support the management option that benefits your "occupation."

Encourage students to revisit the data that do not support their chosen option as well as data that do support it. Then students should prepare responses to criticism that their option may receive from other stakeholders.

8. Choose a representative from your team as your teacher directs. That person will present a brief explanation (3 to 4 minutes) to the class for the option your team has chosen.

Be sure to provide relevant data and logical arguments. Be ready as a team to answer questions and respond to comments from classmates representing the same or other roles. Also be ready to ask questions of your classmates as they present the results of their analyses.

Allow each team to present its position to the class without interruption before opening the floor to questions and comments. Encourage students to ask challenging questions phrased from the perspectives of their roles. If the debate does not begin without your help, assume a role yourself and demonstrate the type of questioning or criticism you would like the students to provide. The following table provides some of the reasons for and against the three management options:

Reasons For and Against Three Management Options

Close the Fisheries	
Reasons for	*Reasons against*
◆ This option will allow fish stocks time to recover. ◆ Because a stock assessment is an estimate not a census, fish stocks may be in worse condition than the data indicate; this may be the only action that will protect them. ◆ This option will spur people who now depend on the fisheries or consume lots of fish products to find other employment and to use other products, thus reducing pressure on the fisheries when they reopen. ◆ The government could provide federal aid to ease the financial impact on fishing-dependent communities. ◆ This option will serve as a lesson to all of us not to let this type of situation develop again. ◆ Regardless of whether such a severe measure is required, it would be an ecologically good thing to do.	◆ This action may be more extreme than what is actually required to protect the stocks. ◆ This option would have a devastating impact on fishing-dependent communities. ◆ This option would lead to the dismantling of the fishing industry in the area, making restarting the industry more costly in the future. ◆ This option would lead to great and unfair personal heartache to small-boat fishermen because fishing is their way of life and they are less responsible for the problem than large-boat fishermen. ◆ This option does not acknowledge or correct other causes of the problem except overfishing.

Open the Fisheries	
Reasons for	*Reasons against*
◆ This option will allow the free market to reign; fishermen who are not skilled at fishing and/or business will go out of business, which will eventually reduce pressure on the fish stocks. ◆ Catching and selling all the fish now and investing the profits might be a viable way for New England to finance a future that does not depend on fishing.	◆ This option might lead to the complete and irrecoverable collapse of many important fish stocks. ◆ This option might eventually lead to a worse collapse of the area's fishing industry than temporarily closing the fisheries would.

Manage the Fisheries	
Reasons for	*Reasons against*
◆ This option may allow us to maximize both the health of the fish populations and the long-term benefits for the fishing industry. ◆ This option avoids extreme positions that are sure to be difficult and painful for many people. ◆ This option avoids destroying either the fish population or the fishing industry overnight. ◆ This option uses all that we know about the reproduction, growth, and habits of these fish to promote a good end.	◆ Successful management depends on stock assessments that may not be accurate. ◆ It is costly to develop and enforce management policies. ◆ It is not clear that management has worked in the past, and there is no reason to think it will be effective in the future. ◆ The process for developing management plans is highly political and may lead to regulations that favor one group of stakeholders over another.

Analysis

1. Participate in a class discussion. Vote on the best management option for the Gulf of Maine fisheries.

   Vote as an individual, not as a team or as a representative of your earlier role.

   At this point in the activity, students should drop their role-play positions and be guided through a metacognitive analysis of their stakeholder experience. Encourage students who were silent or spoke little during the role play to share their observations and perceptions.

   Ask students to vote on a secret ballot that you collect and count so that each student participates fully. While you count the votes, students should proceed with Analysis question 2, explaining their individual choice.

2. Record your vote in your journal. Write a paragraph explaining your choice.

   Expect that students will explain their chosen option by stating reasons similar to those given in the previous table. Encourage the students to include a brief statement about how they would defend their choice in light of the criticisms given in the class discussion.

3. With your teammates, discuss what general principles you saw in the Gulf of Maine example that apply to all of earth's resources. In your journal, record the three strongest ideas your team discussed. Explain each briefly.

Expect students to identify that shared resources can decline or be entirely exhausted unless the people involved adopt strategies to prevent it; that unmanaged commons degrade because individuals receive all of the benefits from using the resource (in this case, fish), whereas the costs (resource depletion) are shared by everyone; and that several strategies exist to save resources from becoming tragically depleted, and each strategy has certain advantages and disadvantages.

4. Compare the Gulf of Maine ecosystem to the fictional Tri-Lakes ecosystem. How are those systems similar? How are they different?

Expect that students will quickly recognize that both ecosystems are aquatic and involve a declining fish population. However, the Tri-Lakes ecosystem is disrupted primarily by abiotic changes (temperature, acidity, oxygen levels, etc.), leading to a declining food supply for the bass. The Gulf of Maine ecosystem is also affected by abiotic factors in the system, but the predominant pressure disrupting the fish population is human overfishing. The bass in Tri-Lakes are affected indirectly by human interactions. In addition, students should recognize that both situations represent changes that will affect many other interdependent, living organisms and alter the abiotic factors in the ecosystems.

Elaborate   Are There Limits?

Major Concepts Analyzing complex systems; ethical analysis; modeling population growth in a system; comparing and contrasting logistic and exponential growth

Overview

In this activity, students will deepen their understanding of the interrelationship between population growth and limiting factors within ecosystems by using their knowledge to analyze information about human population growth. They also will understand growth trends further through introductions to the concepts of exponential and logistic population growth.

First, students will observe and discuss a video that poses the question of whether earth's resources and ability to support human populations are limited. Next, the students will view an animation of human population growth across time and discuss the implications of the observed growth trend. Then students will use a computer model to build a deeper understanding of exponential growth and the effects of starting size, growth rate, and time on the final size of a population growing exponentially. Finally, a computer animation will facilitate comparisons between exponential and logistic growth, and the students will consider differences in resource consumption and interactions that occur in the two growth types.

Materials   (teams of 2–4)

The Commons CD
computers with CD-ROM drives

Outcomes and Indicators of Success

The following indicators allow you to assess the students' level of success with the activity and to assess their process of learning.

By the end of this activity, the learners should

1. have a more complete understanding of the complex ecological scenario on earth.

   They will demonstrate their ability to recognize and explain earth's complex ecological situation by

   a. analyzing the patterns of change in human population growth across time, and

   b. articulating a position regarding the impact human population growth may have on earth's carrying capacity for humans.

2. recognize the difficulty of predicting the effects of humanity's intervention in the biosphere.

   They will demonstrate their recognition by comparing two opposing, scholarly views of earth's condition.

3. understand the basic concepts of exponential and logistic growth.

   They will demonstrate their understanding by writing a compare-and-contrast statement about the two types of growth.

4. understand how the carrying capacity of an ecosystem affects exponential growth.

   They will demonstrate their understanding by explaining how resource consumption and interactions differ in exponential and logistic growth.

5. understand that the concepts of exponential growth and carrying capacity have implications for human populations.

   They will demonstrate their understanding by comparing the earth to an island and discussing the implications.

Preparations

This activity involves using computers and *The Commons* CD. You will need to arrange that access and decide on team sizes (depending on the number of computers available).

Background Information

Most of your students will recognize immediately that the issues involved in determining the earth's carrying capacity are so complex that a complete analysis is not possible. Thinking about what that number of people might be—or what factors might influence that number—is, nevertheless, a useful and interesting exercise.

Many individuals think that we already have exceeded the earth's carrying capacity, certainly in specific countries or areas of countries, and possibly, for the world. One only has to look at the many examples of famine and starvation around the world to appreciate their point. When we factor the world's potential for further population growth, the picture that emerges is sobering. In this light, the recent commitment by the world nations to stabilize the world's population at or below 9.8 billion by the year 2050 takes on a special significance.

Although the focus in this chapter is on human needs (on the earth's carrying capacity for *human* population), it is important to recognize that our efforts to make the earth yield evermore for ourselves are diminishing its ability to support millions of other types of life.

The relationship between human activity and the welfare of other forms of life can be seen in calculations of the percentage of the earth's *net primary productivity* that humans use, either directly or indirectly. The earth's net primary productivity (NPP) is defined as the total amount of solar energy converted into biochemical energy through plant photosynthesis minus the energy that those plants use for their own life processes. Because this biochemical energy is the basic food source for virtually all terrestrial organisms, NPP provides one definition of the outer limit of the earth's carrying capacity. Some estimates indicate that prior to human impact, the earth's NPP was some 150 billion tons of organic matter per year (for example, see Worldwatch Institute's *State of the World, 1994*). These estimates also indicate that humans have destroyed the ecosystems responsible for about 12 percent of the earth's terrestrial NPP and now directly or indirectly use another 27 percent. This means that one species (humans) has appropriated nearly 40 percent of the terrestrial food supply, leaving only 60 percent remaining for other terrestrial organisms.

One of the most important issues your students need to address to answer the question posed to them is what the term *carrying capacity* means. Students were introduced to the term in Chapter 15. Carrying capacity is commonly defined as the largest number of any species that a particular habitat can support indefinitely. If that maximum number is exceeded, the foundation of resources that sustains the population will begin to decline, eventually affecting the population.

The key phrase in the definition for carrying capacity is "support indefinitely." Carrying capacity is a measure of the population size that the habitat can sustain, not a measure of the size that it can support for the short term. The question of the earth's capacity to support human life has to do with more than just its ability to provide our most basic food needs today. Instead, it relates to the earth's ability to provide us with a "quality of life" as well as its ability to absorb and neutralize our waste products, not just today but *indefinitely*.

Three important trends have contributed heavily to the pressures now being placed on the earth's ecosystems. These trends include the relentless growth of the world's population, the widening gap in the distribution of income and resources, and the rapid growth in the world's economic output that has taken place since the Industrial Revolution. The first trend—the increase in the earth's population—will be familiar to your students. Experience with the Chapter 15 pasture simulation and the activity *Mystery on Easter Island*, for example, should have given your students a good sense of the effect of the growing population on the earth's capacity to meet human desires.

Likewise, your students have had some experience dealing with the second trend, the distribution of income and resources. They may not recognize the issue explicitly as a problem of resource distribution. Their discovery in the simulation that conditions may be better for all if developed nations share some of their good fortune, speaks to issues of equity. Phrased negatively, research indicates that the chasm between the richest and the poorest people on earth is a major cause of environmental decline. This is because it encourages overconsumption at the top of the ladder at the same time that it fosters equally environmentally unsound activities at the bottom (see Worldwatch Institute's *State of the World, 1995*). The poor often must cut trees, overgraze land, produce more children, and behave in otherwise environmentally damaging ways simply to survive. The wealthy, on the other hand, use resources, generate waste products, and alter environments far out of proportion to their numbers.

The third trend, the rapid rise in the world's economic activity, has been fueled, in part, by the introduction of fossil fuels into human life and the related industrialization that has taken place subsequently. The relentless rise in industrial production has been particularly noticeable in the last 60 years. What was produced in the first 2 ½ months of 1990 is as much as was produced in the entire year of 1950. The extent to which such production damages the environment and undermines our base of resources depends on the technology used during production. Unfortunately, much of this production tends to be of the environment-damaging type. This problem will be compounded by the earth's growing population. As countries and individuals seek to raise their standard of living, their needs and desires will generate even greater pressures on the earth's capacity to support them. A variety of relatively straightforward calculations reveals that the earth does not possess the capacity to support even the present population if everyone's consumption level matched that of people living in developed nations. (For example, estimates show that the earth probably does not possess the total amount of energy and the volume of raw materials that would be needed to produce the finished products required to raise the standard of living of each person already in the world to that of the average American.)

An important unknown in this situation, of course, is the role that changing technology will play in helping us support the world's current and future inhabitants. Critical to our success in avoiding serious environmental destruction will be our ability to distinguish between technologies that simply allow us to meet more needs and demands regardless of the environmental cost, and technologies that meet needs and demands in an *environmentally sustainable* manner. The decrease in the earth's total arable land, for example, means that meeting future food needs will depend almost exclusively on raising the productivity of the land. During the last few decades, the world has shown remarkable gains in productivity, but it is not clear that this rate of increase can continue indefinitely.

Strategies for Guiding Learners

PROCESS AND PROCEDURES

As a class, read orally or silently all introductory materials for the activity and the Process and Procedures to help students build connections between concepts and activities. Use the time spent reading to bring the student's attention into focus.

PART A Humans in the World System

1. With your teammates, begin *The Commons* CD at "The World." Watch the video "Are There Limits?" (see Figure 16.4).

    In this video, the students hear Julian Simon and Paul Ehrlich express their fundamental positions on whether the earth has limits. Students also examine their personal views of the present and likely future state of the earth.

2. Discuss the following questions with your teammates. Record your own answers in your journal.

    a. What is the central question discussed in the video?

    b. What is the major difference between the views expressed by Julian Simon and Paul Ehrlich?

The central question addressed in the video is whether there are limits to earth's capacity to continue to meet the growing human population's needs for natural resources. Simon believes that there are no such limits; Ehrlich insists that it is clear that there are.

3. Take the *Earth Issues Survey* individually. Consider your results. Write a paragraph in your journal explaining whether you tend to agree more with Julian Simon or Paul Ehrlich.

Include specific examples from the video that you agree or disagree with. You may review the video if needed.

After students have had sufficient time to write their responses, ask them to share their survey results with the other members of the class or a partner. Encourage the students to discuss the differences in perspectives and experiences that might lead an individual to answer each survey question in a particular way. Challenge the students to consider the types of data that would support their position (boomster or doomster) on each question.

4. With your teammates, watch the animation "People and More People."

The animation of world population growth, originally produced by Zero Population Growth (ZPG) and used with permission on *The Commons* CD, helps students picture the exponential population growth that occurred after the Industrial Revolution. In the animation, the 2,000-year time span from AD 0 to 2000 is compressed into a few minutes. Population growth during this time is displayed as dots that appear on a map of the world. Each dot represents 1 million people. Students should be able to visualize the explosive character of exponential growth as the map fills rapidly at the end of the animation after relatively little change during most of the time period.

Before the students begin the animation, you might check that they can identify various parts of the world on the map. In particular, India, China, Europe, Africa, South America, and the United States should be familiar to them before they begin the animation.

You may wish to suggest that students view the full animation two or three times in silence before they discuss what they observed. Point out that after they have watched the animation from beginning to end, they may wish to use the pointer on the control bar to selectively view the map at particular dates.

Because the timeline starts at AD 0, it does not represent the time of the agricultural revolution, which occurred around 8000 BC. Students will find the agricultural revolution if they view the timeline of important events related to human population growth "Back in Time" in step 5.

5. Discuss the following questions with your teammates:

   a. What relationship between time and human population growth did you notice?
      World population grew very slowly until the 19th century.

   b. What relationship between space and human population growth did you notice?
      Expect students to notice that there are particular distribution patterns, such as the localization of a high number of people in China, India, and on the eastern coast, and later, on the western coast of the United States.

c. When did you see major changes in population size or in its distribution?

> Students should see that in the early world history, India and China had the major share of the world's population. As time passed, the numbers began to increase in Europe and then the United States. Between 1900 and 2000, the population seemed to explode in all parts of the world except the extreme northern and southern geographic areas.

d. Does the greatest increase in population take place at a time that corresponds to any historical events that you know about?

> You may want to view *The Commons* CD section "Back in Time" to see major historical events in human history.
>
> Students may recognize that the Industrial Revolution is the principle event. Expect that students will suggest other events, and ask them to explain why they think there is a relationship.

e. Did the animation give you any new insights about human population growth? Did it raise any questions about environmental issues?

> Students may express surprise or confusion at seeing a pattern of population growth that they did not expect. Encourage them to include concepts from the last two chapters in their discussions.

f. Is there any sense in which the animation gives a false picture of what is really happening?

> Students may identify at least two ways in which the animation gives a false picture. One is that there are almost no dots in the Americas until about 300 years ago. That is because pre-Columbian populations were mostly disperse, not living in local areas with populations of 1 million or more (the value of one dot), with the exception of the Valley of Mexico. There also certainly were millions of native North Americans, but no dots appear on the map because these people were very dispersed.
>
> The second deceptive thing about the animation is that each dot measures only population size, not the population's environmental impact. Seeing many dots in China and fewer in North America makes one feel that the human population in China must be having a greater environmental impact than the human population in North America. What this hides is the issue of resource consumption and its impact.

6. Participate in a class discussion of the questions from step 5.

> Guide the discussion to include the ecological principles studied in Unit 6. For example, ask students to consider the impact that human population growth has had on interactions, interdependence, resource consumption, and carrying capacity in the ecosystems of the world.

7. Read the essay *Environmental Ethics and You* (page 654). Add a brief description of your environmental ethics views to your *Earth Issues Survey* summary.

PART B Exponential Growth

1. With your teammates, study and run "The E-Growth Model" section and the "Hardin Pond" simulation on *The Commons* CD (see Figure 16.5).

   This simulation is based on a fable in which the owner of a pond notices that a water weed—called Hardin's water lily—has been introduced into her pond and is spreading. Concerned that it will cover the pond's surface and prevent boating, the owner takes some measurements and estimates that the area covered by the weed is doubling every day and that the pond will be totally covered in about 3 weeks.

   The owner decides to do something to get rid of it when the pond surface is one-half covered. She reasons that even then there will be plenty of room for boating and plenty of time for action. The challenge to students is to determine when the pond will be one-half full and the owner ready to do something about it.

2. How does the example of Hardin Pond relate to the human population growth that you saw in "People and More People?"

   Expect students to recognize that populations grow exponentially if the environment provides optimal conditions and unlimited supplies of resources.

3. Complete the following questions as a team. Read and use the essays *Growing, Growing, Grown* (page 656) and *Endless Interactions* (page 658) as resources. Record your answers in your journal.

   a. How do differences in the starting size of a population affect population growth? How do differences in the number of offspring produced per parent seed affect population growth?

   The larger the starting size, the larger its final size, if the growth rate and time are held constant. However, expect students to observe that the general shape of the curve does not change—it is J-shaped regardless of the size of the starting population. What does change are the values along the *y*-axis, that is, the total number of people in the population at each point in time and the number of people added.

   Increasing the number of offspring increases the growth rate. Increasing growth rate makes the resulting curve's J-shape sharper and more pronounced. The faster the growth rate, the greater the difference between a population's starting size and its final size, when starting size and time are held constant.

   b. How would increasing the time between reproduction events affect population growth?

   Increasing the time interval between reproduction events would reduce the growth rate. Decreasing the growth rate makes the resulting curve's J-shape less steep. The slower the growth rate, the less difference between a population's starting size and its final size, when starting size and time are held constant.

   c. How would decreasing the time between reproduction events affect population growth?

   This would increase the growth rate and have the same effect as increasing the number of offspring.

d. In what ways is this simulation of population growth on Hardin Pond realistic? How is it unrealistic?

Use concepts from the essays and *The Commons* CD to explain your answers. Include specific examples of types of growth and interactions.

Expect that students will suggest that the exponential growth shown by the lilies on Hardin Pond represents a realistic growth pattern. Populations do increase in size through reproduction by contributing more offspring generation by generation. However, they also should realize that the simulation does not take into account the limiting factors that would be at work in a natural setting or the population dynamics that also would be at work.

PART C   Logistic Growth

1. View the "Logistic Growth" animation on *The Commons* CD with your team. Discuss the differences and similarities between exponential and logistic growth.

Expect students to recognize that the two trends show different patterns of growth because exponential growth proceeds without limit, and logistic growth occurs when a population's growth is restricted by limiting factors. Circulate among teams during this brief discussion time, and encourage students to use terminology like *limiting factors*, *resources*, and *carrying capacity* to describe their observations.

2. In your journal, explain how resource consumption and interactions differ in exponential and logistic growth.

Students should be able to describe that resources must be freely available for exponential growth to occur. In addition, the interactions occurring must not place restrictions on the growth rate for an exponentially growing population within an ecosystem. In contrast, resource consumption is limited in an ecosystem that sustains a population exhibiting logistic growth. There may be interactions, such as predator-prey relationships or competition for resources, that place pressures on the population and restrict its growth as well.

Analysis

1. Think about what you have learned in this activity and about the information you have recorded in your journal. Explain whether you think there is the potential for a human population problem. Give specific examples of interactions and components in the earth system to explain your answer.

Whether or not the students think that there is a human population problem right now, they should realize after completing this activity that there is the *potential* for a problem. Even though humans have been able to solve problems and increase the production of food supply through technology, there are still limited resources and limited space on the earth. Some students may recognize that some problems already exist today because of the distribution of resources and the strain on the food supply.

2. Say that half of the nations in the world reduced their growth rate to zero. Would that change the type of population growth humans are experiencing on a global level? Why or why not?

Students should realize that the severity of the problem may be slowed somewhat but that eventually the problem would still face us.

3. In what ways is the earth system as a whole similar to an island ecosystem such as Easter Island? Use specific examples of resource consumption and interactions to explain your answer.

Expect the students to indicate that the earth is similar to an island because the planet itself is a limited, self-contained ecosystem, although much larger than an island. We are limited by finite space and resources. Expect students to indicate that the earth is only capable of supporting a certain number of humans, but because of advances in technology, humans have been able to keep increasing the value of that number. We may not know what that number is, but it is likely that there is such a number. Some students may take the position that we will find ways through technology, such as space stations, to continue to increase the number of humans who can live on earth.

Evaluate Tri-Lakes: Public Policy

Major Concepts The nature of science as it relates to public policy used to govern natural resources within complex ecosystems

Overview

The students write a reply letter to the Tri-Lakes Association to evaluate their current understanding of the situation. They also practice giving each other feedback. This activity allows the students to conclude the Tri-Lakes activity, make a connection to the nature of science, and synthesize the concepts from Unit 6 to make a public policy recommendation that reveals deep understanding of system analysis as it applies to ecological studies.

Materials (per class of 30)

30 copies of the rubric *Tri-Lakes Letter*

Outcomes and Indicators of Success

The following indicators allow you to assess the learners' level of success with the activity and to assess their process of learning.

By the end of this activity, the students should be able to evaluate their understanding of the Tri-Lakes situation.

They will indicate their understanding by

a. writing a letter that uses references from the data packet and the labs to support the policy they are advocating,

b. identifying the key components, interactions, and stakeholders in the Tri-Lakes ecosystem,

c. recognizing the multiple perspectives likely held by stakeholders in the Tri-Lakes community, and

d. constructively critiquing other students' letters.

Strategies for Guiding Learners

PROCESS AND PROCEDURES

As a class, read orally or silently all introductory materials for the activity and the Process and Procedures to help students build connections between concepts and activities. Use the time spent reading to bring the students' attention into focus.

1. Develop a response to the letter from the Tri-Lakes Association. Obtain a rubric for the letter from your teacher. Discuss the criteria with your partner before writing your response.

   The students will work individually to write a letter back to Chris Tackle. In the letter, they should describe what they think the problem in the Tri-Lakes is and what the community should do about it. A strong letter will describe new information related to the Tri-Lakes situation and identify what is still unknown. This activity provides an opportunity for embedded assessment. It also will help you determine how well the learners can synthesize their work.

2. Exchange letters with another person as your teacher directs. Analyze the letter you received according to the rubric.

   Direct the students to exchange letters with another student. Each student then will critique the other student's letter. You may need to clarify this step to the learners if they have not had experience critiquing another person's work. A strong critique indicates the strengths of the letter, points out missing parts, and offers specific suggestions for improving it. You may want to have students use highlighters to mark the words in the rubric that describe the letter they are critiquing.

3. Provide the person whose letter you analyzed with at least 3 specific comments about their letter.

   Your feedback should be a mix of statements. Provide positive statements that indicate the strengths of the letter. Other statements should identify weak areas that need to be revised.

4. Revise your letter to reflect the feedback that you received.

   Assign the revision of the letter as homework, and then collect the revised letters. You can decide whether you want one letter from each student or from each team.

5. Share your letter with your teacher and class as your teacher directs.

6. Participate in a class discussion. Talk about the changes in particular components that likely affected the Tri-Lakes ecosystem and the recommendations for public policies to address the problems.

   Use this discussion as an opportunity for students to use their oral skills to advocate their positions. Students who had difficulty expressing their ideas in the written letter may be able to show their understanding more easily in this discussion format. Facilitate the conversation while probing for understanding. Ask students who critique other students' ideas to justify their criticisms with data and logical reasoning.

7. In your journal, briefly summarize the difference between an explanation based on a single, limited analysis and one based on a combination of related analyses. Explain how this difference should affect the way you interpret scientific studies that are reported in the news.

An analysis based on a combination of analyses is more complete and likely to be more accurate than a limited analysis. Learners should support their answers with an explanation that reveals an awareness that the level of complexity described in their final Tri-Lakes analyses was likely much greater after sharing class data than it would have been if it was based solely on data gathered by their team. Because more information generally translates into greater reliability and a better ability to predict outcomes, the students now should be more alert to the accuracy of science stories reported in the news. When a reported breakthrough appears to have occurred in a new research area, it generally is prudent to be skeptical and to wait for further experiments that replicate the results and add more data before proclaiming the success or importance of the breakthrough.

8. Write a general statement that assesses our ability to predict the consequences of introducing new, humanmade components into the environment. Provide reasons that support your statement.

The introduction of any new component into the environment (such as the temperature increase brought about by cooling plastics in Tri-Lakes) has the potential to disrupt an interaction that is not well understood by ecologists. Therefore, it is probably prudent to anticipate that certain introduced components might produce unpredictable consequences. A relatively minor disruption for one organism may manifest itself as a major disruption for an organism several trophic levels away. These effects occur because ecosystems are so interdependent. Of course, *every* disruption of the environment does not cause catastrophic ecological failure. Natural ecosystems have a tremendous ability to absorb change and regenerate themselves, but beyond a certain limit, long-term and possibly irreversible damage may result.

Thinking like a Biologist

This final section of *BSCS Biology: A Human Approach* serves as an evaluate exercise for the entire program; we designed it for use as a final exam. The Evaluate Section takes into account the authentic assessment requirements of this conceptually oriented biology program. As in the rest of the program, students take the role of active learners as they analyze one or two scenarios, answer challenge questions, or complete a portfolio to provide you and themselves with a showcase of their learning. The exact combination of activities and questions you use in this section will be based on how you taught the course. We have provided more material than is necessary for a complete assessment so that you can tailor the Evaluate Section to your students' needs and strengths.

The section begins with an activity in which the learners articulate their understanding of the six unifying principles and then try to identify those principles in one of two scenarios that illustrate the importance of understanding biology in real-life applications. This activity is followed by *Chapter Challenges*, a section of questions that provides an opportunity for the students to analyze and synthesize their understanding of each chapter in the program. For teachers who have included portfolio assessment in their teaching, we have included a portfolio activity that is summative in nature.

Major Concepts
Six unifying principles of biology: evolution; homeostasis; matter, energy, and organization; genetics and the continuity of information; development; ecology

ACTIVITIES	
Part A	Recognizing Biology in Medicine
Part B	Chapter Challenges

Unit 1 Evolution: Patterns and Products of Change in Living Systems

Unit 2 Homeostasis: Maintaining Dynamic Equilibrium in Living Systems

Unit 3 Energy, Matter, and Organization: Relationships in Living Systems

Unit 4 Continuity: Reproduction and Inheritance in Living Systems

Unit 5 Development: Growth and Differentiation in Living Systems

Unit 6 Ecology: Interaction and Interdependence in Living Systems

Alternate	Building a Portfolio of Scientific Literacy

Outcomes and Indicators of Success

The following indicators allow you to assess the students' level of success with the activity and to assess their process of learning.

By the end of this section, the learners should

1. understand how to apply their conceptual understanding of biology to novel situations.

   They will demonstrate this understanding by

   a. articulating the significance of a biological scenario that they read,

   b. stating and describing the unifying principles of biology, and

   c. describing how these principles interrelate and operate in the scenario they have read.

2. recognize and understand important, specific biological concepts and methods of inquiry.

   They will indicate this ability by

   a. accurately representing the concepts as they answer a series of questions that assesses their knowledge of fundamental biological topics covered in this program,

   b. conducting performance assessments and critical-thinking tasks,

   c. explaining each choice of material for their portfolios (optional), and

   d. improving on their execution of earlier activities (optional).

3. evaluate their own progress (optional).

   They will indicate this ability by

   a. choosing work for their own portfolio, and

   b. justifying their choice of work.

Part A Recognizing Biology in Medicine

Overview

This activity provides an opportunity for students to tie together their understanding of the six unifying principles of biology that structure this program. To begin, students read one or two biology-relevant scenarios and demonstrate their understanding of how the unifying principles operate and interrelate in the situation described.

We offer two scenarios, one dealing with a commonplace trip to a doctor's office and the other reporting new research findings that may link the presence of an allele for cystic fibrosis to an increased chance of surviving cholera infection. Several choices for how to use the scenarios are listed in Preparations. In each case, students need to process what they have read at a primary level and show how the unifying principles of biology are illustrated in the scenario.

Preparations

To choose how you want to use this activity, read over the questions asked of the students and review each scenario. We offer the following three strategies to maximize the learning opportunities available to your students. Tailor these suggestions to fit the diversity of student abilities in your classroom.

◆ **Assign One Scenario**

   If your students have demonstrated a fairly thorough conceptual understanding of biology and can apply the unifying principles, assign one scenario for individual work. Scenario 2, *Cystic Fibrosis and Cholera*, is probably a greater challenge. Scenario 1, *Iguanas and Aspirin, Shots and Antibiotics*, also offers multiple examples of the interaction among all the unifying principles but in a somewhat obvious manner.

◆ **Have Students Choose**

   If your students have a good grasp of the unifying principles, but your class has a fairly large range of abilities, you may want to let students choose the scenario they use. The different styles of the two scenarios will appeal to different learning styles.

◆ **Use One Scenario as a Trial Run**

   If you feel that your students will have considerable difficulty handling an assignment that requires them to make conceptual connections in a new situation, consider working through Scenario 1, *Iguanas and Aspirin, Shots and Antibiotics*, as a class. You might let the students work in teams, combine results, and then discuss the significance of the type of analysis necessary to accomplish such a task. This approach adds time to the evaluation process, but it gives you and the students a chance to assess this type of reasoning in a formative manner. After this preparation, the students should be ready to complete Scenario 2, *Cystic Fibrosis and Cholera*, individually.

Preview the scoring rubric on the *GACD* and make changes as needed.

Background Information

We designed *BSCS Biology: A Human Approach* around the six unifying principles of biology outlined in *Developing Biological Literacy* (BSCS, 1993). We used these principles as a foundation upon which students could construct a conceptual framework for biology that would enable them to make sense of any biological topic. A strong conceptual understanding of biology, combined with critical-thinking and inquiry skills, should prepare the students for life as biologically literate citizens. To assess the students' level of preparedness in this regard, we designed this portion of the Evaluate Section to mimic the type of biologically relevant medical research news that might confront students in their adult lives.

The source for the information on the effects of CF heterozygosity on cholera is "Cystic Fibrosis Heterozygote Resistance to Cholera Toxin in the Cystic Fibrosis Mouse Model," by S.E. Gabriel, et al., 7 October 1994, *Science*, Vol. 266, pp. 107–109. The source for the information on the effects of fever as a defense mechanism is P. Ewald (1994), *Evolution of Disease*, Oxford University Press.

Strategies for Guiding Learners

PROCESS AND PROCEDURES

As a class, read orally or silently all introductory materials for the activity and the Process and Procedures to help students build connections between concepts and activities. Use the time spent reading to bring the students' attention into focus.

1. Obtain a scoring rubric from your teacher. Study the requirements for completing this activity successfully.

    Discuss the rubric with your partner. Ask your teacher to answer any questions that you have about the project.

    > Review the scoring rubric for this activity with your students. Provide time for them to question what the categories on the rubric mean and to clarify what it means to do an excellent job. Be sure they understand your expectations for success in this activity.

2. In your journal, identify each of the 6 unifying principles. Write a statement describing what each one means.

    The unifying principles of biology were the foundation for this course. They are in the title of each unit.

    > To make this step a little more fun, you might consider running a contest. In teams or individually, the students could race to list the six unifying principles. Or, see which team can list the most principles without using a resource such as the book or their journal. The six unifying principles are as follows:

    - ◆ Evolution
    - ◆ Homeostasis
    - ◆ Matter, energy, and organization
    - ◆ Continuity
    - ◆ Development
    - ◆ Ecology

    > After identifying the unifying principles, the learners should work reflectively to write a statement describing the meaning of each principle as they have come to know it through this course. This may be a good homework assignment. Figure TEv.1, which follows these strategies, provides a summary of how each chapter presented the ideas. It is unlikely that students will articulate their understanding as concisely as the phrases provided in the table; the table is designed to be a tool for you to provide hints or guidance.

3. Review both scenarios that follow. Choose one that you will use to complete the Analysis.

    > You may need to modify the student instructions for this step depending on the method you use to match the students with the scenario(s). You may decide to assign the reading of the scenario as homework, regardless of which strategy you use.

4. In a few sentences, describe 2 or more interesting things that you learned from reading the scenario.

Accept all responses that indicate the scenario was read and the students were interested in some aspect of it. For instance, in Scenario 1, some students might be surprised that anyone would question a physician's diagnosis. In this case, emphasize that it is appropriate to ask *why* the physician came to a particular conclusion.

Scenario 1 (*Iguanas and Aspirin, Shots and Antibiotics*) describes

- how patients can ask questions of their doctor to understand what is happening
- how fever may be a useful defense mechanism to fight infection (by reducing activity to conserve energy and possibly by directly interfering with the pathogen)
- how studies in animal systems offer data that may support observations in humans
- that when viruses such as influenza and chicken pox cause a fever, taking aspirin may be dangerous
- that antibiotics that are useful against bacterial infections do not fight viral illnesses such as influenza or the common cold
- that vaccines not only protect the vaccinated individual, they also indirectly lower the risk of infection for the entire population

Scenario 2 (*Cystic Fibrosis and Cholera*) describes

- the molecular basis of cystic fibrosis
- a molecular defect in the CFTR protein that leads to CF
- how mutant CFTR proteins fail to regulate the exchange of chloride ions
- how an ion imbalance can lead to a water imbalance
- the effect of excess mucus on the function of the gas exchange and digestive systems
- that cholera is caused by a bacterium that produces a toxin
- the way the cholera bacteria exploit a normal cellular protein (CFTR) to cause diarrhea, which aids in the transmission of the bacterium to other hosts
- an experiment in mice that demonstrates a beneficial effect of being a carrier of the CF allele (heterozygotes have less functional CFTR, and thus cholera has less normal CFTR to exploit)

Figure TEv.1 Key concepts in each chapter

Unit	Chapter	Concepts
1 Evolution: Patterns and Products of Change in Living Systems	1 The Human Animal	The distinguishing characteristics of humans; the similarities among humans and other animals
	2 Evolution: Change across Time	Evidence for evolution; natural selection; geologic and evolutionary time
	3 Products of Evolution: Unity and Diversity	Common properties of life; adaptations result in diversity; biological classification
2 Homeostasis: Maintaining Dynamic Equilibrium in Living Systems	4 The Internal Environment of Organisms	Internal and external environments; systems; compartments
	5 Maintaining Balance in Organisms	Maintaining internal balance; restoring mechanisms; regulation
	6 Human Homeostasis; Health and Disease	Disruption of homeostasis; defense mechanisms; cost/benefit analysis; ethical analysis
3 Energy, Matter, and Organization: Relationships in Living Systems	7 Performance and Fitness	Human performance requires matter and energy (food); athletic fitness versus fitness for life; many factors affect fitness
	8 The Cellular Basis of Activity	Forms of energy; cells alter energy and matter to stay alive; metabolism includes photosynthesis, cellular respiration, and other biosynthesis reactions that are key processes for making energy and matter accessible to living systems; energy is neither created nor destroyed but may be unavailable for living systems
	9 The Cycling of Matter and the Flow of Energy in Communities	Flow of energy and matter in communities; cycling of matter
4 Continuity: Reproduction and Inheritance in Living Systems	10 Reproduction in Humans and Other Organisms	Reproduction is necessary for continuity; asexual versus sexual reproduction; culture influences mating behavior
	11 Continuity of Information through Inheritance	The flow of genetic information from one generation to the next provides continuity for species and allows for evolution; in each generation, genetic information interacts with the environment to produce phenotype
	12 Gene Action	Transfer and expression of genetic information (structure of DNA, replication, transcription, and translation); the impact of genetic engineering
5 Development: Growth and Differentiation in Living Systems	13 Processes and Patterns of Development	Development is a lifelong process; development through growth and differentiation is an expression of a genetic plan; multicellularity depends on development
	14 The Human Life Span	Human life stages have physical, emotional, cognitive, and social aspects
6 Ecology: Interaction and Interdependence in Living Systems	15 Interdependence among Organisms in the Biosphere	Limiting factors affect interactions; carrying capacity; all organisms are dependent on each other in some manner
	16 Decision Making in a Complex World	The complexity of decisions and living systems

Analysis

Unless your students never complete writing assignments outside of class, the majority of the essay assignment in the Analysis makes an ideal homework assignment. Encourage the students to use their journals, readings, student resources or outside resources, and other people to develop the ideas in their essays. You may consider organizing a peer review of the first drafts in which the students have a partner read their essays and make comments, then revise their work based on those comments and their additional reflection. As they plan their essays, they should be outlining, drawing concept maps or webs, or making notes about important ideas. If your students lack these skills, you may need to stop and model one or more of these techniques.

If students have difficulty connecting all six unifying principles to the scenario, have them first make a list of the unifying principles and examples from the story that could be evidence of each principle at work. Then they can build their essay about interrelationships from this intermediate step.

We cannot suggest full student responses because the connections will depend largely on the particular examples they choose. However, for each scenario, we provide a sample of how the connections could be made.

Scenario 1: *Iguanas and Aspirin, Shots and Antibiotics*

Sample Essay

In this scenario, all six unifying principles are represented. There is evidence of *evolution* when the doctor refers to the bacteria that are resistant to certain antibiotics. The discussion about the role of fever is an example of the restoring mechanisms the body has for maintaining *homeostasis* or returning to a balanced state after a disruption. When the father asks whether Miguel should eat or drink, the response from the doctor emphasizes the role of *matter, energy, and organization* because the fever will use energy stored in the body as glycogen and fat, and Miguel will need to replenish these stores. The manner in which penicillin helps fight bacterial infection represents an interference with the pathogen's ability to maintain *continuity* of information through inheritance; the antibiotic disrupts the production of the cell wall during cell division, which prevents bacterial reproduction. The reference to the dangers of rubella for a developing fetus represents a connection to *development*. Finally, the balance of bacteria in the intestine is an example of *ecology*. As the penicillin wipes out the "good bacteria," the yogurt containing live cultures helps replenish the population.

Connections between the unifying principles include the way the evolution of resistant bacteria affects the ecology of their interactions with humans. The birth defects caused by rubella in a developing fetus show an alteration in the organization of living material. There is a connection between energy use during illness and the body's ability to fight off infection using the immune system to restore homeostasis.

Scenario 2: *Cystic Fibrosis and Cholera*

Sample Essay

The most obvious unifying principle in this scenario is *homeostasis* because of the detailed descriptions of the disruptions to the health of the CF victim. A specific example is the loss of regulation of chlorine ions that leads to a loss of water balance and increased mucus secretions. *Evolution* is evident in the scenario because there appears to be a selective advantage in surviving cholera for individuals who have one CF allele. This feature highlights one of the key concepts in the principle of *continuity*: different genotypes can be passed from parent to offspring and lead to different phenotypes. For example, a homozygous CF individual will develop serious symptoms of cystic fibrosis and may not live past 30 years old. Heterozygous CF individuals do not have CF, but if they are exposed to cholera, they are not affected as seriously as homozygous normal individuals, who also do not have CF. The interaction between host (human) and pathogen (cholera) represents an *ecological* interaction.

Delivery systems such as the intestines and bloodstream, which deliver nutrients, water, and regulatory molecules such as pancreatic enzymes, exemplify how *development* of complex tissues with differentiated cells makes homeostasis possible. The mutation in the CF allele is a change in the *organization of matter*, which in this case results in altered information and a nonfunctional CFTR protein. Thus, organization of matter can have genetic effects that alter continuity.

Other connections include the relationship between the host/parasite interaction between cholera and humans and the impact of this interaction on natural selection for humans with the CF allele (*evolution*). Also, natural selection for heterozygotes with one copy of the CF allele depends on reproduction (*continuity*) because *evolution* occurs through many generations.

<table>
<tr><td>**Part B**</td></tr>
</table>

Chapter Challenges

Overview

This part of the Evaluate Section provides an opportunity for students to express their understanding of important, specific biological concepts covered in this program. It includes a selection of challenging questions, problems, and performance tasks that correlate to particular chapters in the program. You should select a set of questions appropriate for the emphasis and coverage you allotted to each chapter.

Strategies for Guiding Learners

To assess your students' understanding of the specific ideas in the chapters of *BSCS Biology: A Human Approach*, choose the questions for them that best reflect the program as you taught it. Encourage students to answer the questions using materials from the entire program and outside resources. The list of questions by chapter is an organizational tool that should make selecting easier for you; it is not intended to suggest that all of the information necessary to answer the question can be found in a particular chapter.

As you choose the questions that will best reflect what you taught, keep in mind the time spent on different chapters as well as the students' interest in various concepts. Alternatively, you could have the learners choose five or six questions that most interest them and supplement their list with several others. The responses below are one way to answer each question. You may need to modify the focus of the response to reflect the emphasis you gave when teaching a particular concept.

Unit 1 Evolution: Patterns and Products of Change in Living Systems

Chapter 1 The Human Animal

1. Long before humans developed ways to write their languages, they passed on information about their lives and the world around them by telling stories, drawing pictures, acting out plays, dancing, or singing. As the collection of information grew, people needed very good memories to pass along all the information.

   a. How have written language and modern electronic communication altered the way information is stored and transmitted?

   b. Explain how you think these changes may have affected human cultures.

   The use of written and electronically communicated information (television, radio, FAX, telephone, electronic mail, etc.) allows much larger amounts of information to be stored and accessed than human memory alone can. Visual information can be stored in a better way, and factual information may remain more accurate in written form than if it is transmitted by one person telling another. The number of people to whom information can be communicated is also greater, and information is available instantaneously in many cases. These changes make cultural differences smaller. In addition, as stored information is shared throughout the world and across generations, it allows people to take better advantage of the learning of those who came before.

Chapter 2 Evolution: Change across Time

1. Describe two examples of how evolution is happening today.

   Evolution is happening today as populations of varied individuals in a species are subjected to natural selection. Traits that are advantageous at a particular time are more likely to be represented in offspring than traits that are disadvantageous. Conversely, disadvantageous traits tend to become rare. Many modern examples of evolution are the result of unintended consequence of human technologies. For example, the use of pesticides results in selection for insects that are resistant to these toxins, and antibiotics have promoted the evolution of resistant bacteria strains. Human destruction of habitat or direct hunting have caused many species, such as passenger pigeons, to become extinct or endangered. Human agricultural practices over the last 4,000–6,000 years have artificially selected for many new plants. Corn (*Zea mays*), for instance, is not found in the wild at all. Evolution in more natural settings continues as well. For example, the fastest and most alert gazelles still survive cheetah attacks better than less-well-adapted gazelles. Thus, the continuity of genetic information from one generation to the next still reflects the reproductive success of the best-adapted members of a population.

2. How does technology play a role in helping scientists collect evidence of biological change across long periods of time?

   Technologies that permit the accurate dating of materials (such as carbon dating) are very useful in determining the age of fossil species. Computer tools are useful for carefully recording details about fossil evidence or modeling a complete organism from partial evidence. The development of techniques for determining the sequence of DNA provides a powerful tool for identifying molecular similarities between species. This technology is much more accurate for identifying homologies than simple observation.

3. Scientists have hypothesized that modern whales are descended from land mammals that moved into the water environment between 50 to 60 million years ago. In 1994, scientists found two exciting fossil discoveries, both whalelike creatures with legs.

   a. Look at the data presented in Figure Ev.9. Explain how this information supports an evolutionary explanation for the origin of modern whales from an ancestor that lived on land and had legs.

   The intermediate fossils (*Rodhocetus* and *Prozeuglodon*) between the modern legless whales and the earlier ancestors that could walk easily on land (*Mesonychid* and *Ambulocetus*) support the idea that as these early whale ancestors spent increasingly more time in the water, their walking legs became less advantageous, and a strong tail for swimming became more advantageous. This series of fossils and their time of occurrence are consistent with the idea that the aquatic whale species gradually emerged through changes in their land-based ancestors during many generations and millions of years.

   For more information on these discoveries, see the article "Back to the Sea," by Carl Zimmer in *Discover*, January 1995, pp. 82–84.

Chapter 3   Products of Evolution: Unity and Diversity

1. Develop a reasonable scientific explanation for this statement: Birds are related to dinosaurs.

   Fossil evidence from dinosaurs and anatomical evidence from modern birds indicate certain physical homologies, such as limb structure. Both dinosaurs and birds could have had a common ancestral species. In time, the dinosaur line became extinct, while the gradual changes through time that resulted in modern birds have left these species still capable of surviving.

2. The Nature Conservancy is an example of a conservation organization that seeks to protect land from human development. How could the activities of an organization such as this have an effect on biological diversity? Give specific examples using this organization or a similar one.

   Responses will depend on the organization students choose. The Nature Conservancy's impact on diversity depends on its buying and preserving land that offers natural habitats to many species, some of which are endangered. An important goal of this organization is to obtain large enough tracts of undisturbed land to be effective. Other organizations may save seeds from endangered plant species or try to educate people to maintain habitats in ways as simple as providing wildflowers or nesting boxes that songbirds need.

Unit 2 Homeostasis: Maintaining Dynamic Equilibrium in Living Systems

Chapter 4   The Internal Environment of Organisms

1. An astronaut in space depends on a space vehicle or a space suit to create an environment that can support his or her life. The data in the need to know box show the average daily dietary and metabolic needs of an astronaut in space.

   a. Make a table that shows the types of output that each astronaut would produce given the input shown. (You do not need to use numerical values, but you can identify what types of waste will be produced.)

b. Consider the output you listed in your chart. What technological adaptations would be necessary to maintain a healthy and clean living environment in the space vehicle? How does your answer relate to the concepts of this chapter?

Output would include carbon dioxide from respiration; waste water in the form of urine, wash water, and food preparation water; some water vapor from respiration and from perspiration; and solid waste in the form of feces. The space vehicle or space suit must have regulatory systems to control, recycle, or dispose of these products as they build up. This need is similar to regulatory systems in the human body, but once wastes leave the body on earth, they do not stay as close to the body as they do in the space vehicle, which is a closed environment. However, waste products on earth do have an effect on their surroundings (as mentioned in Chapters 8, 9, 15, and 16).

Chapter 5   Maintaining Balance in Organisms

1. What role does the brain have in maintaining the body's balance of temperature, water, gas exchange, and blood pressure?

The students should describe the general role of the brain as a stimulus detector and response regulator. The brain is responsible for coordinating the specific regulatory responses of many interactive organ systems and thus for maintaining homeostasis. For example, if blood pressure is low, the brain responds by sending signals that increase heart rate, constrict arteries, and conserve water through changes in kidney function.

Chapter 6   Human Homeostasis: Health and Disease

1. A human body is continuously subjected to changes in its external environment. Use one or two examples to explain why these changes normally do not cause problems for the body. Under what circumstances can homeostasis become disrupted?

There is a difference between adjusting to fluctuations in the internal or external environment to maintain life-supporting conditions and trying to respond to a severe disruption. For instance, bleeding from a minor cut stops quickly through the clotting of blood, which is regulated through positive feedback. New tissue starts to heal over the wound, and the immune system sends in protective cells to avoid infection. This response requires a certain amount of time, but minor perturbations allow the body time to respond. A deep cut or a severed artery, however, may result in such rapid blood loss that clotting is not quick enough to protect the body from an extreme alteration in internal conditions. Alternatively, a relatively minor cut could be a problem for a person with an impaired immune system or one suffering from the clotting disorder called hemophilia. In these cases, either the severity of the disruption or the impairment of regulatory systems can cause a loss in homeostasis.

2. How do AIDS and autoimmune diseases keep the body from maintaining a healthy condition?

The HIV virus enters T-helper cells of the immune system and multiplies inside those cells, eventually killing them. Without healthy T-helper cells, which are critical to the function of B-cells and killer T-cells, the immune system ceases to be effective. It loses the ability to combat other infections, and these opportunistic infections prevent the maintenance of a healthy condition. Other autoimmune disorders, such as lupus, allergies, and certain forms of arthritis, have debilitating effects on health but for different reasons. In these cases, the immune system is not disabled, but it fails to distinguish self from nonself. The result is an immune system attack on the body's own tissues.

Unit 3 Energy, Matter, and Organization: Relationships in Living Systems

Chapter 7 Performance and Fitness

1. Have you ever watched someone race-walk? The unusual twisting motion of the hips makes it look as if it would be so much easier for the racers to pick up their feet and run. What is the difference between running and walking? Humans, like many other vertebrates including horses, dogs, cats, and deer, have different ways of moving their legs for locomotion. If you ever have ridden a horse, you know that the jarring bounce you feel when the horse trots is very different from a gallop or a canter. Use the data displayed in Figure Ev.10 to answer the questions below.

    a. At a speed of 5 km/hour (about 3 miles per hour), is running or walking more energy efficient? Is the same true at 8 km/hour (about 5 miles per hour)? Explain how the data in Figure Ev.10 support your answers.

    At 5 km/hour, walking is more efficient than running, using about two-thirds as much energy. At 8 km/hour, running is slightly more energy efficient than walking; the curves for the two types of movement cross at about 7.6 km/hour.

    b. During very fast running, above 16 km/hour (10 miles per hour), most people are exercising anaerobically. If this is the case, would the type of data measured in Figure Ev.10 be an appropriate way to determine their energy efficiency? Explain your answer.

    No, the data in this figure are not appropriate because they are derived from oxygen consumption. Oxygen consumption is not an accurate way to measure energy use at higher speeds because much of the energy is provided by glycolysis in the muscle cells, an anaerobic process. Although oxygen still is being used for aerobic respiration, it accounts for only part of the actual energy use.

Chapter 8 The Cellular Basis of Activity

1. Metabolism includes the series of chemical reactions that break down macromolecules. These include glycolysis, fermentation, and aerobic respiration. It also includes the reactions that build up macromolecules, such as protein synthesis or (in plants and certain prokaryotes) photosynthesis.

    a. Can both types of reactions happen in the same cells of the same organism? Explain your answer.

    b. Show how your answer to question 1a relates to activity in a living system.

    Both types of reactions are needed at different times in the same cells. Regulatory signals control which reactions are happening at a given time. Different sets of enzymes carry out the different reactions.

For example, immediately after you eat a meal high in sugar, your liver and muscle cells may take up glucose and use it to make glycogen, a biosynthetic reaction. When you need energy for running, your muscle cells will break down some of the glycogen to have glucose available for the anaerobic energy-releasing reactions of glycolysis or for aerobic respiration (the Krebs cycle). Your liver cells also may break down the glycogen, but some of the resulting glucose is released into the bloodstream for transport to other cells.

2. To grow and develop, a seed must germinate (sprout) as the embryonic plant begins to grow. Germination requires water. For example, lettuce seeds germinate in about 48 hours after being soaked in water. Germination also may be sensitive to light. Some seeds require light to germinate. In other species, light inhibits germination.

   a. Design and carry out an experiment to test whether light affects the germination of common garden seeds. You will need to use seeds that germinate quickly, such as Grand Rapids lettuce seeds.

   b. Report your results and conclusions. Include a possible explanation of why the seeds you selected behaved as they did.

   c. Explain the sources of energy and matter for a germinating seed *before* the sprout emerges and leaves grow. Do the same for *after* the sprout is aboveground and the leaves are open.

      Students' experimental designs will vary but should reflect an attention to controls and variables. Seeds vary in their response to light, and individual strains may vary as well. Phytochrome, the regulatory protein involved in response to light, controls processes such as flowering and change from etiolation (lack of chloroplasts) to green tissue. Germination of Grand Rapids lettuce seeds is reported to be stimulated by light, while germination of pansy seeds is inhibited. Perhaps this switch is triggered by the level of soil coverage appropriate for growth and affects the success of germination.

      As germination begins, energy and matter must come from macromolecules stored in the seed. This requirement explains why seeds of many plants, such as peas, beans, and sunflowers, are good sources of food. As soon as the new plant has sufficient tissue exposed to sunlight, it can begin photosynthesis, during which it obtains energy from light, matter from water and nutrients (via roots), and carbon dioxide from the air (via stomates).

Chapter 9   The Cycling of Matter and the Flow of Energy in Communities

1. Explain the flow of energy in a compost pile. What happens to the matter? What is the connection between the flow of energy and the changes in the matter?

   A compost heap is a classic example of organic recycling. Students should be able to explain that decomposers break down complex organic matter and release simpler molecules that other organisms can use. For instance, carbon dioxide that microorganisms in the heap release through cellular respiration can enter the atmosphere and be fixed by plants undergoing photosynthesis. The decomposition process produces energy that is released as heat, but microorganisms also manage to use some of the energy released by reactions that break down complex molecules in the organic matter. They use this energy to build macromolecules required for their own maintenance and to perform other cellular work. Ultimately, energy is transferred from one molecule to another until most of it is converted into heat.

2. Identify a population of organisms that lives in your community. Draw or construct a food web that shows the connections among the organisms in that population. Include a discussion of what happens to the energy as you move to higher trophic levels. Illustrate those relationships.

Students should be able to identify a population in their community. From here, they should draw a relatively complex web that illustrates the interactions between producers, herbivores, omnivores, predators, and decomposers that are indigenous to your community. All webs should include green plants and indicate that energy in the form of sunlight enters the system.

Unit 4 Continuity: Reproduction and Inheritance in Living Systems

Chapter 10 Reproduction in Humans and Other Organisms

1. Use the population data shown in Figure Ev.11 to answer the following questions:

   a. Explain how birthrate and death rate work together to determine both continuity and size of a population of organisms.

   b. What other factors contribute to the size of a population of organisms? How?

   Reproduction produces new individuals in a population, so even though individuals die, the population or species continues. However, the size of the population is based on a balance between birthrate and death rate. The data in this graph show that after 1900, there was a sharp increase in population size. Either the number of offspring being born has increased dramatically or the rate of death has decreased. The statement comparing infant mortality between 1940 and 1980 offers a clue. The rate of survival of newly born offspring has greatly increased, reflecting improved hygiene, nutrition, and medical practices (particularly the advent of antibiotics and vaccines).

2. The behavior of animals such as crickets plays an important role in reproductive success. Read this short description from *Science* magazine about the results of a research project that used a robot model of a cricket.

   See the need to know box on page 676 of the student text.

   a. Explain how these results relate to what you know about mating behavior in animals, including humans.

   The answers will depend largely on students' earlier observations in Chapter 10. Similarities between this report and the live crickets that students observed include both crickets sensing the call and responding by moving toward it. In addition, the recognized call is specific, an aspect of mating behavior that encourages locating a member of the opposite sex and same species. Humans, like many other sexually reproducing animals, have behaviors that encourage receptiveness of the opposite sex. Nonhuman animals also have physical signals (such as the cricket song or pheromones) that attract a mate. It is not clear whether humans have similar signals, but there are cultural behaviors (such as dress) that enhance sexual attractiveness, and these may play an analogous role. For more information on the robot cricket behavior described here, see S. Bains (1994), *Science, 266*, p. 1809.

3. Say you were to invent two new types of contraceptives, one hormonal and the other physical. What would they be and how would they work?

   Accept any response that indicates an understanding of the anatomy and physiology of the relevant reproductive system.

Chapter 11   Continuity of Information through Inheritance

1. In the laboratory, scientists can use enzymes to remove the cell walls from plant cells in growing tissue. This produces protoplasts. Protoplasts then can be placed on a growth medium in a petri dish. If the medium contains the proper mixture of plant hormones, a single isolated protoplast can divide and eventually produce a whole plant.

   a. What does this observation tell you about the genetic material of a plant cell?

   b. How does genetic material affect continuity in sexually reproducing organisma? in asexually reproducing organisms?

   A single plant cell contains all the genetic information necessary to direct the growth of the entire plant. As each cell divides, it passes along information that ensures continuity. (The fact that every cell does not normally give rise to a complete new plant, however, suggests that additional factors must influence how genetic information is expressed to direct the growth of organisms. Unit 5 covers the topic of development.) The inheritance of genetic information is the basis for continuity in a species or population.

Chapter 12   Gene Action

1. How is the molecular structure of genetic information important to the replication and expression of genes? In your response, describe the similarities and differences among the following molecular processes: replication, transcription, and translation.

   The genetic information in DNA is stored in two linear sequences of nucleotides, and these two sequences form base pairs in a specific, complementary fashion with one another. This complementarity allows the double helix to serve as a template for its own copying, a process known as DNA replication. During replication, one old strand is copied to produce a new strand, and ultimately two double helices result, each of which has one new and one old strand. An analogous reaction begins the process of gene expression, called transcription, except that in this case an RNA copy of the information in DNA, which often encodes a protein or ribosomal RNA, is made from the DNA template. If the RNA thus produced corresponds to a gene for a protein, it is called messenger RNA, and it will subsequently be translated into protein structure. The information in the triplet codons of this messenger RNA (and the DNA gene from which it was copied) is what determines the sequence of amino acids added to a growing protein chain during the process of translation.

2. How is it possible that a change in a single nucleotide of a gene can produce a mutant protein? Will such a change in a nucleotide always produce a mutant protein? Explain.

   If one nucleotide in the sequence of a gene is substituted for another, such as a T for a C, then the meaning of a three-nucleotide codon, which represents a particular amino acid, could be altered. Consequently, the protein that results from expression of the altered gene could be a mutant form. However, several different codons can specify the same amino acid. If the altered nucleotide happened to result in a new codon corresponding to the same amino acid, there would be no change in the protein being specified. (A single nucleotide deletion, however, can shift the entire frame for reading the gene and cause a substantial change in the encoded information.)

Unit 5 Development: Growth and Differentiation in Living Systems

Chapter 13   Processes and Patterns of Development

See the need to know box on page 677 of the student text.

1. Plants and animals adjust to environmental changes in many ways. Read the following brief description of several adaptations to change. Then complete the task below.

    Use either deciduous trees or insects as an example. Describe how their pattern of development represents an adaptation for extreme seasonal differences in temperature.

    These organisms exemplify adaptational strategies that take advantage of differences in the physical structures typical of various developmental stages. Each of these species has adapted to winter through evolutionary processes that selected for the coincidence of hardy developmental phases during periods of harsh conditions. For example, the tree loses the parts that would be most subject to damage by freezing (the broad deciduous leaves). Trees survive such a dramatic change in physiology because their developmental pattern permits them to slow activity and stop growth during the winter and to replace the leaves needed for photosynthesis in the spring. Similarly, insects in different developmental stages can occupy quite different habitats. Consider the difference in the crawling caterpillar and flying mature butterfly. By coordinating developmental stages with seasonal changes, insects have a useful adaptation to survive freezing temperatures.

2. A tumorous disease of tomato and tobacco plants known as crown gall can result from the action of a bacterium, called *Agrobacterium tumefaciens*. This bacterium infects a wound on the plant stem (see Figure Ev.13). Those bacteria contain copies of a DNA plasmid with special genes that can transform the growth regulation of plant cells. The bacterial genes incorporate into the plant's genetic material. Here those genes direct plant cells to make unusual amino acids that are useless to the plant but serve as food for the bacteria. A mass of undifferentiated tissue at the infected site soon grows into a tumor.

    Describe how that bacteria-induced tumor compares with cancer in humans. How is the tumor different from cancer?

    Like cancer in humans, crown gall involves unregulated growth of undifferentiated tissue to form a tumor. It also involves changes in the genetic material that bring about this loss of developmental regulation. However, in humans, there are no cancers known to be caused by an invading bacterial species, although a number of viruses are known to be involved.

Chapter 14   The Human Life Span

1. People go through the same life stages. Each generation, however, does so at a different time in history. A high school student named Rachel was 15 years old in 2003. Her parents were 15 in 1974. They listened to music by the Beatles and the Rolling Stones recorded on large vinyl records. Rachel's grandparents were 15 in 1949, shortly after World War II. They liked to dance to a big band sound and listen to shows on the radio.

   a. Make a table that compares the physical biology and the cultural setting for a single life stage of three generations. For example, your chart could include you, your parents at your age, and your grandparents at your age. (If you prefer not to use your own family, use a family that you know about or have read about.) You can use any life stage as long as you have information that corresponds to each generation.

   b. Make two columns. Label one *Physical Biology* and the other *Cultural Setting*. Under each column, describe the characteristics that apply to each of your individuals.

   c. Write a few sentences that describe the differences in the life stage of the various individuals according to the historical setting in which they take place.

   There are too many variables in the potential responses to offer a survey. However, you can look for accuracy in the descriptions of the physical characteristics that should be relatively similar, particularly for younger life stages. (These might include rapid growth, development of secondary sex characteristics, pregnancy, etc.) For task c, look for thoughtful responses that consider the interplay between culture, history, technology, and life stage. For instance, in old age, a person in the oldest generation might have suffered blindness while a person at that age today could undergo surgery for cataracts. This question offers a good opportunity to blend scientific and technological information with creativity.

Unit 6 Ecology: Interaction and Interdependence in Living Systems

Chapter 15   Interdependence among Organisms in the Biosphere

1. An instrument aboard NASA's *Nimbus-7* satellite records data from the surface water of the Atlantic Ocean off the U.S. coast. This instrument is called a Coastal Zone Color Scanner, or CZCS. It measures infrared radiation and concentrations of chlorophyll pigments. The pattern of radiation corresponds to water temperature. The patterns of both radiation and chlorophyll correspond to currents and tidal mixing. The highest concentrations of chlorophyll pigments are found near the shore. The lower concentrations are found in the relatively unmixed waters of the warm Gulf Stream current.

   To answer the following questions about interdependence, keep in mind that some places in the ocean have high concentrations of phytoplankton. Phytoplankton are photosynthetic microorganisms that drift with ocean currents. (You also may find it useful to review the discussion of photosynthesis in Chapter 8.)

   a. The CZCS instrument on board the *Nimbus-7* can take measurements only from the surface water of the ocean. Is this where you would expect to find phytoplankton? Explain the basis for your answer.

b. How could the *Nimbus-7* data be useful for managing commercial fisheries?

You would expect to find phytoplankton concentrated at the surface of ocean waters because they are photosynthetic and thus dependent on sunlight. The fact that phytoplankton are unevenly distributed in the oceans suggests that they are not adapted to live equally well in all environments. Temperature as well as sunlight appears to be important.

Commercial fisheries might find the *Nimbus-7* data useful because many fish, which are consumers, depend directly or indirectly on phytoplankton, which are producers. For instance, phytoplankton are a food source for many small crustaceans, which in turn serve as food for fish. Therefore, areas of high phytoplankton concentration are likely areas of high fish concentration.

2. Population growth rates are easy to see on graphs. They typically have a characteristic shape that reflects the involvement of limiting factors. Use your knowledge of these types of graphs to complete the following task:

   a. Draw a graph that illustrates the growth of any population of organisms over a period of at least 10 generations.

   You can pick a general type of organism such as insects for your graph.

   b. Label your graph. Make sure the reader can tell how many generations have passed and what type of organism is represented.

   c. Pick three distinct points on different parts of your graphed line. Label them A, B, C. Describe what is happening to the population at points A, B, and C.

   Include a discussion of limiting factors to help explain your answer.

   d. What point on the graph represents the carrying capacity for your population? Explain.

   Look for graphs that follow the parameters you have established for the year, such as where and how to title the graph and how to label the axes. Then look for a number of offspring that is reasonable for the chosen organism. For example, elephants should not be giving birth to 10 babies a year. The three labels should describe points such as where the population is growing slowly, increasing dramatically, leveling out, or declining. The learners should be able to explain that carrying capacity is the size of population they think can be sustained indefinitely.

Chapter 16   Decision Making in a Complex World

1. A panel of lawmakers has met to consider zoning for 200 acres of land near a large forest that currently includes wetlands and a meadow. One development company wants to build a shopping center and apartments on most of this land. Another company proposes building a manufacturing plant there. Conservation groups want to protect the wetlands. Various specialists have provided reports that mention the following observations about natural land and human development:

   ◆ Nitrogen acts as a fertilizer for leafy parts of plants and for some microorganisms. Too much of this fertilizer causes plants to grow large tops and insufficient roots.

   ◆ Forests may help protect the world from global warming by converting carbon dioxide to plant mass by way of photosynthesis.

   ◆ Acid rain results from certain air pollutants produced by industrial processes. Its effects on living systems are complex.

♦ Nitrogen cycling is the conversion of atmospheric nitrogen into nitrogen that living organisms can use. In this process, nitrogen-fixing bacteria convert nitrogen gas, N_2, into chemical forms that biological systems can use (such as ammonium, nitrates, and nitrites). When an organism dies, different microorganisms (called denitrifying bacteria) decompose the organism's body. This releases some of its nitrogen back into nonbiological systems. Many denitrifying bacteria live in boggy wetland environments.

The panel is ready to make a decision, but now a new finding is presented.

See the need to know box on page 680 of the student text.

Your task is to discuss the following:

a. How do the data in Figure Ev.14 support the concerns of scientists who claim that acid rain and excessive nitrates from pollution cause damage to trees?

b. List all of the possible biological and nonbiological consequences of developing the land. Then list the consequences of not developing the land.

c. Think about the findings reported in Figure Ev.14 and those from the earlier reports. How might these findings influence the panel's decision about how or whether the land in question should be developed?

d. What would you decide to do? Why?

The data do support the idea that as a forest becomes less healthy, more and more nitrates may pass through it without entering biological systems. This result appears to be a combination of less growth of trees and a possible decrease in populations of soil microorganisms. The situation is actually quite complex with many variables, some of which are not taken into account by the information given here. For example, the amount of acid rain in Germany may far exceed that in the proposed site. Is there any evidence that this stand of trees is shunting too much growth to leafy tops due to excess nitrates or that the roots are weakened and excess nitrates are passing through the habitat? Would the proposed industry emit large amounts of pollutants? Would maintenance of the wetland be sufficient to save the forest if it were indeed in danger?

Once these questions were answered satisfactorily, there still would be no clear choice for the panel. Now a question of individual or community values would come into play.

Consider the students' response in light of logical thinking and the ability to look for variables and identify connections. A wide range of responses could demonstrate an understanding of the interdependence of living systems, both with one another and with abiotic factors. For more on this issue, see J. Raloff (1995), *Science News*, pp. 90–91.

Building a Portfolio of Scientific Literacy

Overview

We designed this portfolio activity to help learners review the year's work in a manner that requires them to reflect on the major concepts in each chapter and evaluate their past and current understanding of them. They have several means to present a portfolio that represents their progress with each chapter. They can select from existing work; they can revisit activities and improve on them; and/or they can respond to any of the questions in *Chapter Challenges* that represent a sampling of the chapter concepts. The resulting portfolio may be a collection of old and new work that demonstrates not only the students' understanding of key biological concepts, but also their maturity in selecting and displaying the work.

Materials   (per class of 30)

30 copies of the rubric *Biology Portfolio* and Rubric: *Oral Portfolio Presentation* (see Preparations)
other needs based on how you tailor the assignment

Preparations

If you plan to have students build portfolios, it is best to tell them so when they first begin your course, and remind them regularly to save all of their work. You may wish to provide your classes with a file or other designated space where they can store journals that have been filled or other artifacts from their work throughout the year. You also will need to save posters that students have created if you plan to allow them in portfolios. Consider offering students the option of using a photograph of a poster if they wish to include it in the portfolio. If you have access to a digital camera, you can photograph posters and presentations throughout the year.

Some students may wish to create electronic portfolios in the form of Web pages or PowerPoint-type presentations. You may need to arrange for computer time to accommodate those students. If you let the students repeat activities or use the DVDs to prepare materials for their portfolios, you will need to arrange for materials as well.

As the students work on the questions, they may want additional resources. You could set up a collection of materials in your classroom, in the school library, or on the Internet. SciLinks and digital library resources will be valuable assets.

Another interesting option you may want to offer the students is an opportunity to interview a scientist. Use the scientist's field of study to determine which slot in the portfolio the interview would fill.

Preview the portfolio rubrics on the *GACD*, and determine whether you will have students present their portfolios in class. Modify the rubric(s) you decide to use as needed.

Background Information

A portfolio is a collection of a person's best work as well as reflections about that work. An entire portfolio may have a particular focus, such as improvement, conceptual understanding, or creativity. Alternatively, an entire portfolio may be a diverse collection of work representing the range of talents an individual possesses. Advocates of portfolio assessment contend that portfolios offer a richer and more complete picture of a student's competency as compared with the data collected solely from traditional forms of assessment. The richness of portfolios comes from the strategy's flexibility, which allows students to show their strengths through varieties of evidence, as well as its utility, in which students demonstrate their understanding in personally compelling applications.

A complete portfolio has the following components:

◆ Container/holder labeled with the learner's name and class

◆ Collection of work that has been thoughtfully selected and revised as necessary

◆ Caption for each entry that lists its title, what it illustrates, and the reason for its selection

It takes a long time to assess portfolios. Before making the assignment, refine your rubric and the point scheme for assessing portfolios. Take advantage of peer review, parental review, and in-school writing resources as ways to provide feedback efficiently and effectively to students about their portfolios. Create a clear timeline for students to complete key stages in portfolio building.

There is more information on portfolios in the assessment section of the *GACD*.

Strategies for Guiding Learners

PROCESS AND PROCEDURES

As a class, read orally or silently all introductory materials for the activity and the Process and Procedures to help students build connections between concepts and activities. Use the time spent reading to bring the students' attention into focus.

1. Obtain a rubric for the portfolio from your teacher. Read the rubric carefully. Discuss the criteria with your partner.

   Ask your teacher any questions about the project that you or your partner cannot answer from the rubric.

2. Review the chapters. Record in your journal what you think the main concepts are from each chapter. Do this by making a table. Create one column for the titles of the chapters in each unit. Add a second column to record the main concepts or ideas from each chapter.

   Encourage the students to use their journals, the opening stories, the titles, and the chapter overviews to efficiently identify the main concepts of each chapter you taught. Learners should record the concepts in a chart in their journals. As you review the charts, look for evidence that they understand the key idea(s) in each chapter and are not concentrating on individual topics or activities. Be liberal in your expectations of how the students articulate the larger concepts of biology. Look for expressions of key ideas and functional knowledge, not isolated facts.

3. Let your teacher review your table of concepts before you prepare your portfolio.

4. Look over your work for each chapter. Select the examples you think will make up the best portfolio for your interview as a scientifically literate citizen. Follow the criteria in the rubric for selecting work.

   a. Decide how to display your samples of work to make a portfolio for your interview.

   b. Find an example of work to illustrate the key concept(s) of each chapter. Use examples of your work just as they are. Or make corrections or additions if you think you understand the concepts and the particular activity better than when you did it.

   Remember, you can use additional resources to help you improve an existing activity. Use the essays, your journal, your teammates, or outside references.

   c. If you are missing good examples of work from some chapters, add new work to your portfolio. Choose at least one chapter question to answer from the collection of questions in the *Chapter Challenges*.

   You can put this new work in the portfolio along with the samples of your previous work.

   Before the students begin working on their portfolios, you will need to explain clearly your expectations for size, location, style, and due date of the portfolio. We have left that aspect of the activity open intentionally so that you can tailor it to your setting and timeline.

   As the students develop their portfolios, encourage them to refer to their table from step 2. Each portfolio entry should reflect the main ideas that the students articulated for each chapter. You may need to prompt their creativity to make these connections. They should be able to use answers to questions, data charts, experiment summaries, or even reflective entries to indicate their level of understanding of each set of concepts. In addition, you may offer the option of revisiting key hands-on activities.

   After the students have perused their extant work and modified it to meet their current understandings, they may find some holes in their portfolio selections. They may choose to create new portfolio entries that demonstrate their understanding of a particular concept. We recommend that not more than one-third of the entries be new, but do not dampen students' enthusiasm to answer additional questions if they are so inclined.

5. Prepare a caption for each example in the portfolio. Each caption should include the information explained in the portfolio rubric.

   Include a caption for all work in the portfolio, both existing work and new work.

   If your students are new to writing captions, this step provides guidance. Encourage the students to focus their captions on two things: how the entry represents the chapter concepts and why they chose the entry as their best representation of a particular concept. You may need to model this process for your students if they are new to the activity of building a portfolio.

Analysis

1. When you think your portfolio is complete, take time to look through it. Decide if you would get the job as a scientifically literate citizen. Be sure that you have organized your portfolio so that any reader can easily find and understand your work examples.

2. Have your portfolio reviewed as your teacher directs.

   Encourage students to be constructive in their feedback about the portfolios they review. A parental/guardian review adds both another opportunity for students to get feedback and it informs parents or guardians about their child's progress through the program.

3. Revise your portfolio based on your self-evaluation and feedback that you receive.

   As a part of the revision process, students should create a table of contents that indicates what is in the portfolio they have completed.

References

Unit One
Engage

Andrews, W. A. (Ed.). (1972). *A guide to the study of freshwater ecology.* Englewood Cliffs, NJ: Prentice Hall.

Chen, J., Henderson, G., & Laine, R. A. (1998). Isolation of 2-phenoxyethanol from a ballpoint pen ink as a trail-following substance of *Coptotermes formosanus Shiraki* and *Reticulitermes* sp. *Journal of Entomological Science, 33,* 97–105.

Dempsey, B. C., & Betz, B. J. (2001, April). Biological drawing: A scientific tool for learning. *The American Biology Teacher, 63,* 271–279.

Pearson, H. (2001, September 12). *Doctors examine art: Art appreciation class improves student doctors' diagnosis.* Retrieved September 17, 2001, from http://www.nature.com/nsu/010913/010913-11.html

Chapter 1

Aitken, M. J., Mellars, P. A., & Stringer, C. B. (1993). *The origin of modern humans and the impact of chronometric dating.* Princeton, NJ: Princeton University Press.

American Medical Association (AMA) Division of Drugs. (1983). *AMA drug evaluation* (5th ed.). Chicago, IL: American Medical Association.

Bloom, F. E., Lazerson, A., & Hofstadter, L. (1985). *Brain, mind, and behavior.* New York: W. H. Freeman.

Bonner, J. T. (1980). *The evolution of culture in animals.* Princeton, NJ: Princeton University Press.

Bouchard, C. B. (1988). *Life and society in the west: Antiquity and the middle ages.* New York: Harcourt, Brace, & Jovanovich Publishers.

Brookhart, S., & Hanna, K. (n.d.). *Exploring the brain.* Washington, DC: National Foundation for Brain Research.

Brown, A. (1968). *Invitation to sailing.* New York: Simon & Schuster.

Corballis, M. C. (1991). *The lopsided ape.* New York: Oxford University Press.

Corina, D. P., Vaid, J., & Bellugi, U. (1992, March). The linguistic basis of left hemisphere specialization. *Science, 255,* 1258–1260.

Damasio, A. R., & Damasio, H. (1992, September). Brain and language. *Scientific American, 267,* 88–95.

Eccles, J. (1989). *Evolution of the brain: Creation of the self.* London, England: Routledge.

Fischbach, G. D. (1992, September). Mind and brain. *Scientific American, 267,* 48–57.

Goodall, J. (1986). *The chimpanzees of Gombe: Patterns of behavior.* Cambridge, MA: Harvard University Press.

Goodall, J. (1988). *In the shadow of man.* Boston, MA: Houghton Mifflin.

Goodall, J. (1990). *Through a window: My thirty years with the chimpanzees of Gombe.* Boston, MA: Houghton Mifflin.

Gould, J. L., & Gould, C. G. (1994). *The animal mind.* New York: W. H. Freeman.

Hickman, C. P., Roberts, L. S., & Hickman, F. (1984). *Integrated principles of zoology* (7th ed.). St. Louis, MO: Times Mirror/Mosby College Publishing.

Jolly, A. (1972). *The evolution of primate behavior.* New York: Macmillan Publishing.

Klivington, K. (1989). *The science of mind.* Cambridge, MA: The MIT Press.

Linden, E. (1993, March 22). Can animals think? *Time, 141*(12), 54–61.

McCrone, J. (1991). *The ape that spoke: Language and the evolution of the human mind.* New York: Avon Books.

McKim, R. H. (1980). *Thinking visually: A strategy manual for problem solving.* Palo Alto, CA: Dale Seymour Publications.

Montgomery, S. (1991). *Walking with the great apes: Jane Goodall, Dian Fossy, and Birute Galdikas.* Boston, MA: Houghton Mifflin.

Napier, J. (1970). *The roots of mankind.* New York: Harper and Row.

Posner, M. I. & Raichle, M. E. (1994). *Images of Mind.* New York: Scientific American Library, a division of HPHLP.

Rumbaugh, D. M. (1977). *Language learned by chimpanzees: The Lana project.* New York: Academic Press.

Sagan, C. (1977). *The dragons of Eden.* New York: Random House.

Sebook, T. A. (1980). *Speaking of apes: A critical anthology of two-way communication with man.* New York: Plenum Press.

Solomon, E. P., Schmidt, R. R., & Adragna, P. J. (1990). *Human anatomy and physiology* (2nd ed.). Philadelphia, PA: Saunders College Publishing.

Spector, W. S. (Ed.). (1961). *Handbook of biological data.* Philadelphia, PA: Saunders College Publishing.

Stebbins, G. L. (1992). *Darwin to DNA, molecules to humanity.* San Francisco, CA: W. H. Freeman.

Strachan, T. (1992). *The human genome.* Oxford, England: BIOS Scientific Publishers.

Strange, P. G. (1992). *Brain biochemistry and brain disorders.* New York: Oxford University Press.

Tullar, R. M. (1977). *The human species: Its nature, evolution, and ecology.* New York: McGraw-Hill.

U.S. Department of Health and Human Services. Alcohol, Drug Abuse, and Mental Health Administration. (1989). *Approaching the 21st Century: Opportunities for NIMH neuroscience research* (DHHS Publication No. ADM 89-1580) (Library of Congress Catalog No. 88-601969). Washington, DC: U.S. Government Printing Office.

Zeki, S. (1992, September). The visual image in mind and brain. *Scientific American, 267,* 68–76.

Chapter 2

Bar-Yosef, O., & Vandermeersch, B. (1993, April). Modern humans in the levant. *Scientific American, 268,* 94–100.

Basetti, R. (1998, November 30). More on Haeckel's dictum [Letter to the publisher/editor]. Retrieved September 4, 2001, from http://naturalscience.com/ns/letters/ns_let17.html

BBC-Television & Time-Life Television. (1980). *The voyage of Charles Darwin* (7-part series).

Beck, W. S., Liem, K. F., & Simpson, G. G. (1991). *Life: An introduction to biology* (3rd ed.). New York: HarperCollins.

Britten, R. J., Jr. (1986, March). Rates of DNA sequence evolution differ between taxonomic groups. *Science, 230,* 1393–1398.

BSCS. (1992). *Evolution: Inquiries into biology and earth science.* Seattle, WA: Videodiscovery.

Campbell, B. G. (1992). *Humankind emerging* (6th ed.). New York: HarperCollins.

Campbell, N. A. (1990, November). *Biology* (2nd ed.). Redwood City, CA: The Benjamin/Cummings Publishing Company.

Cavalli-Sforza, L. L. (1991, November). Genes, peoples and languages. *Scientific American, 265*, 104–110.

Cohen, Chiscon, & Hoyer (1972). Evolution of primate DNA sequence. *Journal of Human Evolution, 1,* 627–644.

Creager, J. G., Black, J. G., & Davison, V. E. (1990). *Microbiology: Principles and applications.* Englewood Cliffs, NJ: Prentice Hall.

Dalziel, I. W. D. (1995, January). Earth before Pangea. *Scientific American, 272*, 58–63.

Darwin, C. (1975). *On the origin of species: A facsimile of the first edition.* Cambridge, MA: Harvard University Press. (Original work published 1859.)

Dodson, E. O., & Dodson, P. (1976). *Evolution: Process and product.* New York: D. Van Nostrand.

Dubos, R. (1968). *So human an animal.* New York: Charles Scribner & Sons.

Edey, M. A., & Johanson, D. C. (1989). *Blueprints. Solving the mystery of evolution.* New York: Penguin Books.

Ewald, P. W. (1994). *Evolution of infectious disease.* New York: Oxford University Press.

Felsenstein, J. (1988). Phylogenies from molecular sequences: Inference and reliability. *Annual Review of Genetics, 22,* 521–565.

Fritz, S. (1993, February). Who was the Iceman? *Popular Science, 242,* 46–50.

Gould, S. J. (1982). *The panda's thumb.* New York: W. W. Norton.

Grant, P. R. (1991, October). Natural selection and Darwin's finches. *Scientific American, 265,* 82–87.

Haeckel and the vertebrate archetype. (1997, October 3). Retrieved September 4, 2001, from http://zygote.swarthmore.edu/evo5.html

Haldane, J. B. S. (1990). *The causes of evolution.* Princeton, NJ: Princeton University Press.

Harrison, G. A., Tanner, J. M., Pilbeam, D. R., & Baker, P. T. (1988). *Human biology: An introduction to human evolution, variation, growth, and adaptability* (3rd ed.). New York: Oxford University Press.

Jaroff, L., & Rademaekers, W. (1992, October 26). The Iceman's secrets. *Time, 140,* 62–69.

Jeffreys, A. J. (1982). Evolution of globin genes. In G. A. Dover & R. B. Flavell (Eds.), *Genome evolution* (pp. 157–176). Orlando, FL: Academic Press.

Johanson, D. C., & Edey, M. A. (1981). *Lucy: The beginnings of humankind.* New York: Simon & Schuster.

Johanson, D. C., Johanson, L. C., & Edgar, B. (1994). *Ancestors: In search of human origins.* New York: Villard Books.

Lewin, R. (1993). *The origin of modern humans.* New York: W. H. Freeman.

Lewin, R. (1988). Conflict over DNA clock results. *Science, 241,* 1598-1600, 1756-1759.

Loomis, W. F. (1988). *Four billion years: An essay on the evolution of genes and organisms.* Sunderland, MA: Sinauer Associates.

Mayr, E. (1991). *One long argument: Charles Darwin and the genesis of modern evolutionary thought.* Cambridge, MA: Harvard University Press.

Mayr, E. (1988). *Toward a new philosophy of biology: Observations of an evolutionist.* Cambridge, MA: Harvard University Press.

McKinney, L. (1972). *Wallace and natural selection.* New Haven, CT: Yale University Press.

Mystery over: Arrow killed Iceman. (2001, July 26). *The Gazette,* p. A14.

Napier, J. (1970). *The roots of mankind: The story of man and his ancestors* (Rev. ed.). New York: Smithsonian Institute Press.

Nickels, M. K. (1987). Human evolution: A challenge for biology teachers. *The American Biology Teacher, 49*(3), 143–148.

Press, F., & Siever, R. (1986). *Earth* (4th ed.). New York: W. H. Freeman.

Roberts, D., & Garrett, K. (1993, June). The Iceman: Lone voyager from the Copper Age. *National Geographic, 183,* 36–67.

Scharmann, L. C. (1990). Enhancing an understanding of the premises of evolutionary theory: The influence of a diversified instructional strategy. *School Science and Mathematics, 90*(2), 91–100.

Sherris, J. (Ed.). (1990). *Medical microbiology.* Publisher unknown.

Spindler, K. (1994). *The man in the ice.* New York: Harmony Books.

Stanley, S. M. (1985). Rates of evolution. *Paleobiology, 11,* 13–26.

Stanley, S. M. (1986). *Earth and life through time.* New York: W. H. Freeman.

Stringer, C. B. (1990, December). The emergence of modern humans. *Scientific American, 263,* 98–104.

Tattersall, I. (2000, January). Once we were not alone. *Scientific American, 282,* 56-62.

Chapter 3

Abbott, I. A, & Dawson, E. Y. (1978). *How to know the seaweeds* (2nd ed.). Dubuque, IA: William C. Brown.

American Association for the Advancement of Science. (1989). *Science for all Americans: A project 2061 report on literacy goals in science, mathematics, and technology.* Washington, DC: Author.

Arrod, R., Bramwell, M., Parker, S., Stidworthy, J., O'Toole, C., & Bailey, J. (1991). *Children's encyclopedia of the animal kingdom.* New York: Dorset Press.

Barnes, R. D., Dorit, R. L., & Walker, W. F., Jr. (1991). *Zoology.* Philadelphia, PA: Saunders College Publishing.

Barnhart, P. S. (1936). *Marine fishes of Southern California.* Berkeley, CA: University of California Press.

Beck, W. S., Liem, K. F., & Simpson, G. G. (1991). *Life: An introduction to biology.* (3rd ed.). New York: HarperCollins.

Berry, R. J., & Hallam, A. (Eds.). (1987). *The encyclopedia of animal evolution.* New York: Facts On File Publications.

Bliss, D. E. (1990). *Shrimps, lobsters and crabs.* New York: Columbia University Press.

Brower, K. (1991). *Realms of the sea* (1st ed.). Washington, DC: National Geographic Society.

BSCS. (1993). *Developing biological literacy.* Colorado Springs, CO: Author.

BSCS. (2001). *BSCS Biology: A molecular approach* (8th ed.) [teacher's edition]. Chicago, IL: Everyday Learning.

BSCS. (2002). *BSCS Biology: An ecological approach* (9th ed.) [teacher's edition]. Dubuque, IA: Kendall/Hunt.

Burn, D. M. (Ed.). (1980). *The complete encyclopedia of the animal world.* London, England: Octopus Books, Ltd.

Calvin, J., & Ricketts, E. F. (1968). *Between pacific tides* (4th ed.). Stanford, CA: Stanford University Press.

Chandler, D. L. (1979). *Life on Mars.* New York: E. P. Dutton.

Cooper, H. S. F., Jr. (1980). *The search for life on Mars: Evolution of an idea.* New York: Holt, Rinehart, and Winston.

Creager, J. G., Black, J. G., & Davison, V. E. (1990). *Microbiology: Principles and applications.* Englewood Cliffs, NJ: Prentice Hall.

DeWit, H. C. D. (1966). *Plants of the world: Higher plants* (Vol. 1). New York: E. P. Dutton.

Dolhinow, P. (Ed.). (1972). *Primate patterns.* University of California at Berkeley: Holt, Rinehart, and Winston.

Futuyma, D. J. (1986). *Evolutionary biology.* Sunderland, MA: Sinauer Associates.

Gibbons, B. (1984). *A guide to plant biology: How flowers work.* Dorset, England: Blandford Press.

Gleick, J. (1987). *Chaos: Making a new science.* New York: Penguin Books.

Gould, S. J. (1977). *Ever since Darwin: Reflections in natural history.* New York: W. W. Norton.

Headstrom, R. (1985). *Lobsters, crabs, shrimps, and their relatives.* New York: Dover Publications.

Heywood, V. H. (Ed.). (1978). *Flowering plants of the world.* New York: Mayflower Books.

Hickman, C. P., Jr., Roberts, L. S., & Hickman, F. M. (1984). *Integrated principles of zoology* (7th ed.). St. Louis, MO: Times Mirror/Mosby College Publishing.

Interdisciplinary workshop on the Synthesis and Simulation of Living Systems. (1987). *Artificial life: The proceedings of an interdisciplinary workshop on the synthesis and simulation of living systems* (held September 1987 in Los Alamos, NM). Redwood City, CA: Addison-Wesley Publishing.

Jolly, A. (1972). *The evolution of primate behavior.* New York: Macmillan Publishing.

Kauffman, S. A. (1993). *The origins of order: Self-organization and selection in evolution.* New York: Oxford University Press.

Kutter, G. S. (1987). *The universe and life: Origins and evolution.* Boston, MA: Jones and Bartlett.

Mabberley, D. J. (1987). *The plant book: A portable dictionary of the higher plants.* Cambridge, England: Cambridge University Press.

Macdonald, D. (Ed.) (1984). *The encyclopedia of mammals.* New York: Facts On File Publications.

Margulis, L. (1981). *Symbiosis in cell evolution.* San Francisco, CA: W. H. Freeman.

Margulis, L., & Sagan, D. (1988). *A practical guide to the subvisible world: Garden of microbial delights.* New York: Harcourt, Brace, & Jovanovich Publishers.

Margulis, L., & Schwartz, K. V. (1988). *Five kingdoms: An illustrated guide to the phyla of life on earth* (2nd ed.). New York: W. H. Freeman.

Mauseth, J. D. (1991). *Botany: An introduction to plant biology.* Philadelphia, PA: Saunders College Publishing.

McMahon, T. A., & Bonner, J. T. (1983). *On size and lift.* New York: W. H. Freeman.

Moore, J. (1984). Science as a way of knowing I: Evolutionary biology. *The American Zoologist, 24,* 467–534.

Moore, J. (1989, December). Science as a way of knowing VII: A conceptual framework for biology (Part III), *The American Zoologist,* (Part II).

Morton, J. E. (1967). *Molluscs.* London, England: Hutchinson University Library.

Moss, S. A. (1984). *An introduction for the amateur naturalist: Sharks.* Englewood Cliffs, NJ: Prentice Hall.

Nadeau, R. L. (1991). *Mind, machines and human consciousness.* Chicago, IL: Contemporary Books.

National Geographic. (1981). *Book of mammals* (Vol. 2) [Special Publication]. Washington DC: National Geographic Society.

Nowak, K. M. (1991). *Walker's mammals of the world.* Baltimore, MD: The Johns Hopkins University Press.

Palmer, E. L. (1949). *Fieldbook of natural history.* New York: McGraw-Hill.

Perrier, E. (1879). The beginnings of life. *Scientific American.* (Suppl. 188).

Peterson, R. T. (1947). *A field guide to the birds* (2nd ed.). Boston, MA: Houghton Mifflin.

Raven, P. H., Evert, R. F., & Curtis, H. (Eds.). (1981). *Biology of plants* (3rd ed.). New York: Worth.

Ristori, A. (1992). *The salt water fish identifier.* London, England: Quintet Publishing Limited and New York: Mallard Press.

Robbins, C. S., Bruun, B., & Zim, H. S. (1983). *A guide to field identification: Birds of North America.* Racine, WI: Western Publishing.

Ruthen, R. (1993, January). Adapting to complexity. *Scientific American, 268,* 130–140.

Steel, R. (1985). *Sharks of the world.* New York: Facts On File Publications.

Udvardy, M. D. F. (1977). *The Audubon Society field guide to North American birds, western region.* New York: Alfred A. Knopf.

Walker, E. P. (1964). *Mammals of the world.* Baltimore, MD: The Johns Hopkins University Press.

Ward, P. D. (1992). *Living fossils and the great extinctions: On Methuselah's trail.* New York: W. H. Freeman.

Wilson, E. O. (1984). *Biophila.* Cambridge, MA: Harvard University Press.

Wilson, E. O. (1992). *The diversity of life.* Cambridge, MA: Belknap Press.

Wilson, E. O., & Peter, F. M. (Eds.). (1988). *Biodiversity.* Washington, DC: National Academy Press.

Unit Two

Chapters 4 and 5

Beck, W. S., Liem, K. F., & Simpson, G. G. (1991). *Life: An introduction to biology* (3rd ed.). New York: HarperCollins.

Berger, R. A. (1982). *Applied exercise physiology.* Philadelphia, PA: Lea and Febiger.

Creager, J. G., Black, J. G., & Davison, V. E. (1990). *Microbiology: Principles and applications.* Englewood Cliffs, NJ: Prentice Hall.

Darnell, J., Lodish, H., & Baltimore, D. (1990). *Molecular cell biology* (2nd ed.). Scientific American Library. New York: W. H. Freeman.

Guyton, A. C. (1991). *Textbook of medical physiology* (8th ed.). Philadelphia, PA: W. B. Saunders.

Hess, F. C. (1984). *Chemistry made simple.* (revised by Thomas, Arthur L.) New York: Doubleday.

Hickman, C. P., Jr., & Roberts, L. S. (1994). *Biology of animals* (6th ed.). Dubuque, IA: William C. Brown.

Hickman, C. P., Jr., Roberts, L. S., & Hickman, F. M. (1982). *Biology of animals* (3rd ed.). St. Louis, MO: C. V. Mosley Company.

Hoar, W. S. (1983). *General and comparative physiology* (3rd ed.). Englewood Cliffs, NJ: Prentice-Hall.

Hole, J. W., Jr. (1993). *Human anatomy and physiology* (6th ed.). Dubuque, IA: William C. Brown.

Kreighbaum, E., & Barthels, K. M. (1985). *Biomechanics: A qualitative approach for studying human movement* (2nd ed.). New York: Macmillan Publishing.

Martini, F. (1992). *Fundamentals of anatomy and physiology* (2nd ed.). Englewood Cliffs, NJ: Prentice Hall.

McMahon, T. A., & Bonner, J. T. (1983). *On size and life.* Scientific American Library. New York: Scientific American Books.

Moroff, S. V., & Bass, D. E. (1965). Effects of overhydration on man's physiological response to work in heat. *Journal of Applied Physiology, 20,* 267.

Noakes, T. D. (1991). *Lore of running* (3rd ed.). Champaign, IL: Leisure Press.

Raven, P. H., Evert, R. F., & Eichhorn, S. E. (1991). *Biology of plants* (5th ed.). New York: Worth Publishers.

Raven, P. H., & Johnson, G. B. (1991). *Understanding biology* (2nd ed.). St. Louis, MO: Mosby-Year Book Publishing.

Rhoades, R., & Pflanzer, R. (1992). *Human physiology* (2nd ed.). Philadelphia, PA: Saunders College Publishing.

Seeley, R., Stephens, T., & Tate, P. (1992). *Anatomy and physiology* (2nd ed.). St. Louis, MO: Mosby-Year Book Publishing.

Sherwood, L. (1991). *Fundamentals of physiology.* St. Paul, MN: West Publishing.

Solomon, E. P., Schmidt, R. R., & Adragna, P. J. (1990). *Human anatomy and physiology* (2nd ed.). Philadelphia, PA: Saunders College Publishing.

Starr, C., & Taggart, R. (1992). *Biology: The unity and diversity of life* (6th ed.). Belmont, CA: Wadsworth Publishing.

Stryer, L. (1981). *Biochemistry* (2nd ed.). San Francisco, CA: W. H. Freeman.

Tolkien, J. R. R. (1966). *The hobbit.* Boston, MA: Houghton Mifflin.

Vander, A. J., Sherman, J. H., & Luciano, D. S. (1985). *Human physiology: The mechanisms of body junction* (4th ed.). New York: McGraw-Hill.

Vander, A. J., Sherman, J. H., & Luciano, D. S. (1994). *Human physiology* (6th ed.). New York: McGraw-Hill.

Whitney, E., & Rolfes, S. R. (1993). *Understanding nutrition* (6th ed.). Minneapolis, MN: West Publishing.

Zubray, G. (1983). *Biochemistry.* Reading, MA: Addison-Wesley.

Chapter 6

About cardiovascular disease. (n.d.). Retrieved July 2, 2002, from the Centers for Disease Control and Prevention, National Center for Chronic Disease Prevention and Health Promotion Web site: http://www.cdc.gov/cvh/aboutcardio.htm

Accidental deaths lowest in 70 years. (1993, August). *USA Today, 122* (2579), 4.

Alcohol. (1990, January). Apparent per capita ethanol consumption—United States, 1975–1986. *Journal of American Medical Association, 263*(3), 354.

American Cancer Society. (2002). *Cancer facts & figures 2002* (02-250M-No. 5008.02). Atlanta, GA: Author.

American Heart Association. (n.d.). *Women, heart disease and stroke.* Retrieved July 2, 2002, from http://www.americanheart.org/presenter.jhtml?identifier=4786

America's children: Key national indicator of well-being, 2001. (2001). Retrieved July 2, 2002, from http://www.childstats.gov/ac2001/toc.asp

Anatomy of a hospital bill. (1993, November). *Consumer Reports, 58*(11), 736–737.

Atherosclerosis: Battling the bad fat. (1992, January). *Harvard Health Letter, 17*(3), 6–8.

The Boston Women's Health Book Collective. (1984). *The new our bodies, ourselves.* New York: Simon & Schuster.

Browner, W. S., Westenhouse, J., & Tice, J. A. (1991, June 26). What if Americans ate less fat? A quantitative estimate of the effect on mortality. *Journal of American Medical Association, 265*(24), 3285–3292.

BSCS & The American Medical Association. (1992). *Mapping and sequencing the human genome: Science, ethics, and public policy.* Colorado Springs, CO and Chicago, IL: Authors.

Centers for Disease Control and Prevention. (1993, January). Selected behaviors that increase risk for HIV infection, other sexually transmitted diseases and unintended pregnancy among high school students—United States, 1991. *Journal of American Medical Association, 269*(3), 329–330.

Centers for Disease Control and Prevention. (1997, March). *U.S. childhood immunization update: Measles.* Retrieved November 30, 2001, from the National Foundation for Infectious Diseases Web site: http://www.nfid.org/factsheets/measlesupdate.html

Centers for Disease Control and Prevention, National Center for Chronic Disease Prevention and Health Promotion. (n.d.). *Prostate cancer control initiatives.* Retrieved July 2, 2002, from http://www.cdc.gov/cancer/prostate/index.htm

Centers for Disease Control and Prevention, National Center for Health Statistics. (n.d.). *Accidents / unintentional injuries.* Retrieved July 3, 2002, from http://www.cdc.gov/nchs/fastats/acc-inj.htm

Centers for Disease Control and Prevention, National Center for Health Statistics. (n.d.). *Alcohol use.* Retrieved July 11, 2002, from http://www.cdc.gov/nchs/fastats/ alcohol.htm

Centers for Disease Control and Prevention, National Center for Health Statistics. (n.d.). *Suicide.* Retrieved July 3, 2002, from http://www.cdc.gov/nchs/fastats/suicide.htm

Centers for Disease Control and Prevention, National Center for HIV, STD, and TB Prevention. (2002, February 28). *Basic Statistics* [summary from *HIV/AIDS Surveillance Report, 13*(1)]. Retrieved July 2, 2002, from http://www.cdc.gov/hiv/ stats.htm

Centers for Disease Control and Prevention, National Center for Injury Prevention and Control. (2000, April 7). *Motor vehicle–related crashes among teenagers.* Retrieved July 3, 2002, from http://www.cdc.gov/ncipc/factsheets/teenmvh.htm

Centers for Disease Control and Prevention, National Immunization Program. (2001, August). *What would happen if we stopped vaccinations?* Retrieved November 30, 2001, from http://www.cdc.gov/nip/publications/fs/gen/whatifstop.htm

Clayre, A. (1984). *The heart of the dragon.* Boston, MA: Houghton Mifflin.

Colorado: Cigarette smoking rate by gender, 1998. (1999, December). Retrieved November 29, 2001, from http://www.statehealthfacts.kff.org/cgi -bin/healthfacts.cgi?action=profile&area=Colorado&category=Health+Status& subcategory=Smoking&topic=Rate+by+Gender

Colorado: Distribution of personal health care spending by service, 1998. (n.d.). Retrieved November 29, 2001, from http://www.statehealthfacts.kff.org/cgi-bin/healthfacts.cgi ?action=profile&area=Colorado&category=Health+Costs+%26+Budgets& subcategory=Personal+Health+Care+Expenditures&topic=Spending+by+Service

Colorado: Hospital adjusted expenses per inpatient day, 1999. (1999). Retrieved November 29, 2001, from http://www.statehealthfacts.kff.org/cgi-bin/healthfacts.cgi?action=profile&area=Colorado&category=Health+Costs+%26+Budgets&subcategory=Hospital+Expenses&topic=Adjusted+Expenses+per+Inpatient+Day

Colorado: New AIDS cases, reported July 1999–June 2000. (2001). Retrieved November 29, 2001, from http://www.statehealthfacts.kff.org/cgi-bin/healthfacts.cgi?action=profile&area=Colorado&category=HIV%2fAIDS&subcategory=New+AIDS+Cases&topic=All+Ages

Colorado: Number of heart disease deaths per 100,000 population by gender, 1998. (1998). Retrieved November 29, 2001, from http://www.statehealthfacts.kff.org/cgi-bin/healthfacts.cgi?action=profile&area=Colorado&category=Health+Status&subcategory= Heart+Disease&topic=Death+Rate+per+100%2c000+by+Gender

Colorado: Number of stroke deaths per 100,000 population by gender, 1998. (1998). Retrieved November 29, 2001, from http://www.statehealthfacts.kff.org/cgi-bin/healthfacts.cgi?action=profile&area=Colorado&category=Health+Status&subcategory=Stroke&topic= Death+Rate+per+100%2c000+by+Gender

Colorado: Overweight and obesity rate, 1998. (1999, December). Retrieved November 29, 2001, from http://www.statehealthfacts.kff.org/cgi-bin/healthfacts.cgi?action=profile&area=Colorado&category=Health+Status&subcategory=Obesity&topic=Overweight+and+Obesity+Rate

Commentary—Perspectives on cost containment. (1993, February). No pain, no gain. *Journal of American Medical Association, 269*(5), 631.

Cosgriff, J. H. (1984). *The practice of emergency care: Emergency procedures and management.* Philadelphia, PA: Lippincott.

Council on Scientific Affairs. (1993, March). Health services for adolescents. *Journal of American Medical Association, 269*(11), 1420–1423.

County Alcohol and Drug Treatment: Thomas, C., Center of Disease Control: Schwartz, P., Women, Infants, and Children Program: Murphy, J. *Department of Health and Environment, El Paso County, Colorado Springs, Colorado* and Cost Information Coordinator: Stimpson-Smith, L. *Penrose-St. Francis Healthcare System, Colorado Springs, Colorado.*

Creager, J., Black, J., & Davison, V. (1990). *Microbiology: Principles and applications.* Englewood Cliffs, NJ: Prentice Hall.

Deaf or hard of hearing population statistics. (n.d.). Retrieved July 1, 2002, from the League for the Hard of Hearing Web site: http://www.lhh.org/research/stats.htm

DiClemente, R. J. (Ed.). (1992, March). *Adolescents and AIDS: A generation in jeopardy.* Newbury Park, CA: Sage Publications.

Do we know what causes lung cancer? (2001). Retrieved July 1, 2002, from the American Cancer Society Web site: http://www.cancer.org/eprise/main/docroot/CRI/content/CRI_2_4_2X_Do_we_know_what_causes_lung_cancer_26?sitearea=&level=

Farley, D. (1992, April). Eating disorders. *FDA Consumer, 26*(2), 27–29.

Faulke, J. (1992). Good news about good nutrition. *FDA Consumer, 26*(3), 37–39.

Grant, H. D., Murray, R. H., Jr., & Bergeron, J. D. (1982). *Emergency care* (3rd ed.). Bowie, MD: Robert J. Brady.

Greeley, A. (1991, May). No safe tan. *FDA Consumer, 2–5*(4), 17–21.

Guidelines for the use of antiretroviral agents in HIV-infected adults and adolescents: Goals of therapy. (2001, August 13). Retrieved November 29, 2001, from [updated url] http://www.hivatis.org/guidelines/adult/May23_02/AAMay23.pdf

Guyton, A. C. (1991). *Textbook of medical physiology* (8th ed.). Philadelphia, PA: W. B. Saunders.

Hahn, R. A., Teutsch, S. M., Rothenberg, R. B., & Marks, J. S. (1990). Excess deaths from nine chronic diseases in the United States. *Journal of American Medical Association, 264*(20), 2654–2660.

Hamilton, E. (1942). *Mythology.* New York: Mentor Books-The New American Library.

Healthcare Cost and Utilization Project, Agency for Healthcare Research and Quality. (2001, September). *1997 National statistics: Results-principal procedures: Outcomes for multiple specific procedures.* Retrieved November 29, 2001, from http://hcup.ahrq.gov/hcupnet.asp

Hellinger, F. J. (1992, Fall). Forecasts of the costs of medical care for persons with HIV: 1992–1995. *Inquiry, 29,* 356–65.

Hellinger, F. J. (1993, July). The lifetime cost of treating a person with HIV. *Journal of American Medical Association, 270*(4), 474–478.

Help for infants and pregnant women. (1993, April). [Special Newsletter Edition]. *USA Today, 121*(2575), 6.

The Henry J. Kaiser Family Foundation. (2000, August). *Teen sexual activity* [Fact Sheet package code 3040]. Menlo Park, CA: Author.

Hepatitis C. (2000, April). Retrieved November 29, 2001, from the American Academy of Family Physicians Web site: http://familydoctor.org/handouts/071.html

Holinger, P. C., Offer, D., Barter, J. T., & Bell, C. C. (1994). *Suicide and homicide among adolescents.* New York: The Guilford Press.

James, D. K., & Stirrat, G. M. (Eds.). (1988). *Pregnancy and risk: The basis for rational management.* New York: John Wiley & Sons.

Johnston, L. D., O'Malley, P. M., & Bachman, J. G. (1989). *Drug use, drinking, and smoking: National survey results from high school, college and young adult populations, 1975–1988.* DHHS Publishing No. (ADM)89–1638. Rockville. MD: ADAMHA.

Key facts about measles. (1996, August). Retrieved November 30, 2001, from the National Foundation for Infectious Diseases Web site: http://www.nfid.org/factsheets/measles.html

Larson, D. E. (Ed.). (1990). Smoking risks. *Mayo Clinic Family Health Book.* New York: William Morrow.

Lemberg, R. (Ed.). (1992). *Controlling eating disorders with facts, advice, and resources.* Phoenix, AZ: The Onyx Press.

Lewis, T. (1983). *The youngest science: Notes of a medicine watched.* New York: Viking Press.

Marwick, C. (1993, June). Increasing use of chewing tobacco especially among younger persons alarms surgeon general. *Journal of American Medical Association, 269*(2), 195.

Maryland Department of Health & Mental Hygiene, Epidemiology & Disease Control Program. (n.d.). *Measles fact sheet.* Retrieved November 30, 2001, from http://edcp.org/html/measlesfact.html

Maryland Department of Health & Mental Hygiene, Epidemiology & Disease Control Program. (n.d.). *Mumps fact sheet.* Retrieved November 30, 2001, from http://edcp.org/html/mumps.html

Maryland Department of Health & Mental Hygiene, Epidemiology & Disease Control Program. (n.d.). *Tuberculosis fact sheet*. Retrieved November 30, 2001, from http://edcp.org/html/tubercul.html

Maryland Department of Health & Mental Hygiene, Epidemiology & Disease Control Program. (1996, May). *Hepatitis B fact sheet*. Retrieved November 30, 2001, from http://edcp.org/html/hep_b.html

Medicaid coverage for anti-AIDS drugs would be cost effective. (2001, August 31). Retrieved November 29, 2001, from the Harvard School of Public Health Web site: http://www.hsph.harvard.edu/press/releases/press8312001.html

Miller, L. S., Zhang, X., Rice, D. P., & Max, W. (1998). *State estimates of total medical expenditures attributable to cigarette smoking, 1993.* Retrieved November 30, 2001, from http://socialwelfare.berkeley.edu/faculty/lmiller_report.html

Minino, A. M., & Smith, B. L. (2001). Deaths: Preliminary data for 2000. *National Vital Statistics Report, 49*(12). Hyattsville, MD: National Center for Health Statistics.

Moyers, B. (1993). *Healing and the mind.* New York: Doubleday Publishing.

The National Clearinghouse for Alcohol and Drug Information. (1995, Spring). *Health care costs, the deficit, & alcohol, tobacco, and other drugs* [Fact Sheet] (NCADI Inventory Number ML007). Rockville, MD: Author.

National Coalition for Adult Immunization. (1997, March). *Hepatitis B: What every teen should know.* Retrieved November 30, 2001, from the National Foundation for Infectious Diseases Web site: http://www.nfid.org/factsheets/hbagadol.html

National Coalition for Adult Immunization. (2001, August). *Facts about mumps for adults.* Retrieved November 30, 2001, from the National Foundation for Infectious Diseases Web site: http://www.nfid.org/factsheets/mumpsadult.html

National Committee for Quality Assurance. (2001). *Childhood immunization status* (The State of Managed Care Quality Report). Retrieved November 30, 2001, from http://www.ncqa.org/somc2001/child_imm/somc_2001_cis.html

National Highway Traffic Safety Administration. (2000). *Traffic safety facts 2000: Occupant protection* (DOT HS 809 327). Washington, DC: National Center for Statistics & Analysis.

National Institute on Alcohol Abuse and Alcoholism (NIAAA). (2001, February). *Areas of the brain that can be damaged in utero by maternal alcohol consumption.* Retrieved November 29, 2001, from http://www.niaaa.nih.gov/gallery/fetal/mattson.htm

National Institutes of Health. (2002, January 22). *What you need to know about cancer of the cervix* (NIH Publication No. 95-2047). Retrieved July 1, 2002, from the National Cancer Institute Web site: http://www.cancer.gov/cancer_information/doc_wyntk.aspx?viewid=1529727f-0309-4f59-aa5f-a17a761f10d9

National Safety Council. (2000, June 23). *Sun safety.* Retrieved July 1, 2002, from http://www.nsc.org/library/facts/sunsafet.htm

National, state, and urban area vaccination coverage levels among children aged 19–35 months—United States, July 1996–June 1997. (1998, February 20). *MMWR, 47,* 108–116.

New York State Office of Alcoholism and Substance Abuse Services. (1998, January). The costs and consequences of addiction and the benefits of prevention and treatment: *Findings and conclusions about addiction prevention and treatment in America.* Albany, NY: Author.

Nossel, I. (1996, September). Pregnancy and childbearing among younger teens. Retrieved November 30, 2001, from http://www.advocatesforyouth.org/publications/factsheet/fsyoungerteens.htm

Potosky, A. L., Miller, B. A., Albertsen, P. C., & Kramer, B. S. (1995, February). The role of increasing detection in the rising incidence of prostate cancer. *Journal of the American Medical Association, 273,* 548–552.

Rhoades, R., & Pflanzer, R. (1992). *Human physiology* (2nd ed.). Philadelphia, PA: Saunders College Publishing.

Rosen, W. G. (Ed.). (1989). *High school biology: Today and tomorrow.* National Research Council. Washington. DC: National Academic Press.

Scitovsky, A. A., Cline, N. W., & Cebrams, D. I. (1990). Effects of the use of AZT on the medical care costs of persons with AIDS in the first 12 months. *Acquired Immune Deficiency Syndromes, 3*(9), 904–912.

Scitovsky, A. A., & Over, M. (1988). AIDS: Costs of care in the developed and the developing world. *AIDS, 2* (Suppl. 1), S71–S81.

Selin, H. (1993, March). Science across cultures (Part I): African and Native American achievements. *The Science Teacher, 60*(3), 34–42.

Selin, H. (1993, April). Science across cultures (Part II): Chinese and Islamic achievements. *The Science Teacher, 60*(4), 32–36.

Skolnick, A. A., & Manack, L. (1993, November). Medical news and perspectives. *Journal of American Medical Association, 270*(20), 2418.

Smokeless tobacco. (2001, September). Retrieved July 3, 2002, from http://kidshealth.org/teen/drug_alcohol/tobacco/smokeless_p2.html

Smoking. (1993, September 22–29). Cigarette smoking: Attributable mortality and years of potential life lost—United States 1990. *Journal of American Medical Association, 270*(12), 1408–1413.

Solomon, E., Schmidt, R., & Adragna, P. (1990). *Human anatomy and physiology* (2nd ed.). Philadelphia, PA: Saunders College Publishing.

Stephens, R. C. (1991). *The street addict role: A theory of heroin addiction.* Albany, NY: State University of New York Press.

Stine, G. J. (1993). *Acquired immune deficiency syndrome: Biological, medical, social, and legal issues.* New Jersey: Prentice Hall.

Substance Abuse and Mental Health Services Administration. (n.d.). *Binge drinking in adolescents and college students.* Retrieved November 29, 2001, from http://www.health.org/govpubs/rpo995/

Substance Abuse and Mental Health Services Administration, National Household Survey on Drug Abuse (NHSDA) Report. (2001, December 14). *Alcohol use.* Retrieved July 3, 2002, from http://www.samhsa.gov/oas/2k2/alcns/alcns.htm

Tizard, I. (1992). *Immunology: An introduction* (3rd ed.). Philadelphia, PA: Saunders College Publishing.

Trends in the prevalence of alcohol use among high school seniors: Monitoring the future study, 1975–2001. (2002, February). Retrieved July 1, 2002, from the National Institute on Alcohol Abuse and Alcoholism (NIAAA) Web site: http://www.niaaa.nih.gov/databases/dkpat10.txt

Tuberculosis: A global emergency. (1999, April). Retrieved November 30, 2001, from the National Foundation for Infectious Diseases Web site: http://www.nfid.org/factsheets/tb.html

U.S. Department of Health and Human Services. (1985). *The health consequences of smoking, cancer and chronic lung disease in the workplace.* Rockville, MD: Public Health Service Office on Smoking and Health.

U.S. Department of Health and Human Services. (1990, January). *Alcohol and health.* Washington, DC: U.S. Government Printing Office.

U.S. Department of Health and Human Services. (1992, April). *Reducing the health consequences of smoking: 25 years of progress* (82-500 M-Rev. 4/92-No. 2023-LE). A Report of the Surgeon General.

U.S. Department of Health and Human Services. (1993, February). *Epidemiology, prevention, and control of vaccine preventable diseases.* Atlanta, GA: Centers for Disease Control and Prevention (CDC).

U.S. Congress, Office of Congressional Budget Study. (1992, October). *Economics of rising health care costs* (Publication No. 92-0623-P). Washington, DC: U.S. Government Printing Office.

Wayner, D. S. (2002, April 4). *Hearing loss.* Retrieved July 2, 2002, from the Deafness Research Foundation Web site: http://www.drf.org/cms/index.cfm?displayArticle=15

Ways and Means Commerce, House of Representatives. *Health care resource book* (Y4.W36:WMCP 103-4). Washington, DC: Microfilm.

Weighing the costs: Annual cost per drug addict. (1998). Retrieved November 29, 2001, from the Brown University, Center for Alcohol and Addictions Studies Web site: http://center.butler.brown.edu/plndp/Resources/pl16.gif

Weinstock, C. P. (1990, October). Children with AIDS. *FDA Consumer, 24*(8), 8–11.

What are the risk factors for lung cancer? (2001). Retrieved July 1, 2002, from the American Cancer Society Web site: http://www.cancer.org/eprise/main/docroot/CRI/content/CRI_2_4_2X_What_are_the_risk_factors_for_lung_cancer_26

Whitney, E. J., & Behr, T. S. (1982 approx. date). *Physician education manual for cardiovascular risk management program.* Laughlin AFB, TX: USAF Hospital Laughlin.

Who dares? Smoking. (1993, September). *The Economist, 328*(7830), 32–33.

Willems, J. S., & Sanders, C. R., (Eds.). (1981). *The Journal of Infectious Diseases. 144*(5), 486–493.

Williams, R. (1992, May). Enjoy, protect the best ears of your life. *FDA Consumer, 26*(4), 25–27.

Willis, J. L. (1993, June). Preventing STD's. *FDA Consumer, 27*(5), 33–35.

Vesalius, A. (1950). *Illustrations from the works of Andrea Vesalius.* New York: Dover Books.

Unit Three

Chapter 7

Alexander, R. M. (1992). *Exploring biomechanics: Animals in motion.* New York: Scientific American Library.

Alexander, R. M. (1992). *The human machine.* New York: Columbia University Press.

Bruess, C., & Richardson, G. (1992). *Decisions for health.* Dubuque, IA: William C. Brown.

Byer, C. O., & Shainberg, C. O. (1991). *Living well.* New York: HarperCollins.

Cairney, W. J., & Dixon, J. P. (Eds.). (1992). *Selected topics in aerospace and hyperbaric physiology.* Colorado Springs, CO: USAF Academy and Air Training Command.

NIH/National Institute on Drug Abuse. (2001, May 2). *Researchers find evidence that prenatal use of ecstasy can cause long-term memory loss and other impairments in offspring.* Retrieved January 11, 2002, from http://www.sciencedaily.com/releases/2001/05/010501074739.htm

Unit Four

Chapter 10

Adamo, S. A., & Hoy, R. R. (1994). Mating behaviour of the field cricket *Gryllus bimaculatus* and its dependence on social and environmental cues. *Animal Behaviour, 47,* 857–868.

Beck, W. S., Liem, K. F., & Simpson, G. G. (1991). *Life: An introduction to biology* (3rd ed.). HarperCollins.

BSCS. (2001). *BSCS Biology: A molecular approach* (8th ed.). Chicago, IL: Everyday Learning.

BSCS. (2002). *BSCS Biology: An ecological approach* (9th ed.). Dubuque, IA: Kendall/Hunt.

Cade, E. S., & Cade, W. H. (1992). Male mating success, calling and searching behaviour at high and low densities in the field cricket, *Gryllus integer. Animal Behaviour, 43,* 49–56.

Chu, H. F. (1949). *How to know the immature insects.* Dubuque, IA: William C. Brown.

Clutton-Brock, T. H. (Ed.). (1988). *Reproductive success.* Chicago, IL: University of Chicago Press.

Cohn, B. S. (1971). *India: The social anthropology of a civilization.* Englewood Cliffs, NJ: Prentice-Hall.

Creager, J. G., Black, J. G., & Davison, V. E. (1990). *Microbiology: Principles and applications.* Englewood Cliffs, NJ: Prentice-Hall.

Deloach, N. (Ed.). (1993). *Reef coral identification.* Jacksonville, FL: New World Publications.

Diamond, J. (1993). Sex and the female agenda. *Discover, 14*(9), 86–93.

Dorit, R. L., Walker, W. F., Jr., & Barnes, R. D. (1991). *Zoology.* Philadelphia, PA: Saunders College Publishing.

Dubinsky, Z. (Ed.). (1990). *Ecosystems of the world: 25 coral reefs.* New York: Elsevier Science Publishers.

Encyclopedia Britannica. (1973). Volumes 7, 9, 14, 15, 19. Chicago, IL: William Benton Publishers.

Encyclopedia Britannica. (1985). Volumes 5, 13, 14, 23, 26. Chicago, IL: Encyclopedia Britannica.

Fisher, H. E. (1992). *Anatomy of love: The natural history of monogamy, adultery, and divorce.* New York: W. W. Norton & Company.

Gould, J. L., & Gould, C. G. (1989). *Sexual selection.* New York: Scientific American Library.

Hickman, C. P., Jr., Roberts, L. S., & Hickman, F. M. (1984). *Integrated principles of zoology* (7th ed.). St. Louis, MO: Times Mirror/Mosby College Publishing.

Hole, J. W., Jr. (1993). *Human anatomy and physiology* (6th ed.). Dubuque, IA: William C. Brown.

Kluckhohn, C. & Leighton, D. (1962). *The Navaho* (Rev. ed.). Garden City, NY: Anchor Books, Doubleday & Company.

Kudo, R. R. (1966). *Protozoology* (5th ed.). Springfield, IL: Charles C. Thomas.

Levy, M. R., Dignan, M., & Shirreffs, J. (1992). Instructor's manual to accompany *Life and health: Targeting wellness.* New York: McGraw-Hill.

Locke, R. F. (1992). *The book of the Navajo* (5th ed.). Los Angeles, CA: Mankind Publishing Company.

Margulis, L., & Sagan, D. (1986). *Origins of sex: Three billion years of genetic recombination.* New Haven, CT: Yale University Press.

McClane, A. J. (1965). *McClane's new standard fishing encyclopedia and international angling guide.* New York: Holt, Rinehart and Winston.

Palmer, E. L. (1949). *Fieldbook of natural history.* New York: McGraw-Hill.

Prabhu, P. H. (1963). *Hindu social organization* (3rd ed.). Bombay, India: Popular Prakashan.

Preston, R. J., Jr. (1968). *Rocky Mountain trees* (Rev. ed.). New York: Dover Publications.

Raven, P. H., Evert, R. F., & Eichhorn, S. E. (1992). *Biology of plants* (5th ed.). New York: Worth Publishers.

Rhoades, R., & Pflanzer, R. (1992). *Human physiology* (2nd ed.). Philadelphia, PA: Saunders College Publishing.

Riddle, J. M., Estes, J. W., & Russell, J. C. (1994, March/April). Birth control in the ancient world. *Archeology, 47*(2), 29–35.

Sagan, C., & Druyan, A. (1992). *Shadows of forgotten ancestors: A search for who we are.* New York: Random House.

Scott, D. (1992). Swans Semper Fidelis. *Natural History, 7*(92), 26–33.

Shuttleworth, F. S., & Zim, H. S. (1967). *Non-flowering plants.* New York: Golden Press.

Simmons, L. W. (1988). Male size, mating potential and lifetime reproductive success in the field cricket, *Gryllus bimaculatus (De Geer). Animal Behaviour, 36,* 372–379.

Solomon, E. P., Schmidt, R. R., & Adragna, P. J. (1990). *Human anatomy & physiology* (2nd ed.). Philadelphia, PA: Saunders College Publishing.

Starr, C., & Taggert, R. (1992). *Biology: The unity and diversity of life* (6th ed.). Belmont, CA: Wadsworth Publishing Company.

The New Encyclopedia Britannica (15th ed.). (1985). Chicago: Encyclopedia Britannica.

Tyndale-Biscoe, H., & Renfree, M. (1987). *Reproductive physiology of marsupials* [Monograph]: *Monographs on Marsupial Biology.* Cambridge, MA: Cambridge University Press.

Van De Graaff, K. M., & Fox, S. I. (1989). *Concepts of human anatomy and physiology* (2nd ed.). Dubuque, IA: William C. Brown.

Vander, A. J., Sherman, J. H., & Luciano, D. S. (1994). *Human physiology* (6th ed.). New York: McGraw-Hill.

Vander, A. J., Sherman, J., & Luciano, D. (1985). *Human physiology: The mechanisms of body function* (4th ed.). New York: McGraw-Hill.

Whitney, S. (1985). *Western forests: National Audubon Society nature guides.* New York: Chanticleer Press.

Wood, E. M. (1983). *Corals of the world.* Neptune City, NJ: TFH Publications.

Wymelenberg, S. (1990). *Science and babies: Private decisions, public dilemmas.* Washington, DC: National Academy Press.

Chapter 11

Bronowski, J. (1973). *The ascent of man.* Boston, MA: Little, Brown and Company.

Gardner, E. J. (1983). *Human heredity.* New York: John Wiley & Sons.

Goldsby, R. A. (1979). *Biology* (2nd ed.). New York: Harper & Row.

Goodenough, U. (1984). *Genetics* (3rd ed.). Philadelphia, PA: Saunders College Publishing.

Hartl, D. L. (1983). *Human genetics.* New York: Harper & Row.

Ingram, J. (1989). *The science of everyday life.* Markham, Ontario, Canada: Viking Press.

Jones, R. (1994, Spring). Genetic testing for Huntington's Disease—What's new? *Marker,* 6.

Lison, M., Blondheim, S. H., & Melmed, R. N. (1980). A polymorphism of the ability to smell urinary metabolites of asparagus. *British Medical Journal, 281,* 1676–1678.

Mange, E. J., & Mange, A. P. (1994). *Basic human genetics.* Sunderland, MA: Sinauer Associates.

McGee, H. (1984). *On food and cooking: The science and lore of the kitchen.* New York: Charles Scribner & Sons.

McKusick, V. A. (1992). *Mendelian inheritance in man* (10th ed.). (Vols. 1–2). Baltimore, MD: Johns Hopkins University Press.

Moore, R. (1962). *Life nature library: Evolution.* New York: Time Incorporated.

Nora, J. J., & Fraser, F. C. (1981). *Medical genetics: Principles and practice* (2nd ed.). Philadelphia, PA: Lea & Febiger.

Spencer, E. W. (1967). *Basic concepts of historical geology* (7th ed.). Chicago, IL: Thomas C. Crowell Company.

Stanbury, J. B., Wyngaarden, J. B., & Fredrickson, D. S. (Eds.). (1960). *The metabolic basis of inherited disease* (4th ed.). New York: McGraw-Hill.

Stille, D. R. (Ed.). (1994). *The world book health and medicine annual.* Chicago, IL: World Book.

University of Colorado Health Sciences Center. (1988). *Genetic applications: A health perspective.* Lawrence, KS: Learner Managed Designs.

Weaver, R. F., & Hendrick, P. W. (1992). *Genetics* (2nd ed.). Dubuque, IA: William C. Brown.

Chapter 12

Alberts, B., Bray, D., Lewis, J., Raff, M., Roberts, K., & Watson, J.D. (1989). *Molecular biology of the cell* (2nd ed.). New York: Garland Publishing.

Bloom, M. V. (1994, October). Polymerase chain reaction. *Carolina Tips, 57,* 1,14–18.

Bush awards congressional gold medals to Navajo code talkers. (2001, July 26). Retrieved July 25, 2001, from http://www.foxnews.com/story/0,2933,30613,00.html

Darnell, J., Lodish, H., & Baltimore, D. (1990). *Molecular cell biology* (2nd ed.). New York: W. H. Freeman & Company.

Dr. Arthur Caplan: Ethics of human cloning. (2001, August 7). Retrieved August 7, 2001, from http://www.cnn.com/2001/COMMUNITY/08/07/caplan.cnna/index.html

Editorial reviews: The Romanovs: The final chapter. (n.d.). Retrieved July 25, 2001, from http://www.amazon.com/exec/obidos/ASIN/0345406400/qid=1030723560/sr=2-1/ref=sr_2_1/002-6919716-4957654

Farnsworth, J. (2000, April 7). *To clone or not to clone: The ethical question.* Retrieved August 8, 2001, from http://farnsworthfamily.tripod.com/Humancloning/cloning_m.htm

In re Fishback, J., Brief Times Reporter (15) 1689 (Colo. App. 1991), No. 90CA0936 (City and County, D.C., Denver, CO, Dec. 5, 1991).

Gibbs, R. A. (n.d.). *Polymerase chain reaction.* Retrieved August 6, 2001, from http://encarta.msn.com/index/conciseindex/AC/0AC84000.htm?z=1&pg=2&br=

Griffin, H. (1997, December 12). *Briefing notes on Dolly.* Retrieved August 8, 2001, from http://www.ri.bbsrc.ac.uk/library/research/cloning/dolly.html

In re Lindsey, G., Brief Times Reporter (17) 43 (Colo. App. 1993), No. 90CA0556 (El Paso County, D.C., CO, Jan. 7, 1993).

Lewin, B. (1987). *Genes* (3rd ed.). New York: John Wiley & Sons.

Mullis, K. B. (1990, April). The unusual origin of the polymerase chain reaction. *Scientific American, 262*, 56–65.

Rothwell, N. V. (1993). *Understanding genetics: A molecular approach.* New York: Wiley-Liss.

Russell, P. J. (1990). *Genetics* (2nd ed.). Glenview, IL: Scott, Foresman and Company.

Sattelle, D. B. (1990). *Biotechnology in perspective.* Washington, DC: Industrial Biotechnology Association (IBA).

Scientists to clone humans. (2001, March 12). Retrieved August 8, 2001, from http://www.yahooligans.com/content/news/top_story/200103122.html

Singer, M., & Berg, P. (1991). *Genes and genomes: A changing perspective.* Mill Valley, CA: University Science Books.

Soble, S. P. (Ed.). (1993). *New bio news: Information on biotechnology.* St. Louis, MO: Monsanto Company.

Thompson, W. C., & Ford, S. (1992, April). DNA testing: Debate update. *Trial*, 52–61.

U.S. Congress, Office of Technology Assessment. (1990, July). *Genetic witness: Forensic uses of DNA tests.* (OTA-BA-438).Washington, DC: U.S. Government Printing Office.

Wertz, D. C. (1998, August 1). *Twenty-one arguments against human cloning, and their responses.* Retrieved August 8, 2001, from http://www.geneletter.com/archives/twentyonearguments.html

Unit Five

Chapter 13

Audubon Society. (1983). *Field guide to North American fishes, whales, dolphins.* New York: Alfred A. Knopf.

Berkow, R. (Editor-in-chief). (1992). *The Merck manual* (16th ed.). Rahway, NJ: Merck Research Laboratories.

BSCS. (2001). *BSCS Biology: A molecular approach* (8th ed.). Chicago, IL: Everyday Learning.

BSCS. (2002). *BSCS Biology: An ecological approach* (9th ed.). Dubuque, IA: Kendall/Hunt.

Chiras, D. D. (1993). *Biology, the web of life.* Minneapolis, MN: West.

Coleman, S., Silberstein, G. B., & Daniel, C. W. (1988, June). Ductal morphogenesis in the mouse mammary gland: Evidence supporting a role for epidermal growth factor. *Developmental Biology, 127*(2), 304–315.

Dorst, J., & Dandelot, P. (1970). *Larger mammals of Africa.* Boston, MA: Houghton Mifflin.

Enger, E. D., Kormelink, J. R., Ross, F. C., & Smith, R. J. (1991). *Concepts in biology.* Dubuque, IA: William C. Brown.

FDA proposes to delete warning label on hormone. (1999, July). *Pharmaceutical and Medical Packaging News*, p. 67. Retrieved February 19, 2002, from http://www.devicelink.com/pmpn/archive/99/07/009.html

Feduccia, A., & McCrady, E. (1991). *Torrey's morphogenesis of the vertebrates* (5th ed.). New York: John Wiley & Sons.

Gilbert, S. F. (1991). *Developmental biology* (3rd ed.). Sunderland, MA: Sinauer Associates.

Hopper, A. R., & Hart, N. H. (1985). *Foundations of animal development* (2nd ed.). New York: Oxford University Press.

Illmensee, K. & Mahowald, A. P. (1974). Transplantation of posterior polar plasm in *Drosophila*. Induction of germ cells at the anterior pole of the egg. *Proceedings of the National Academy of Sciences, 71*(4), 106–1020.

Jenkins, J. B. (1990). *Human genetics*. New York: Harper and Row.

Levine, J. S., & Suzuki, D. (1993). *The secret of life: Redesigning the living world*. Boston, MA: WGBH Boston.

Lewis, R. (1994). *Genes V*. New York: Oxford University Press.

Lewis, R. (1994). *Human genetics, concepts and applications*. Dubuque, IA: William C. Brown.

Macdonald, D. (1984). *The encyclopedia of mammals*. New York: Facts On File Publications.

Mader, S. (1988). *Human biology*. Dubuque, IA: William C. Brown.

Mange, A. P., & Mange, E. J. (1990). *Genetics: Human aspects* (2nd ed.). Sunderland, MA: Sinauer Associates.

Marc Kirschner, Ph.D. (n.d.). Retrieved February 21, 2002, from the Harvard Medical School Department of Cell Biology Web site: http://cellbio.med.harvard.edu/faculty/kirschner/

Martin, G. R. (1980). Teratocarcinomas and mammalian embryogenesis. *Science*, 768–776.

McConnaughey, B. H., & McConnaughey, E. (1985). *Pacific coast, national Audubon nature guide*. New York: Alfred A. Knopf.

Mix, M. C., Farber, D., & King, K. I. (1993). *Biology, the network of life*. New York: HarperCollins.

Moore, K. L. (1983). *Before we are born: Basic embryology and birth defects* (2nd ed.). Philadelphia, PA: W. B. Saunders Company.

Moore, R. (1962). *Life Nature Library: Evolution*. New York: Time Incorporated.

Morholt, E., Brandwein, P. F., & Joseph, A. (1966). *A sourcebook for the biological sciences* (2nd ed.). New York: Harcourt, Brace, & World.

Nora, J. J. (1981). *Medical genetics: Principles and practice* (2nd ed.). Philadelphia, PA: Lea & Febiger.

Nossal, G. J. V. (1993, September). Life, death, and the immune system. *Scientific American, 269*, 53–62.

Palmiter, R. D., Brinster, R. L, Hammer, R. E., Trumbauer, M. E., Rosenfeld, M. G., Birnberg, N. C., & Evans, R. M. (1982). Dramatic growth of mice that develop from eggs microinjected with metallothionein-growth hormone fusion genes. *Nature, 300*, 611–615.

Rischer, C. E., & Easton, T. (1992). *Focus on human biology*. New York: HarperCollins.

Saunders, J. W., Jr., Gasseling, M. T., Errick, J. E. (1976, May). Inductive activity and enduring cellular constitution of a supernumerary apical ectodermal ridge grafted to the limb bud of the chick embryo. *Developmental Biology, 50*(1), 16–25.

Shostak, S. (1991). *Embryology: An introduction to developmental biology*. New York: HarperCollins.

Snively, G. (1978). *Exploring the seashore in British Columbia, Washington, and Oregon*. Vancouver, Canada: Gordon Soules Book Publishers, Ltd.

Thomas, C. L. (Ed.) (1993). *Taber's encyclopedic medical dictionary* (17th ed.). Philadelphia, PA: F.A. Davis Company.

University of Colorado Health Sciences Center. (1988). *Genetic applications: A health perspective*. Lawrence, KS: Learner Managed Designs.

Wallace, R. A. (1991). *Biology, the science of life*. New York: HarperCollins.

Wolpert, L. (1994, October 28). Do we understand development? (Frontiers in Biology: Development). *Science 266*(5185), 571–572.

Wolpert, L. (1991). *The triumph of the embryo*. Oxford, England: Oxford University Press.

Chapter 14

Arms, K., & Camp, P. S. (1987). *Biology*. New York: Saunders.

Batchelor, J. (1927). *Ainu life and lore: Echoes of a departing race*. Tokyo, Kyobunkwan, Japan: The Japan Advertiser Press.

Beck, W. S., Liem, K. F., & Simpson, A. R. (1991). *Life: An introduction to biology* (3rd ed.). New York: HarperCollins.

Brittain, W.L. (1979). *Creativity, art, and the young child*. New York: Macmillan Publishing.

Bronowski, J. (1973). *The ascent of man*. (Text edition). Boston: Little, Brown and Company.

Chiras, D. D. (1991). *Human biology: Health, homeostasis, and the environment*. St. Paul, MN: West Publishing.

Cole, M., & Cole, S. (1989). *The development of children*. New York: W. H. Freeman.

Edwards, B. (1989). *Drawing on the right side of the brain* (Rev. ed.). New York: Putnam Publishing.

Fogel, A., & Melson, G. (1988). *Child development: Individual family, and society*. St. Paul, MN: West Publishing.

Hostetler, J. A. (1980). *Amish society* (3rd ed.). Baltimore: Johns Hopkins University Press. Ingram, J. (1992). *Talk, talk, talk: An investigation into the mystery of speech*. Toronto, Canada: Penguin Books.

Kotre, J., & Hall, E. (1997). *Seasons of life: Our dramatic journey from birth to death*. Boston, MA: Little, Brown and Co.

Kraybill, D. B. (1989). *The riddle of Amish culture*. Baltimore, MD: Johns Hopkins University Press.

Lecours, A. (1982). Correlates of developmental behavior in brain maturation. In T. Bever (Ed.), *Regressions in mental development*. Hillsdale, NJ: Erlbaum Publishers.

Lownefeld, V., & Brittain, W.L. (1987). *Creative and mental growth* (8th ed.). New York: Macmillan Publishing.

Luria, A. (1973). *The working brain*. New York: Basic Books.

Mader, S. S. (1992). *Human biology*. Dubuque, IA: William C. Brown.

Munroe, R. L., & Munroe, R. H. (1975). *Cross-cultural human development*. Monterey, CA: Brooks/Cole.

Oxford atlas of the world (2nd ed.). (1993). New York: Oxford University Press.

Scarr, S., Weinberg, R., & Levine, A. (1986). *Understanding development*. New York: Harcourt, Brace, & Jovanovich Publishers.

Sears, R., & Feldman, S. (Eds.). *The seven ages of man*. Los Altos, CA: William Kaufmann.

Seitz, R. H. (1991). *Amish ways*. Harrisburg, PA: RB Books.

Sigelman, C. K., & Shaffer, D. R. (1995). *Life-span human development* (2nd ed.). Pacific Grove, CA: Brooks/Cole Publishing.

Skolnick, A. (1986). *The psychology of human development*. New York: Harcourt, Brace, & Jovanovich Publishers.

Super, C. M., & Harkness, S. (Eds.). (1980). *Anthropological perspectives on child development*. San Francisco: Jossey-Bass.

The first year of life. (1982). *American Baby, 44*(4).

Van De Graaf, K., & Fox, S. (1989). *Concepts of human anatomy and physiology* (2nd ed.). Dubuque, IA: William C. Brown.

Wallace, K. A., Sanders, G. P., & Ferl, R. J. (1991). *Biology: The science of life* (3rd ed.). New York: HarperCollins.

Whistler, N. (1979). *Oral history workshop guide.* Denver, CO: Denver Public Library.

White, S. (1965). Evidence for a hierarchical arrangement of learning processes. In L. Lipsitt and C. Spiker (Eds.), *Advances in child development and behavior* (Vol. 2). New York: Academic Press.

Unit Five Assessment

Aase, J. M. (1993). *Fetal alcohol syndrome: A training manual.* Prepared for New Mexico Disability Prevention Project.

Clarren, S. K., & Smith, D. W. (1979). The fetal alcohol syndrome. *New England Journal of Medicine, 298*(19), 1063.

Little, B. B., Snell, L. M., Rosenfeld, C. R., Gilstrap, L. C., & Gant, N. F. (1990). Failure to recognize fetal alcohol syndrome in newborn infants. *American Journal of Diseases of Children, 144,* 1142.

U.S. Department of Health & Human Services. (1990, January). *Alcohol & health* (DHHS Publication No. ADM 90-1656). Washington, DC: U.S. Department of Health & Human Services.

Unit Six

Evaluate

Alexander, R. M. (1992). *Exploring biomechanics: Animals in motion.* New York: Scientific American Library.

Bains, S. (1994). Even a robot cricket always gets her mate. *Science, 266*(5192), 1809.

Beck, W. S., Liem, K. F., & Simpson, G. G. (1991). *Life: An introduction to biology* (3rd ed.). New York: HarperCollins.

Ewald, P. W. (1994). *Evolution of infectious disease.* New York: Oxford University Press.

Gabriel, S. E., Brigman, K. N., Koller, B. H., Boucher, R. C., & Stutts, M. J. (1994). Cystic fibrosis heterozygote resistance to cholera toxin in the cystic fibrosis mouse model. *Science, 266,* 107–109.

Galston, A. W. (1994). *Life processes of plants.* New York: Scientific American Library.

Guyton, A. C. (1991). *Textbook of medical physiology* (8th ed.). Philadelphia, PA: Saunders College Publishing.

Halfpenny, J. C., & Ozanne, R. D. (1989). *Winter, an ecology handbook.* Boulder, CO: Johnson Publishing.

Larson, E. E. (Ed.). (1990). *Maya Clinic family health book.* New York: William Morrow & Company.

Mange, E. J., & Mange, A. P. (1994). *Basic human genetics.* Sunderland, MA: Sinauer Associates.

Massachusetts Medical Society. (1994, October). Summary of notifiable diseases, United States, 1993. In *Morbidity and mortality weekly report*. Waltham, MA: Massachusetts Medical Society.

NASA. (1984). Phytoplankton and temperature patterns. In *Oceanography from space* (Publication No. 1984-784-583). Washington, DC: U.S. Government Printing Office.

Nora, J. J., & Fraser, F. C. (1991). *Medical genetics: Principles and practice* (2nd ed.). Philadelphia, PA: Lea & Febiger.

Raloff, J. (1995, February 11). When nitrate reigns. *Science News, 147,* 90–91.

Rhoades, R., & Pflazer, R. (1992). *Human physiology* (2nd ed.). Philadelphia, PA: Saunders College Publishing.

Solomon, E. P., Schmidt, R. R., & Adragna, P. J. (1990). *Human anatomy and physiology*. Philadelphia, PA: Saunders College Publishing.

Terborgh, J. (1992). *Diversity and the tropical rainforest*. New York: Scientific American Library.

Tizard, I. R. (1992). *Immunology: An introduction* (3rd ed.). Philadelphia, PA: Saunders College Publishing.

Wieland, P. O. (1994). *Designing for human presence in space: An introduction to environmental control and life support systems.* (NASA Reference Publication No. 1324). Huntsville, AL: George C. Marshall Space Flight Center.

Zimmer, C. (1995). Back to the sea. *Discover, 16*(1), 82–84.

Chapter 15

Botkin, D. B. (1990). *Discordant harmonies: A new ecology for the twenty-first century.* New York: Oxford University Press.

Bradley, P. V. (1994). Otter limits. *Natural History, 103*(11), 36–46.

Brewer, R. (1994). *The science of ecology* (2nd ed.). Philadelphia, PA: Saunders College Publishing.

Brown, L. R., Lenssen, N., & Kane, H. (1995). *Vital signs.* Worldwatch Institute. New York: W. W. Norton and Co.

BSCS. (1994). *Middle school science & technology, level C.* Dubuque, IA: Kendall/Hunt.

BSCS. (2002). *BSCS Biology: An ecological approach* (9th ed.). Dubuque, IA: Kendall/Hunt.

Buchsbaum, R., & Buchsbaum, M. (1972). *Basic ecology.* Pittsburgh, PA: The Boxwood Press.

Buettner, D. (1994, December). So close to infinity. *Bicycling 35*(11), 77–83, 112.

Croall, S., & Rankin, W. (1982). *Ecology for beginners.* New York: Pantheon Books.

Cunningham, W. P. & Saigo, B. W. (1992). *Environmental science: A global concern* (2nd ed.). Dubuque, IA: William C. Brown.

Curtis, W. (1984). *The nature of things.* New York: The Ecco Press.

Darwin, C. (1872). *The origin of species* (6th ed.). New York: Collier Books Edition.

Devall, B., & Sessions G. (1985). *Deep ecology.* Salt Lake City, UT: Gibbs M. Smith.

Elfring, C. (1989). Yellowstone: Fire storm over fire management. *BioScience, 39,* 667–672.

Hanson, J. K., & Morrison, D. (1992). *Of kinkajous, capybaras, horned beetles, and seladangs.* New York: HarperPerennial.

Hardin, G. (1993). *Living within limits: Ecology, economics, and population taboos.* New York: Oxford University Press.

Shugart, H. H., & O'Neill, R. V. (Eds.). (1979). *Systems ecology.* PA: Dowden, Hutchinson & Ross.

Simmons, L. M., Jr. (Ed.). (1992). *The Bulletin of the Santa Fe Institute, 7,* 1. Santa Fe, NM: Santa Fe Institute.

Solomons, T. W. G. (1976). *Organic chemistry* (2nd ed.). New York: John Wiley & Sons.

Staff. (1992, May/June). Eastern enigma. *Audubon, 94.*

Staff. (1992, November). Eagles on the rise. *National Geographic, 182.*

Stewart, D. (1993). Good news and bad about Superior's Bald Eagles. *National Wildlife, 31.*

Thorp, J. H., & Covich, A. P. (Eds.). *Ecology and classification of North American invertebrates.* San Diego, CA: Academic Press.

Turbak, G. (1989, October/November). America's other eagle. *National Wildlife, 27.*

U.S. Department of Commerce, Bureau of Economic Analysis. (1992). *Business statistics.* Washington, DC: U.S. Government Printing Office.

Vikbanski, L. (1989, September). Zone park. *Discover, 32.*

Ward's Natural Science Establishment, Inc. *Rearing of* Daphnia *and related arthropods.* Rochester, NY: Author.

West, D. (1992, June/July). Taking aim at deadly chemicals. *National Wildlife, 30.*

Wetzel, R. G. (1975). *Limnology.* Philadelphia, PA: Saunders College Publishing.

Whitfield, P. (Ed.). (1984). *Macmillan illustrated animal encyclopedia.* New York: Macmillan Publishing.

Williams, T. (1988, March). Let them eat steel. *Audubon, 90.*

Evaluate

Creager, J. G., Black, J. G., & Davison, V. E. (1990). *Microbiology: Principles and applications.* Englewood Cliffs, NJ: Prentice-Hall.

Index

A

Abiotic environment, 539, 543, 547, 557, 577, 584

Absorption, in digestion, 266

Abstaining from sex, 231

Achondroplasia, 507

Acidity, 187, 192. *See also* pH

Acquired traits, 26, 119, 392–394

Active transport, 170

Activity/rest cycle, 202

Adaptation: natural selection *versus*, 26; unity and diversity in, 116–125; variation and, 91–92

Adaptive characteristics, 124, 135, 453

Adolescence, 520

Adulthood, 53, 520

Advertisements, 253–254

Advocating skills, 570, 592

Aerobic conditioning, 271, 274, 276

Aerobic respiration, 302, 316

Africa, 32

Africa in My Blood: An Autobiography in Letters (Goodall), 34

Aging, 520

Agriculture, 338, 588

AIDS, 220, 231

Alcohol abuse, 45, 232–234, 507

Algae, 120–121

Alleles, 414; for cystic fibrosis, 407–408; dominant and recessive, 409; for genetic disorders, 430; for Huntington's disease, 407; segregation of, 402; for sickle-cell disease, 458, 462, 476

Alloying, 93

Alzheimer's disease, 46–47

American Association of Retired Persons (AARP), 524

American Biology Teacher, The, 288, 441

American Cancer Society, 503

American Family Physician, 151

American Sign Language, 34

Amino acids, 312; in aerobic respiration, 316; mutations in, 458–459; radioactive labeled, 314–315; on ribosomes, 466; sequence of, 462–463, 468–469

Amylase, 264

Anaerobic respiration, 279, 309, 341

Analysis skills, 319

Anaphase, of mitosis, 496

Ancestral Puebloans, 336–337

Animal Einstein (Scientific American Frontiers), 55

Animals, nonhuman, 113–116, 378–379

Anorexia nervosa, 266

Anthropologists, 70–72, 79–80

Antibacterial soaps, 99

Antibiotics: resistance to, 97–99, 470; viruses and, 219, 599

Anxiety, 227

Aqueous solvents, 164

Aristotle, 382

Articulation skills, 60

Artifacts, 92–96

Art terms, 13

Ascus, of yeast, 389, 402

Asexual reproduction. *See* Reproduction

Aspirin, 599

Assessment, 301; chapter challenges, 602–613; embedded, 184; journals in, 12; peer, 433, 578; performance, 596; self, 206

Assortment, independent, in genetics, 408, 415, 420

Athletic fitness, 247–249. *See also* Performance and fitness

Atkins, John, 447

Atlas of Science Literacy, 5, 26, 242, 362

Atoms, 286, 292–293

ATP: as energy-matter link, 287; kinetic and potential energy and, 293; light energy for, 309; mitochondria increase and, 278; for muscle contraction, 270, 273, 302

Australopithecine fossils, 79

Australopithecus afarensis, 79

Autoimmune diseases, 218

Automatic physiological responses, 186

Automobiles, 253. *See also* Alcohol abuse

Autosomes, 419, 430

Averages, calculating, 300

B

Bacteria, 58; antibiotic resistance of, 98–99; infections from, 227; kingdom classification of, 113–116; toxins from, 215

Bacteriophages, 115–116

Balance in organisms, 174–204; body responses for, 177–180; chapter implementation, 175–176; cooling for, 199–202; in "critter," 202–204; as equilibrium, 173; heat and, 171; pH in, 193–199; pulse and breathing rates in, 186–192; temperature and, 180–186

Bar graphs, 89

Behavior. *See also* Culture: for cooling, 200; genetic role in, 388; for homeostasis, 202; human, 49; illness and, 215; mating, 378–379; mental disorders and, 42–47; risk and, 228, 234; as stress response, 180; of termites, 19

Bell-shaped distributions, 422

Incubation, 52
Incubators, 388, 390–391, 399
Independence, Kentucky, 435
Independent assortment, in genetics, 408, 415, 420
Indicators of success. *See* Success indicators
Inductive reasoning, 46
Industrial Revolution, 586, 589
Infancy, 520
Infections: antibiotics and, 97–99; bacterial, 58; fever and, 599; fluid exchange and, 230–231; viruses and, 227
Inferences. *See also* Change: from artifacts, 93–94; on common ancestor, 79; from evidence, 43, 68; experimental, 157; prognosis from, 219; in relationships, 132
Influenza, 219, 599
Information gathering, 356–357
Ingram, Jay, 393
Inherited traits, 26, 98–99, 119, 123–124. *See also* Continuity; Reproduction
Innovations, impact of, 528
Inquiry skills, 281. *See also* Scientific inquiry
Insomnia, 220
"Instant society," 253
Institute for Human and Machine Cognition, 152
Instructional model for text (5Es), 4
Instrumentation, 150
Intensity, in art, 13
Interbreeding, 134
Interdependence, 541–567; chapter implementation, 542; "critter" and, 564–567; on Easter Island, 559–564; interactions and, 546–549; observing, 543–545; shared resources and, 549–558
Intermarriage, 394, 420
Internal environment of organisms, 147–173; cell activity in, 153–161; cell model for, 161–167; chapter implementation, 148–149; heat and, 150–153, 170–173; regulating, 167–170
Internet, 83, 356, 377
Interphase, of mitosis, 495
Interpretation skills, 513
Interviewing, 523–528, 614
In the Shadow of Man (Goodall), 34
Investigation practices, 20
Iodine solution, 162, 165, 262
Irritants, in laboratory, 289–290
Isotopes, radioactive, 314

J

Jigsaw activities, 72–74, 120, 231–233
Journals, scientific. *See* Scientific journals
Jurassic Park (Crichton), 477
Justification skills, 60

K

Kahn, Herman, 560
Karyotypes, 431
Kentucky, 435
Kidneys, 170–172
Kinetic energy, 287, 289–290, 293
Kingdoms, in classification, 111–116
Knowledge-applying skills, 60
Kotre, J., 529

L

Laboratory experiences, 1, 12, 245. *See also* Experiments
Lactic acid, 273
Land bridges, 79
Landfills, 325
Language, 34, 51–55, 432
Large intestine, 266
Learning, 51–55, 182, 263
Learning strategies: on adaptation, 118–123; on animal reproduction, 379; on athletic fitness *versus* fitness for life, 248–249; on biological thinking, 598–599; on cell activity, 155–159; on cell models, 163–166; on change, 72–74, 427–431; on childhood, 52–53; on classification schemes, 126–131; on common characteristics, 104–105; on cooling, 200–201; on "critter" example, 141–143, 203–204, 383–384, 565–567; on culture, 93–95, 381, 534–535; on development, 498–500, 509–510, 520–522, 531–532; on DNA models, 447–455; on earth history modeling, 65–67; on Easter Island, 560–562; on energy, 263–266, 284–285, 288–292, 315–316, 343–347. *See also* Heat energy; Photosynthesis; on evolution, 82–84, 97; on experiments, 354–359; on fitness determination, 250–253; on five-kingdom classification, 112–114; on food, 256–259, 297–301; on genetics, 415–419, 437–439, 441–444, 459–462, 472–476, 479–480; on growth and differentiation, 492–496; on Gult of Maine example, 580–583; on health and disease, 212–215, 236–239, 504–506; on heat energy, 151, 171–172, 339–341; on homeostasis disruption, 209; on humans, 32–33, 49–50, 52–53, 56–57, 375–377, 422–424, 515; on immune system, 218–227; on inheritance, 393–394, 404–406, 410–413; on interactions and interdependence, 329–332, 544–545, 546–549, 576–578; on light energy, 305–308; on limits to growth, 587–591; on living organism characterization, 107–109; on "Lucy" hominid fossil, 62; on marathon running, 274–277; on metabolism, 311–313; on muscle function, 267–269; on natural selection modeling, 87–90; on oral history, 526–528; overview of,

Mouth, in digestive system, 266
Movement, 36–39, 41, 49, 63
mRNA (messenger RNA), 457–459, 461–462, 464, 466–467, 500
Mucus, 231
Multicellular organisms, 120–121, 189
Multiple sclerosis, 218
Muscle fatigue, 270, 273
Muscles, 266–271, 273, 499
Muscular dystrophy, 425
Mutations, 92; adaptations and, 124; in DNA, 458; predicting effects of, 468–470; as replication error, 456; replication of, 453–454; variations from, 431, 441, 444–445
Mutualism, 547
Myers-Briggs learning style inventory, 55
My Thirty Years with the Chimpanzees of Gombe (Goodall), 34

N

National Association of Biology Teachers, 82
National Center for Science Education, 82
National Geographic, 34, 63
Native American cultures, 33, 336, 382
Natural defense systems. *See* Immune function
Natural selection: adaptation *versus*, 26; detrimental traits and, 430; human populations and, 425; modeling, 86–92; reproduction and, 368; teleolgic view *versus*, 141
Nature of Sex, The (Nature), 374, 379
Nature (Public Broadcasting System), 366
Navajo language, 432
Negative controls, in experiments, 259
Nephron tubules, of kidneys, 170, 172
Nervous system, 49, 187, 189
Net primary productivity (NPP), 586
Neuromuscular effects, in muscle fatigue, 274
New Chimpanzees, The (National Geographic Society), 34
Nicotine, 507. *See also* Smoking
Nilsson, Lennart, 375
Nirenberg, Marshall, 314
Nitrates, 325
Nitrogen, 292
Nondisjunction, in genetics, 430
Nonspecific defense mechanisms, 218. *See also* Immune function
Note taking, 11
NOVA, 374–375
Nucleic acids, 449
Nucleotide sequence, 466
Nucleus of cells, 448
Nursing, 52
Nutrients, 257, 260, 271, 278, 325. *See also* Diet; Food
Nutrition, 253, 283. *See also* Diet; Food

O

Objectivity, 15, 20
Observations, 1–2, 388; drawings as records of, 12–14; qualitative *versus* quantitative, 155; in scientific inquiry, 20, 37; skills in, 513–514, 521, 539, 543–545; of temperature regulation, 200
Offspring, variation in, 92
Oils, 259–260
Old age, 520
Olfactory bulb, of brain, 41
Omnivores, 335, 345
Onion: cells of, 158–160; DNA extraction from, 436–439
Opener strategies, 4
Optic lobe, of brain, 41
Oral history, 523–528
Orangutans, 39
Orders, in classification, 129
Organization, 140, 241–243. *See also* Cell activity; Communities; Performance and fitness
Organizational skills, 3, 245
Osmosis, 173
Outcomes, indicators of. *See* Success indicators
Overconsumption, 586
Oxygen: bonding with, 292; in circulatory system, 169, 187, 192; depletion of, 294; geological evidence for, 68; in muscles, 271; to muscles, 278; from photosynthesis, 121, 308–309, 345; in sickle-cell hemoglobin, 460

P

Paleontologists, 69, 71–72, 74–75
Pancreas, 266
Parasitism, 547
Parental care, 371
Pathogens, 219, 222–223, 225–226
Patterns. *See also* Development; Reproduction: in data, 357; in evidence, 68; in graphs, 191; in line graphs, 184–185; in meiosis, 409–414; in Mendelian inheritance, 403–409; in zebra stripes, 132
Patterson, Penny, 34
PBS (Public Broadcasting System), 47, 62, 99, 216, 366
Peer assessment, 19, 433, 578
Penicillin, 97, 219
Performance and fitness, 244–279. *See also* Cell activity; athletic *versus* fitness for life, 247–249; chapter implementation, 245–246; determining, 249–254; energy for, 261–266; factors in, 272–279; food components and, 254–261; muscle function in, 266–271
Permeability, 163, 166, 172–173
Permission forms, 517–519, 521